CADES 2013 Camping Touring & Motor Caravan Site Guide

GW00360668

Compiled and Edited by
Reg Cade

Published by
Cade's Guides Limited,
Fairbourne Drive, Atterbury, Milton Keynes, MK10 9RG
Tel: 0844 504 9500
Email: enquiries@cades.co.uk
Website: www.cades.co.uk

Design and Administration
Mary Soper

Advertisement Manager
Malcolm Johnson

Printed by
Acorn Web Offset, Normanton, West Yorkshire

Distribution (Booktrade)
Kuperard
59 Hutton Grove, London, N12 8DS

(Camping and Caravan Trade)
Cade's Guides Limited (address above)

ISBN 1 - 905963 - 12 - 2

Get closer to the **great outdoors** with Haven

There's lots to discover with a choice of 23 UK touring and camping holiday parks. From golden beaches to heated pools, sports activities and kids' clubs, there's so much to do and it's all included in your pitch price. And, there's also an exciting range of 'pay as you go' activities including fencing, archery and golf.

As well as all the fun, we've covered the essentials

- Pick of 6 pitch types - from basic grass to fully serviced hard-standing
- We welcome tourers, motorhomes, tents and trailer tents
- Modern shower blocks and amenities
- 24-hour security with touring wardens on many parks
- Beach access on or near all parks
- Pets welcome for only £1* a night

Save up to **50%*** on 2013 holidays

To find out more, order a brochure and to book

Call: **0843 308 7817** Quote: TO_CADES13

Calls cost 5p per minute plus network extras. Open 7 days a week, 9am-9pm

Visit: **haventouring.com/tocades13**

Haven touring +camping

Britain's Favourite Seaside Holida

Welcome to the 2013 edition of Cade's camping, Touring and motor Caravan Site Guide.

Cade's have been providing quality touring park information to the discerning holidaymaker for over forty years. Our guide is updated annually and all the information contained within it has been provided or verified by the parks owners or operators.

Why still a printed guide in the age of the internet? Have a flick through the pages of this guide as you hold it. Stop and look at a particular county. Either side of where you are looking are details on other parks in the same area, allowing you to instantly compare their facilities at a glance. Try that on the internet and you will soon have an unwieldy array of windows open featuring an equally unwieldy array of formats from which to try and make your choice. Using Cade's Camping, Touring and Motor Caravan Site Guide makes the selection process far easier.

Of course we do not dismiss the internet, indeed all the information in this guide is featured on our own website but the guide itself should be considered perhaps, as an internet directory. Once you have shortlisted the sites you think may suit you by checking their facilities in these pages, then you can visit their websites to find out more. Where individual parks have website and email addresses, these are featured in their entries, making the next stage of your selection process easier for you. If you use the guide in this way, please be sure to mention to our advertisers that you initially found their website details in 'Cade's Guide', this will help us to continue providing you with quality park information for years to come.

Remember to use the 'Pitch Fee Discount Vouchers' at the back of this guide, you could save yourself up to £40. Parks accepting the vouchers show a 🖃 symbol in their entries.

Finally, there have been some very tragic camping accidents throughout 2012, most of which could have been avoided! Campers and caravanners and their families have been poisoned by carbon monoxide fumes when taking a barbecue in to their tent or awning. Even if you think the barbecue is extinguished, for hours it will still produce lethal carbon monoxide gas. DO NOT COOK INSIDE YOUR TENT OR AWNING OR USE THE RESIDUAL HEAT FOR WARMTH - IT WILL KILL YOU! Always make certain your family are safe when camping or caravanning.

Have a very enjoyable touring season in 2013.

The Cade's Team

INDEX

4

5

SYMBOLS/SYMBOLES FRANCAISE

⋏ Tents	⋏ Tentes
🚐 Motor Caravans	🚐 Auto-Caravanes
🚐 Touring Caravans	🚐 Caravanes
🚐 U.S. R.V.'s	🚐 Auto-Caravanes (Etats Unis)
⇌ Nearest Station	⇌ Gare Locale
♿ Facilities for Disabled	♿ Handicapés
🏍 No Motorcycles	⌁ Branchments Electrique Pour Caravanes
⌁ Electricity Hook-ups	▣ Emplacement Service Complet
▣ Fully Serviced Pitches	▣ Emplacement Surface Dure
▣ Hard Standings	🏍 Motorcyclettes Non-Admises
🚽 Flush Toilets	🚽 Toilettes
⚲ Water	⚲ Eau
⌐ Showers	⌐ Douches
⊙ Shaver Points	⊙ Prises Electrique pour Rasoirs
🛁 Washing Facilities	🛁 Bains
🔲 Ironing Facilities	🔲 Repassage
▣ Launderette	▣ Laverie Automatique
♟ Chem. Toilet Disposal	♟ Décharge pour W.C. Chemique
S🏪 Site Shop	S🏪 Magasin du Terrain
M🏪 Mobile Shop	M🏪 Magasin Mobile
l🏪 Local Shop	l🏪 Magasin du Quartier
⊖ Gas	⊖ Gaz
☎ Public Telephone	☎ Cabines Téléphoniques
✕ Café Restaurant	✕ Café
♀ Licensed Club	♀ Club/Bar Patenté
📺 T.V.	📺 Salle de Télévision
♠ Games Room	♠ Salle de Jeux
⋔ Childs Play Area	⋔ Terrain de Jeux Enfants
⌁ Outdoor Pool	⌁ Piscine du Terrain
⌁ Indoor Pool	⌁ Piscine a l'interieur
✿ Sports Area	✿ Terrain de Sports et de Jeux
🐾 Pets Welcome	✎ Pêche sur place
✎ Fishing on Site	▣ Stationment à côté de la caravane permis
▣ Parking by Unit	⊞ Carte Credit Accepter
⊞ Credit Cards Accepted	▣ Bon Remise 'Cades' Accepter
▣ Money-Off Vouchers	A Camping Seulment Adulte
A Adults Only Park	⋇ Emplacements pour La Saison
⋇ Seasonal Pitches	⋏ Gardiennage
⋏ Secure Storage	📶 Wi-Fi
📶 Wi-Fi Access	

the Bestof British

Quality family owned Touring
and Holiday Parks to suit
all tastes, with a warm
and friendly welcome

View or download our brochure online

the Bestof British
quality touring and holiday parks
www.bob.org.uk

PO Box 28249, Edinburgh, EH9 2YZ

ENGLAND
BERKSHIRE
DORNEY REACH
Amerden Caravan Site, Off Old Marsh Lane, Dorney Reach, Nr Maidenhead, Berkshire, SL6 0EE
Tel: 01628 627461
Email: beverly@amerdencaravanpark.co.uk
www.amerdencaravanpark.webs.com
Pitches For A ⊕ ⊕ **Total** 40
Acreage 3 **Open** Apr to Oct
Access Good **Site** Level
Nearest Bus Stop (Miles) 1¼
Near River Thames.
Facilities ⓕ ∮ Ⓦ ⌐ ⌐ ⊙ ⌐ ⚌ ⌐ ☎
⚑ ⌐ ⌐ ⌐ ☎
Nearest Town Maidenhead
Directions Leave M4 junc 7, Slough West, then A4 towards Maidenhead. Turn left at second set of traffic lights signposted Dorney Reach and caravan site, then first turn right.
⇥ Taplow

HURLEY
Hurley Riverside Park, Hurley, Nr Maidenhead, Berkshire, SL6 5NE
Tel: 01628 824493/823501
Email: info@hurleyriversidepark.co.uk
www.hurleyriversidepark.co.uk
Pitches For A ⊕ ⊕ ⊕ᐸ **Total** 200
Acreage 15 **Open** Mar to Oct
Access Good **Site** Level
Nearest Bus Stop (Miles) Outside
Family-run Park alongside the River Thames with access to the Thames Path. Ideal for visiting Legoland® Windsor, Oxford and Henley. Discounted tickets for Legoland available to purchase. Disabled toilets. Slipway, nature trail and riverside picnic

ground. David Bellamy Gold and Special Distinction Awards. Fully serviced Caravan Holiday Homes and ReadyTents for hire.
Facilities ⓕ ∮ ⌐ Ⓗ Ⓦ ⌐ ⌐ ⊙ ⌐ ⚌ ⌐ ☎
⚑ ⚑ ⓘ ⊙ ⚌ ⌐ ⌐ ⌐ ☎
Nearest Town Henley-on-Thames
Directions Maidenhead, A4130 west towards Henley. After 3¼ miles turn right, ¾ mile past Hurley Village, into Shepherds Lane. Entrance 200 yards on left.
⇥ Maidenhead/Henley-on-Thames

NEWBURY
Oakley Farm Caravan Park, Oakley Farm House, Penwood Road, Wash Water, Newbury, Berkshire, RG20 0LP
Tel: 01635 36581
Email: info@oakleyfarm.co.uk
www.oakleyfarm.co.uk
Pitches For A ⊕ ⊕ **Total** 30
Acreage 3 **Open** Mar to Oct
Access Good **Site** Gentle Slope
Nearest Bus Stop (Miles) ½
Not suitable for caravans over 22 foot long.
Facilities ∮ ⌐ Ⓦ ⌐ ⌐ ⊙ ⌐ ☎ ⚑ ⌐
Nearest Town Newbury
Directions From the A34 south of Newbury take the exit marked Highclere and Wash Common. Turn left onto the A343 towards Newbury, turn right after ¼ mile (by car sales garage) into Penwood Road. Site is then 400 metres on your left.
⇥ Newbury

RISELEY
Wellington Country Park, Odiham Road, Riseley, Berkshire, RG7 1SP
Tel: 01189 326444
Email: info@wellington-country-park.co.uk
www.www.wellington-country-park.co.uk
Pitches For A ⊕ ⊕ **Total** 82
Open Mar to Nov

Access Good **Site** Level
Nearest Bus Stop (Miles) ¼
Forest location with free access to country park and facilities.
Facilities ∮ ⌐ Ⓗ Ⓦ ⌐ ⌐ ⊙ ⌐ ⚌ ⌐ ☎
⚑ ⊙ ⚌ Ⓧ ⌐ ⌐ ⌐ ☎
Nearest Town Reading
Directions From the M4 junction 11 follow the A33 south towards Basingstoke.
⇥ Reading

BRISTOL (COUNTY OF)
BRISTOL
Baltic Wharf Caravan Club Site, Cumberland Road, Bristol, BS1 6XG
Tel: 0117 926 8030
www.caravanclub.co.uk
Pitches For ⊕ ⊕ **Total** 55
Acreage 2½ **Open** All Year
Access Good **Site** Level
Nearest Bus Stop (Miles) Outside
Quiet waterside site ½ mile from the town centre. River ferry service to the city centre in Summer. Near to Bristol Zoo, SS Great Britain and museums. Non members welcome. Booking essential.
Facilities ⓕ ∮ Ⓦ ⌐ ⌐ ⌐ ⊙ ⌐ ⚌ ⌐ ☎
⚑ ⊙ ⚌ ⚑ ⌐ ⌐ ☎
Nearest Town Bristol
Directions Leave M5 at junc. 18 take the A4. After Clifton Suspension Bridge keep in lt lane and follow signs to harbour. At lights stay in rt lane through Hotwells, over the crossing and move to lt lane, go over bridge following signs for SS Great Britain. Site is 500 yds on the lt.
⇥ Bristol Temple Meads

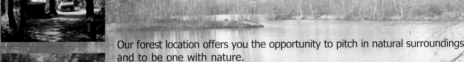

BUCKINGHAMSHIRE

BEACONSFIELD

Highclere Farm Country Touring Park,
Newbarn Lane, Seer Green, Nr
Beaconsfield, Buckinghamshire, HP9 2QZ
Tel: 01494 874505
Email: highclerepark@aol.com
www.highclerefarmpark.co.uk
Pitches For 🏕 ⬛ 🚐 **Total** 100
Acreage 6 **Open** Mar to Jan
Access Good **Site** Level
Nearest Bus Stop (Miles) Outside
Near to Legoland, Chiltern Air Museum,
Miltons Cottage, Odds Farm (Rare Breeds),
Bekonscot, Amersham and London.
Facilities ⬛ ✆ 🔒 ▦ ⬛ ℙ ⊙ ⊿ ▦ ◻ ☎
♨ ℙ ⬛ 🅿 🔲
Nearest Town Beaconsfield
Directions Leave the M40 at junction 2, go
into Beaconsfield and take the A355 towards
Amersham. After 1 mile turn right to Seer
Green and follow tourist signs.
🚏 Seer Green

MILTON KEYNES

**Gulliver's Milton Keynes Camping &
Caravanning Club Site,** Livingstone Drive,
Milton Keynes, Buckinghamshire, MK15
0DT
Tel: 02476 475580
Email: gullivers.site@thefriendlyclub.co.uk
**www.campingandcaravanningclub.co.uk/
gullivers**
Pitches For 🏕 ⬛ 🚐 **Total** 90
Open 31-Mar to 04-Nov
Access Good **Site** Level
Nearest Bus Stop (Miles) ½
Adjacent to Gulliver's Land Theme Park and
near a lake. Just a short drive to Central
Milton Keynes. Pods for Glamping. Excellent
location for footpaths and cycle routes. Non
members welcome. You can also call us on
0845 130 7633.
Facilities ⬛ ✆ 🔒 ▦ ⬛ ℙ ⊙ ⊿ ◻ ☎
🔒 ⬛ ▦ 🅿 🔲 🛜
Nearest Town Milton Keynes
Directions From the M1 take the A509
towards Central Milton Keynes and follow
signs for Gullivers Theme Park (on the V10
Brickhill Street).
🚏 Milton Keynes

NEWPORT PAGNELL

Lovat Meadow Touring Caravan Park, c/
o Middleton Pool, Tickford Street, Newport
Pagnell, Buckinghamshire, MK16 9BG
Tel: 01908 610477
Email: middletonpool@newport-
pagnell.org.uk
www.newport-pagnell.org.uk
Pitches For ⬛ 🚐 **Total** 40
Open Apr (TBC) to Oct
Access Good **Site** Lev/Slope
Nearest Bus Stop (Miles) ¼
Situated by a small river. Ideal for Central
Milton Keynes with its shopping centre and
Xscape, also for the MK Bowl.
Facilities ⬛ ☎ 🔲 ⬛ ▦ 🅿 🔲
Nearest Town Newport Pagnell

Directions 1½ miles from the M1 junction
14. From Newport Pagnell town centre, turn
into St Johns Street, go over the iron bridge
onto London Road and the Park entrance is
on the right after the BP Garage.
🚏 Milton Keynes

OLNEY

Emberton Country Park, Olney Road,
Emberton, Buckinghamshire, MK46 5FJ
Tel: 01234 711575
Email: embertonpark@milton-
keynes.gov.uk
Pitches For 🏕 ⬛ 🚐 🚐 **Total** 48
Open Apr to Oct
Access Good **Site** Level
Nearest Bus Stop (Miles) ¼ mile
Country Park
Facilities ⬛ ✆ 🔒 ▦ ℙ ⊿ ◻ ☎
🔒 ✗ ▦ 🅿 ⬛ ⊿ 🔧
Nearest Town Olney
Directions On the A509, 6 miles north of the
M1 junction 14.
🚏 Milton Keynes

CAMBRIDGESHIRE

CAMBRIDGE

Appleacre Park, London Road, Fowlmere,
Cambridgeshire, SG8 7RU
Tel: 01763 208354
Email: tony@appleacrepark.co.uk
www.appleacrepark.co.uk
Pitches For 🏕 ⬛ 🚐 **Total** 23
Acreage 3 **Open** All Year
Access Good **Site** Level
Nearest Bus Stop (Miles) Entrance
A small pleasant Park at the southern end of
the village. Only 3 miles from Duxford
Imperial War Museum. RSPB Nature
Reserve just a 20 minute walk away.
Facilities ✆ 🔒 ▦ ⬛ ℙ ⊙ ⊿ ◻ ☎
℄ ▦ 🅿 🔲
Nearest Town Cambridge
Directions 9 miles south of Cambridge on
the B1368 through Fowlmere Village on the
left hand side.
🚏 Foxton

CAMBRIDGE

**Cambridge Cherry Hinton Caravan Club
Site,** Lime Kiln Road, Cherry Hinton,
Cambridgeshire, CB1 8NQ
Tel: 01223 244088
www.caravanclub.co.uk
Pitches For 🏕 ⬛ 🚐 **Total** 60
Acreage 5½ **Open** All Year
Access Good **Site** Level
Nearest Bus Stop (Miles) ½
Set in old quarry works with imaginative
landscaping. Only ½ a mile from Cambridge
town centre. Close to the American War
Cemetary, Duxford Imperial War Museum,
Wicken Fen Nature Reserve, Wimpole Hall
and Audley End House & Gardens. Non
members welcome. Booking essential.
Facilities ⬛ ✆ 🔒 ▦ ⬛ ℙ ⊙ ⊿ ◻ ☎
℄ 🔒 ⬛ ▦ 🅿 🔲 🛜
Nearest Town Cambridge

Directions From south west on A10, pass over
M11 junc 11 and continue onto A1309 sp
Cambridge. At the fifth set of traffic lights turn
right into Long Road(A1134) After 1½ miles
at the r/about continue to Queen Ediths Way,
after 1 mile turn right into Lime Kiln Road.
🚏 Cambridge

CAMBRIDGE

Highfield Farm Touring Park, Highfield
Farm, Long Road, Comberton, Cambridge,
Cambridgeshire, CB23 7DG
Tel: 01223 262308
Email:
enquiries@highfieldfarmtouringpark.co.uk
www.highfieldfarmtouringpark.co.uk
Pitches For 🏕 ⬛ 🚐 **Total** 120
Acreage 8 **Open** Apr to Oct
Access Good **Site** Level
Nearest Bus Stop (Miles) ½
Well maintained, long established family run
Touring Park. 1½ miles of farmland walks.
Close to the historic University City of
Cambridge, and the Imperial War Museum,
Duxford. Calor Caravan Park Awards 2002,
Best Park in England (Finalist).
Facilities ✆ 🔒 ▦ ⬛ ℙ ⊙ ⊿ ◻ ☎
♨ ℙ ℙ ⬛ ⬛ ▦ ✚ ▦ 🔲
Nearest Town Cambridge
Directions From Cambridge - Leave A1303/
A428 (Bedford) after 3 miles, follow camping
signs to Comberton. From M11 - Leave
junction 12, take A603 (Sandy) for ½ mile
then B1046 to Comberton (2 miles).
🚏 Cambridge

CAMBRIDGE

Roseberry Tourist Park, Earith Road,
Willingham, Cambridgeshire, CB24 5LT
Tel: 01954 260346
Email: info@roseberrytouristpark.co.uk
www.roseberrytouristpark.co.uk
Pitches For 🏕 ⬛ 🚐 🚐 **Total** 90
Acreage 10 **Open** All Year
Access Good **Site** Level
Nearest Bus Stop (Miles) 1
Ideal for touring Cambridge and surrounding
Market towns of St. Ives, Huntingdon and Ely.
Facilities ✆ 🔒 ▦ ⬛ ℙ ⊙ ⊿ ◻ ☎
℄ ▦ 🅿 🔲 ⊿ 🔧
Nearest Town Cambridge
Directions Northwest of Cambridge on A14
Junc 29 Bar Hill, Follow B1050 towards
Willingham. Site 1 mile north of Willingham
🚏 Cambridge/Waterbeach

EARITH

Westview Marina, High Street, Earith,
Huntingdon, Cambridgeshire, PE28 3PN
Tel: 01487 841627
Email: elainefidler@homecall.co.uk
Pitches For ⬛ 🚐 **Total** 28
Acreage 2 **Open** March to October
Access Good **Site** Level
Nearest Bus Stop (Miles) Outside
River frontage. Ideal touring.
Facilities 🔒 ▦ ℙ 🅿 🔲 ⊙ ⊿ ⊿ ⊿
Nearest Town St. Ives (Cambs)
Directions 5 miles from St. Ives and 12 miles
from Cambridge.
🚏 Huntingdon

ELY

Riverside Caravan & Camping Park, 21
New River Bank, Littleport, Ely,
Cambridgeshire, CB7 4TA
Tel: 01353 860255
Email: riversideccp@btopenworld.com
www.riversideccp.co.uk
Pitches For ▲ ⊞ ⊟ **Total** 49
Acreage 4½ **Open** All Year
Access Good **Site** Level
Nearest Bus Stop (Miles) ¼
ADULTS ONLY site alongside the River Ouse
for fishing and boating. 5 miles from the
historic city and cathedral of Ely.
Facilities ⌁ ⌂ ⎙ ♒ ⌐ ⊙ ⊐ ☕
♿ ⊙ ⊬ ⊟ △ ⅍ ☎
Nearest Town Ely
Directions On the A10, 5 miles north of Ely,
cross the River Ouse and turn right at the
roundabout.
⚏ Littleport

GRAFHAM

Grafham Water Caravan Club Site,
Church Road, Grafham, Huntingdon,
Cambridgeshire, PE28 0BB
Tel: 01480 810264
www.caravanclub.co.uk
Pitches For ⊞ ⊟ **Total** 87
Acreage 6 **Open** Mar **to** Nov
Access Good **Site** Level
Nearest Bus Stop (Miles) ½
Near to Grafham Water. Refurbished amenity
block. David Bellamy Gold Award for
Conservation 2005. Non members welcome.
Booking essential.
Facilities ⌁ ⌂ ⎙ ♒ ⌐ ⊙ ⊐ ☕
♿ ⊙ ⊠ ⊬ ⊟ ⊡ ⅍ ☎
Nearest Town Huntingdon
Directions From the A1 at Buckden
roundabout follow caravan park signs. From
the A14 leave at Ellington and follow caravan
park signs from the village.
⚏ Huntingdon

GREAT SHELFORD

**Cambridge Camping & Caravanning
Club Site,** 19 Cabbage Moor, Great
Shelford, Cambridgeshire, CB22 5NB
Tel: 01223 841185
Email:
cambridge@thefriendlyclub.co.uk
www.campingandcaravanningclub.co.uk/
cambridge
Pitches For ▲ ⊞ ⊟ **Total** 120
Open 21-Mar **to** 04-Nov
Site Level
Nearest Bus Stop (Miles) ¼
On the outskirts of the city of Cambridge. 6
miles from Duxford Imperial War Museum
and the American Cemetery. Boat launching.
Dog Walk. 4 Star Graded and AA 3 Pennants.
Non members welcome. You can also call
us on 0845 130 7633.
Facilities ⌁ ⎙ ♒ ⌐ ⊙ ⊐ ☕
♿ ⊙ ⊠ ⊬ ⊟ ☎
Directions Leave the M11 at junction 11 onto
the B1309 signposted Cambridge. At the first
set of traffic lights turn right, after ½ mile you
will see the site sign on the left hand side
pointing down the lane.
⚏ Great Shelford

HUNTINGDON

Burleigh Hill Farm, Somersham Road, St
Ives, Huntingdon, Cambridgeshire, PE27
3LY
Tel: 01480 462173
Email: mschwier@talk21.com
Pitches For ▲ ⊞ ⊟ ⊟ **Total** 40
Acreage 8 **Open** All Year

Access Good **Site** Level
Nearest Bus Stop (Miles) ½
Relaxing picturesque parkland area.
Walkways and trees around the farm with
information plaques and environmental
projects to see. Ideal for nature lovers and
walkers. You can also call us on Mobile:
07855 286238.
Facilities ⌁ ⌂ ⎙ ♒ ⌐ ⊙ ⊐ ☕ ⅍ ♒
Nearest Town St Ives
Directions From the M11 north of Cambridge
(which becomes the A14 to Huntingdon), take
the A1096 to St. Ives, cross the river bridge
and roundabout and follow the B1040
towards Somersham. Go past St. Ives
Industrial Estate on the left, at the mini
roundabout turn left. After a third of a mile
the farm is on the left, continue down the
private tarmac drive.
⚏ Huntingdon

HUNTINGDON

Houghton Mill Caravan Club Site, Mill
Street, Houghton, Huntingdon,
Cambridgeshire, PE28 2AZ
Tel: 01480 466716
www.caravanclub.co.uk
Pitches For ▲ ⊞ ⊟ **Total** 54
Acreage 8½ **Open** March **to** Nov
Access Good **Site** Level
Nearest Bus Stop (Miles) ½
On the banks of the River Great Ouse.
Adjacent to Houghton Mill working museum.
Ideal for walkers, bird watchers and wildlife
enthusiasts. Non members welcome.
Booking essential.
Facilities ⌁ ⌂ ⎙ ♒ ⌐ ⊙ ♿ ⊙ ⊠ ⊬ ⊡
Nearest Town Huntingdon
Directions From the A1(M)/A1 turn onto the
A14 sp Huntingdon, then take the A141. At
Texaco roundabout turn onto the A1123 sp
Houghton, after 1¼ miles turn right sp
Houghton, continue into Mill Street, pass the
church and site is on the left.
⚏ Huntingdon

HUNTINGDON

Huntingdon Boathaven & Caravan Park,
The Avenue, Godmanchester, Huntingdon,
Cambridgeshire, PE18 8AF
Tel: 01480 411977
Email: boathaven.hunts@virgin.net
www.huntingdonboathaven.co.uk
Pitches For ▲ ⊞ ⊟ **Total** 35
Acreage 2 **Open** Mar **to** Oct
Access Good **Site** Level
Nearest Bus Stop (Miles) ¼
Marina and caravan park situated on the
Great River Ouse. Near to many tourist
attractions. Limited fishing on site.
Facilities ⌁ ⌁ ⌂ ⎙ ♒ ⌐ ⊙ ☕
♿ ⊙ ⊠ ⊟ ⌀ ⅍
Nearest Town Cambridge
Directions From the A14 turn off to
Godmanchester and travel towards
Huntingdon. Turn left before the fly-over to
Huntingdon Boathaven.
⚏ Huntingdon

HUNTINGDON

Quiet Waters Caravan Park, Hemingford
Abbots, Huntingdon, Cambridgeshire,
PE28 9AJ
Tel: 01480 463405
Email: quietwaters.park@btopenworld.com
www.quietwaterscaravanpark.co.uk
Pitches For ▲ ⊞ ⊟ **Total** 20
Acreage ½ **Open** April **to** October
Access Good **Site** Level
Nearest Bus Stop (Miles) Outside
In the centre of a riverside village, good for
fishing and boating.

Facilities ⌁ ⌁ ⎙ ⎙ ♒ ⌐ ⊙ ⊐ ☕
♿ ⊙ ⊠ ⊬ ⊟ ⊡ ⌀ ⅍ ☎
Nearest Town St Ives/Huntingdon
Directions Junction 25 off the A14. West of
Cambridge on the A14, after 12 miles look
for Hemingford Abbots, we are 1 mile into
the village. 3 miles east of Huntingdon on
the A14.
⚏ Huntingdon

HUNTINGDON

Stroud Hill Park, Fen Road, Pidley,
Huntingdon, Cambridgeshire, PE28 3DE
Tel: 01487 741333
Email: stroudhillpark@btconnect.com
www.stroudhillpark.co.uk
Pitches For ▲ ⊞ ⊟ **Total** 60
Open All Year
Access Good **Site** Lev/Slope
Nearest Bus Stop (Miles) ½
Quiet, attractive, rural, ADULTS ONLY site.
Set in ancient bluebell woodland on a 150
acre family farm. Tennis on site. 18 hole golf
course next door.
Facilities ⌁ ⌂ ⎙ ♒ ⌐ ⊙ ⊐ ☕ ⎐ ⊡ ☎
♿ ⊙ ⊠ ⊗ ⌀ ⊬ ⊟ ⊡ ⌀ ⅍ ☎
Nearest Town St Ives
Directions Take the A141 signposted March,
4 miles from St Ives and 7 miles from
Huntingdon.
⚏ Huntingdon

HUNTINGDON

The Willows Caravan Park, Bromholme
Lane, Brampton, Huntingdon,
Cambridgeshire, PE18 8NE
Tel: 01480 437566
Email: willows@willows33.freeserve.co.uk
www.willowscaravanpark.com
Pitches For ▲ ⊞ ⊟ ⊟ ⊑ **Total** 70
Acreage 4 **Open** All Year
Access Good **Site** Level
Nearest Bus Stop (Miles) ¼
Situated in Ouse Valley Way, attractive
walks. Launching area for boats and canoes.
Fishing and boating available. Separate tent
field. No groundsheets. Heated toilet block.
Resident wardens on site. Country park,
Grafham Water and sports facilities nearby.
Site is Caravan Club, Camping &
Caravanning Club and AA Listed.
Facilities ⌁ ⌂ ⎙ ♒ ⌐ ⊙ ⊐ ☕
♿ ⊗ ⌀ ⊬ ⊟ ⅍
Nearest Town Huntingdon
Directions Brampton is situated between the
A1 and the A14 (formerly A604). Follow the
B1514 through Brampton towards
Huntingdon, taking right hand signposted
turning into Bromholme Lane.
⚏ Huntingdon

PETERBOROUGH

Ferry Meadows Caravan Club Site, Ham Lane, Peterborough, Cambridgeshire, PE2 5UU
Tel: 01733 233526
www.caravanclub.co.uk
Pitches For ▲ ⛺ 🚐 **Total** 265
Acreage 30 **Open** All Year
Access Good **Site** Level
Nearest Bus Stop (Miles) ½
Set in a country park with plenty of activities available nearby, and a 6 acre shopping complex. Near to Nene Valley Steam Railway. Non members welcome. Booking essential.
Facilities ⬥ ♦ 🌳 🅭 ⌂ 🏳️ ⚲ ☂
🏧 🛈 🛒 🔌 ☎
Nearest Town Peterborough
Directions From South on the A1, do not turn onto the A1139, instead turn left at next junction just past the service station sp Showground. At the T-junction turn left, continue and turn left sp Nene Park, continue and site is on the left.
➤ Peterborough

ST. NEOTS

Camping & Caravanning Club Site, Hardwick Road, Eynesbury, St. Neots, Cambridgeshire, PE19 2PR
Tel: 01480 474404
Email: stneots.site@thefriendlyclub.co.uk
www.campingandcaravanningclub.co.uk/stneots
Pitches For ▲ ⛺ 🚐 **Total** 180
Acreage 11 **Open** 21-Mar **to** 05-Nov
Access Good **Site** Level
Nearest Bus Stop (Miles) ½
On the banks of the River Ouse for boating, fishing and walking. Plenty of sports facilities in the area. Non members welcome. You can also call us on 0845 130 7633.
Facilities ⬥ ♦ 🌳 🅭 ⌂ ⚲ ☂ 🏧 🛈 🛒 🔌 ☎ 🛜
Nearest Town Cambridge
Directions From the A1 take the A428 to Cambridge, at the second roundabout turn left to Tescos, go past the sports centre and follow the international signs to the site.
➤ Cambridge

WISBECH

Virginia Lake Caravan Park, Smeeth Road, St Johns Fen End, Wisbech, Cambridgeshire, PE14 8JF
Tel: 01945 430167/430585
Email: louise@virginialake.co.uk
www.virginialake.co.uk
Pitches For ▲ ⛺ 🚐 🚐 **Total** 98
Acreage 7 **Open** All Year
Access Good **Site** Level
Nearest Bus Stop (Miles) ½
Set in Fenland countryside with a fishing lake and clubhouse. 30 minutes from the beach.
Facilities ⬥ ♦ 🌳 🅭 ⌂ ⚲ ☂ 🏳️ 🛈 🛒
🏧 🛈 🛒 🔌 🍴 🚻 🔌 🛒 ☎ 🛜 ⚲ 🔥 ⚓
Nearest Town Wisbech/Kings Lynn
Directions From either direction, turn off the A47 halfway between Wisbech and Kings Lynn at the junction to Terrington St John.
➤ Kings Lynn

CHANNEL ISLES

JERSEY

Rozel Camping Park, La Grande Route De Rozel, Rozel, St Martin, Channel Isles, JE3 6AX
Tel: 01534 855200
Email: rozelcampingpark@jerseymail.co.uk
www.rozelcamping.co.uk
Pitches For ▲ ⛺ 🚐 **Total** 200
Open Mid May **to** Mid Sept
Access Good **Site** Level
Nearest Bus Stop (Miles) Outside
Near beach with views to France.
Facilities ⬥ ♦ 🅭 ⌂ ⚲ ☂ 🏳️ 🛒 🖥 ☎
🏧 🛈 🛒 🔌 🍴 🛒 🔌 🚻 🔌 🛒 🛜
Nearest Town Rozel Bay
Directions On leaving Elizabeth Harbour by La Route du Port Elizabeth, take the A1 to the east, then the A17, go to the 4th set of traffic lights and turn left onto the A6. Stay in the middle lane and continue on the A6 to Five Oaks, then St Martins Church. Take the B38 to Rozel and the Park is on the right hand side.

CHESHIRE

CHESTER

Chester Fairoaks Caravan Club Site, Rake Lane, Little Stanney, Chester, Cheshire, CH2 4HS
Tel: 0151 355 1600
www.caravanclub.co.uk
Pitches For ▲ ⛺ 🚐 **Total** 100
Acreage 8 **Open** All Year
Access Good **Site** Level
Nearest Bus Stop (Miles) ½
Pleasant open and level site with oak tree boundaries. Close to the delightful city of Chester. Non members welcome. Booking essential.
Facilities ⬥ ♦ 🌳 🅭 ⌂ ⚲ ☂ 🏳️ ⚓ ☎
🏧 🛈 🛒 🔌 🚻 🔌 🛒 🛜
Nearest Town Chester
Directions Leave the M53 at junction 10 and take the A5117 signposted Queensferry. After ¼ mile in Little Stanney turn left signposted Chorlton. Site is ¼ mile on the left.
➤ Chester

CHESTER

Manor Wood Country Caravan Park, Manor Wood, Coddington, Chester, Cheshire, CH3 9EN
Tel: 01829 782990
Email: info@manorwoodcaravans.co.uk
www.manorwoodcaravans.co.uk
Pitches For ▲ ⛺ 🚐 **Total** 25
Acreage 8 **Open** All Year
Access Good **Site** Level
Nearest Bus Stop (Miles) ¼
Excellent views. Only 15 minutes from Chester City. Fishing on site. Fantastic walks and cycleways. Golf courses within 5 minutes drive.
Facilities ⬥ ♦ 🌳 🅭 ⌂ ⚲ ☂ 🏳️ 🛒 🖥 ☎
🏧 🛈 🛒 🔌 🍴 🛒 🔌 🚻 🔌 🛒 🛜 ⚲ 🔥 ⚓
Nearest Town Chester
Directions From the A41 Whitchurch to Chester road, at Broxton roundabout take the A534 signposted Wrexham. Turn opposite the Cock O Barton Pub and the Park is 500 yards on the left.
➤ Chester

CHESTER

Netherwood Touring Site, Netherwood House, Whitchurch Road, Nr Chester, Cheshire, CH3 6AF
Tel: 01244 335583
Email: netherwood.chester@btinternet.com
www.netherwoodtouringsite.co.uk
Pitches For ⛺ 🚐 **Total** 15
Acreage 1½ **Open** March **to** 31-Oct
Access Good **Site** Level
Nearest Bus Stop (Miles) Outside
ADULTS ONLY site on the Shropshire Union Canal. 5 miles from a Zoo.
Facilities ♦ 🅭 ⌂ ⚲ ☂ 🏳️ 🛈 🛒 🔌 🍴 ⚲ 🅰
Nearest Town Chester
Directions On A41, approx. 1 mile from Chester bypass.
➤ Chester

KNUTSFORD

Royal Vale Caravan Park, London Road, Allostock, Knutsford, Cheshire, WA16 9JD
Tel: 01565 722355
Email: canistay@royalvale.co.uk
www.royalvale.co.uk
Pitches For ▲ ⛺ 🚐 🚐 **Total** 52
Access Good **Site** Level
ADULTS ONLY PARK situated in the heart of Cheshire countryside, 3 miles south of the historic market town of Knutsford, which has an excellent shopping centre, fine restaurants and old inns. Country walks direct from the Park. Historic homes nearby including Tatton Park, Gawsworth Hall and Little Moreton Hall.

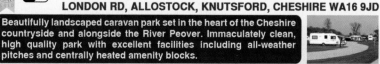
13

Facilities ⚅ ✦ ⊟ ◫ ◱ ⌐ ⊙⌐ ⊿ ◨ ▣ ☎
◨ ✕⊟◨ ▣ ☒ ▲ ☀ ⎌

Nearest Town Knutsford
Directions Just off the A50 midway between Knutsford and Holmes Chapel.
⚏ Knutsford

KNUTSFORD

Woodlands Park, Wash Lane, Allostock, Cheshire, WA16 9LG
Tel: 01565 723429
Email: jane@rongrundy.co.uk
Pitches For ▲ ⊟ ⊟ **Total** 20
Open Mar **to** 06-Jan
Access Good **Site** Level
Nearest Bus Stop (Miles) ¼
Facilities ⚅ ✦ ◫ ◱ ⌐ ⊙ ▣ ⊿⊟✕☀
Directions Take the A50 Knutsford road, Wash Lane is left turn after Boundary Water Park.
⚏ Goostrey

MACCLESFIELD

Strawberry Wood Caravan Park, Home Farm, Farm Lane, Lower Withington, Macclesfield, Cheshire, SK11 9DU
Tel: 01477 571407
Email:
info@strawberrywoodcaravanpark.co.uk
www.strawberrywoodcaravanpark.co.uk
Pitches For ⊟ ⊟ **Total** 25
Acreage 5 **Open** March **to** October
Access Good **Site** Level
Unique site set amongst mature woodland. Large coarse fishing pond adjacent to the site.
Facilities ✦ ◫ ◱ ⌐ ⊙ ⊟ ▣ ✎ ☀ ✎
Nearest Town Macclesfield
Directions Leave the M6 at junction 18 and take the A54 to Holmes Chapel. Then take the A535 to Macclesfield, after 4 miles turn right onto the B5392 (Farm Lane). The site entrance is 700 yards on the right hand side.
⚏ Goostrey

NORTHWICH

Delamere Forest Camping & Caravanning Club Site, Station Road, Delamere, Northwich, Cheshire, CW8 2HZ
Tel: 01606 889231
Email:
delamere.forest@thefriendlyclub.co.uk
www.campingandcaravanningclub.co.uk/
delamere
Pitches For ▲ ⊟ ⊟ **Total** 80
Acreage 6 **Open** All Year
Access Good **Site** Level
Ideal for walking and cycling (bike hire). Near to Chester Zoo, Go Ape Adventure Playground, Oulton Park Raceway, Railway Age Museum and Beeston Castle. Non members welcome. You can also call us on 0845 130 7633.
Facilities ⚅ ✦ ◫ ◱ ⌐ ⊙⌐ ⊿ ◨ ▣
◨ ⊟✕⊟▣ ⎌
Nearest Town Frodsham
Directions From the A556 in Delamere turn into Station Road and the Site is located on the opposite side of the train tracks.
⚏ Northwich

NORTHWICH

Woodbine Cottage Caravan Park, Warrington Road, Acton Bridge, Northwich, Cheshire, CW8 3QB
Tel: 01606 852319
Email: jjdone@woodbinecottage-caravanpark.co.uk
Pitches For ▲ ⊟ ⊟ **Total** 55
Acreage 2½ **Open** March **to** Oct
Access Good **Site** Lev/Slope

Situated on the banks of the River Weaver. Nearby attractions including Blakemere Crafts and Anderton Boat Lift. Within easy reach of Chester, Liverpool, Manchester and the North Wales coast. Static caravans for hire. You can also contact us on Mobile: 07747 175327.
Facilities ✦ ◫ ◱ ⌐ ⊙⌐ ⊿ ◨ ▣
◨ ▣ ☒ ▲ ✕☀
Nearest Town Northwich
Directions Leave the M56 at Junction 10 and take the A49 towards Whitchurch. Continue across Acton Swing Bridge and the Park entrance is on the left after the Riverside Inn.
⚏ Acton Bridge

WINSFORD

Lamb Cottage Caravan Park, Dalefords Lane, Whitegate, Northwich, Cheshire, CW8 2BN
Tel: 01606 882302
Email: info@lambcottage.co.uk
www.lambcottage.co.uk
Pitches For ⊟ ⊟
Open Mar **to** Oct
Access Good **Site** Level
Peaceful retreat for Adults only. Ideal for touring the heart of Cheshire.
Facilities ✦ ⊟ ◫ ◱ ⌐ ⊙⌐ ⊿ ◨ ▣ ☎
◨ ⊟✕⊟▣ ☒ ▲ ☀ ⎌
Nearest Town Winsford
Directions 1 mile from the A556.
⚏ Cuddington

CORNWALL

BODMIN

Lanarth Hotel & Caravan Park, St Kew Highway, Bodmin, Cornwall, PL30 3EE
Tel: 01208 841215
Email: lanarthhotel@live.co.uk
www.lanarthhotel.co.uk
Pitches For ▲ ⊟ ⊟ **Total** 86
Acreage 10 **Open** April **to** October
Access Good **Site** Level
Beautiful rural setting, conveniently situated for beaches and moors. Ideal for touring Cornwall and Devon.
Facilities ✦ ◫ ◱ ⌐ ⊙ ⊿ ◨ ☒ ▣ ☎
Nearest Town Wadebridge
Directions On the A39 at St. Kew Highway, approx 4 miles east of Wadebridge and 8 miles west of Camelford.
⚏ Bodmin

BUDE

Bude Camping & Caravanning Club Site, Gillards Moor, St Gennys, Bude, Cornwall, EX23 0BG
Tel: 01840 230650
Email: bude@thefriendlyclub.co.uk
www.campingandcaravanningclub.co.uk/
bude
Pitches For ▲ ⊟ ⊟ **Total** 100
Acreage 6 **Open** 30-Apr **to** 30-Sep
Site Lev/Slope
Nearest Bus Stop (Miles) 1
Near the coastal paths in the heart of King Arthurs Country. Table tennis on site. BTB 4 Star Graded and AA 3 Pennants. Non members welcome. You can also call us on 0845 130 7633.
Facilities ✦ ◫ ◱ ⌐ ⊙⌐ ⊿ ◨ ▣ ☎
◱ ◨ ☒ ▲ ⌐◫⊟▣
Directions Going south on the A39 the site is on the right in lay-by 9 miles from Bude. Going north on the A39 the site is on the left in lay-by 9 miles from Camelford, approx. 3 miles from the B3262 junction. Brown camping signs ½ mile either side of the site, also on both ends of the lay-by.
⚏ Bodmin

BUDE

Budemeadows Touring Park, Widemouth Bay, Bude, Cornwall, EX23 0NA
Tel: 01288 361646
Email: holiday@budemeadows.com
www.budemeadows.com
Pitches For ▲ ⊟ ⊟ **Total** 145
Acreage 9 **Open** All Year
Access Good **Site** Level
Nearest Bus Stop (Miles) Outside
1 mile from sandy beaches, cliff walks and the rolling surf of Widemouth Bay. Spectacular coastal scenery. Licenced Bar and heated pool.
Facilities ⚅ ✦ ⊟ ◫ ◱ ⌐ ⊙⌐ ⊿ ◨ ▣ ☎
☒ ◨ ▣ ☒ ▲ ⟋ ⌐ ✕⊟▣ ☒ ☀ ⎌
Nearest Town Bude
Directions From Bude take the A39 south for 3 miles.
⚏ Exeter

BUDE

Penhalt Farm Holiday Park, Widemouth Bay, Bude, Cornwall, EX23 0DG
Tel: 01288 361210
Pitches For ▲ ⊟ ⊟ **Total** 100
Acreage 7 **Open** Easter **to** Oct
Access Good **Site** Lev/Slope
Nearest Bus Stop (Miles) 1
2 miles from Widemouth Bay, ideal for surfing and swimming. 5 miles from Bude.
Facilities ⚅ ✦ ◫ ◱ ⌐ ⊙⌐ ⊿ ◨ ▣ ☎
☒ ◨ ▣ ☒ ▲ ✕⊟▣
Nearest Town Bude
Directions On the A39 about 4 miles south of Bude, take the second turn right for Widemouth Bay. Turn left by Widemouth Manor Hotel and the site is two thirds of a mile on the left.
⚏ Exeter

BUDE

Upper Lynstone Camping & Caravan Park, Upper Lynstone Farm, Bude, Cornwall, EX23 0LP
Tel: 01288 352017
Email: reception@upperlynstone.co.uk
www.upperlynstone.co.uk
Pitches For ▲ ⊟ ⊟ **Total** 65
Acreage 5 **Open** Easter **to** October
Access Good **Site** Level
Nearest Bus Stop (Miles) ¼
Facilities ⚅ ✦ ◱ ⌐ ⊙⌐ ⊿ ◨ ▣ ☎
☒ ◨ ✕⊟▣
Directions ½ mile south of Bude on the old coast road.
⚏ Exeter

BUDE

Willow Valley Holiday Park, Dye House, Bush, Bude, Cornwall, EX23 9LB
Tel: 01288 353104
Email: willowvalley@talk21.com
www.willowvalley.co.uk
Pitches For ▲ ⊟ ⊟ **Total** 40
Open Easter **to** Sept
Access Good **Site** Level
Nearest Bus Stop (Miles) 1
2 miles from beach, river runs through site.
Facilities ⚅ ✦ ◫ ◱ ⌐ ⊙⌐ ⊿ ◨ ▣ ☎
☒ ◨ ▣ ✕⊟
Nearest Town Bude
Directions Just off the A39 between Bude and Kilkhampton.

BUDE

Wooda Farm Holiday Park, Poughill, Bude, Cornwall, EX23 9HJ
Tel: 01288 352069
Email: enquiries@wooda.co.uk
www.wooda.co.uk

Pitches For Å ♥ ♥ **Total** 200
Acreage 12 **Open** April **to** October
Access Good **Site** Lev/Slope
Nearest Bus Stop (Miles) Outside
Overlooks sea and coastline. Woodland walks, coarse fishing, large childrens play area, tennis court, badminton court, gym, dog exercise field and short golf course. Sandy beaches 1½ miles. Licensed bar and takeaway. Off License on site.
Facilities ⅊ ∱ ⊞ Ⓜ↯ґ⊙⌂☕⊡♥
ⓈⓁⒾⓄ☺✕⛱♠⋔☀⊁⊟♥⋗♦
Nearest Town Bude
Directions Take road to Poughill 1¼ miles, go through village. At crossroads turn left. Site 200yds along road on right hand side.
⇥ Exeter

BUDE

Woodview Caravan & Camping Park
Little Youlstone, Nr Kilkhampton, Bude, Cornwall, EX23 9PU
Tel: 01288 331492
Email: info@woodviewcampsite.co.uk
www.woodviewcampsite.co.uk
Pitches For Å ♥ ♥ **Total** 100
Acreage 4 **Open** Jan **to** Jan
Access Good **Site** Sloping
Beach 5 miles. Fishing 5 miles. 100 metres to Woodland walks. Riverside stream on site.
Facilities ⅊ ∱ ⊞ Ⓜ↯ґ⊙⌂☕⊡♥
ⓈⒾ⛱♠⋔♠♥☀
Nearest Town Bude
Directions Kilkhampton to Bideford A39. Take first right, then first left.
⇥ Exeter/Barnsatple

CAMELFORD

Lakefield Caravan Park, Lower Pendavey Farm, Camelford, Cornwall, PL32 9TX
Tel: 01840 213279
Email:
lakefieldequestriancentre@btconnect.com
www.lakefieldcaravanpark.co.uk
Pitches For Å ♥ ♥ **Total** 40
Acreage 5 **Open** Apr **to** Sept
Access Good **Site** Level
Nearest Bus Stop (Miles) ½
3 miles from the beach and 1 mile from local amenities. Full equestrian facilities providing lessons, site rides and hacks for all the family. Close to the Moors and 2 miles form a golf course.
Facilities ∱ ↯ґ⊙⌂☕⊡♥
ⓈⓁⒾⓄ✕⛱☀⊁⊟⊟♥
Nearest Town Camelford
Directions 1 miles north of Camelford on the B3266 Boscastle road.
⇥ Bodmin

CARLYON BAY

Carlyon Bay Camping Park, Cypress Avenue, Carlyon Bay, St Austell, Cornwall, PL25 3RE
Tel: 01726 812735
Email: holidays@carlyonbay.net
www.carlyonbay.net
Pitches For Å ♥ ♥ **Total** 180
Acreage 18 **Open** Easter **to** Oct
Access Good **Site** Level
⇥ Par

COVERACK

Little Trevothan Caravan Park, Coverack, Helston, Cornwall, TR12 6SD
Tel: 01326 280260
Email: sales@littletrevothan.co.uk
www.littletrevothan.co.uk
Pitches For Å ♥ ♥
Acreage 10½ **Open** Mar **to** Dec
Access Good **Site** Level
Nearest Bus Stop (Miles) 1
¾ miles from the beach in an area of outstanding natural beauty.
Facilities ∱ Ⓜ↯ґ⊙⌂☕⊡♥
ⓈⓁⒾⓄ⛱♠⋔♠⊁⊟☀♥♦
Nearest Town Helston
Directions Take the A39 to Helston, then follow the B3083 to Culdrose, turn left onto the B3293 signposted Coverack. Go past BT Goonhilly, turn right before Zoar Garage, third turning on the left, site is 300yds on the right.
⇥ Redruth

COVERACK

Penmarth Farm Camp Site, Coverack, Helston, Cornwall,
Tel: 01326 280389
Pitches For Å ♥ ♥ **Total** 28
Acreage 2 **Open** March **to** October
Access Good **Site** Level
Nearest Bus Stop (Miles) ¼
¼ mile woodland walk to the sea and beach.
Facilities ⚹ Ⓜ↯ґ⊙⌂☕ ⓁⒾⓄ⋔
Nearest Town Helston
Directions From Helston take the B3293 for approx. 10 miles.
⇥ Cambourne

CRACKINGTON HAVEN

Hentervene Park, Crackington Haven, Bude, Cornwall, EX23 0LF
Tel: 01840 230365
Email: contact@hentervene.co.uk
www.hentervene.co.uk
Pitches For ♥ ♥ **Total** 11
Acreage 8 **Open** Mar **to** Oct
Access Good **Site** Level
Nearest Bus Stop (Miles) Outside
Beautiful and peaceful Park situated in North Cornish countryside. 2 miles from the beach

for sands, swimming and surfing. Self catering accommodation also available.
Facilities ∱ ⊞ Ⓜ↯ґ⊙⌂☕⊡♥
⚹☺♠⋔⊁⊟⊡⊞☀♥
Nearest Town Bude
Directions From Bude take the A39 Wadebridge road. Approx 1½ miles after Wainhouse Corner, turn right sp Crackington Haven. At the junction in ¾ miles turn right and see the Hentervene sign, Park is ½ a mile on the right.
⇥ Bodmin Parkway

CRANTOCK

Quarryfield Holiday Park, Crantock, Newquay, Cornwall, TR8 5RJ
Tel: 01637 830338/872792
Email: info@quarryfield.co.uk
www.quarryfield.co.uk
Pitches For Å ♥ ♥ **Total** 125
Acreage 4½ **Open** Easter **to** End Oct
Access Good **Site** Lev/Slope
Nearest Bus Stop (Miles) ¼
Just a 10 minute walk to the village, Crantock beach and the River Gannel.
Facilities ⅊ ∱ Ⓜ↯ґ⊙⌂☕⊡♥
ⓈⓁⒾⓄ⛱♠⋔☀⊁⊟⊟♥
Nearest Town Newquay
Directions From the A3075 Newquay to Redruth road, turn off signposted Crantock Village, site is approx. 2½ miles.
⇥ Newquay

CRANTOCK

Treago Farm Caravan & Camping Site, Treago Farm, Crantock, Nr Newquay, Cornwall, TR8 5QS
Tel: 01637 830277
Email: info@treagofarm.co.uk
www.treagofarm.co.uk
Pitches For Å ♥ ♥ **Total** 81
Open Easter **to** Early Oct
Access Good **Site** Level
Nearest Bus Stop (Miles) ½
Within walking distance to Crantock and two sandy beaches.
Facilities ⅊ ∱ Ⓜ↯ґ⊙⌂☕⊡♥
ⓈⒾⓄ⛱♠⋔⊁⊟⊟♦
Nearest Town Newquay
Directions 2 miles south west of Newquay. Turn right off the A3075 and follow camping signs.
⇥ Newquay

FALMOUTH

Pennance Mill Farm Touring Park, Pennance Mill Farm, Maenporth Road, Falmouth, Cornwall, TR11 5HJ
Tel: 01326 317431
Email: jewellshj@bt.internet.com
Pitches For Å ♥ ♥ ♥ ⚃ **Total** 75

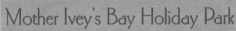
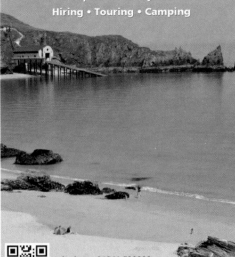

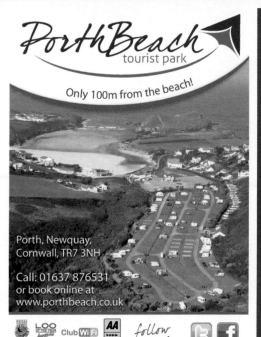

Acreage 8 **Open** Easter **to** Oct
Access Good **Site** Lev/slope
Nearest Bus Stop (Miles) Outside
½ mile to beach, private path to beach.
Facilities ∫ ⊞ ⊟ ⎈ ⎗ ⌐ ⌣ ↰ ⌂ ◎ ⌓
⌕ ◉ ◔ ☂ ⋀ ⋈ ⊹ ⊞
Nearest Town Falmouth
Directions A390 turn right at Hillhead Roundabout, follow campsite signs 2 miles off roundabout.
⇌ Penmere

FALMOUTH

Retanna Holiday Park, Edgcumbe, Helston, Cornwall, TR13 0EJ
Tel: 01326 340643
Email: retannaholpark@btconnect.com
www.retanna.co.uk
Pitches For ⋏ ⌓ **Total** 24
Acreage 8 **Open** March **to** Nov
Access Good **Site** Lev/Slope
Nearest Bus Stop (Miles) Entrance
Just a short drive to The Flambards Experience, Gweek Seal Sanctuary and Poldark Mine.
Facilities ∫ ⌐ ⎗ ⌐ ⌣ ↰ ⌂ ◎ ⌓
⌕ ◉ ◔ ☂ ⋀ ⋈ ⊞ ⊟ ⋈
Nearest Town Falmouth
Directions Midway between Falmouth and Helston on the A394, on the right hand side after passing through Edgcumbe.
⇌ Falmouth/Truro

FALMOUTH

Tregedna Farm Touring Caravan & Camping Park, Maenporth, Falmouth, Cornwall, TR11 5HL
Tel: 01326 250529
www.tregednafarmholidays.co.uk
Pitches For ⋏ ⌓ ⌯ **Total** 40

Acreage 12 **Open** Easter **to** End Sept
Access Good **Site** Sloping
Nearest Bus Stop (Miles) ¼
Situated in the beautiful Maen Valley, just minutes from the beach and surrounded by wooded countryside.
Facilities ∫ ⎗ ⌐ ⌣ ↰ ⌂ ◎ ⌓
⌕ ◉ ◔ ☂ ⋈ ⊞
Nearest Town Falmouth
Directions Take the A39 from Truro to Falmouth, 2½ miles to Falmouth on the Maenporth to Mawnan Smith road.
⇌ Penmere

FOWEY

Penhale Caravan & Camping Park, Fowey, Cornwall, PL23 1JU
Tel: 01726 833425
Email: info@penhale-fowey.co.uk
www.penhale-fowey.co.uk
Pitches For ⋏ ⌓ ⌯ **Total** 56
Acreage 5 **Open** April **to** October
Access Good **Site** Lev/Slope
Splendid views, close to sandy beaches with many lovely walks nearby. Central for touring.
Facilities ∫ ⎗ ⌐ ⌣ ↰ ⌂ ◎ ⌓
⌕ ⌕ ◉ ◔ ☂ ⋈ ⊞ ⊟ ⋈ ⚡
Nearest Town Fowey
Directions 1 mile west of Lostwithiel on the A390, turn left onto the B3269. After 3 miles turn right at the roundabout onto the A3082. Penhale is 500yds on the left.
⇌ Par

FOWEY

Penmarlam Caravan & Camping Park, Bodinnick-by-Fowey, Fowey, Cornwall, PL23 1LZ
Tel: 01726 870088
Email: info@penmarlampark.co.uk

www.penmarlampark.co.uk
Pitches For ⋏ ⌓ ⌯ ⌯ **Total** 65
Acreage 4 **Open** Easter **to** Oct
Access Good **Site** Lev/Slope
Quiet site with two areas, one sheltered and one with stunning views. Near the Eden Project. Boat launching and storage.
Facilities ◔ ∫ ⌐ ⎗ ⌐ ⌣ ↰ ⌂ ◎ ⌓
⌕ ◉ ⊞ ⊞ ⊟ ⋈ ⚡
Nearest Town Fowey
Directions From the A38 eastbound, pass Liskeard and turn left onto the A390 sp St. Austell. In East Taphouse turn left onto the B3359 sp Polperro & Looe. After 5 miles turn right sp Bodinnick. Site is on the right in 5 miles.
⇌ Liskeard/Par/Looe

FOWEY

Polruan Holidays - Camping & Caravanning, Polruan-by-Fowey, Cornwall, PL23 1QH
Tel: 01726 870263
Email: polholiday@aol.com
www.polruanholidays.co.uk
Pitches For ⋏ ⌓ ⌯ **Total** 47
Acreage 2 **Open** Easter **to** 1st October
Access Good **Site** Lev/Slope
Nearest Bus Stop (Miles) Outside
Coastal park surrounded by sea, river and National Trust farmland.
Facilities ∫ ⊞ ⊟ ⎗ ⌐ ⌣ ↰ ⌂ ◎ ⌓
⌕ ◉ ◔ ☂ ⋈ ⊞
Nearest Town Fowey
Directions From Plymouth A38 to Dobwalls, left onto A390 to East Taphouse, then left onto B3359. After 4¼ miles turn right signposted Polruan.
⇌ Par

GOONHAVERN

Roseville Holiday Park, Goonhavern, Nr Truro, Cornwall, TR4 9LA
Tel: 01872 572448
Email: roseville.park@btconnect.com
www.rosevilleholidaypark.co.uk
Pitches For A ⊞ ⊟ **Total** 90
Acreage 8 **Open Easter to** October
Access Good **Site** Level
Nearest Bus Stop (Miles) ¼
Ideal for North Cornwall. Quiet, private site. Families and mature persons only.
Facilities ⚅ ⨍ ⊞ ⌶ ⌻ ↑ ⊡ ⌖ ⊡ ☎
⌂ ⌕ ⌆ ⌀ ⌰ ↑ ⊟ ⌦ ⌇ ⚘
Nearest Town Truro
Directions 6 miles from Newquay on the A3075.
⊭ Truro

GORRAN HAVEN

Trelispen Caravan & Camping Park, Gorran Haven, St Austell, Cornwall, PL26 6NR
Tel: 01726 843501
Email: trelispen@care4free.net
www.trelispen.co.uk
Pitches For A ⊞ ⊟ **Total** 75
Acreage 1½ **Open** Apr **to** Oct
Access Good **Site** Level
Nearest Bus Stop (Miles) ¼
Within walking distance of Gorran Haven with its beach and fine cliff scenery.
Facilities ⨍ ⌻ ⌶ ⌀ ⊡ ⌖ ↑ ⊡
Nearest Town Mevagissey
Directions From St. Austell take the B3273 south following signs for Gorran Haven. Nearing Gorran Haven look for brown tourism signs to Trelispen.
⊭ St. Austell

HAYLE

Beachside Holiday Park, Hayle, Cornwall, TR27 5AW
Tel: 01736 753080
Email: reception@beachside.co.uk
www.beachside.co.uk
Pitches For A ⊞ ⊟ **Total** 83
Acreage 20 **Open Easter to** Sept
Access Good **Site** Sloping
Nearest Bus Stop (Miles) Outside
Right beside a golden sandy beach. Sea fishing from site.
Facilities ⨍ ⌻ ⌶ ⌀ ⊡ ⌖ ⊡ ☎
⌤ ⌆ ⌖ ⌕ ⌰ ↑ ⌺ ⊡ ⊟ ⌇ ⚘
Nearest Town Hayle
Directions Leave the A30 at roundabout signed Hayle, turn right opposite the Jet Petrol Station and the entrance is ½ a mile on the right.
⊭ Hayle

HAYLE

Gwithian Farm Campsite, Gwithian, Hayle, Cornwall, TR27 5BX
Tel: 01736 753127
Email: holidays@gwithianfarm.co.uk
www.gwithianfarm.co.uk
Pitches For A ⊞ ⊟ **Total** 130
Acreage 8 **Open** 23-Mar **to** 01-Oct
Access Good **Site** Level
Nearest Bus Stop (Miles) Outside

Just a 10 minute walk from a stunning 3 mile long beach. Friendly, family run site in a village, opposite a good pub.
Facilities ⚅ ⨍ ⌶ ⌻ ⌶ ⌀ ⊡ ⌖ ⌦ ☎
⌤ ⊡ ↑ ⊟ ⌇
Nearest Town St. Ives
Directions Leave the A30 at Hayle roundabout and turn right onto the B3301 signposted Portreath. After 2 miles in Gwithian, the site is on the left opposite the Red River Inn.
⊭ Camborne/Hayle

HAYLE

Higher Trevaskis Caravan & Camping Park, Gwinear Road, Connor Downs, Hayle, Cornwall, TR27 5JQ
Tel: 01209 831736
www.highertrevaskiscaravanpark.co.uk
Pitches For A ⊞ ⊟ **Total** 75
Acreage 5¼ **Open** April **to** October
Access Good **Site** Level
Nearest Bus Stop (Miles) ½
Friendly, secluded, family run, countryside park. Spacious, level pitches in small enclosures. Designated play areas and our renowned spotlessly clean facilities.
Facilities ⨍ ⌶ ⌻ ⌶ ⌀ ⊡ ⌖ ⌦ ⊡ ☎
⌤ ⌇ ⌀ ⌆ ⌰ ⌀ ↑ ⊟ ⌦ ⚘
Nearest Town Hayle
Directions From the A30 at the Hayle roundabout (McDonalds) take the first exit signposted Connor Downs. After 1 mile turn right to Carnhell Green. Park is on the right in ¾ miles.
⊭ Hayle

HAYLE

Parbola Holiday Park, Wall, Gwinear, Cornwall, TR27 5LE
Tel: 01209 831503
Email: bookings@parbola.co.uk
www.parbola.co.uk
Pitches For A ⊞ **Total** 110
Acreage 14 **Open** April **to** September
Access Good **Site** Level
Nearest Bus Stop (Miles) Outside
No dogs allowed during July and August. Hair and make-up room.
Facilities ⚅ ⨍ ⌶ ⌻ ⌶ ⌀ ⊡ ⌖ ⌦ ⊡ ☎
⌤ ⌇ ⌆ ⌕ ⌰ ↑ ⌺ ⊡ ⌇ ⚘
Nearest Town Hayle
Directions Travel on A30 to Hayle, at roundabout leave first exit to Connor Downs. At end of village turn right to Carnhell Green, right at T-Junction, Parbola is 1 mile on the left.

HAYLE

Sunny Meadow Holiday Park, Lelant Downs, Hayle, Cornwall, TR27 6LL
Tel: 01736 752243
Email: sunnymeadow@tiscali.co.uk
www.sunnymeadowholidaypark.co.uk
Pitches For A ⊞ ⊟ **Total** 3
Open All Year
Access Good **Site** Level
Nearest Bus Stop (Miles) ¼
Quiet, safe site in the countryside, only 3 miles from St Ives. Rural walks and coastal paths nearby.

Facilities ⨍ ⌶ ⌻ ⌶ ⌀ ⊡ ⌖ ⌦ ⊡ ⌀ ⌰ ⌖
Nearest Town St Ives
Directions Stay on the A30 until you reach the Penzance/St Ives roundabout, then take the A3074 for St Ives. At the second mini roundabout turn left, and the site is 2/3rds of a mile.
⊭ St Erth

HAYLE

Treglisson Touring Park, Wheal Alfred Road, Hayle, Cornwall, TR27 5JT
Tel: 01736 753141
Email: steve@treglisson.co.uk
www.treglisson.co.uk
Pitches For A ⊞ ⊟ **Total** 26
Acreage 2½ **Open** Easter **to** Oct
Access Good **Site** Lev/Slope
Nearest Bus Stop (Miles) 1
Just 5 minutes from the beaches of St Ives Bay. Centrally situated, ideal for touring West Cornwall.
Facilities ⚅ ⨍ ⌶ ⌻ ⌶ ⌀ ⊡ ⌖ ⌦ ⊡ ☎
⌤ ⌆ ⌀ ⌰ ↑ ⊟ ⊡ ⌇
Nearest Town Hayle/St. Ives
Directions Take the A30 to roundabout outside Hayle and take the 4th exit to Hayle. At the first mini roundabout turn left, after a mile (past the golf course) theres a sign on the left.
⊭ Hayle

HELSTON

Gunwalloe Caravan Park, Gunwalloe, Helston, Cornwall, TR12 7QP
Tel: 01326 572668
Pitches For A ⊞ ⊟ **Total** 40
Acreage 3½ **Open** April **to** October
Access Good **Site** Level
Nearest Bus Stop (Miles) 1
One mile form the beach. Ideal for touring the Lizard Peninsula.
Facilities ⨍ ⌶ ⌻ ⌶ ⌀ ⊡ ⌖ ☎ ⌀ ↑ ⊟
Nearest Town Helston
Directions From Helston take the A3082 towards The Lizard, after 2 miles turn right to Gunwalloe for 1 mile, site is signposted.
⊭ Redruth

CORNWALL

HELSTON

Lower Polladras Touring Park, Carleen, Helston, Cornwall, TR13 9NX
Tel: 01736 762220
Email: lowerpolladras@btinternet.com
www.lower-polladras.co.uk
Pitches For Å ⊞ ⊟ **Total** 60
Acreage 4 **Open** 01-Apr **to** 04-Jan
Access Good **Site** Level
Nearest Bus Stop (Miles) ½
Rural and quite.
Facilities
Nearest Town Helston
Directions From Helston take the A394 to Penzance and turn right onto the B3302. take 2nd right. Continue 2 miles in Carleen Village take 2nd right and follow signs to the park.
⇌ Camborne

HELSTON

Poldown Caravan & Camping Site, Carleen, Breage, Helston, Cornwall, TR13 9NN
Tel: 01326 574560
Email: stay@poldown.co.uk
www.poldown.co.uk
Pitches For Å ⊞ ⊟ **Total** 13
Acreage 1¼ **Open** Apr **to** Sept
Access Good **Site** Level
Nearest Bus Stop (Miles) Outside
Small, secluded, pretty site. 2 hard standings and 6 fully serviced pitches available. Glamzing safari tents, Ideal for touring West Cornwall. ETB 4 Star Graded.
Facilities
Directions Take A394 (signed Penzance) from Helston. At top of the hill on outskirts of Helston take the B3303 signed Hayle/St Ives. Take the second left on this road and we are ¼ mile along.
⇌ Penzance

ISLES OF SCILLY

Garrison Holidays, Tower Cottage, The Garrison, St Marys, Isles of Scilly, Cornwall, TR21 0LS
Tel: 01720 422670
Email: tedmoulson@aol.com
www.garrisonholidays.com
Pitches For Å **Total** 120
Acreage 9½ **Open** Easter **to** October
Site Level
Small, family orientated campsite. Electric hook-ups (10) on marked pitches, rest of site is not formally marked. Small fields, mostly sheltered. No vehicles on site. Transport for luggage is available from the ferry to the site for a small charge. Childrens play area adjacent to site.
Facilities
Nearest Town St Mary's
Directions From Penzance take a boat, skybus or helicopter to Isles of Scilly. Park is 10 minutes walk from Hugh Town, St Marys.
⇌ Penzance

ISLES OF SCILLY

St. Martins Campsite, Middle Town, St Martins, Isles of Scilly, Cornwall, TR25 0QN
Tel: 01720 422888
Email: camping@stmartinscampsite.co.uk
www.stmartinscampsite.co.uk
Pitches For Å **Total** 50
Open Mar **to** Oct
Site Lev/slope
On own beach,easy walk to shop & pub etc. Sheltered family site.

Facilities
Directions Take a ferry, plane or helicopter from Penzance to St. Marys. Launch from St. Marys to St. Martins.
⇌ Penzance

ISLES OF SCILLY

Troytown Farm Campsite, Troytown Farm, St Agnes, Isles of Scilly, Cornwall, TR22 0PL
Tel: 01720 422360
Email: enquiries@troytown.co.uk
www.troytown.co.uk
Pitches For Å **Total** 36
Open March **to** Nov
Site Lev/Slope
Spectacular views across the western rocks towards Bishop Rock Lighthouse. It also has its own sandy beach.
Facilities
Nearest Town St. Agnes
Directions Take the ferry from Penzance or fly from south west airports. NB: It is not possible to bring your car to Scilly.
⇌ Penzance

JACOBSTOW

Edmore Tourist Park, Edgar Road, Wainhouse Corner, Jacobstow, Bude, Cornwall, EX23 0BJ
Tel: 01840 230467
Email: enquiries@cornwallvisited.co.uk
www.cornwallvisited.co.uk
Pitches For Å ⊞ ⊟ **Total** 28
Acreage 3 **Open** 1 week before Easter **to** 1st Week Oct
Access Good **Site** Level
Nearest Bus Stop (Miles) ¼
Rural area with coastal walks. 2½ miles from the beach. Good touring base.
Facilities
Nearest Town Bude
Directions On the A39 Bude to Camelford road, 9 miles west of Bude.
⇌ Exeter

LANDS END

Cardinney Caravan & Caravan Park, Main A30, Lands End Road, Crows-an-Wra, Lands End, Cornwall, TR19 6HX
Tel: 01736 810880
Email: cardinney@btinternet.com
www.cardinney-camping-park.co.uk
Pitches For Å ⊞ ⊟ **Total** 90
Acreage 5 **Open** All Year
Access Good **Site** Level
Nearest Bus Stop (Miles) Outside
Sennen Cove Blue Flag, scenic coastal walks, ancient monuments, scenic flights, Minack Ampitheatre, trips to the Isles of Scilly. Ideal for touring Lands End Peninsula.
Facilities
Directions From Penzance follow Main A30 to Lands End, approx 5¼ miles. Entrance on right hand side on Main A30, large name board at entrance.
⇌ Penzance

LISKEARD

Great Trethew Manor, Horningtops, Liskeard, Cornwall, PL14 3PY
Tel: 01503 240663
Email: great_trethew_manor@yahoo.com
www.great-trethew-manor.co.uk
Pitches For Å ⊞ ⊟ **Total** 55
Acreage 30 **Open** April **to** Oct
Access Good **Site** Level
Nearest Bus Stop (Miles) 0.5

On site Pony Trekking, Ideal location for touring Devon and Cornwall.
Facilities
Nearest Town Liskeard
Directions From Liskeard take A38 towards Plymouth turn right onto B3251 in ¼ mile turn left.
⇌ Menheniot

LISKEARD

Pine Valley Park, Double Bois, Liskeard, Cornwall, PL14 6LE
Tel: 01579 321041
Pitches For Å ⊞ ⊟ **Total** 40
Acreage 3 **Open** All Year
Access Good **Site** Level
Nearest Bus Stop (Miles) ¼
Close to Eden Project, Looe and Plymouth.
Facilities
Nearest Town Liskeard
Directions 3 miles from Liskeard towards Bodmin. Just off the main A38 signposted to St Austell.
⇌ Liskeard

LISKEARD

Trenant Chapel House, Trenant Caravan Park, St Neot, Liskeard, Cornwall, PL14 6RZ
Tel: 01579 320896
Pitches For Å ⊞ ⊟ **Total** 8
Acreage 1 **Open** April **to** October
Site Level
Close to Siblyback and Colliford Reservoirs for fishing, boardsailing and bird watching. Situated in a sheltered corner of Upper Fowey Valley and bounded by tributary of Fowey river. Close to Bodmin moor, ideal for walking and touring.
Facilities
Nearest Town Liskeard
Directions Take St Cleer road off the A38 at Dobwalls, after 1 mile turn left signposted St. Neot, after 1 mile turn right signposted Trenant, ½ mile turn right signposted Trenant.
⇌ Liskeard

LOOE

Bay View Farm, St Martins, Looe, Cornwall, PL13 1NZ
Tel: 01503 265922
Email: mike@looebaycaravans.co.uk
www.looebaycaravans.co.uk
Pitches For Å ⊞ ⊟ **Total** 25
Acreage 3 **Open** All Year
Access Good **Site** Lev/Slope
Nearest Bus Stop (Miles) 1
Near to the beach, The Eden Project and many National Trust properties. We have eight shire horses on the farm. You can also contact us on Mobile: 07967 267312.
Facilities
Nearest Town Looe
Directions From Plymouth or Liskeard take the A38 to Trerulefoot roundabout, then take the (A387) B3253 to No-Mans-Land. Follow signs for the Monkey Sanctuary and Bay View Farm is at the end of the lane.
⇌ Looe

LOOE
Camping Caradon Touring Park,
Trelawne, Looe, Cornwall, PL13 2NA
Tel: 01503 272388
Email: enquiries@campingcaradon.co.uk
www.campingcaradon.co.uk
Pitches For Å 🛖 🚐 **Total** 85
Acreage 3 **Open** All Year
Access Good **Site** Level
Nearest Bus Stop (Miles) Site Entrance
In a rural location, within easy reach of all of Cornwall. The Eden Project is only 20 miles away. 2½ miles from Looe and 2 miles from Polperro. Free Wi-Fi. Family/disabled facilities. On local bus route. November to March by prior booking only.
Facilities 🛁 🍴 🕽 🔚 ⚹ 🕽 ⊙ 🍴 🚐 🗑 🛒
🍸 🐕 🛞 🔊 ⚡ 🌐
Nearest Town Looe/Polperro
Directions From Looe take the A387 towards Polperro. After 2 miles turn right onto the B3359. Take the next turning right, and Camping Caradon is clearly signposted.
🚆 Looe

LOOE
Polborder House Caravan & Camping Park, Bucklawren Road, St Martin, Looe, Cornwall, PL13 1QS
Tel: 01503 240265
Email: reception@polborderhouse.co.uk
www.polborderhouse.co.uk
Pitches For Å 🛖 🚐 **Total** 36
Acreage 3 **Open** All Year
Access Good **Site** Level
Nearest Bus Stop (Miles) ½
Small, select, award winning park set in beautiful countryside, 1¼ miles from the sea. Holiday caravans also available for rent. Top 100 UK Parks Regional winner.
Facilities 🛁 🍴 🖪 🔚 🚐 🕽 🔚 🚐 🗑 🛒
🍸 ⊙ 🔊 🛞 🔚 🚆 🌐
Nearest Town Looe
Directions 2¼ miles east of Looe off B3253, follow signs for Polborder and Monkey Sanctuary.
🚆 Looe

LOOE
Tencreek Holiday Park, Polperro Road, Looe, Cornwall, PL13 2JR
Tel: 01503 262447
Email: reception@tencreek.co.uk
www.dolphinholidays.co.uk
Pitches For Å 🛖 🚐
Acreage 20 **Open** All Year
Access Good **Site** Lev/Slope
Nearest Bus Stop (Miles) ¼
Excellent coastal and countryside views. Good park facilities including indoor pool and a large modern club house with entertainment.
Facilities 🛁 🍴 🖪 🔚 🕽 ⊙ 🚐 🗑 🛒
🍸 ⊙ 🐕 ✕ 🛞 🔊 🔚 ⚡ 🛞 🔚 🚆 🐾
🌐
Nearest Town Looe
Directions 1¼ miles west of Looe on the A387 Looe to Polperro road.
🚆 Looe

LOOE
Trelay Farmpark, Pelynt, Nr Looe, Cornwall, PL13 2JX
Tel: 01503 220900
Email: stay@trelay.co.uk
www.trelay.co.uk
Pitches For Å 🛖 🚐 **Total** 70
Acreage 4½ **Open** 01-Apr to 31-Oct
Access Good **Site** Sloping
Nearest Bus Stop (Miles) ¼
A small, uncommercialised Park surrounded by farmland, with a friendly, family atmosphere. Good sized grass pitches. 3 miles from Looe and the pretty fishing village of Polperro.
Facilities 🛁 🍴 🕽 🔚 ⚹ 🕽 ⊙ 🚐 🗑 🛒
🕽 ⊙ 🐕 ✕ 🛞 🔚 🚆 🔊 🌐
Nearest Town Looe
Directions From Looe take the A387 over the bridge towards Polperro. After 2 miles turn right onto the B3359 towards Pelynt and Trelay Farmpark is exactly 1 mile on the right.
🚆 Looe

LOSTWITHIEL
Eden Valley Holiday Park, Lanlivery, Bodmin, Cornwall, PL30 5BU
Tel: 01208 872277
Email:
enquiries@edenvalleyholidaypark.co.uk
www.edenvalleyholidaypark.co.uk
Pitches For Å 🛖 🚐 **Total** 57
Acreage 12 **Open** Easter to Oct
Access Good **Site** Level
Nearest Bus Stop (Miles) 3
Stream runs through the park. Woodland and river walks.
Facilities 🛁 ✏ 🍴 🖪 🔚 🕽 ⊙ 🚐 🗑 🛒
🕽 ⊙ 🐕 🛞 🔊 🔚 🚆 🔊 🐾 🔧
Nearest Town Fowey
Directions From Lostwithiel take the A390 for 1½ miles.
🚆 Lostwithiel

MARAZION
Trevair Touring Site, South Treveneague Farm, St Hilary, Penzance, Cornwall, TR20 9BY
Tel: 01736 740647
Email: info@trevairtouringpark.co.uk
www.trevairtouringpark.co.uk
Pitches For Å 🛖 🚐 **Total** 35
Acreage 3½ **Open** End Mar to Oct
Access Good **Site** Level
Nearest Bus Stop (Miles) 1
Everyone is welcome at our clean and friendly site. Set in the peace and quiet of the countryside, yet within 2 to 3 miles of beaches, shops and pubs.
Facilities 🍴 🔚 🕽 ⊙ 🚐 🗑 🛒 🔊 🔚
Nearest Town Marazion
Directions 3 miles from Marazion, B3280 through Goldsithney signposted South Treveneague.
🚆 St. Erth

MAWGAN PORTH
Magic Cove Touring Park, Mawgan Porth, Newquay, Cornwall, TR8 4BD
Tel: 01637 860263
Email: magic@magiccove.co.uk
www.magiccove.co.uk
Pitches For Å 🛖 🚐 **Total** 18
Acreage 1 **Open** Easter to Sept
Access Good **Site** Level
Nearest Bus Stop (Miles) ¼
300yds from a sandy beach. Ideal centre for North Cornwall coast. Water adjacent to each pitch and TV points.
Facilities 🍴 🔚 🕽 ⊙ 🚐 🗑 🛒 🔚 🚆 🔊 🌐
Nearest Town Newquay
Directions Exit the A30 at Highgate Hill Junction (A39) sp Newquay & Airport. Follow Airport signs to Trekenning roundabout and take the first exit. Continue to follow Airport signs, go past the Airport, at the T-Junction turn right to Mawgan Porth. Turn right by Pitch n Putt. Campsite is 300 yards on the left.
🚆 Newquay

MAWGAN PORTH
Marver Touring Park, Marver Chalets, Mawgan Porth, Nr Newquay, Cornwall, TR8 4BB
Tel: 01637 860493
Email: familyholidays@aol.com
www.marverholidaypark.co.uk
Pitches For Å 🛖 🚐 **Total** 15
Acreage 2½ **Open** April to Oct
Access Good **Site** Level
Nearest Bus Stop (Miles) Outside
Peaceful location in a valley with superb views. 300 yards to the beach, excellent coastal walks. Ideal base for touring Cornwall.
Facilities 🍴 🔚 🕽 ⊙ 🚐 🗑 🛒 🔊 🔚 🚆 🔊
Nearest Town Newquay
Directions From Newquay take the B3276 coast road to Padstow. After 6 miles, on entering Mawgan Porth, turn right at the Mawgan Porth Stores, park is 300 yards on the left.
🚆 Newquay

MAWGAN PORTH
Sun Haven Valley Holiday Park, Mawgan Porth, Cornwall, TR8 4BQ
Tel: 0800 634 6744
Email: bookings@sunhavenvalley.com
www.sunhavenvalley.com
Pitches For Å 🛖 🚐 **Total** 109
Acreage 7 **Open** Easter to Oct
Access Good **Site** Level
Nearest Bus Stop (Miles) Outside
Just a 10 minute walk from the large sandy beach.
Facilities 🍴 🔚 🕽 ⊙ 🚐 🗑 🛒 🔊 🔚
🍸 🛞 ⊙ 🐕 🛞 🔚 🚆 🌐
Nearest Town Padstow
Directions Leave the A30 at Highgate Hill for Newquay and follow signs for the airport. Go past the airport and turn right at the T-Junction for Mawgan Porth. At the beach turn right on the only road inland (with crazy golf on the left), ¼ mile to the s-bend and the Park is ½ a mile further on.
🚆 Newquay

MEVAGISSEY

Tregarton Park, Gorran, Nr Mevagissey, St Austell, Cornwall, PL26 6NF
Tel: 01726 843666
Email: reception@tregarton.co.uk
www.tregarton.co.uk
Pitches For ▲ 🚐 🚙 **Total** 125
Acreage 12 **Open** April **to** October
Access Good **Site** Lev/Terraced
Nearest Bus Stop (Miles) Outside
Beautiful sheltered park with glimpses of the sea through the valley. 1½ miles to the nearest beach, 2½ miles from the Lost Garden of Heligan and 9 miles from The Eden Project.
Facilities 🔊 ✆ 🛢 🔟 🗑 🏧 ⊙ ⏚ 🛒 🔲 🍴
🏸 🏇 🖩 🗗 🛢 ✕ 🎣 🔱 🎪 ↖ 🐾 🗗 ⛲
Nearest Town St. Austell
Directions From St Austell take the B3273 signposted Mevagissey. After 4 miles, at the top of Pentewan Hill turn right signposted Gorran Haven. Park is 3 miles on the right (signposted).
🚲 St. Austell

MULLION

Franchis, Cury Cross Lanes, Mullion, Helston, Cornwall, TR12 7AZ
Tel: 01326 240301
Email: enquiries@franchis.co.uk
www.franchis.co.uk
Pitches For ▲ 🚐 🚙 **Total** 70
Acreage 4 **Open** Easter **to** Oct
Access Good **Site** Lev/Slope
Nearest Bus Stop (Miles) ½
Set in 17 acres of woodland and fields. Near to beaches and Helford River.
Facilities ✆ 🛢 🗑 🏧 ⊙ ⏚ 🔲 🍴 🏸 🛢 🗗 🍴
Directions On the A3083, 5 miles south of Helston and 2 miles north of Mullion.
🚲 Redruth

MULLION

Little trethvas Camping Site The Lizard, Helston, Cornwall, TR12 7AT
Tel: 01326 290344
Email: farmliz@orange.net
www.littletrethvas.co.uk
Pitches For ▲ 🚐 🚙 **Total** 29
Acreage 2 **Open** Mar **to** Oct
Access Good **Site** Level
Nearest Bus Stop (Miles) ¼
Within walking distance to Kyncnce,Cadgwith and Mullion. Also open 23Dec-1Jan
Facilities ✆ 🛢 🗑 🏧 ⏚ 🍴 🗗 🔲 🌿
Nearest Town Mullion
Directions At Helston take signs for the Lizard, site 2 miles further on from Mullion turn on lane signposted to Cadgwith.
🚲 Falmouth

MULLION

Mullion Holiday Park, Ruan Minor, Nr Helston, Cornwall, TR12 7LJ
Tel: 01326 280428
Email: parkdean.com
www.parkdeanholidays.com
Pitches For ▲ 🚐 🚙 **Total** 97
Open Mar **to** Nov
Access Good **Site** Level
Nearest Bus Stop (Miles) Outside
Very near beach, ideal touring the most southerely point The Lizard
Facilities 🔊 ✆ 🛢 🔟 🗑 🏧 ⊙ ⏚ 🔲 🍴
🏸 🖩 🛢 🗗 ✕ 🎣 🔟 🎪 ↖ ⛲ 🐾
🗗 🔲 🗗 🌿 ⛲
Nearest Town Helston
Directions From the A30 take the A39 through Truro towards Falmouth. Then take the A394 to Helston then the A3083 for The Lizard. Park is 7 miles on the left.
🚲 Penzance

NEWQUAY

Carvynick Country Club Summercourt, Newquay, Cornwall, TR8 5AF
Tel: 01872 510716
Email: info@carvynick.co.uk
www.carvynick.co.uk
Pitches For 🚐 🚙 ≋ **Open** All Year
Nearest Bus Stop (Miles) ¼
Situated in the heart of Cornwall amidst the rolling hills of the beautiful South West, Carvynick Holiday Park in Newquay extends a warm welcome to those seeking tranquil family holidays in Cornwall. Located only 10 minutes from the stunning Newquay beaches, dramatic Cornish coastline and only 14 miles from the world famous Eden Project. Our central location provides easy access to all of Cornwall•™ many attractions.
Facilities ✆ 🛢 🔟 🗑 🏧 ⏚ 🔲 🍴
✕ 🎪 🖩 🗗 🔲
Nearest Town Newquay
Directions From the A30 heading west, take the Summercourt exit signposted A3058 Newquay. Travel into Summercourt, at the traffic lights turn right and the Park is first on the left.
🚲 Newquay

NEWQUAY

Cottage Farm Touring Park, Treworgans, Cubert, Newquay, Cornwall, TR8 5HH
Tel: 01637 831083
Email: info@cottagefarmpark.co.uk
www.cottagefarmpark.co.uk
Pitches For ▲ 🚐 🚙 **Total** 45
Acreage 2 **Open** April **to** End Sept
Access Good **Site** Level
Nearest Bus Stop (Miles) ¼

Within easy reach of three National Trust beaches. Small, family site, peaceful and in a rural location.
Facilities ✆ 🔟 🗑 🏧 ⏚ ⊙ ⏚ 🛒 🔲 🍴 🗗
Nearest Town Newquay
Directions Newqauy to Redruth road A3075, turn right onto High Lanes, follow signs to Cubert, at Cubert Village turn right at the mini roundabout sp Crantock-Wesley road. Continue for ½ a mile passing Cubert Primary School on your left, then look for Blue Cottage Farm sign on the left hand side.
🚲 Newquay

NEWQUAY

Crantock Plains Touring Park, Crantock, Newquay, Cornwall, TR8 5PH
Tel: 01637 830955
Email: crantockplainstp@btinternet.com
www.crantock-plains.co.uk
Pitches For ▲ 🚐 🚙 **Total** 60
Acreage 4 **Open** April **to** Sept
Access Good **Site** Level
Nearest Bus Stop (Miles) ¼
Spacious park set in peaceful countryside. 2½ miles from Newquay.
Facilities 🔊 ✆ 🛢 🔟 🗑 🏧 ⊙ ⏚ 🛒 🔲 🍴
🏸 🖩 🔟 🎪 ↖ 🗗 🔲 🌿 🔍
Nearest Town Newquay
Directions Turn off the A30 onto the A392. Approx. 9 miles past Morrisons turn onto the A3075, after 1 mile follow signs.
🚲 Newquay

NEWQUAY

Hendra Holiday Park, Newquay, Cornwall, TR8 4NY
Tel: 01637 875778
Email: enquiries@hendra-holidays.com
www.http://www.hendra-holidays.com
Pitches For ▲ 🚐 🚙 **Total** 548
Open Easter **to** Beginning of Nov
Access Good **Site** Level
Nearest Bus Stop (Miles) Outside
Country views. Only 1½ miles from beaches. Indoor and outdoor Oasis Fun Pools.
Facilities 🔊 ✆ 🛢 🔟 🗑 🏧 ⏚ 🛒 🔲 🍴
🏸 🏇 🖩 🗗 🛢 ✕ 🎣 🔟 🎪 ↖ 🐾 🗗 🔲 🌿
⛲
Nearest Town Newquay
Directions 1½ miles from Newquay on the A392.
🚲 Newquay

NEWQUAY

Holywell Bay Holiday Park, Holywell Bay, Cornwall, TR8 5PR
Tel: 0844 335 3732
Email:
touringandcamping@parkdeanholidays.com
www.parkdeantouring.com

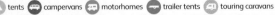

Pitches For ⋀ ⊕ ⊟ **Total** 40
Acreage 40 **Open** Mar **to** Oct
Access Good **Site** Level
Nearest Bus Stop (Miles) Outside
Beach is a short stroll from the park, with Newquay town centre only 5 miles away. Heated outdoor pool, bar and restaurant on Park. FREE kids clubs and live family entertainment.
Facilities ⸙ ⬛ ⌂ ⬛
◨ ♨ ⬛ ⬛ ✕ ⛱ ⬛ ⚑ ⬛ ⬚ ⬛ 🞱 ⬛ ⬛ 🛜
Nearest Town Newquay
Directions Follow the M4 to Exeter and take the A30 to Okehampton. Turn off at the first slip road to Newquay (A39), continue over the roundabout to the A3075 towards Redruth, the park is 2 miles.
⇌ Newquay

NEWQUAY
Newperran Holiday Park, Rejerrah, Newquay, Cornwall, TR8 5QJ
Tel: 01872 572407
Email: holidays@newperran.co.uk
www.newperran.co.uk
Pitches For ⋀ ⊕ ⊟ **Total** 400
Acreage 25 **Open** Easter **to** Oct
Access Good **Site** Level
Nearest Bus Stop (Miles) ¼
Concessionary green fees, scenic views and central to nine golden beaches. Quality in Tourism 5 Stars, AA 4 Pennants and BH&HPA.
Facilities ⬛ ⸙ ⬛ ⬛ ⌂ ⬛ ⬚ ⬛ ⬛
♨ ⬛ ◨ ⬛ ✕ ⬛ ⬛ 🞱 ⬛ 🛜 ⬛ ⬛ 🞱
🞱
Nearest Town Newquay
Directions Take the A30 towards Redruth, turn right onto the B3285 signposted Perranporth and Goodhavern. At the junction at Goodhavern turn right onto the A3075 and turn left at the Newperran sign.
⇌ Newquay

NEWQUAY
Newquay Holiday Park, Newquay, Cornwall, TR8 4HS
Tel: 0844 0
Email: touringandcamping@parkdeanholidays.com
www.parkdeantouring.com
Pitches For ⋀ ⊕ ⊟ **Total** 50
Acreage 60 **Open** March **to** Oct
Access Good **Site** Sloping
Nearest Bus Stop (Miles) Outside
Set in rolling Cornish countryside, only 2 miles from a choice of 11 beaches. Three heated outdoor pools. FREE kids clubs and live family entertainment.
Facilities ⸙ ⬛ ⬛ ⌂ ⬚ ⬛ ⬛ ⬛ ⬛
♨ ⬛ ✕ ◨ ⬛ 🞱 ⬛ 🞱 ⬛ ⬛ 🛜
Nearest Town Newquay
Directions Follow the M4 to Exeter and take the A30 to Okehampton. Continue until you see the turn off for St. Mawgan, go along the road and take the A3059 to Newquay.
⇌ Newquay

NEWQUAY
Porth Beach Tourist Park, Porth, Newquay, Cornwall, TR7 3NH
Tel: 01637 876531
Email: info@porthbeach.co.uk
www.porthbeach.co.uk
Pitches For ⋀ ⊕ ⊟ ⊞ ≷ **Total** 200
Acreage 7 **Open** March **to** End Oct
Access Good **Site** Level
Nearest Bus Stop (Miles) Outside
Beach across road, stream running down the side of park. Beautiful coastal walks.

Facilities ⸙ ⬛ ⬛ ⌂ ⬛ ⬛ ⬚ ⬛ ⬛ ⬛
⬛ ◨ ✕ ⛱ ⬛ ⚑ ⬛ ⬛ 🞱 ⬛ 🛜
Nearest Town Newquay
Directions Follow main road W of Newquay towards Padstow. Porth is the first bay.
⇌ Newquay

NEWQUAY
Riverside Holiday Park, Lane, Newquay, Cornwall, TR8 4PE
Tel: 01637 873617
Email: info@riversideholidaypark.co.uk
www.riversideholidaypark.co.uk
Pitches For ⋀ ⊕ ⊟ **Total** 58
Acreage 7 **Open** Easter **to** Oct
Site Level
Nearest Bus Stop (Miles) 1
In a peaceful position, beside the River Gannel. Only 2½ miles from the spectacular coastline and sandy beaches.
Facilities ⸙ ⬛ ⬛ ⌂ ⬛ ⬚ ⬛ ⬛ ⬛
♨ ⬛ ◨ ⬛ ✕ ⬛ ⬛ 🞱 ⬛ ⬛ 🛜
Nearest Town Newquay
Directions Approx. 2½ miles from Newquay town centre, situated 1 mile off the A392 Newquay road.
⇌ Newquay

NEWQUAY
Rosecliston Park, Trevemper, Newquay, Cornwall, TR8 5JT
Tel: 01637 830326
Email: info@rosecliston.co.uk
www.rosecliston.co.uk
Pitches For ⋀ **Total** 126
Acreage 12 **Open** Late May **to** Sept
Access Good **Site** Lev/Slope
Nearest Bus Stop (Miles) Outside
ADULTS ONLY PARK. 18 to 30s camping site. Close to Newquay with its nightlife, shopping and excellent surfing beaches.
Facilities ⸙ ⬛ ⌂ ⬛ ⌂ ⬚ ⬛
⬛ ♨ ◨ ⬛ ⬛ ⬛ ⬛ ⬛ ◨ ⬛
Nearest Town Newquay
Directions On the A3075 Newquay to Redruth road, 1 mile from Newquay Boating Lake.
⇌ Newquay

NEWQUAY
Trebarber Farm, St Columb Minor, Newquay, Cornwall, TR8 4JT
Tel: 01637 873007
Email: trebarberfarm@talktalk.net
www.trebarberfarmholidays.com
Pitches For ⋀ ⊕ ⊟
Acreage 5 **Open** May **to** Oct
Access Good **Site** Level
Quiet, ideal family centre for touring and beaches. Within walking distance of Porth Reservoir (coarse fishing) and a golf course.
Facilities ⬛ ⌂ ⬚ ⬛ ⬛ ⬛ 🛜 ⬛
Nearest Town Newquay
Directions 3 miles from Newquay on A3059, Newquay to St. Columb Major road.
⇌ Newquay

NEWQUAY
Tregurrian Camping & Caravanning Club Site, Tregurrian, Nr Newquay, Cornwall, TR8 4AE
Tel: 01637 860448
Email:
tregurrian.site@thefriendlyclub.co.uk
www.campingandcaravanningclub.co.uk/
tregurrian
Pitches For ⋀ ⊕ ⊟ **Total** 90
Acreage 4½ **Open** 21-Mar **to** 04-Nov
Access Good **Site** Level
Nearest Bus Stop (Miles) ¼

The glorious sandy beach of Watergate Bay is just ¾ miles away. There is a pretty coastal walk from the site to the beach. BTB 4 Star Graded, AA 3 Pennants and Loo of the Year Award. Non members welcome. You can also call us on 0845 130 7633.
Facilities ⸙ ⬛ ⌂ ⬛ ⌂ ⬚ ⬛ ⬛ ⬛
⬛ ◨ ⬛ ⚑ ⬛ 🛜
Nearest Town Newquay
Directions Leave the A30 after a prominent railway bridge by turning right signposted Newquay Airport, St Columb Major at roundabout on the A39. Join the A3059 to Newquay, after 1½ miles turn right signposted Newquay Airport and follow signs to Watergate Bay.
⇌ Newquay

NEWQUAY
Trekenning Tourist Park, Trekenning, Newquay, Cornwall, TR8 4JF
Tel: 01637 880462
Email: holidays@trekenning.co.uk
www.trekenning.co.uk
Pitches For ⋀ ⊕ ⊟ **Total** 75
Acreage 6½ **Open** All Year
Access Good **Site** Sloping
Nearest Bus Stop (Miles) ½
Family site, family run. Holiday homes for sale.
Facilities ⸙ ⬛ ⌂ ⬛ ⌂ ⬚ ⬛ ⬛ ⬛
♨ ⬛ ◨ ⬛ ✕ ⬛ ⬛ 🞱 ⬛ 🞱 ⬛ ⬛ 🞱
🛜
Nearest Town Newquay
Directions From Newquay take the A3059 to the Trekenning roundabout, site entrance is 20 yards on the right before the roundabout.
⇌ Newquay

NEWQUAY
Treloy Touring Park, Newquay, Cornwall, TR8 4JN
Tel: 01637 872063/876279
Email: stay@treloy.co.uk
www.treloy.co.uk
Pitches For ⋀ ⊕ ⊟ ≷ **Total** 223
Acreage 12 **Open** April **to** Sept
Access Good **Site** Lev/Slope
Nearest Bus Stop (Miles) Outside
Ideal site for touring the whole of Cornwall. Coarse fishing nearby. Own golf course close by with concessionary Green Fees. Free entertainment.
Facilities ⸙ ⬛ ⌂ ⬛ ⌂ ⬚ ⬛ ⬛ ⬛
♨ ⬛ ◨ ⬛ ✕ ⬛ ⬛ 🞱 ⬛ 🞱 ⬛ ⬛ 🞱
🛜
Nearest Town Newquay
Directions 3 miles from Newquay off the A3059 Newquay to St Columb Major Road.
⇌ Newquay

NEWQUAY
Trenance Holiday Park, Edgcumbe Avenue, Newquay, Cornwall, TR7 2JY
Tel: 01637 873447
Email:
enquiries@trenanceholidaypark.co.uk
www.trenanceholidaypark.co.uk
Pitches For ⋀ ⊕ ⊟ **Total** 134
Acreage 15 **Open** April **to** Oct
Access Good **Site** Sloping
Nearest Bus Stop (Miles) Outside
1 mile from Newquay town centre and next door to Newquay Zoo.
Facilities ⸙ ⬛ ⌂ ⬚ ⬛ ⬛ ⬛ 🛜
♨ ⬛ ◨ ✕ ⬛ ⬛ ⬛ ⬛
Nearest Town Newquay
Directions On the main A3075 Newquay to Truro road, approx 1 mile from Newquay town centre.
⇌ Newquay

ESCAPE
EXPLORE
DISCOVER

CORNWALL'S FINE STAR HOLIDAY PARK

CORNWALL'S
FINEST FIVE STAR
HOLIDAY PARK

trevornick
holiday park

DOG FRIENDLY! DOG FRIENDLY!

★★★★★
HOLIDAY PARK

www.trevornick.co.uk - 0843 453 5531
Holywell Bay Nr. Newquay Cornwall TR8 5PW

•• TOURING •• CAMPING •• EUROTENTS ••

NEWQUAY

Trencreek Holiday Park, Trencreek, Newquay, Cornwall, TR8 4NS
Tel: 01637 874210
Email: trencreek@btconnect.com
www.trencreekholidaypark.co.uk
Pitches For Å ₩ ₩ **Total** 150
Acreage 10 **Open** April **to** September
Access Good **Site** Level
Nearest Bus Stop (Miles) Outside
Coarse fishing on site, 15 minutes footpath walk to Newquay, 1 mile by road.
Facilities ...
Nearest Town Newquay
Directions A392 to Quintrell Downs, turn right Newquay East/Porth, at Porth crossroads, ¾ miles outside Newquay, turn left to Trencreek.
≠ Newquay

NEWQUAY

Trethiggey Touring Park, Quintrell Downs, Newquay, -, -, Cornwall, TR8 4QR
Tel: 01637 877672
Email: enquiries@trethiggey.co.uk
www.trethiggey.co.uk
Pitches For Å ₩ ₩ ₩ **Total** 157
Acreage 16 **Open** 02-Mar **to** 02-Jan
Access Good **Site** Lev/Slope
Nearest Bus Stop (Miles) 0.25
Nearest Town Newquay
≠ Quintrell Downs

NEWQUAY

Trevella Park, Crantock, Newquay, Cornwall, TR8 5EW
Tel: 01637 830308
Email: holidays@trevella.co.uk

www.trevella.co.uk
Pitches For **Total** 270
Acreage 15 **Open** Easter **to** October
Access Good **Site** Level
≠ Newquay

NEWQUAY

Trevornick Holiday Park, Holywell Bay, Newquay, Cornwall, TR8 5PW
Tel: 01637 830531
Email: bookings@trevornick.co.uk
www.trevornick.co.uk
Pitches For Å ₩ ₩ **Total** 600
Acreage 30 **Open** 23-Mar **to** 13 Apr Then 18 May 14 Sept
Access Good **Site** Level
Nearest Bus Stop (Miles) Outside
Right next to the beach with stunning sea views. On site 18 hole golf course and 18 hole pitch n putt. Tourers and static tents.
Limited facilities until 25 May and from 31 Aug.
Facilities ...
Nearest Town Newquay
Directions Take Newquay to Perrenporth A3075 road. Take turning for Cubert/Holywell.
≠ Newquay

NEWQUAY

Watergate Bay Touring Park, Watergate Bay, Newquay, Cornwall, TR8 4AD
Tel: 01637 860387
Email: email@watergatebaytouringpark.co.uk
www.watergatebaytouringpark.co.uk
Pitches For Å ₩ ₩ ₩ **Total** 171
Acreage 30 **Open** Mar **to** End Oct
Access Good **Site** Level

Nearest Bus Stop (Miles) Outside
½ mile from Watergate Bay in a rural location in an area of outstanding natural beauty.
Facilities ...
Nearest Town Newquay
Directions 4 miles north of Newquay on the B3276 Coast Road to Padstow. Follow directions shown from Watergate Bay.
≠ Newquay

PADSTOW

Carnevas Farm Holiday Park, Carnevas Farm, St Merryn, Padstow, Cornwall, PL28 8PN
Tel: 01841 520230
Email: carnevascampsite@aol.com
www.carnevasholidaypark.co.uk
Pitches For Å ₩ ₩ **Total** 198
Acreage 8 **Open** April **to** October
Access Good **Site** Lev/Slope
Nearest Bus Stop (Miles) ½
Well run family park in a lovely rural position, near to numerous sandy beaches. Ideal touring. AA 4 Pennants and ETB 4 Star Park.
Facilities ...
Nearest Town Padstow
Directions From Padstow take the B3726 Newquay coast road, turn right at Tredrea Inn just before getting to Porthcothan Bay. Site ¼ mile up road on right.
≠ Newquay

PADSTOW

Dennis Cove Camping Ltd., Dennis Cove, Padstow, Cornwall, PL28 8DR
Tel: 01841 532349
Pitches For Å ₩ ₩ **Total** 42
Acreage 5 **Open** Apr **to** Sept

Access Fair **Site** Lev/Slope
Nearest Bus Stop (Miles) ¼
Scenic views. Site adjoins Camel Trail cycle track. 10 minute walk to Padstow centre. 5 electric hook-ups. No groups, Reservation essential.
Facilities ⬥ ♂ 📶 📛 ☎ ⌂ ⊙ ↵ ▣ ◱ ♜
📶 ⬙ ↯⬙
Nearest Town Padstow
Directions Signposted off A389 on outskirts of Padstow Town.
⚇ Bodmin Parkway

PADSTOW

Harlyn Sands Holiday Park, Lighthouse Road, Trevose Head, Padstow, Cornwall, PL28 8SQ
Tel: 01841 520720
Email: enquiries@harlynsands.co.uk
www.harlynsands.co.uk
Pitches For ⬥ ♣ ♠ **Open** Easter **to** Oct
Access Good **Site** Level
Nearest Bus Stop (Miles) ¼
Near the beach. Fun pool on site.
Facilities ⬥ ♂ 📶 📛 ☎ ⌂ ⊙ ↵ ▣ ◱ ♜
📶 ⬙ ⊛ ✕ ♞ ♫ ♜ ⊣ ▣ ◲ ↯ ☀
Nearest Town Padstow
Directions From Padstow take the B3276 Newquay coast road. After 1 mile follow signs for Harlyn Sands.
⚇ Bodmin

PADSTOW

Mother Ivey's Bay Holiday Park, Trevose Head, Padstow, Cornwall, PL28 8SL
Tel: 01841 520990
Email: info@motheriveysbay.com
www.motheriveysbay.com
Pitches For ⬥ ♣ ♠ **Total** 100
Acreage 10 **Open** April **to** October
Access Good **Site** Level
Nearest Bus Stop (Miles) ¼
Own private sandy beach. Beautiful coastal walks.
Facilities ⬥ ♂ 📶 📛 ☎ ⌂ ⊙ ↵ ▣ ◱ ♜
📶 ⬙ ⊛ ♜ ⊣ ▣ ◲ ↯ ☀
Nearest Town Padstow
Directions 4 miles from Padstow. Signposted off the B3276 Padstow to Newquay coastal road (Trevose Head).
⚇ Bodmin

PADSTOW

Music Water Touring Park, Rumford, Wadebridge, Cornwall, PL27 7SJ
Tel: 01841 540257
www.wix.com/musicwater/touringpark
Pitches For ⬥ ♣ ♠ **Total** 140
Acreage 8 **Open** April **to** Oct
Access Good **Site** Lev/Slope
5 miles from beaches. Cafe/restaurant nearby. Ideal touring base.
Facilities ♂ 📶 📛 ☎ ⌂ ⊙ ↵ ▣ ◱ ♜
📶 ⬙ ⊘ ♞ ♫ ⤳ ⊛ ♜ ⊣ ▣ ◲ ↯ ✦
Nearest Town Padstow
Directions From Wadebridge take the A39 to Winnards Perch roundabout, then take the B3274. Turn first left and site is on the right.
⚇ Bodmin

PADSTOW

Padstow Holiday Park, Cliffdowne, Padstow, Cornwall, PL28 8LB
Tel: 01841 532289
Email: mail@padstowholidaypark.co.uk
www.padstowholidaypark.co.uk
Pitches For ⬥ ♣ ♠ **Total** 50
Acreage 7 **Open** Mar **to** Dec
Site Level
Nearest Bus Stop (Miles) Outside

Quiet location in open countryside with no club or bar. Near to several sandy beaches. Footpath to Padstow (1 mile). 1 mile from a Tesco store.
Facilities ♂ 📶 ☎ ⌂ ⊙ ↵ ▣ ◱ ♜
📶 ⬙ ⊛ ♜ ♛ ▣ ◲ ♜
Nearest Town Padstow
Directions From Wadebridge take the A389 to Padstow, site is on the right hand side 1½ miles before Padstow.
⚇ Bodmin

PADSTOW

Padstow Touring Park, Padstow, Cornwall, PL28 8LE
Tel: 01841 532061
Email: bookings@padstowtouringpark.co.uk
www.padstowtouringpark.co.uk
Pitches For ⬥ ♣ ♠ ♞ ⅊ **Total** 180
Acreage 13¼ **Open** All Year
Access Good **Site** Level
Nearest Bus Stop (Miles) Outside
Quiet family park with panoramic views. Several sandy beaches within 3 miles. Footpath to padstow. Three amenity blocks.
Facilities ⬥ ♂ 📶 📛 ☎ ⌂ ⊙ ↵ ▣ ◱ ♜
📶 ⬙ ◱ ♜ ♜ ↯ ▣ ◲ ◱ ☀ ✦ ↯ ▣ ◱ ♜
Nearest Town Padstow
Directions On A389 1 mile south south west of Padstow.

PADSTOW

Seagull Tourist Park, St Merryn, Padstow, Cornwall, PL28 8PT
Tel: 01841 520117
Pitches For ⬥ ♣ ♠ **Total** 100
Acreage 4 **Open** Easter/1 April **to** Oct
Access Good **Site** Level
Nearest Bus Stop (Miles) ½
Quiet family site near the fishing port of Padstow, and with seven golden sandy beaches, cliff walks and surfing all within a 15 minute drive.
Facilities ♂ 📶 ☎ ⌂ ⊙ ↵ ▣ ◱ ♜ 📶 ⬙ ⊛ ↯
✦
Nearest Town Padstow
Directions From St Columb take the B3274 towards Padstow, head for St Merryn and go past the old airfield.
⚇ Bodmin Parkway

PENRYN

Menallack Farm, Treverva, Penryn, Cornwall, TR10 9BP
Tel: 01326 340333
Email: cheese@menallack.co.uk
Pitches For ⬥ ♣ ♠ **Total** 20
Acreage 1½ **Open** Apr **to** Oct
Access Good **Site** Level
Nearest Bus Stop (Miles) ½
Secluded, simple quite site. Beautiful views, peaceful countryside. Easy reach of both north and south coasts.
Facilities ♂ 📶 ☎ ⌂ ⊙ ↵ ▣ 📶 ⬙ ↯⬙ ↯
Nearest Town Falmouth
Directions From take the A39 "Asda" roundabout turn right up the hill to Mabe Burnthouse. At the crossroads turn left and follow the road, at crossroads turn right to Gweek, site is signposted 1½ miles.
⚇ Penryn

PENZANCE

Bone Valley Caravan & Camping Park, Heamoor, Penzance, Cornwall, TR20 8UJ
Tel: 01736 360313
www.bonevalleyholidaypark.co.uk
Pitches For ⬥ ♣ ♠ **Total** 17
Acreage 1 **Open** All Year
Access Good **Site** Level
Nearest Bus Stop (Miles) Outside

---

1 mile from Penzance, 3 miles from St Michaels Mount and 10 miles from Lands End. Coastal footpaths.
Facilities ⬥ ♂ 📶 📛 ☎ ⌂ ⊙ ↵ ▣ ◱ ♜
📶 ⬙ ⊙ 📶 ♞ ♜ ▣ ◲ ↯
Nearest Town Penzance
Directions A30 to Penzance to Heamoor signposted approx 1 mile from Penzance
⚇ Penzance

PENZANCE

Garris Farm, Gulval, Penzance, Cornwall, TR20 8XD
Tel: 01736 365806
Pitches For ⬥ ♣ ♠
Acreage 8 **Open** May **to** Oct
Access Good **Site** Sloping
Nearest Bus Stop (Miles) ¼
Sailing and water skiing with own equipment
Facilities 📛 ♂ ♜ ▣ ◱ ♜
Nearest Town Penzance
Directions Leave A30 turning right at Growlas on road to Luogvan B3309 to Castlegate. Follow road to Chysauster ancient village.
⚇ Penzance

PENZANCE

River Valley Country Park, Relubbus, Penzance, Cornwall, TR20 9ER
Tel: 01736 763398
Email: rivervalley@surfbay.co.uk
www.surfbayholidays.co.uk
Pitches For ♣ **Total** 40
Acreage 18 **Open** 24th Mar **to** 22nd Sept
Access Good **Site** Sloping
Nearest Bus Stop (Miles) ¼
Seasonal touring pitches available at our tranquil, partly wooded park, along the banks of a clear shallow stream. Near to beaches, pubs, golf course and St Michaels Mount.
Facilities ⬥ ♂ 📶 📛 ☎ ⌂ ⊙ ↵ ▣ ◱ ♜
📶 ⬙ ♜ ⊣ ▣ ◲ ↯ ✦
Nearest Town Penzance
Directions From the A30 at St. Michaels Mount roundabout, take the A394 towards Helston. At the next roundabout turn left onto the B3280 to Relubbus, after 3 miles go over the bridge and River Valley is on the left.
⚇ Penzance

PENZANCE

Sennen Cove Camping & Caravanning Club Site, Higher Tregiffian Farm, St Buryan, Penzance, Cornwall, TR19 6JB
Tel: 01736 871588
Email: sennen.covesite@thefriendlyclub.co.uk
www.campingandcaravanningclub.co.uk/sennencove
Pitches For ⬥ ♣ ♠ **Total** 75
Acreage 4 **Open** 15-Mar **to** 04-Nov
Access Good **Site** Level
Nearest Bus Stop (Miles) ¼
Situated on a farm in peaceful countryside. 2½ miles from the beach at Sennen Cove which has won numerous awards. BTB 4 Star Graded and AA 3 Pennants. Non members welcome. You can also call us on 0845 130 7633.
Facilities ⬥ ♂ 📶 📛 ☎ ⌂ ⊙ ↵ ▣ ◱ ♜
📶 ⬙ ⊛ 📶 ♜ ⊣ ▣ ◲ ♜ ✦
Nearest Town Penzance
Directions Follow the A30 towards Lands End, turn right onto the A3306 St. Just to Pendeen road, site is 50 yards on the left.
⚇ Penzance

PENZANCE

Wayfarers Caravan & Camping Park, St Hilary, Penzance, Cornwall, TR20 9EF
Tel: 01736 Penzance 763326
Email: elaine@wayfarerspark.co.uk
www.wayfarerspark.co.uk
Pitches For Å ⊕ ⊕ **Total** 39
Acreage 4 **Open** May **to** Sept
Access Good **Site** Level
Nearest Bus Stop (Miles) Outside
ADULTS ONLY PARK. Tranquil, landscaped surroundings. Graded Excellent by the English Tourist Board. Pitches with 16amp hook-ups and awnings from £17 per night Four luxury holiday homes for hire.
Facilities ⬡ ⬡ symbols
Nearest Town Marazion
Directions 2 miles east of Marazion on the B3280.
⇌ Penzance

PERRANPORTH

Penrose Holiday Park, Halt Road, Goonhavern, Near Perranporth, Truro, Cornwall, TR4 9QF
Tel: 01872 573185
Email: info@penroseholidaypark.com
www.penroseholidaypark.com
Pitches For Å ⊕ ⊕ ⊕ **Total** 111
Acreage 10 **Open** 01-Apr **to** Oct
Access Good **Site** Level
Nearest Bus Stop (Miles) ¼
Dog friendly, family site, Take away, 2 miles to Perranporth beach.
Facilities symbols
Nearest Town Perranporth
Directions From the East, take the A30, continue past Bodmin and Indian Queens. Shortly after the wind farm take the B3285 to Perranporth, site is on the left.
⇌ Truro

PERRANPORTH

Perran Springs Holiday Park, Goonhavern, Truro, Cornwall, TR4 9QG
Tel: 01872 540568
Email: info@perransprings.co.uk
www.perransprings.co.uk
Pitches For Å ⊕ ⊕
Acreage 21 **Open** Easter **to** Oct
Access Good **Site** Level
Nearest Bus Stop (Miles) ½
Award winning, friendly, quiet family park offering: Coarse Fishing Lakes, Nature Trail and Pond, Spacious Level Pitches, Electric Hook-ups, Caravan Holiday Homes to buy and hire, Eurotents, Shop, Launderette, Childrens Play Area and Panoramic Countryside Views. 4 Star Park and Bellamy Gold Award.
Facilities symbols
Nearest Town Perranporth
Directions Leave the A30 and turn right onto the B3285 signposted Perranporth. Follow the brown tourism signs marked Perran Springs for 1½ miles. Entrance will then be clearly seen.
⇌ Truro

PERRANPORTH

Perranporth Camping & Touring Park, Budnick Road, Perranporth, Cornwall, TR6 0DB
Tel: 01872 572174
Pitches For Å ⊕ ⊕ **Total** 150
Acreage 6 **Open** Easter **to** Sept
Access Good **Site** Lev/Slope
Nearest Bus Stop (Miles) ¼

½ a mile from the town and beach. Adjoining a golf course and 300 metres from stables.
Facilities symbols
Nearest Town Perranporth
Directions ½ a mile north east of Perranporth town centre, off the B3285 Perranporth to Newquay road.
⇌ Truro

POLZEATH

South Winds Camping & Caravan Park, Old Polzeath Road, Polzeath, Nr Wadebridge, Cornwall, PL27 6QU
Tel: 01208 863267
Email: info@southwindscampsite.co.uk
www.polzeathcamping.co.uk
Pitches For Å ⊕ ⊕ **Total** 100
Acreage 7 **Open** May **to** September
Access Good **Site** Level
Nearest Bus Stop (Miles) ¼
Outstanding views of countryside and sea. ½ a mile from Polzeath Beach.
Facilities symbols
Nearest Town Polzeath
⇌ Bodmin Road

POLZEATH

Tristram Camping & Caravan Park, Polzeath, Nr Wadebridge, Cornwall, PL27 6TD
Tel: 01208 862215
Email: info@tristramcampsite.co.uk
www.polzeathcamping.co.uk
Pitches For Å ⊕ ⊕ **Total** 150
Acreage 10 **Open** March **to** Nov
Access Good **Site** Level
Nearest Bus Stop (Miles) ¼
Set on a cliff top overlooking Polzeath beach. Private access onto the beach.
Facilities symbols
Nearest Town Polzeath
Directions From Wadebridge take the B3314 and follow signs to Polzeath.
⇌ Bodmin

POLZEATH

Valley Caravan Park, Polzeath, Wadebridge, Cornwall, PL27 6SS
Tel: 01208 862391
Email: info@valleycaravanpark.co.uk
www.valleycaravanpark.co.uk
Pitches For Å ⊕ ⊕ **Total** 100
Acreage 10 **Open** Apr **to** Oct
Access Good **Site** Level
Nearest Bus Stop (Miles) ¼
Near the beach.
Facilities symbols
Nearest Town Wadebridge
Directions From Wadebridge take the B3314 to Polzeath and enter the village. Entrance is between shops, opposite the beach.
⇌ Bodmin Parkway

PORTHTOWAN

Porthtowan Tourist Park, Mile Hill, Porthtowan, Truro, Cornwall, TR4 8TY
Tel: 01209 890256
Email: admin@porthtowantouristpark.co.uk
www.porthtowantouristpark.co.uk
Pitches For Å ⊕ ⊕ **Total** 80
Acreage 5½ **Open** Easter **to** Sept
Access Good **Site** Level
Nearest Bus Stop (Miles) 1
A level site with spacious pitches in an area of outstanding natural beauty. Close to a sandy surfing beach, cycle trail and coastal

path. Superb toilet/laundry facilities with free showers and family rooms. Ideal touring base.
Facilities symbols
Nearest Town Porthtowan/Truro
Directions Take signpost off A30 Redruth/ Porthtowan. Cross the A30, through north country to T-Junction, right up the hill, park is ½ a mile on the left.
⇌ Redruth

PORTREATH

Cambrose Touring Park, Portreath Road, Redruth, Cornwall, TR16 4HT
Tel: 01209 890747
Email:
cambrosetouringpark@supanet.com
www.cambrosetouringpark.co.uk
Pitches For Å ⊕ ⊕ **Total** 60
Acreage 7 **Open** April **to** Oct
Access Good **Site** Level
Nearest Bus Stop (Miles) ½
1½ miles from the beach. Near to tramway. Ideal for walking and touring.
Facilities symbols
Nearest Town Portreath
⇌ Redruth

PORTREATH

Tehidy Holiday Park, Harris Mill, Illogan, Portreath, Cornwall, TR16 4JQ
Tel: 01209 216489
Email: holiday@tehidy.co.uk
www.tehidy.co.uk
Pitches For Å ⊕ ⊕ ⊕ **Total** 28
Acreage 4½ **Open** March **to** November
Access Good **Site** Level
Nearest Bus Stop (Miles) Outside

⇌ Redruth

PORTSCATHO

Treloan Coastal Holidays, Treloan Lane, Portscatho, The Roseland, Truro, Cornwall, TR2 5EF
Tel: 01872 580989
Email: info@treloancoastalholidays.co.uk
www.treloancoastalholidays.co.uk
Pitches For Å ⊕ ⊕ **Total** 65
Open All Year **Site** Lev/Slope
Nearest Bus Stop (Miles) ¼
3 selcluded beaches/caves. Walking distance of 3 pubs
Facilities symbols
Nearest Town Truro
Directions From Truro take the A390 through Tresillian and onto the by-pass, take second right turn onto the A3078 sp Tregony and St. Mawes. At Trewithian turn left sp Portscatho and follow signs to Gerrans.
⇌ Truro/St. Austell

PORTSCATHO

Trewince Farm Touring Park, Trewince Farm, Portscatho, Truro, Cornwall, TR2 5ET
Tel: 01872 580430
Email: bookings@trewincefarm.co.uk
www.trewincefarm.co.uk
Pitches For Å ⊕ ⊕ **Total** 25
Acreage 3 **Open** May **to** Sept
Access Good **Site** Lev/Slope
Nearest Bus Stop (Miles) ½
Near the beach in an area of outstanding natural beauty. Close to village pubs and shops.
Facilities symbols
Nearest Town Truro

CORNWALL

Directions From St. Austell take the A390, then turn left onto the B3287 to Tregony, then the A3078 to St. Mawes. Leave at Trewitian and follow the road to St. Anthony.
⚏ Truro

REDRUTH

Chiverton Park, East Hill, Blackwater, Truro, Cornwall, TR4 8HS
Tel: 01872 560667
Email: info@chivertonpark.co.uk
www.chivertonpark.co.uk
Pitches For Å ♊ ♊ **Total** 12
Acreage 4 **Open** Mar **to** oct
Access Good **Site** Level
Nearest Bus Stop (Miles) ¼
Quiet park, close to beaches. Easy access to the north and south coast.
Facilities ⚓ ∮ ⊟ ⊞ ⅏ ⌐ ⌐ ⊙ ⌐ ⓐ ⊙ ♥
⌕ ⚘ ⌂⋈⊡⊟ ☀ ☂
Nearest Town St Agnes
Directions Travel along the A30 to Chiverton Cross roundabout follow signs to Blackwater,turn right approx 400 yds
⚏ Truro

REDRUTH

Globe Vale Holiday Park, Radnor, Redruth, Cornwall, TR16 4BH
Tel: 01209 891183
Email: info@globevale.co.uk
www.globevale.co.uk
Pitches For Å ♊ ♊ **Total** 138
Acreage 9 **Open** All Year
Access Good **Site** Level
Just a 10 minute drive from Portreath and Porthtowan beaches. Good access from the A30, ideal for visiting St. Ives, Penzance and Truro.
Facilities ∮ ⊟ ⊞ ⅏ ⌐ ⌐ ⌐ ⓐ ⊙ ♥
⌕ ⊙ ⚛ ⌕ ⌂⋈⊡⊟ ☀ ☂
Nearest Town Redruth
Directions From Redruth follow signs to Portreath and Porthtowan from the A30 roundabout. At the double roundabout take the third exit to North Country. At the crossroads turn right signposted Radnor and follow signs. Approx. 4 miles from Redruth.
⚏ Redruth

REDRUTH

Lakeside Camping, The Golden Lion Inn, Stithians Lake, Menherion, Redruth, Cornwall, TR16 6NW
Email: enquiries@golden-lion-inn.co.uk
www.golden-lion-inn.co.uk
Pitches For Å ♊ ♊ ♊ **Total** 14
Open All Year **Access** Good **Site** Level
Nearest Bus Stop (Miles) 1
Set behind the gardens of an award winning pub and restaurant. 50 yards from a lake for windsurfing, sailing and kayaking. Fly fishing permits.
Facilities ⚓ ∮ ⊞ ⅏ ⌐
⚔ ⌂⋈⊡⊟ ☀ ☂
Nearest Town Redruth
Directions Leave the A30 at Redruth and take the B3297 signposted Four Lanes and Helston. Turn right at signpost for Golden Lion.
⚏ Redruth

REDRUTH

Lanyon Holiday Park, Loscombe Lane, Four Lanes, Redruth, Cornwall, TR16 6LP
Tel: 01209 313474
Email: lanyonadmin@btconnect.com
www.lanyonholidaypark.co.uk
Pitches For Å ♊ ♊ ♊ **Total** 50
Acreage 14 **Open** April **to** Oct
Access Good **Site** Level
Nearest Bus Stop (Miles) ¼
Surrounded by open countryside. 6 miles to Portreath surfing beach. 3¼ miles from Stithians Lake and close to the Great Flat Lode Trail.
Facilities ∮ ⊟ ⊞ ⅏ ⌐ ⌐ ⊙ ⌐ ⓐ ⊙ ♥
⌕ ⚘ ⌓ ⊡ ⚘ ⌂⋈⊡⊟ ☀ ☂
Directions Leave the A30 at Camborne/Pool A3047 exit, keep to the left hand lane and drive straight ahead through the next two sets of traffic lights. Pass Tesco Extra (on your left) and turn next right over railway bridge (sp Four Lanes). Follow this road up the hill [approx 1½ miles], at T-Junction turn right then take 2nd right at Pencoys Village Hall. Park is on the left hand side after approx 400 metres.
⚏ Redruth

REDRUTH

St Day Touring Holidays Church Hill, St Day, Redruth, Cornwall, TR16 5LE
Tel: 01209 821086
Email: holidays@stdaytouring.co.uk
www.stdaytouring.co.uk
Pitches For Å ♊ ♊ ♊ **Total** 32
Acreage 4 **Open** All Year
Access Good **Site** Level/Sloping
Nearest Bus Stop (Miles) Outside
ADULTS ONLY small, peaceful Park in rural surroundings. Central location.
Facilities ∮ ⊟ ⊞ ⅏ ⌐ ⌐ ⊙ ⌐ ⓐ ⊙ ♥
⌕ ⌂⋈⊟⚘ ☂
Nearest Town Redruth
Directions 1½ miles from the A30 at Scorrier.
⚏ Redruth

REDRUTH

Wheal Rose Caravan & Camping Park, Wheal Rose, Scorrier, Redruth, Cornwall, TR16 5DD
Tel: 01209 891496
Email: whealrose@aol.com
www.whealrosecaravanpark.co.uk
Pitches For Å ♊ ♊ **Total** 50
Acreage 6½ **Open** Mar **to** Dec
Access Good **Site** Level
Nearest Bus Stop (Miles) Outside
Adjacent to a mineral tramway. Cenral for all of West Cornwalls attractions. AA 4 Pennants.
Facilities ⚓ ∮ ⊟ ⊞ ⅏ ⌐ ⌐ ⊙ ⌐ ⓐ ⊙ ♥
⌕ ⌓ ⊙ ⚘ ⊟ ⚘ ⚛ ⌂⋈⊡⊟ ☂
Nearest Town Redruth
Directions From the A30 take the Scorrier slip road and turn right at the Plume of Feathers, follow signs to park.
⚏ Redruth

RUAN MINOR

The Friendly Camp & Caravan Park, Tregullas Farm, Ruan Minor, Helston, Cornwall, TR12 7LJ
Tel: 01326 240387
Email: jbwbennetts@tiscali.co.uk

Pitches For Å ♊ ♊ **Total** 8
Open Easter or 1 April **to** Oct
Access Good **Site** Level
Nearest Bus Stop (Miles) ¼
Ideal centre for touring the Lizard Peninsula.
Facilities ∮ ⊟ ⊞ ⅏ ⌐ ⌐ ⊙ ⌐ ⓐ ⊙ ♥
Directions Take the A3083 Helston to Lizard road, the Park is situated on the left just before the junction of the B3296 to Mullion.
⚏ Redruth

SALTASH

Dolbeare Park, Landrake, Saltash, Cornwall, PL12 5AF
Tel: 01752 851332
Email: reception@dolbeare.co.uk
www.dolbeare.co.uk
Pitches For Å ♊ ♊ ♊ **Total** 60
Acreage 9 **Open** All Year
Access Good **Site** Level
Nearest Bus Stop (Miles) ¾
Centrally located between beaches and the moors, ideal for exploring both Cornwall and Devon. Easy access. Close to Looe, Polperro and Plymouth. Take-away on site.
Facilities ⚓ ∮ ⊟ ⊞ ⅏ ⌐ ⌐ ⊙ ⌐ ⓐ ⊙ ♥
⌕ ⊙ ⚘ ⌓ ⌂⋈⊡⊟ ☀ ☂ ☂
Nearest Town Saltash
Directions From Saltash take the A38 west for 4 miles to Landrake. At the footbridge turn right and follow signs to the site. ¾ miles from the A38.
⚏ Saltash

SENNEN

Seaview Holiday Park, Sennen, Lands End, Cornwall, TR19 7AD
Tel: 01736 871266
Email: bookings@seaview.org.uk
www.seaview.org.uk
Pitches For Å ♊ ♊ **Total** 120
Acreage 12½ **Open** mar **to** Dec
Access Good **Site** Level
Nearest Bus Stop (Miles) Outside
Lands End, Minials theatre, cable station.
Facilities ∮ ⊟ ⊞ ⅏ ⌐ ⌐ ⊙ ⌐ ⓐ ⊙ ♥
⌕ ⌕ ⚔ ⌓ ⌂⋈⊡⊟ ☀ ☂
Nearest Town Penzance
Directions From Penzance take the A30 signposted Lands End. go through Sennen village to the other side. on the left.
⚏ Penzance

ST. AGNES

Beacon Cottage Farm Touring Park, Beacon Drive, St Agnes, Cornwall, TR5 0NU
Tel: 01872 552347
Email: beaconcottagefarm@lineone.net
www.beaconcottagefarmholidays.co.uk
Pitches For Å ♊ ♊ **Total** 70
Acreage 4 **Open** 01-Apr **to** 30-Sep
Access Good **Site** Level
Nearest Bus Stop (Miles) ½
On a working farm, surrounded by National Trust land. Sandy beach 1 mile, beautiful sea views.
Facilities ∮ ⊞ ⅏ ⌐ ⌐ ⊙ ⌐ ⓐ ⊙ ♥
⌕ ⌓ ⊙ ⚘ ⌂⋈⊡⊟ ☀ ☂
Nearest Town St Agnes
Directions From the A30, take the B3277 to St. Agnes, take road to the Beacon and follow signs to the site.

ST. AGNES

Presingoll Farm Caravan & Camping Park, St Agnes, Cornwall, TR5 0PB
Tel: 01872 552333
Email: pam@presingollfarm.co.uk
www.presingollfarm.co.uk
Pitches For ⚠ ⬜ ➡ **Total** 90
Acreage 5 **Open** Easter **to** End October
Access Good **Site** Level
Nearest Bus Stop (Miles) Outside
Working farm overlooking the North Cornwall coastline. Near the Cornish Coastal Path and surf beaches within 2 miles. Ideal for walking. Dogs must be kept on a lead.
Facilities 🚻 ✆ 🛁 ⬛ ⌂ ⊙ ⬜ 🕴 ▣ 🛒 ♨ ▤ ⊡
Nearest Town St. Agnes
Directions Leave the A30 at Chiverton Cross roundabout and take the B3277 for St. Agnes. Site is 3 miles on the right.
➘ Truro

ST. AUSTELL

Croft Farm Holiday Park, Luxulyan, Bodmin, Cornwall, PL30 5EQ
Tel: 01726 850228
Email: enquiries@croftfarm.co.uk
www.croftfarm.co.uk
Pitches For ⚠ ⬜ ➡ **Total** 52
Acreage 5 **Open** 21-Mar **to** 21-Jan
Access Good **Site** Lev/Slope
1 mile from the Eden Project.
Facilities ✆ 🛁 ⬛ ⌂ ⊙ ⬜ 🕴 ▣ 🛒
🕴 ⊙ ⬛ ♨ ▤ ✚ ▣ ⊡ ☀ ☂
Nearest Town St Austell
Directions From St Austell follow signs for the Eden Project, Croft Farm is 1 mile from the main entrance.
➘ Luxulyan

ST. AUSTELL

Pensagillas Park, Grampound, Truro, Cornwall, TR2 4SR
Tel: 01872 530808
Email: sales@pensagillas-park.co.uk
www.pensagillas-park.co.uk
Pitches For ⚠ ⬜ ➡ **Total** 65
Acreage 10 **Open** Mar **to** Oct
Access Good **Site** Level
2 acre course fishing lake, 5 miles from beach, 4 miles from Mevagissey.
Facilities ✆ 🛁 ⌂ ⊙ ⬜ 🕴 ▣
🕴 ⊙ ⬛ ▽ ⬛ ♨ ▤ ✚ ▣ ⊡ ✍ ☀ ☂
Nearest Town Mevagissey
➘ St Austell

ST. AUSTELL

River Valley Holiday Park, London Apprentice, St Austell, Cornwall, PL26 7AP
Tel: 01726 73533
Email: mail@cornwall-holidays.co.uk
www.rivervalleyholidaypark.co.uk
Pitches For ⚠ ⬜ ➡ **Total** 40
Acreage 9 **Open** April **to** Oct
Access Good **Site** Level
Nearest Bus Stop (Miles) Outside
Alongside a river with woodland walk and cycle trail to the beach.
Facilities ✆ 🛁 ⬛ ⌂ ⊙ ⬜ 🕴 ▣
🕴 ⊙ ⬛ ♨ ▽ ✖ ▣ ⊡ ☀ ☂
Nearest Town St Austell
Directions Take the B3273 from St Austell to Mevagissey, 1 mile to London Apprentice, site is on the left hand side.
➘ St Austell

ST. AUSTELL

Treveor Farm Caravan & Camping Site, Gorran, St Austell, Cornwall, PL26 6LW
Tel: 01726 842387
Email: info@treveorfarm.co.uk
www.treveorfarm.co.uk
Pitches For ⚠ ⬜ ➡ **Total** 50
Acreage 4 **Open** April **to** Oct
Access Good **Site** Level
1 mile to the beach and coastal path. 3 miles from the Lost Gardens of Heligan and only 15 miles from the Eden Project.
Facilities ✆ 🛁 ⌂ ⊙ ⬜ 🕴 ▣
🕴 ▤ ✚ ▣ ⊡
Nearest Town St Austell/Gorran Haven
Directions Take the B3273 from St Austell towards Mevagissey. After Pentewan at top of the hill turn right to Gorran. After approx 4 miles turn right into the park at the signboard.
➘ St Austell

ST. BURYAN

Tower Park Caravans & Camping, St Buryan, Penzance, Cornwall, TR19 6BZ
Tel: 01736 810286
Email: enquiries@towerparkcamping.co.uk
www.towerparkcamping.co.uk
Pitches For ⚠ ⬜ ➡ **Total** 102
Acreage 12 **Open** March **to** October
Access Good **Site** Level
Nearest Bus Stop (Miles) ¼
Peaceful, family run campsite in West Cornwall. Short walk to the village pub and shop. Holiday caravans for hire.
Facilities 🚻 ✆ 🛁 ⌂ ⊙ ⬜ 🕴 ▣
🕴 ⊙ ⬛ ♨ ▽ ⬛ ♨ ▤ ✚ ▣ ⊡ ☀ ☂
Nearest Town Penzance
Directions From the A30 Lands End road turn left onto the B3283 towards St. Buryan. In the village turn right then right again and the park is 300 yards on the right.
➘ Penzance

ST. IVES

Ayr Holiday Park, Ayr, St Ives, Cornwall, TR26 1EJ
Tel: 01736 795855
Email: recept@ayrholidaypark.co.uk
www.ayrholidaypark.co.uk
Pitches For ⚠ ⬜ ➡ ⬛ **Total** 80
Acreage 6 **Open** All Year
Access Good **Site** Level/Sloping
Nearest Bus Stop (Miles) Outside
Beautiful coastal views. Just a 10 minute walk to the town centre, harbour and beaches of St Ives.
Facilities 🚻 ✆ 🛁 ⬛ ⌂ ⊙ ⬜ 🕴 ▣
🕴 ⊙ ⬛ ♨ ▽ ✚ ▣ ⊡ ☂
Nearest Town St Ives
Directions From the A30 take the St Ives exit following signs to St Ives for heavy vehicles, day visitors and Tate Gallery. Join the B3311 then the B3306 and follow brown tourism signs to the Park.
➘ St Ives

ST. IVES

Balnoon Camping Site, Balnoon, Nr Halsetown, St Ives, Cornwall, TR26 3JA
Tel: 01736 795431
Email: nat@balnoon.fsnet.co.uk
www.balnooncampsite.co.uk
Pitches For ⚠ ⬜ ➡ **Total** 23
Acreage 1 **Open** Easter **to** Oct
Access Good **Site** Level
Nearest Bus Stop (Miles) Outside
Situated in the countryside with views of adjacent rolling hills. Equidistant from the beautiful beaches of Carbis Bay and St. Ives, approx. 2 miles.
Facilities ✆ 🛁 ⌂ ⊙ ⬛ ▣ 🕴 ⊙ ✚ ⊡
Nearest Town St. Ives
Directions From the A30 take the A3074 for St. Ives, at the second mini-roundabout turn first left signposted Tate St.Ives (B3311), turn second right signposted Balnoon. Approx. 3 miles from the A30.
➘ St. Ives

ST. IVES

Higher Chellew, Nancledra, Penzance, Cornwall, TR20 8BD
Tel: 01736 364532
Email: higherchellew@btinternet.com
www.higherchellewcamping.co.uk
Pitches For ⚠ ⬜ ➡ **Total** 30
Acreage 1½ **Open** Easter **to** End Sept
Access Good **Site** Level
Nearest Bus Stop (Miles) Outside
Peaceful and private small site with views of Trencrom and glimpses of the sea. Spectacular walks in the area. Near St Michaels Mount. A few fully serviced pitches available.

Facilities ♿ ∱ 🚽🚿🅿📶⊙🍴 ♨ 🏪 🍺 🛝
Nearest Town St Ives/Penzance
Directions On the B3311 in between Penzance and St Ives.
🚊 St Ives/Penzance

ST. IVES

Penderleath Caravan & Camping Park, Towednack, St Ives, Cornwall, TR26 3AF
Tel: 01736 798403
Email: holidays@penderleath.co.uk
www.penderleath.co.uk
Pitches For ▲ 🚐 🚙 **Total** 75
Acreage 10 **Open** Easter **to** Oct
Access Good **Site** Lev/Slope
Nearest Bus Stop (Miles) Outside
Nearest Town St. Ives
🚊 St. Ives

ST. IVES

Polmanter Touring Park, Halsetown, St Ives, Cornwall, TR26 3LX
Tel: 01736 795640
Email: reception@polmanter.co.uk
www.polmanter.co.uk
Pitches For ▲ 🚐 🚙 **Total** 250
Acreage 20 **Open** 29th Mar **to** 27-Oct
Access Good **Site** Level
Nearest Bus Stop (Miles) Entrance
Within walking distance of St Ives and beaches.
Facilities ♿ ∱ 🚽🚿🅿📶⊙🍴 ♨ 🏪 🍺
🛝 ⊙ 🏪 ✕ 🍺 ♨ ♣ 🎣🅿📶 🛝 🍴 📶 🛜
Nearest Town St Ives
Directions From the A30 take the A3074 to St Ives, turn left at the second mini-roundabout via Halsetown. Turn right at the B3311 and turn right at the Halsetown Inn, then first left.
🚊 St Ives

ST. JUST

Kelynack Caravan & Camping Park, Kelynack, St Just, Penzance, Cornwall, TR19 7RE
Tel: 01736 787633
Email: enquiries@kelynackholidays.co.uk
www.kelynackholidays.co.uk
Pitches For ▲ 🚐 🚙 **Total** 30
Acreage 2 **Open** All Year
Access Good **Site** Level
Nearest Bus Stop (Miles) ¼
Small and secluded site nestling alongside a stream. Just 1 mile from the coast in the beautiful Cot Valley.
Facilities ∱ 🚽🚿🅿📶⊙🍴 ♨ 🏪 🍺
🛝 ⊙ 🏪🍴🅿📶 🛜
Nearest Town Penzance

Directions From Penzance take the A3071 to St Just. Just before reaching St Just turn left onto the B3306, follow road down the hill for 1 mile then turn left, after 200 yards turn left again.
🚊 Penzance

ST. JUST

Roselands Caravan Park, Dowran, St Just, Penzance, Cornwall, TR19 7RS
Tel: 01736 788571
Email: info@roselands.co.uk
www.roselands.co.uk
Pitches For ▲ 🚐 🚙 **Total** 38
Acreage 3 **Open** Mar **to** Oct
Access Good **Site** Level
Nearest Bus Stop (Miles) ¼
Nr Lands End, South West Coast Path near Sennen Cove surf beach, in an area of Outstanding natural beauty.
Facilities ∱ 🚽🚿🅿📶⊙🍴 ♨ 🏪 🍺
🛝 ⊙ 🏪 🍺 🏪 ♣ 🅿📶 🛝 🍴 📶 🛜
Nearest Town St Just
Directions From the A30 Penzance by-pass take the A3071 to St Just for 5 miles, turn left at sign and park is 800 yards.
🚊 Penzance

ST. JUST

Secret Garden Caravan Park, Bosavern House, St Just, Penzance, Cornwall, TR19 7RD
Tel: 01736 788301
Email: mail@bosavern.com
www.secretbosavern.com
Pitches For ▲ 🚐 🚙 **Total** 12
Acreage 1 **Open** March **to** October
Access Good **Site** Level
Nearest Bus Stop (Miles) ½
Walled garden site surrounded by trees and flowers. Excellent walking country, good beaches nearby. Local authorities licensed site.
Facilities ∱ 🚽🚿🅿📶⊙🍴 ♨ 🏪 🍺
🏪✕🍴🅿📶 🛝 🛜
Nearest Town St Just/Penzance
Directions Take the A3071 from Penzance towards St. Just. Approximately 550yds before St. Just turn left onto the B3306 signposted Lands End and airport. Secret Garden Caravan Park is 500yds from the turn off, behind Bosavern House.
🚊 Penzance

ST. MAWES

Trethem Mill Touring Park, St Just-in-Roseland, Truro, Cornwall, TR2 5JF
Tel: 01872 580504
Email: reception@trethem.com
www.trethem.com
Pitches For ▲ 🚐 🚙 **Total** 84

Acreage 4 **Open** April **to** Mid Oct
Access Good **Site** Lev/Slope
Nearest Bus Stop (Miles) ¼
Discover the unexplored Roseland, staying on the only 5 Star Park on the Peninsula. Family owned and run, we offer a relaxing and tranquil setting. Ideally located for for walking, sailing, beaches and gardens. National Caravan Park of the Year 2010, England in Excellence Awards.
Facilities ♿ ∱ 🚽🚿🅿📶⊙🍴 ♨ 🏪 🍺
🛝 ⊙ 🏪 🏪🍴🅿📶 🛜
Nearest Town St Mawes
Directions From Tregony follow the A3078 to St. Mawes. Approx. 2 miles after passing through Trewithian look out for caravan and camping sign.
🚊 Truro

ST. MERRYN

Tregavone Farm Touring Park, St Merryn, Padstow, Cornwall, PL28 8JZ
Tel: 01841 520148
Email: info@tregavone.co.uk
www.tregavonefarm.co.uk
Pitches For ▲ 🚐 🚙 **Total** 40
Acreage 4 **Open** March **to** October
Access Good **Site** Level
Quiet family run site situated near sandy surfing beaches, country views, well maintained and grassy. AA 2 Pennants.
Facilities ♿ ∱ 🚽🚿🅿📶⊙🍴 ♨ 🏪 🍺
Nearest Town Padstow
Directions Turn right off A39 (Wadebridge-St. Columb) onto A389 (Padstow) come to a T-junction and turn right, in 1 mile turn left, entrance on left after 1 mile.
🚊 Newquay

ST. MERRYN

Trethias Farm Caravan Park, St Merryn, Padstow, Cornwall, PL28 8PL
Tel: 01841 520323
Email: trethiasfarm@btconnect.com
Pitches For ▲ 🚐 🚙 **Total** 63
Acreage 12 **Open** April **to** September
Access Good **Site** Level
Nearest Bus Stop (Miles) 1
Near beach, scenic views. Couples and family groups only. ETB 3 Star Graded and David Bellamy Gold Award for Conservation 2011.
Facilities ∱ 🚽🚿🅿📶⊙🍴 ♨ 🏪 🍺
🛝 ⊙ 🏪🍴🅿
Nearest Town Padstow
Directions From Wadebridge follow signs to St. Merryn, go past Farmers Arms, third turning right (our signs from here).
🚊 Bodmin Parkway

ST. MERRYN

Trevean Farm Caravan & Camping Park, St Merryn, Padstow, Cornwall, PL28 8PR
Tel: 01841 520772
Email: trevean.info@virgin.net
www.treveancaravanandcamping.net
Pitches For Å ⬠ 🚍 **Total** 68
Acreage 2 **Open** Apr **to** Oct
Access Good **Site** Level
Nearest Bus Stop (Miles) ½
Situated near several sandy, surfing beaches. ETC 4 Star Grading.
Facilities
Nearest Town Padstow
Directions From St. Merryn village take the B3276 Newquay road for 1 mile. Turn left for Rumford, site ¼ mile on the right.
⚞ Newquay

ST. MERRYN

Treyarnon Bay Caravan Park, Treyarnon Bay, Padstow, Cornwall, PL28 8JR
Tel: 01841 520681
Email: enquiries@treyarnonbay.co.uk
www.treyarnonbay.co.uk
Pitches For Å ⬠ 🚍 **Total** 55
Acreage 6 **Open** April **to** Sept
Access Poor **Site** Level/Sloping
Nearest Bus Stop (Miles) Entrance
Family park overlooking Treyarnon Bay and only 200 yards from the beach. Great for surfing and walking.
Facilities
Nearest Town Padstow
Directions From Wadebridge take the A389 west and follow signs to St. Merryn and Treyarnon Bay. 3 miles from Padstow.
⚞ Bodmin/Newquay

TINTAGEL

The Headland Caravan & Camping Park, Atlantic Road, Tintagel, Cornwall, PL34 0DE
Tel: 01840 770239
Email: headland.caravan@talktalkbusiness.net
www.headlandcaravanpark.co.uk
Pitches For Å ⬠ 🚍 🚐 **Total** 60
Acreage 4 **Open** Easter **to** Oct
Access Good **Site** Lev/Slope
Nearest Bus Stop (Miles) ¼
Three beaches within walking distance. Scenic views. Ideal touring centre.
Facilities
Nearest Town Tintagel
Directions Follow camping/caravan signs from B3263 through village to Headland.
⚞ Bodmin Parkway

TINTAGEL

Trewethett Farm Caravan Club Site, Trethevy, Tintagel, Cornwall, PL34 0BQ
Tel: 01840 770222
www.caravanclub.co.uk
Pitches For Å ⬠ 🚍 **Total** 122
Acreage 15 **Open** Mar **to** Nov
Access Good **Site** Level
Breathtaking views overlooking Bossiney Cove. ½ a mile from a sandy beach. Spectacular clifftop walks. Near Tintagel Castle, picturesque ports and harbours. Non members welcome. Booking essential.
Facilities
Nearest Town Tintagel
Directions From NE on the A30, t onto the A395 via slip road. After 11 miles at the T-junc t rt onto the A39, after 1 mile just before the transmitter t lt, at T-junc t rt onto the B3266. After 2½ miles at the junc on the bend turn left onto the B3263, site is on the right.
⚞ Tintagel

TRURO

Carnon Downs Caravan & Camping Park, Carnon Downs, Truro, Cornwall, TR3 6JJ
Tel: 01872 862283
Email: info@carnon-downs-caravanpark.co.uk
www.carnon-downs-caravanpark.co.uk
Pitches For Å ⬠ 🚍 **Total** 150
Acreage 30 **Open** All Year
Access Good **Site** Level
Nearest Bus Stop (Miles) Outside Idea touring
Facilities
Nearest Town Truro
Directions On the A390 Falmouth road, 3 miles South of Truro.
⚞ Truro

TRURO

Chacewater Camping & Caravan Park, Coxhill, Chacewater, Truro, Cornwall, TR4 8LY
Tel: 01209 820762
Email: chacewaterpark@hotmail.co.uk
www.chacewaterpark.co.uk
Pitches For Å ⬠ 🚍 **Total** 100
Acreage 6 **Open** May **to** End Sept
Access Good **Site** Level
Nearest Bus Stop (Miles) Outside
Exclusively for Adults. The ideal holiday base for the Over 30s.
Facilities
Nearest Town Truro
Directions From A30 take the A3047 to Scorrier. Turn left at Crossroads Hotel onto the B3298. 1½ miles turn left to Chacewater, ½ mile sign directs you to the park.
⚞ Truro

TRURO

Cosawes Park, Cosawes Park Homes, Perranarworthal, Truro, Cornwall, TR3 7QS
Tel: 01872 863724
Email: info@cosawes.com
www.cosawestouringandcamping.co.uk
Pitches For Å ⬠ 🚍 🚐 **Total** 50
Acreage 4 **Open** All Year
Access Good **Site** Lev/Slope
Nearest Bus Stop (Miles) ¼
Situated in a 100 acre wooded valley, an area of outstanding natural beauty. Award winning toilet and shower facilities with disabled/family rooms. Fully serviced hard standing pitches. Near to local beaches, Flambards and the city of Truro.
Facilities
Nearest Town Truro/Falmouth
Directions From Truro take the A39, as you exit the village of Perranarworthal take signposted turning on the right.
⚞ Truro/Perranwell

TRURO

Killiwerris Touring Park, Penstraze, Truro, Cornwall, TR4 8PF
Tel: 01872 561356
Email: killiwerris@aol.com
www.killiwerris.co.uk
Pitches For ⬠ 🚍 **Total** 20
Acreage 1 **Open** Easter **to** Oct
Access Good **Site** Level
Nearest Bus Stop (Miles) ½
ADULTS ONLY site. 4 miles from beach, countryside, ideal central location for exploring Cornwall.

TRURO

Facilities
Nearest Town Truro
Directions Chacewater village 1 mile, Truro 4 miles.
⚞ Truro

TRURO

Summer Valley Touring Park, Shortlanesend, Truro, Cornwall, TR4 9DW
Tel: 01872 277878
Email: james@summervalley.co.uk
www.summervalley.co.uk
Pitches For Å ⬠ 🚍 **Total** 50
Acreage 3 **Open** April **to** October
Access Good **Site** Sloping
Nearest Bus Stop (Miles) ¼
Ideal touring centre for all of Cornwall.
Facilities
Nearest Town Truro
Directions 2½ miles north of Truro on the B3284 Perranporth road.
⚞ Truro

TRURO

Veryan Camping & Caravanning Club Site, Tretheake Manor, Veryan, Truro, Cornwall, TR2 5PP
Tel: 01872 501658
Email: veryan.site@thefriendlyclub.co.uk
www.campingandcaravanning.co.uk/veryan
Pitches For Å ⬠ 🚍 **Total** 150
Acreage 9 **Open** 15-Mar **to** 04-Nov
Access Good **Site** Sloping
Nearest Bus Stop (Miles) ¼
Ideal for exploring the beaches and coves of the Cornish Coast. BTB 4 Star Graded and AA 3 Pennants. Non members welcome. You can also call us on 0845 130 7633.
Facilities
Nearest Town Veryan
Directions Take the A390 from St. Austell, leave at the A3078 sign on the left, turn left at the filling station and follow international signs.
⚞ Truro

WADEBRIDGE

Ponderosa Caravan Park, St Issey, Wadebridge, Cornwall, PL27 7QA
Tel: 01841 540359
Pitches For Å ⬠ 🚍 **Total** 40
Acreage 3½ **Open** Easter **to** Oct
Access Good **Site** Level
Nearest Bus Stop (Miles) ¼
Seven beaches within 4 miles. Close to the Camel Trail, Creely Adventre Park and the Eden Project.
Facilities
Nearest Town Padstow
Directions On main Wadebridge to Padstow road.
⚞ Bodmin Parkway

WADEBRIDGE

St. Mabyn Holiday Park, Longstone Road, St Mabyn, Nr Wadebridge, Cornwall, PL30 3BY
Tel: 01208 841677
Email: info@stmabyn.co.uk
www.stmabynholidaypark.co.uk
Pitches For Å ⬠ 🚍 🚐 **Total** 120
Acreage 12 **Open** 15-Mar **to** 03-Nov
Access Good **Site** Level/Sloping
Nearest Bus Stop (Miles) ¼
Situated near Bodmin Moor. Ideal for exploring the whole of Cornwall. Easy access to Eden Project, Truro, Wadebridge, Padstow and many other places of interest.

Facilities ♿ ✦ 🚰 🏠 🕮 🚿 📞 🍴 ☺ 🍳 🛒 🔌 🍽 ♨
♨ 🛢 🐕 🍴 🔥 🏪 🛒 🏕 🥾 ⚓ 📭 🎣 🛒 🏪 🔌 🏕 ☀ 📶
Nearest Town Wadebridge
Directions Take the B3266 from either Camelford or Bodmin. Site is at Longstone crossroads. From Wadebridge take the A389 to Bodmin then the B3266.
🚆 Bodmin Parkway

WADEBRIDGE
The Laurels Holiday Park, Padstow Road, Whitecross, Wadebridge, Cornwall, PL27 7JQ
Tel: 01209 313474
Email: lanyonadmin@btconnect.com
www.thelaurelsholidaypark.co.uk
Pitches For ▲ ⊞ 🚐 **Total** 35
Acreage 2 **Open** April **to** Oct
Access Good **Site** Level
Nearest Bus Stop (Miles) Entrance
6 miles from Padstow, and close to Rock and Port Isaac. Ideal for touring north and south Cornwall.
Facilities ✦ 🕮 🚿 📞 ☺ 🍳 🛒 🔌 ♨
🍴 🏪 🛒 🔌 🐕 🔥
Nearest Town Padstow
Directions On the crossroads of the A39 and the A389 Wadebridge/Padstow junction, close to the Royal Cornwall Showground.
🚆 Bodmin

WADEBRIDGE
Trewince Farm Holiday Park, St Issey, Wadebridge, Cornwall, PL27 7RL
Tel: 01208 812830
Email: enquiries@trewincefarm-holidaypark.co.uk
www.trewincefarm-holidaypark.co.uk
Pitches For ▲ ⊞ 🚐 **Total** 120
Acreage 15 **Open** Easter **to** End Oct
Access Good **Site** Level
Nearest Bus Stop (Miles) ¼
Only 4 miles from picturesque Padstow and the Camel Trail. Ideal for cycling and walking.
Facilities ♿ ✦ 🚰 🏠 🕮 🚿 📞 ☺ 🍳 🛒 🔌 ♨
♨ 🛢 🐕 🍳 🍴 🏪 🔥 🏕 🥾 ⚓ 📭 🎣 🛒 🔌 🐕 ♨
🛒
Nearest Town Padstow
Directions Take the A39 from Wadebridge towards Padstow, turn right onto the A389, site is signposted 1 mile on the left.
🚆 Bodmin Parkway

CUMBRIA
AMBLESIDE
Baysbrown Farm, Great Langdale, Ambleside, Cumbria, LA22 9JZ
Tel: 01539 437150
Email: baysbrowninfo@gmail.com
www.baysbrownfarmcampsite.co.uk
Pitches For ▲ 🚐 **Total** 150
Open Mar **to** Nov
Access Poor **Site** Lev/Slope
Nearest Bus Stop (Miles) ¼
Ideal for walking climbing and other adventures.
Facilities 🕮 📞 ♨ 🍴 🔥
Nearest Town Ambleside

Directions From Ambleside take the A593 to Skelwith Bridge. Turn right onto B5343 Follow to Chapel Stile. 2nd leftafter Wainwright pub
🚆 Windermere

APPLEBY
Hawkrigg Farm, Colby, Appleby-in-Westmorland, Cumbria, CA16 6BB
Pitches For ▲ ⊞
Open All Year
Access Good **Site** Level
Nearest Bus Stop (Miles) 1½
Quiet site with beautiful views. Ideal for touring the Eden Valley.
Facilities ✦ 🕮 🚿 📞 ☺ ♨ 🍳 🍴 🔥
Directions From Appleby take the B6260, turn west onto the Colby road. In Colby turn left onto Kings Meaburn Road, take the first turning right.
🚆 Appleby

APPLEBY
Silverband Park, Silverband, Knock, Nr Appleby, Cumbria, CA16 6DL
Tel: 01768 361218
Pitches For ⊞ 🚐 **Total** 12
Acreage ½ **Open** All Year
Access Good **Site** Sloping
Nearest Bus Stop (Miles) Outside
Ideal for touring the Lakes and Fells. Two fully serviced pitches available. Bus service only once a week.
Facilities ✦ 🚰 🕮 🚿 📞 ☺ ♨
🛢 🍳 🍴 ☀ 🔥
Nearest Town Appleby/Penrith
Directions Turn left off the A66 Penrith to Scotch Corner road at Kirkby Thore. After 2 miles at T-Junction turn left, after 100 yards take the first turn right, site is 1 mile on the right.
🚆 Appleby/Penrith

APPLEBY
Wild Rose Park, Ormside, Appleby, Cumbria, CA16 6EJ
Tel: 017683 51077
Email: reception@wildrose.co.uk
www.harrisonholidays.com
Pitches For ▲ ⊞ 🚐 **Total** 226
Acreage 40 **Open** All Year
Access Good **Site** Lev/Slope
Quiet park in the unspoilt Eden Valley with superb views. Midway between Lakes and Yorkshire Dales. Secure Storage from Nov to March.
Facilities ♿ ✦ 🚰 🏠 🕮 🚿 📞 ☺ 🍳 🛒 🔌 ♨
🛢 🐕 🍳 🍴 🏪 🔥 🏕 🥾 ⚓ 📭 🛒 🔌 ☀
Nearest Town Appleby
Directions Centre Appleby take B6260 Kendal for 1½ miles. Left Ormside and Soulby 1½ miles left, ½ mile turn right.
🚆 Appleby

ARNSIDE/SILVERDALE
Fell End Caravan Park, Slackhead Road, Hale, Nr Milnthorpe, Cumbria, LA7 7BS
Tel: 01524 781453
Email: enquiries@pureleisure-holidays.co.uk

www.fellendcaravanpark.co.uk
Pitches For ⊞ 🚐 **Total** 80
Acreage 12 **Open** All Year
Access Good **Site** Lev/Slope
Nearest Bus Stop (Miles) Outside
In an area of outstanding natural beauty, Fell End is a meticulously kept site with mature gardens and a country inn. Leisure Club with pool, gym, steam room and soft play. Close to Lakes and Dales. Open all year to tourers.
Facilities ♿ ✦ 🚰 🏠 🕮 🚿 📞 ☺ 🍳 🛒 🔌 ♨
🛢 🐕 🍳 🍴 🏪 🔌 🍴 🔥 🏕 🥾 📭 🛒 🔌 ☀ 📶
Nearest Town Arnside/Silverdale
Directions Leave the M6 at junction 35, take the A6 north and turn left at Wildlife Oasis (after passing Esso fuel station). Follow signs to Fell End Caravan Park.
🚆 Arnside

ARNSIDE/SILVERDALE
Hall More Caravan Park, Hale, Nr Milnthorpe, Cumbria, LA7 7BP
Tel: 01524 781453
Email: enquiries@pureleisure-holidays.co.uk
www.hallmorecaravanpark.co.uk
Pitches For ▲ ⊞ 🚐 **Total** 52
Acreage 5 **Open** March **to** January
Access Good **Site** Level
Nearest Bus Stop (Miles) Å¼
Rural location, excellent for walking, rambling, etc.. Camping Pods. Own coarse fishery and trout fishery adjacent. Nearby Leisure Club. Easy access to the Lake District.
Facilities ♿ ✦ 🚰 🕮 🚿 📞 ☺ 🍳 🛒 🔌 ♨
🛢 🐕 🍳 🍴 🏪 🔌 🛒 🐕 ☀
Nearest Town Arnside/Milnthorpe
Directions Leave the M6 at junction 35, take the A6 north and turn left at Wildlife Oasis (after passing Esso fuel station). Follow signs to Fell End Caravan Park and Hall More is signposted from there.
🚆 Arnside

ARNSIDE/SILVERDALE
Silverdale Caravan Park, Cove Road, Silverdale, Nr Carnforth, Lancashire, LA5 0SH
Tel: 01524 701508
Email: reception@holgates.co.uk
www.holgates.co.uk
Pitches For ▲ ⊞ 🚐 **Total** 70
Acreage 10 **Open** All year
Access Good **Site** Lev/Slope
Nearest Bus Stop (Miles) Outside
On Morecambe Bay. In area of outstanding natural beauty. Indoor swimming pool, gym, spa bath, sauna and steam room. Restaurant and bar. Finalist for Cumbria Tourism Awards 2009 Holiday Park of the Year.
Facilities ♿ ✦ 🚰 🏠 🕮 🚿 📞 ☺ 🍳 🛒 🔌 ♨
🛢 🐕 🍳 🍴 🏪 🔌 🍴 🔥 🏕 🥾 📭 🛒 🔌 ☀
🐕 📶
Nearest Town Morecambe
Directions 5 miles northwest of Carnforth, between Silverdale and Arnside.
🚆 Silverdale

CUMBRIA

BROUGHTON IN FURNESS

Birchbank Farm, Birchbank, Blawith, Ulverston, Cumbria, LA12 8EW
Tel: 01229 885277
Email: info@birchbank.co.uk
www.birchbank.co.uk
Pitches For ⚊ ⚊ **Total** 25
Acreage 1 **Open** May **to** October
Access Good **Site** Mostly Level
Small farm site. Next to open Fell, good walking area.
Facilities ⚊ ⚊ ⚊ ⚊ ⚊ ⚊ ⚊ ⚊ ⚊
Nearest Town Coniston Water
Directions A5092 ¼ mile west of Gawthwaite turn for Woodland. Site is 2 miles on the right along an unfenced road.
⚊ Kirkby in Furness

CARLISLE

Dalston Hall Caravan Park, Dalston, Carlisle, Cumbria, CA5 7JX
Tel: 01228 710165
Email: info@dalstonholidaypark.com
www.dalstonhallholidaypark.com
Pitches For ⚊ ⚊ ⚊ ⚊ **Total** 71
Acreage 3½ **Open** March **to** End Jan
Access Good **Site** Level
Nearest Bus Stop (Miles) Outside
Adjacent to a golf course (same ownership). Fishing rights on the adjacent river.
Facilities ⚊ ⚊ ⚊ ⚊ ⚊ ⚊ ⚊
⚊ ⚊ ⚊ ⚊ ⚊ ⚊ ⚊ ⚊ ⚊ ⚊ ⚊ ⚊
Nearest Town Carlisle
Directions Leave the M6 at junction 42 and take the road to Dalston. At Dalston take the B5299 towards Carlisle, site is on the right after 1 mile.
⚊ Dalston

CARLISLE

Dandy Dinmont Caravan & Camping Site, Blackford, Carlisle, Cumbria, CA6 4EA
Tel: 01228 674611
Email: dandydinmont@btopenworld.com
www.caravan-camping-carlisle.co.uk
Pitches For ⚊ ⚊ ⚊ **Total** 47
Acreage 4 **Open** Mar **to** Oct
Access Good **Site** Level
Nearest Bus Stop (Miles) ¼
Now a mainly Adult Park, children are accepted, but there are no ball games or play area. Ideal for historic Carlisle Castle, Cathedral, Roman Wall, Border Country, and only 45 minutes from the Lake District.
Facilities ⚊ ⚊ ⚊ ⚊ ⚊ ⚊
⚊ ⚊ ⚊ ⚊
Nearest Town Carlisle
Directions On A7 at Blackford, 4¼ miles north of Carlisle. Leave M6 at intersection 44, and take the A7 north (Galashiels road), site approx 1½ miles on the right. After Blackford sign, follow road directional signs to site.
⚊ Carlisle

CARLISLE

Englethwaite Hall Caravan Club Site, Armathwaite, Carlisle, Cumbria, CA4 9SY
Tel: 01228 560202
www.caravanclub.co.uk
Pitches For ⚊ ⚊ **Total** 63
Acreage 15 **Open** Mar **to** Nov
Access Good **Site** Lev/Slope
Tranquil 15 acre estate in the Eden Valley with lovely views and Inglewood Forest as a backdrop. Riverside walks. Near the Lake District, Yorkshire Dales and Hadrians Wall. Own sanitation required. Non members welcome. Booking essential.

Facilities ⚊ ⚊ ⚊ ⚊ ⚊ ⚊ ⚊ ⚊ ⚊
Nearest Town Carlisle
Directions Leave the M6 or A6 at junction 42 and take the B6263 signposted Wetheral, after 1¾ miles turn right signposted Armathwaite. Site is approx. 2¾ miles on the right. Warning! - Bumpy road, recommended max speed 35mph.
⚊ Carlisle

CARLISLE

Green Acres Caravan Park, High Knells, Houghton, Carlisle, Cumbria, CA6 4JW
Tel: 01228 675418
Email: info@caravanpark-cumbria.com
www.caravanpark-cumbria.com
Pitches For ⚊ ⚊ ⚊ **Total** 30
Acreage 3 **Open** Easter **to** October
Access Good **Site** Level
ADULT ONLY PARK. Ideal touring base for Hadrians Wall, Carlisle City, the Lake District and the Scottish Borders. AA 3 Pennant Graded.
Facilities ⚊ ⚊ ⚊ ⚊ ⚊ ⚊ ⚊ ⚊ ⚊ ⚊ ⚊
⚊
Nearest Town Carlisle
Directions Leave the M6 at junction 44 (North Carlisle). Take the A689 east for 1 mile, turn left signposted Scaleby. Site is 1 mile on the left.
⚊ Carlisle

COCKERMOUTH

Wheatsheaf Inn, Low Lorton, Cockermouth, Cumbria, CA13 9UW
Tel: 01900 85199
Email: j.williams53@sky.com
www.wheatsheafinnlorton.co.uk
Pitches For ⚊ ⚊ ⚊ **Total** 40
Open Mar **to** 15-Nov
Access Good **Site** Level
Nearest Bus Stop (Miles) ¼
In the town of Cockermouth (Wordsworth) and close to five lakes (osprey), Whinlatter and Go Ape.
Facilities ⚊ ⚊ ⚊ ⚊ ⚊ ⚊ ⚊
⚊ ⚊ ⚊ ⚊ ⚊ ⚊ ⚊
Nearest Town Cockermouth
Directions From Keswick take the A66, turn left at Embleton sign onto the B5292, then take the B5289.
⚊ Workington

COCKERMOUTH

Whinfell Camping, Lorton, Nr Cockermouth, Cumbria, CA13 0RQ
Tel: 01900 85260
Email: ramcclellan@tiscali.co.uk
Pitches For ⚊ ⚊ ⚊ **Total** 3
Acreage 3 **Open** Easter **to** Oct
Access Good **Site** Level
Nearest Bus Stop (Miles) ½
Ideal touring and walking. Near to many attractions including Whinlatter Visitor Centre, Sellafield Visitor Centre, Ravenglass Miniature Steam Railway, Muncaster Castle & Gardens and an Owl centre.
Facilities ⚊ ⚊ ⚊ ⚊ ⚊ ⚊ ⚊
Nearest Town Cockermouth
Directions From Cockermouth take B5292 to Low Lorton, then B5289 through village. Signed from B5289.
⚊ Workington

CONISTON

Coniston Hall Camping Site, Coniston, Cumbria, LA21 8AS
Tel: 015394 41223
Pitches For ⚊ ⚊
Acreage 200 **Open** Mar **to** Oct
Site Level

Nearest Bus Stop (Miles) ½
Lake access. Dogs to be kept on leads.
Facilities ⚊ ⚊ ⚊ ⚊ ⚊ ⚊
⚊ ⚊ ⚊ ⚊ ⚊ ⚊
Nearest Town Coniston
Directions 1 mile south of Coniston.
⚊ Windermere

CONISTON

Coniston Park Coppice Caravan Club Site, Coniston, Cumbria, LA21 8LA
Tel: 01539 441555
www.caravanclub.co.uk
Pitches For ⚊ ⚊ ⚊ **Total** 280
Acreage 20 **Open** Mar **to** Nov
Access Good **Site** Lev/Slope
Nearest Bus Stop (Miles) Outside
Situated between Coniston Water and mountains in 63 acres of National Trust woodland. Ideal for walking and bird watching, especially in Grizedale Forest. Post Office, junior orienteering course and Red Squirrel Nature Trail on site. Non members welcome. Booking essential.
Facilities ⚊ ⚊ ⚊ ⚊ ⚊ ⚊ ⚊ ⚊ ⚊ ⚊
Nearest Town Coniston
Directions On the A593, 1 miles south of Coniston Village, just past the A5084 junction in Torver. NB: Approach is narrow in places.
⚊ Ulverston

CONISTON

Pier Cottage Caravan Park, Pier Cottage, Coniston, Cumbria, LA21 8AJ
Tel: 01539 441252
www.piercottageconiston.co.uk
Pitches For ⚊ ⚊ **Total** 10
Acreage 1 **Open** Mar **to** Oct
Access Good **Site** Level
Nearest Bus Stop (Miles) ¼
Lakeside site with boating, fishing and fellwalking.
Facilities ⚊ ⚊ ⚊ ⚊ ⚊ ⚊ ⚊
Nearest Town Coniston
Directions 1 mile east of Coniston off the B5285 Hawkshead road.
⚊ Windermere

CUMWHITTON

Cairndale Caravan Park, Cumwhitton, Headsnook, Brampton, Nr Carlisle, Cumbria, CA8 9BZ
Tel: 01768 896280
Pitches For ⚊ ⚊ **Total** 5
Acreage 2 **Open** March **to** October
Access Good **Site** Level
Scenic views, ideal touring, quiet site, water and electricity to individual touring sites. Windsurfing nearby.
Facilities ⚊ ⚊ ⚊ ⚊ ⚊ ⚊ ⚊ ⚊ ⚊
Nearest Town Carlisle
Directions Follow A69 to Warwick Bridge and then follow unclassified road through Great Corby to Cumwhitton, approx. 9 miles.
⚊ Carlisle

DENT

Conder Farm Campsite, Deepdale Road, Dent, Sedbergh, Cumbria, LA10 5QT
Tel: 015396 25277
Email: conderfarm@aol.com
Pitches For ⚊ ⚊ **Total** 47
Acreage 1½ **Open** Mar **to** Oct
Access - **Site** Sloping
Nearest Bus Stop (Miles) ¼
Walking
Facilities ⚊ ⚊ ⚊ ⚊ ⚊
Nearest Town Kendal

Directions Leave the M6 at junction 37 and take the road for Sedbergh following signs for Dent for approx. 10 miles. At the George & Dragon take the right hand fork to Dent.
⇌ Dent

DENT

Ewegales Farm, Dent, Sedbergh, Cumbria, LA10 5RH
Tel: 01539 625440
Pitches For Λ ⛺ ⛟ **Total** 60
Acreage 5½ **Open** All Year
Access Good **Site** Level
Nearest Bus Stop (Miles) Outside
Alongside a river for fishing.
Facilities ⚡
Nearest Town Dent
Directions Leave the M6 at junction 37 and head towards Sedbergh then Dent, park is 3½ miles east of Dent Village.
⇌ Dent

DENT

High Lanning Caravan and Camping Park High Lanning Caravan & Camping, High Lanning, Dent, Nr Sedbergh, Cumbria, LA10 5QJ
Tel: 01539 625239
Email: info@highlanning.com
www.highlanning.com
Pitches For Λ ⛺ ⛟
Open All Year
Access Good **Site** Level
Nearest Bus Stop (Miles) ½
3 peaks, Lowland walks, Settle Carlisle Railway.
Facilities ⚡
Nearest Town Dent
Directions From M6 leave at junc 37 signposted Sedbergh A684. Dent is a further 5 miles from Sedbergh
⇌ Dent

EGREMONT

Tarnside Caravan Park, Braystones, Egremont, Cumbria, CA21 2YL
Tel: 01946 822777
Email: reception@seacote.com
www.tarnsidepark.co.uk
Pitches For Λ ⛺ ⛟ **Total** 20
Acreage 2 **Open** Mar to Oct
Access Good **Site** Level
Nearest Bus Stop (Miles) Outside
Beside a lovely beach and tarn. Ideal for walking.
Facilities ⚡
Nearest Town Egremont
Directions From the A595 3 miles south of Egremont, take the B5345 and follow signs for Tarnside Park.
⇌ Braystones

ESKDALE

Eskdale Camping & Caravanning Club Site, Boot, Holmrook, Cumbria, CA19 1TH
Tel: 01946 723253
Email: eskdale2@thefriendlyclub.co.uk
www.campingandcaravanningclub.co.uk/eskdale
Pitches For Λ ⛟ **Total** 80
Acreage 8 **Open** 01-Mar to 14-Jan
Access Good **Site** Level
Close to Scafell Pike, Wastwater, the River Esk, Hardknott Fort, Eskdale Mill and Muncaster Castle. Camping Pods available for hire. Camping barn available. Non members welcome. You can also call us on 0845 130 7633.

Facilities ⚡
Nearest Town Ravenglass
Directions From the A595 turn right onto local road signposted Birkby, continue on to Eskdale.
⇌ Dalegarth

ESKDALE

Fisherground Campsite, Fisherground, Eskdale, Cumbria, CA19 1TF
Tel: 01946 723349
Email: camping@fishergroundcampsite.co.uk
www.fishergroundcampsite.co.uk
Pitches For Λ ⛟ **Total** 215
Acreage 12 **Open** March to October
Site Level/Sloping
Quiet family site in the heart of the Lake District. Near the beach, a river and a waterfall. Plenty of good walks in the area. 7 mile miniature railway at our own private station. Childrens adventure play area. We allow campfires.
Facilities ⚡
Nearest Town Eskdale
Directions Turn right ¾ miles past Broughton on A595 and go up Duddon Valley (signed Ulpha). 4 miles to Ulpha, then turn left (sp Eskdale). 6 miles over Birker Moor, descend to Eskdale and turn right at the King George IV Inn, Site is the first turning on the left.
⇌ Ravenglass

GOSFORTH

Seven Acres Caravan Park & Camping Site, Holmrook, Cumbria, CA19 1YD
Tel: 019467 25480
Email: enquiries@southlakeland-caravans.co.uk
www.southlakeland-caravans.co.uk
Pitches For **Total** 59
Acreage 3 **Open** Mar to Oct
Access Good **Site** Level
At the foot of Wasdale Valley, 3 miles to the coast. Ideal for touring the Western Lake District, walking, golf, fishing, riding and relaxing.
Facilities
Directions Half way between Gosforth and Holmrook on the A595 (Broughton-in-Furness to Workington road) west coast road.
⇌ Seascale

GRANGE-OVER-SANDS

Cartmel Caravan & Camping Park, Wells House Farm, Cartmel, Grange-Over-Sands, Cumbria, LA11 6PN
Tel: 015395 36270
Email: info@cartmelcamping.co.uk
www.cartmelcamping.co.uk
Pitches For Λ **Total** 59
Acreage 5 **Open** March to October
Site Level
Nearest Bus Stop (Miles) Outside
Tranquil park set in picturesque surroundings, yet only 2 minutes from the village square. Cartmel, one of South Lakelands oldest and prettiest villages, has grown up around its famous 12th Century Priory.
Facilities ⚡
Nearest Town Grange-over-Sands
Directions Enter Cartmel from the A590, turn right at the Pig & Whistle, turn next left and the entrance is shortly on the right hand side.
⇌ Grange-over-Sands

GRANGE-OVER-SANDS

Greaves Farm Caravan Park, c/o Prospect House, Barber Green, Grange-over-Sands, Cumbria, LA11 6HU
Tel: 015395 36329/36587
www.greavesfarmcaravanpark.co.uk
Pitches For Λ ⛺ ⛟ **Total** 20
Acreage 3 **Open** March to October
Access Good **Site** Level
Quiet, select, family run park. Ideal base for exploring the Lake District.
Facilities ⚡
Nearest Town Grange-over-Sands
Directions Come off the A590 approx 1 mile south of Newby Bridge at the sign "Cartmel 4 miles". Proceed 1½ miles to sign for caravan park.
⇌ Grange-over-Sands

GRANGE-OVER-SANDS

Meathop Fell Caravan Club Site, Grange-over-Sands, Cumbria, LA11 6RB
Tel: 01539 532912
www.caravanclub.co.uk
Pitches For ⛺ ⛟ **Total** 131
Acreage 10 **Open** All Year
Access Good **Site** Lev/Slope
Peaceful site. Ideal base to explore North Lancashire and Southern Lake District. Close to Brockhole National Park Visitor Centre. Non members welcome. Booking essential.
Facilities ⚡
Nearest Town Grange-over-Sands
Directions Leave M6 at junc 36 take the A590 sp South Lakes. After 3¼ mls t lt via slip rd sp Barrow, at r/about t lt on the B5277 and immediately t lt sp Meathop. Within ¾ miles t rt up incline and keep rt at the top, in 200 yds fork lt at green notice board, site on lt in 150 yds. NB: Steep approach.

KENDAL

Ashes Exclusively Adult Caravan Park, The Ashes, New Hutton, Kendal, Cumbria, LA8 0AS
Tel: 01539 731833
Email: info@ashescaravanpark.co.uk
www.ashescaravanpark.co.uk
Pitches For ⛟ **Total** 25
Acreage 1½ **Open** 01-Mar to 07-Nov
Access Good **Site** Lev/Slope
Nearest Bus Stop (Miles) ½
ADULTS ONLY SITE in a countryside setting with views of the Cumbrian Fells. Popular with walkers and ideal for visiting many local attractions. Close to the Lakes and the Yorkshire Dales.
Facilities ⚡
Nearest Town Kendal
Directions Leave the M6 at junction 37 and take the A684 towards Kendal. In 2 miles at the crossroads turn left signposted New Hutton, site is in ¾ miles on the right.
⇌ Oxenholme

KENDAL

Kendal Camping & Caravanning Club Site, Millcrest, Shap Road, Kendal, Cumbria, LA9 6NY
Tel: 01539 741363
Email: kendal.site@thefriendlyclub
www.campingandcaravanningclub.co.uk/kendal
Pitches For Λ ⛺ ⛟ **Total** 50
Acreage 3 **Open** 14-Mar to 04-Nov
Site Lev/Slope
Nearest Bus Stop (Miles) ½

Right in the middle of the Lake District. Tumble drier and spin drier on site. BTB 4 Star Graded and AA 3 Pennants. Non members welcome. You can also call us on 0845 130 7633.
Facilities ♪ 🖫 📖 ♠ ↿ ⊙ ⌣ ◢ ♥ 🅏 🅘 🅞 🅢 🅐 ❋ ⊁ 🄻 🄓 🄴 ☞
Directions On the A6, 1½ miles north of Kendal, site entrance is 100 yards north of the nameplate Skelsmergh.
⛺ Kendal

KENDAL

Kendal Caravan Club Site, Sedgwick, Kendal, Cumbria, LA8 0JZ
Tel: 01539 560186
www.caravanclub.co.uk
Pitches For ⌺ ⇆ **Total** 141
Acreage 20 **Open** Mar **to** Nov
Nearest Bus Stop (Miles) ½
Peaceful site with varied bird life and wild flowers. River fishing. Non members welcome. Booking essential.
Facilities ⅙ ♪ 🖫 📖 ♠ ↿ 🅞 ♥ 🅞 🅡 🄾 🄽 🄓 🅔 ☞
Nearest Town Kendal
Directions M6 junc 36 take the A590 sp South Lakes, after 3¼ mls leave via slip rd sp Barrow. At r/about follow brown signs t into rd sp Sedgwick, After 150 yds t lt onto road running parallel with the river. Fork rt at the junc, site on lt in ½ a mile.
⛺ Kendal

KENDAL

Waters Edge Caravan Park, Crooklands, Nr Kendal, Cumbria, LA7 7NN
Tel: 015395 67708
Email: info@watersedgecaravanpark.co.uk
www.watersedgecaravanpark.co.uk
Pitches For 𝗔 ⌺ ⇆ **Total** 32
Acreage 3 **Open** Mar **to** Nov
Access Good **Site** Level
Nearest Bus Stop (Miles) ¼
Set in quiet and pleasant countryside. Lakes, Yorkshire Dales and Morecambe Bay within easy reach.
Facilities ⅙ ♪ 🖫 📖 ♠ ↿ ⊙ ⌣ ◢ 🅞 ♥ 🆂🅇 🅘🅞 🅞 🖻 🅣 🄵 ♠ 🄿 🄓 🄴 🖋 ⚡
Nearest Town Kendal
Directions A65 Crooklands, ¾ mile from M6 motorway junction 36.
⛺ Oxenholme

KESWICK

Borrowdale Caravan Club Site, Manesty, Keswick, Cumbria, CA12 5UG
Tel: 01768 777275
www.caravanclub.co.uk
Pitches For ⌺ ⇆ **Total** 60

Acreage 12 **Open** Mar **to** Nov
Access Good **Site** Level
Set in National Trust woodland, close to Derwentwater. Numerous walks from the site. Many visitor attractions within easy reach. Own sanitation required. Non members welcome. Booking essential.
Facilities ♪ 🖫 ♥ ↿ 🅞 🅞 🅐 ➕ 🄿 🄓 🄾
Nearest Town Keswick
Directions M6 at junc 40 take A66, on the outskirts of Keswick keep right onto bypass. At r/about within 1½ mls t lt sp A5271 Keswick, follow signs onto the B5289. After 4¼ mls t rt over the bridge (care required), site on the rt in 1 mile.
⛺ Keswick

KESWICK

Burns Farm Caravan Site, St Johns-in-the-Vale, Keswick, Cumbria, CA12 4RR
Tel: 01768 79225
Email: linda@burns-farm.co.uk
www.burns-farm.co.uk
Pitches For 𝗔 ⌺ ⇆ **Total** 40
Acreage 1¼ **Open** Easter **to** October
Access Good **Site** Level
Nearest Bus Stop (Miles) Outside
Quiet family site with beautiful views. Small charge for use of WiFi. Ideal touring, walking and climbing. AA Graded.
Facilities ⅙ ♪ 🖫 📖 ♠ ↿ ⊙ ⌣ 🅞 ♥ 🅞 🅐 ➕ 🄿 🄓 🄴 🖋 ☞
Nearest Town Keswick
Directions Turn left off the A66 (Penrith to Keswick road) ½ mile past B5322 junction signposted Castlerigg Stone Circle and Burns Farm. Site is on the right, farm is on the left. 2¼ miles from Keswick.
⛺ Penrith

KESWICK

Castlerigg Farm Camping & Caravan Site, Keswick, Cumbria, CA12 4TE
Tel: 01768? 72479
Email: info@castleriggfarm.com
www.castleriggfarm.com
Pitches For 𝗔 ⌺ ⇆ ⇆≲ **Total** 80
Acreage 4½ **Open** Mar **to** Nov
Access Good **Site** Sloping
Nearest Bus Stop (Miles) ¼
Panoramic views quite site for familes, singles or couples. Ideal base for walking.
Facilities ♪ 🖫 📖 ♠ ↿ ⊙ ⌣ ◢ 🅞 ♥ 🆂🅇 🅘🅞 🅞 ➕ 🄿 🄓 🄴 ⚡ ☞
Nearest Town Keswick
Directions From Keswick take the A591 towards Windermere, after approx. 1½ miles turn right at the top of the hill following camping sign and the Site is on the left.
⛺ Penrith

KESWICK

Derwentwater Camping & Caravanning Club Site, Derwentwater Caravan Park, Crow Park Road, Keswick, Cumbria, CA12 5EN
Tel: 01768 772579
Email: linda.watson@thefriendlyclub.co
www.campingandcaravanningclub.co.uk/derwentwater
Pitches For 𝗔 ⌺ ⇆ **Total** 44
Acreage 16 **Open** 28-Feb **to** 05-Jan
Access Good **Site** Level
Nearest Bus Stop (Miles) ½
Within the heart of the Lake District National Park. BTB 4 Star Graded, David Bellamy Gold Award and AA 3 Pennants. Non members welcome. You can also call us on 0845 130 7633.
Facilities ⅙ ♪ 🖫 📖 ♠ ↿ ⊙ ⌣ ◢ 🅞 ♥ 🅞 🅐 🄵 ♠ ☞
Nearest Town Keswick
Directions Leave the M6 at junction 40 and take the A66 signposted Keswick and Workington for 13 miles. Do not take the A591, stay on the A66. At the roundabout turn left signposted Keswick Town Centre, follow signs for caravan park to Derwentwater.
⛺ Penrith

KESWICK

Gill Head Farm Caravan & Camping Park, Troutbeck, Penrith, Cumbria, CA11 0ST
Tel: 01768 79652
Email: enquiries@gillheadfarm.co.uk
www.gillheadfarm.co.uk
Pitches For 𝗔 ⌺ ⇆ **Total** 40
Acreage 10 **Open** March **to** November
Access Good **Site** Sloping
Nearest Bus Stop (Miles) ¼
Situated on a working hill farm in a great location within the Lake District National Park providing superb views. Ideal for families and walkers.
Facilities ♪ 🖫 📖 ♠ ↿ ⊙ ⌣ ◢ 🅞 ♥ 🆂🅇 🅘🅞 🅞 🅐 �ⓣ 🄵 ♠ 🄿 🄓 🄴 ☀ ⚡ ☞
Nearest Town Keswick
Directions Leave the M6 at junction 40 (Penrith), take the A66 west for 9 miles. Then take the A5091 (left) and after 100 yards turn first right.
⛺ Penrith

KESWICK

Keswick Camping & Caravanning Club Site, Crow Park Road, Keswick, Cumbria, CA12 5EP
Tel: 01768 772392
Email: keswick.site@thefriendlyclub.co.uk
www.campingandcaravanningclub.co.uk/keswick
Pitches For ▲ ⊞ ⊟ **Total** 250
Acreage 14 **Open** 15-Feb **to** 05-Jan
Access Good **Site** Level
Nearest Bus Stop (Miles) ½
Situated on the banks of Derwentwater, ideal for fishing and water sports. Boat launching for small boats. Good hillwalking area. Close to the centre of Keswick. All units must have towing vehicle on site overnight. One vehicle per pitch. BTB 4 Star Graded, David Bellamy Gold Award and AA 3 Pennants. Non members welcome. You can also call us on 0845 130 7633.
Facilities ∮ ⬚ ⬚ ⬚ ⬚ ⌐ ⊙ ⌐ ⬚ ⬚ ⬚
⬚ ⊙ ⬚ ⬚ ⬚ ⬚ ⬚ ⬚
Nearest Town Keswick
Directions From Penrith take the A5271, turn left into Main Street (Keswick), turn right to pass Lakes Bus Station, pass the rugby club and turn right, site is on the right.
⇞ Penrith

KESWICK

Scotgate Holiday Park, Braithwaite, Keswick, Cumbria, CA12 5TF
Tel: 017687 78343
Email: info@scotgateholidaypark.co.uk
www.scotgateholidaypark.co.uk
Pitches For ▲ ⊞ ⊟ **Total** 165
Open All Year
Access Good **Site** Level
Nearest Bus Stop (Miles) Entrance
Central for good walks. River nearby. Near to pubs and restaurants. luxury toilet block with under-floor heating.
Facilities ⬚ ∮ ⬚ ⬚ ⌐ ⊙ ⌐ ⬚ ⬚ ⬚
⬚ ⊙ ⬚ ✕ ⬚ ⬚ ⬚ ⬚ ⬚
Nearest Town Keswick
Directions From Keswick head west on the A66 towards Workington, turn left sp Whinlatter Forest Park to Braithwaite Village.
⇞ Penrith

KIRKBY LONSDALE

New House Caravan Park, Kirkby Lonsdale, Cumbria, LA6 2HR
Tel: 015242 71590
Email: colinpreece9@aol.com
Pitches For ⊞ ⊟ **Total** 50
Acreage 3½ **Open** March **to** End Oct
Access Good **Site** Lev/Slope
Situated near to the historic town of Kirkby Lonsdale and Devils Bridge. An ideal location to visit lakes and Yorkshire Dales.
Facilities ⬚ ∮ ⬚ ⬚ ⌐ ⊙ ⌐ ⬚ ⬚ ⬚
⬚ ⊙ ⬚ ⬚ ⬚
Nearest Town Kirkby Lonsdale/Kendal
Directions From Kirkby Lonsdale take the A65 towards Settle, after approx. 1½ miles site is on the right 300 yards past Whoop Hall Inn.
⇞ Carnforth

KIRKBY LONSDALE

Woodclose Caravan Park, High Casterton, Kirkby Lonsdale, Cumbria, LA6 2SE
Tel: 015242 71597
Email: info@woodclosepark.com
www.woodclosepark.co.uk
Pitches For ▲ ⊞ ⊟ **Total** 17
Acreage 9 **Open** March **to** 14-Nov
Access Good **Site** Lev/Slope
An award winning Park set within the beautiful valley of the River Lune between

the Yorkshire Dales and the Lake District National Park. Nine acres providing a unique holiday base in an area of outstanding natural beauty. Wigwams, a great alternative to the tent! Contact us about our holiday home open day offers.
Facilities ⬚ ∮ ⬚ ⬚ ⌐ ⊙ ⌐ ⬚ ⬚ ⬚
⬚ ⊙ ⬚ ⬚ ✦ ⬚ ⬚ ⬚ ⬚
Nearest Town Kirkby Lonsdale
Directions Leave the M6 at junction 36 and take the A65 for approx. 6 miles. Woodclose entrance is past Devils Bridge on the left hand side.

KIRKBY STEPHEN

Pennine View Caravan & Camping Park, Station Road, Kirkby Stephen, Cumbria, CA17 4SZ
Tel: 01768 371717
Pitches For ▲ ⊞ ⊟ **Total** 58
Acreage 2½ **Open** Early Mar **to** Oct
Access Good **Site** Level
Nearest Bus Stop (Miles) ½
On the edge of the River Eden and on the outskirts of the small market town of Kirkby Stephen. Ideal for walking and touring the Yorkshire Dales and the Lake District, Teesdale and Durham.
Facilities ⬚ ∮ ⬚ ⬚ ⌐ ⊙ ⌐ ⬚ ⬚ ⬚
⬚ ⊙ ⬚ ⬚ ⬚ ⬚
Nearest Town Kirkby Stephen
Directions Just off the A685 approx 1 mile from Kirkby Stephen town centre. 11 miles from the M6 junction 38, and 5 miles from the A66 at Brough.
⇞ Kirkby Stephen

LAMPLUGH

Dockray Meadow Caravan Club Site, Lamplugh, Cumbria, CA14 4SH
Tel: 01946 861357
www.caravanclub.co.uk
Pitches For ⊞ ⊟ **Total** 53
Acreage 4½ **Open** Mar **to** Nov
Access Good **Site** Lev/Slope
Nearest Bus Stop (Miles) ½
Sheltered site alongside a stream with fell scenery. Ideal for walkers. Own sanitation required. Non members welcome. Booking essential.
Facilities ⬚ ∮ ⬚ ⬚ ⬚ ⊙ ⬚ ⬚ ⬚
Nearest Town Lamplugh
Directions From the A66 Cockermouth bypass turn onto the A5086 sp Egremont. After 6½ miles (300yds past Lamplugh Tip Pub) turn left at signpost for Loweswater. Within ¾ miles turn right signposted Croasdale, site is 50 yards on the left.

LONGTOWN

Camelot Caravan Park, Sandysike, Longtown, Carlisle, Cumbria, CA6 5SZ
Tel: 01228 791248
Pitches For ▲ ⊞ ⊟ **Total** 20
Acreage 1¼ **Open** March **to** October
Access Good **Site** Level
Nearest Bus Stop (Miles) ¼
Ideal base for the Solway coast, Carlisle Settle Railway, Carlisle Castle, romantic Gretna Green, Hadrians Wall and Border towns. AA 2 Pennants. Waiting List for Secure Storage.
Facilities ⬚ ∮ ⬚ ⌐ ⊙ ⬚ ⬚ ⬚ ⊙ ⬚ ⬚
Nearest Town Longtown
Directions On the A7, 1¼ miles south of Longtown on the left. Leave the M6 northbound at junction 44 and take the A7 (Longtown), Park is on the right in 4 miles.
⇞ Carlisle

LONGTOWN

High Gaitle Caravan Park, Gaitle Bridge, Longtown, Carlisle, Cumbria, CA6 5LU
Tel: 01228 791819
Pitches For ▲ ⊞ ⊟ **Total** 30
Acreage 6 **Open** All Year
Access Good **Site** Level
Nearest Bus Stop (Miles) Outside
Ideal touring location for the Lake District, South Scotland, Borders, Gretna Green and Hadrians Wall. Great for fishing on the world famous River Esk.
Facilities ⬚ ∮ ⬚ ⬚ ⌐ ⊙ ⌐ ⬚ ⬚ ⬚ ⬚ ⬚
Nearest Town Longtown
Directions Leave the M6 at junction 44 and take the A7 for 6 miles through Longtown, then take the A6071 towards Gretna, Site is 1¼ miles on the left.
⇞ Carlisle

MARYPORT

Spring Lea Caravan Park, Allonby, Maryport, Cumbria, CA15 6QF
Tel: 01900 881331
Email: mail@springlea.co.uk
www.springlea.co.uk
Pitches For ▲ ⊞ ⊟ **Total** 35
Acreage 5 **Open** March **to** October
Access Good **Site** Level
Nearest Bus Stop (Miles) ¼
300 yards from the beach with views of Lakeland and Scottish hills. Leisure centre for sauna etc.. Bar/restaurant on site.
Facilities ∮ ⬚ ⬚ ⌐ ⊙ ⌐ ⬚ ⬚ ⬚
⬚ ⊙ ⬚ ✕ ⬚ ✦ ⬚ ⬚ ⬚ ⬚ ⬚
Nearest Town Maryport
Directions 5 miles north of Maryport on the B5300 coast road.
⇞ Maryport

MEALSGATE

The Larches Caravan Park, Mealsgate, Wigton, Cumbria, CA7 1LQ
Tel: 016973 71379 / 71803
Email: thelarches@hotmail.co.uk
www.thelarchescaravanpark.co.uk
Pitches For ▲ ⊞ ⊟ **Total** 73
Acreage 19 **Open** March **to** October
Access Good **Site** Lev/slope
ADULTS ONLY SITE. Ideal for couples, peace and quiet in the countryside with beautiful views. Excellent toilets.
Facilities ⬚ ∮ ⬚ ⬚ ⌐ ⊙ ⌐ ⬚ ⬚ ⬚
⬚ ⊙ ⬚ ⬚ ⬚ ⬚
Nearest Town Wigton
Directions From the north take the A57/A74/A7/A69 to Carlisle, follow the A595 to Mealsgate. From the south leave the M6 at junction 41, take the B5305 Wigton road as far as the A595. Turn left and follow the A595 to Mealsgate.
⇞ Wigton

PENRITH

Beckses Caravan Site, Penruddock, Penrith, Cumbria, CA11 0RX
Tel: 017684 83224
Pitches For ▲ ⊞ ⊟ **Total** 30
Open Apr **to** Oct
Access Good **Site** Lev/Slope
Nearest Bus Stop (Miles) 1
Facilities ⬚ ∮ ⬚ ⌐ ⊙ ⬚ ⬚ ⬚
Directions Take the A66 Penrith to Keswick road then the B5288, site is 400 metres on the right.
⇞ Penrith

PENRITH

Gillside Caravan & Camping Site,
Glenridding, Penrith, Cumbria, CA11 0QQ
Tel: 017684 82346
Email: gillside@btconnect.com
www.gillsidecaravanandcampingsite.co.uk
Pitches For À ⊕ ➡ **Total** 65
Acreage 8 **Open** March **to** Mid Nov
Access Good **Site** Level
Nearest Bus Stop (Miles) ½
Foot of Helvellyn, 5 minutes walk from Lake Ullswater.
Facilities ∮ 🖸 📖⇅୮⊙⊣🔲 ☎
℟ 🖸 ☻➕🔲
Nearest Town Penrith
Directions A592 signposted Ullswater, 14 miles from Penrith. In Glenridding turn right, follow sign for Gillside.
⇌ Penrith

PENRITH

Park Foot Caravan & Camping Park,
Howtown Road, Pooley Bridge, Penrith, Cumbria, CA10 2NA
Tel: 017684 86309
Email: holidays@parkfootullswater.co.uk
www.parkfootullswater.co.uk
Pitches For À ⊕ ➡ 🚐‹ **Total** 332
Acreage 40 **Open** March **to** October
Access Good **Site** Lev/Slope
Nearest Bus Stop (Miles) ½
Family run park beside Lake Ullswater with boat launching access. Licensed bar, restaurant and takeaway. Childrens Club during the summer school holidays and two play areas. Pony trekking, mountain bike hire, tennis and table tennis on site. Own access to the lake where customers can fish using their own equipment.
Facilities ⅋ ∮ 🖸 📖⇅୮⊙⊣🔲 ☎
℟ 🖸 ☻✕ 🌴 🍴 ⛏ 🎿➕🔲🍴 🗲 📶
Nearest Town Pooley Bridge
Directions 5 miles SW of Penrith. Leave M6 at junc 40, then take A66 for Ullswater, next roundabout take A592 then road for Pooley Bridge and 1 mile on Howtown Road to site.
⇌ Penrith

PENRITH

Thacka Lea Caravan Site, Thacka Lea, Penrith, Cumbria, CA11 9HX
Tel: 01768 863319
Pitches For ⊕ ➡ **Total** 25
Acreage 1 **Open** March **to** October
Access Good **Site** Lev/Slope
Nearest Bus Stop (Miles) ¼
Just a 10 minute walk from the town centre. Good touring.
Facilities ⚌ ∮ 🖸 📖⇅୮⊙⊣ ☎➕🔲
Nearest Town Penrith
Directions From south, turn left off the A6, go past the Esso Station at the north end of town. From north, turn right at the Esso Station.
⇌ Penrith

PENRITH

Troutbeck Head Caravan Club Site,
Troutbeck, Penrith, Cumbria, CA11 0SS
Tel: 01768 483521
www.caravanclub.co.uk
Pitches For ⊕ ➡ **Total** 151
Acreage 25 **Open** Mar **to** Nov
Access Good **Site** Level
Set in countryside, alongside a brook with fabulous views. Only 4 miles from Ullswater. Ideal for walkers and nature lovers. Rookin House Farm Centre adjacent offering go-karting, quad bikes, archery, horse riding and much more. Non members welcome. Booking essential.

Facilities ⅋ ∮ 🖸 📖⇅୮⊙⊣🔲 ☎
🖸 ☻🌴✕↴🔲🔲
Nearest Town Penrith
Directions Leave M6 at junc 40 and take A66 sp Keswick. Go straight on at the roundabout and after approx. 7 miles turn left onto A5091. Site is 1¼ miles on the right. NB: No arrivals before 12 noon.
⇌ Penrith

PENRITH

Waterside House Campsite, Waterside Farm, Howtown Road, Pooley Bridge, Penrith, Cumbria, CA10 2NA
Tel: 01768 486332
Email: enquire@watersidefarm-campsite.co.uk
www.watersidefarm-campsite.co.uk
Pitches For À ➡ **Total** 120
Acreage 10 **Open** Mar **to** Oct
Site Lev/Slope
Nearest Bus Stop (Miles) 1
Alongside the lake shore of Ullswater with beautiful views of the lake and fells. Footpath from the site to the local village. Boat and bike hire available.
Facilities ⅋ ∮ 🖸 📖⇅୮⊙⊣ ⛏🔲 ☎
℟ 🖸 ☻➕🔲🔲 🗡
Nearest Town Pooley Bridge/Penrith
Directions Leave the M6 at junction 40 and take the A66 sp Keswick. After 1 mile turn left onto the A592 for Ullswater. Turn left by the lake and go over the bridge, turn first right along Howtown Road. Waterside House is the second campsite on the right (approx. 1 mile).
⇌ Penrith

RAVENGLASS

Ravenglass Camping & Caravanning Club Site, Ravenglass, Cumbria, CA18 1SR
Tel: 01229 717250
www.campingandcaravanningclub.co.uk/ravenglass
Pitches For À ⊕ ➡ **Total** 75
Acreage 6 **Open** 01-Feb **to** 30-Nov
Access Good **Site** Lev/Slope
Set in 5 acres of mature woodland, this is a walkers paradise on Cumbrias Western Coast, where the Lake District National Park meets the sea. Non members welcome. You can also call us on 0845 130 7633.
Facilities ∮ 🖸 📖⇅୮⊙⊣🔲 ☎
℟ 🖸 ☻➕🔲🔲 📶
Nearest Town Egremont
Directions From the A595 turn west for Ravenglass, before village turn left to site.
⇌ Ravenglass

SEDBERGH

Yore House Farm Caravan Park, Yore House Farm, Lunds, Sedbergh, Cumbria, LA10 5PX
Tel: 01969 667358
Email: j.pedley@btinternet.com
Pitches For À ⊕ ➡ **Total** 7
Open Easter **to** Sept
Access Good **Site** Level
Quiet, farm site beside the River Ure. In sight of the famous Settle to Carlisle railway.
Facilities 📖 ☎🍴
Nearest Town Hawes
Directions On the A684 10 miles from Sedbergh and 6 miles from Hawes, near the Moorcock Pub. On the North Yorkshire and Cumbria border.
⇌ Garsdale

SILLOTH

Hylton Caravan Park, Eden Street, Silloth, Cumbria, CA7 4AY
Tel: 016973 31707
Email: enquiries@stanwix.com
www.stanwix.com
Pitches For À ⊕ ➡ **Total** 90
Acreage 18 **Open** 01-Mar **to** 15-Nov
Access Good **Site** Level
Nearest Bus Stop (Miles) ¼
Silloth is on the Solway coast. Beach ½ mile. Base to explore Lakes and Roman Wall.
Facilities ⅋ ∮ 🖸 📖⇅୮⊙⊣🔲 ☎
℟ 🖸 ➕🔲🔲 🍴
Nearest Town Silloth
Directions From the east on entering town follow signs ½ mile
⇌ Carlisle

SILLOTH

Moordale Park, Blitterlees, Silloth, Cumbria, CA7 4JZ
Tel: 016973 31375
Pitches For À ⊕ ➡ 🚐‹ **Total** 12
Acreage 7 **Open** March **to** October
Access Good **Site** Level
Nearest Bus Stop (Miles) Outside
A quiet, simple and spacious site adjacent to the beach and a golf course. Convenient for the Lake District and Scotland.
Facilities ∮ 🖸 📖 ୮⊙⊣🔲 ☎
🖸➕🔲 🎿 🎿
Nearest Town Silloth
Directions 1 miles from Silloth on the B5300 coast road to Maryport.
⇌ Wigton

SILLOTH

Stanwix Park Holiday Centre, Silloth (West), Cumbria, CA7 4HH
Tel: 016973 32666
Email: enquiries@stanwix.com
www.stanwix.com
Pitches For À ⊕ ➡ 🚐‹ **Total** 121
Acreage 18 **Open** All Year
Access Good **Site** Level
Nearest Bus Stop (Miles) Outside
Silloth is on the Solway coast sandy beaches stretching 13 miles to Maryport. Base to explore Lakes and Roman wall.
Facilities ⅋ ∮ 🖸 📖⇅୮⊙⊣🔲 ☎
℟ ℟ 🖸 ☻✕ 🌴 🍴 ⛏🗡 ⟂ 🎿➕🔲🔲 🎿
📶
Nearest Town Silloth
Directions entering Silloth from east follow signs 1 mile. from west entering Silloth site on left.
⇌ Carlisle

SILLOTH

Tanglewood Caravan Park,
Causewayhead, Silloth, Wigton, Cumbria, CA7 4PE
Tel: 016973 31253
Email:
tanglewoodcaravanpark@hotmail.com
www.tanglewoodcaravanpark.co.uk
Pitches For À ⊕ ➡ **Total** 31
Acreage 7 **Open** Mar **to** Jan
Access Good **Site** Level
Nearest Bus Stop (Miles) ¼
Enjoy the promenade at Silloth, the sandy west beach and beautiful sunsets over the Solway Firth. Excellent golf courses.
Facilities ∮ 🖸 📖⇅୮⊙⊣🔲 ☎
🖸 ☻ 🌴 🍴 ➕🔲🔲 🎿 📶
Nearest Town Silloth
Directions On B5302 on left, 4 miles from Abbeytown.
⇌ Wigton

ST. BEES

Seacote Park, St Bees, Cumbria, CA27 0ET
Tel: 01946 822777
Email: reception@seacote.com
www.seacote.com
Pitches For 🏕 🚐 🚐 🚐⚡ **Total** 32
Acreage 4 **Open** Mar **to** Oct
Access Good **Site** Level
Nearest Bus Stop (Miles) Outside
Beside a lovely beach in a historic village. Golf links and walks locally. Hotel adjacent which is owned by the Park.
Facilities ♿ ⅃ 🖻 🖩 🛁 ☎ ⊙↵ 🚮 🖾 ☎
🏵 ⅃ 🗶 🏪 🖩 🐾
Nearest Town Whitehaven
Directions Leave the A595 near Whitehaven or Egremont and take the B5345 following signs to St Bees, then to the beach.
⇥ St. Bees

TEBAY

Westmorland Caravan Site Tebay, Tebay Westmorland Services, M6 Northbound, Cumbria, CA10 3SB
Tel: 01539 711322
Email: caravans@westmorland.com
www.westmorland.com/caravans
Pitches For 🚐 🚐 🚐⚡ **Total** 80
Open Mid-Mar **to** Oct
Access Good
Nearest Bus Stop (Miles) 1
Ideal base for the Lake District and the Yorkshire Dales.
Facilities ⅃ 🖩 🛁 ☎ 🏵 ⊙ 🚮 🖾 🖾 🐾 🗶
Nearest Town Penrith
Directions Situated 1 mile north of junc 38, M6 near orton, reached via tebay services.
⇥ Penrith/Oxenholme

TROUTBECK

Troutbeck Camping & Caravanning Club Site, Hutton Moor End, Troutbeck, Penrith, Cumbria, CA11 0SX
Tel: 01768 779149
Email: troutbeck@thefriendlyclub.co.uk
www.campingandcaravanningclub.co.uk/troutbeck
Pitches For 🏕 🚐 🚐 **Total** 54
Open 01-Mar **to** 01-Dec
Access Good **Site** Level
Nearest Bus Stop (Miles) ½
Superb location in unbeatable walking country with fantastic views. Close to both Keswick and Penrith. 70 main tourist attractions in the district. Non members welcome. You can also call us on 0845 130 7633.
Facilities ♿ ⅃ 🖩 🛁 ☎ ⊙↵ 🖾 ☎
🏵 ⊙ 🍽 🛁 🌸 🚮 🖾 🖾 🗖

Nearest Town Keswick
Directions Leave the M6 at junction 40 and take the A66 towards Keswick. After 8 miles take a sharp left at signpost Wallthwaite, site is on the left.
⇥ Penrith

ULLSWATER

Cove Caravan & Camping Park, Watermillock, Ullswater, Penrith, Cumbria, CA11 0LS
Tel: 01768 486549
Email: info@cove-park.co.uk
www.cove-park.co.uk
Pitches For 🏕 🚐 🚐 **Total** 50
Acreage 3 **Open** 15-Mar **to** 31-Oct
Access Good **Site** Lev/Slope
Small, quiet and peaceful Park, 400 ft above Ullswater. Ideal for touring Ullswater & Helvellyn Range, Keswick and Windermere.
Facilities ♿ ⅃ 🖻 🖩 🛁 ☎ ⊙↵ 🚮 🖾 ☎
🖾 🖾 🖾 🖾 🐾
Nearest Town Penrith
Directions Leave M6 at junction 40 and take A66 west to Rheged roundabout, take A592 to Ullswater. After approx. 4 miles at the T-Junction by the lake turn right onto the A592. After 2 miles turn right at Brackenrigg Inn, Park is 1½ miles on the left.
⇥ Penrith

ULLSWATER

Sykeside Camping Park, Hartsop, Brotherswater, Patterdale, Cumbria, CA11 0NZ
Tel: 01768 482239
Email: info@sykeside.co.uk
www.sykeside.co.uk
Pitches For 🏕 🚐 🚐 🚐⚡ **Total** 80
Acreage 15 **Open** All Year
Access Good **Site** Level/Sloping
Nearest Bus Stop (Miles) Entrance
At the foot of Kirkstone Pass with many walks. ¼ of a mile from Brotherswater for fishing.
Facilities ⅃ 🖩 🛁 ☎ ⊙↵ 🖾 ☎
🏵 ⊙ 🛁 🗶 🖾 🖾 🖾
Nearest Town Ambleside
Directions On the A592 between Windermere and Glennridding (Ullswater).
⇥ Windermere

ULLSWATER

The Quiet Site, Ullswater, Penrith, Cumbria, CA11 0LS
Tel: 07768 727016
Email: info@thequietsite.co.uk
www.thequietsite.co.uk
Pitches For 🏕 🚐 🚐 **Total** 90
Acreage 10 **Open** All Year
Access Fair **Site** Lev/Slope

Nearest Bus Stop (Miles) 1½
Family site set in the idyllic Ullswater Valley. Ideal for walking. The best campsite bar in Britain!. Excellent showers and family bathrooms. Large play field. Carbon neutral.
Facilities ♿ ⅃ 🖩 🖩 🛁 ☎ 🏵 🖾 ☎ 🖾
🏵 ⊙ 🛁 🍽 🏪 🌸 🚮 🖾 🖾 🐾 🗖 ☎
Nearest Town Ullswater
Directions Take A592 from Penrith, turn right at lake and right again at Brackenrigg Hotel follow road for 1½ miles, site on right hand side of road.
⇥ Penrith

ULLSWATER

Ullswater Caravan Camping & Marine Park, Watermillock, Penrith, Cumbria, CA11 0LR
Tel: 00176 84 86666
Email: info@uccmp.co.uk
www.ullswatercaravanpark.co.uk
Pitches For 🏕 🚐 🚐 **Total** 160
Acreage 13 **Open** Mar **to** 14-Nov
Access Good **Site** Level
Nearest Bus Stop (Miles) ½
1 mile up from Lake Ullswater.
Facilities ♿ ⅃ 🖩 🖩 🛁 ☎ ⊙↵ 🚮 🖾 ☎
🏵 ⊙ 🛁 🏪 🌸 🚮 🖾 🖾 🖾 🗖
Nearest Town Ullswater
Directions A592 to Ullswater, reach lakeside road after 5 miles turn right. 2 miles later turn right by telephone box, park situated ½ mile up hill.
⇥ Penrith

ULLSWATER

Waterfoot Caravan Park, Pooley Bridge, Penrith, Cumbria, CA11 0JF
Tel: 017684 86302
Email: enquiries@waterfootpark.co.uk
www.waterfootpark.co.uk
Pitches For 🚐 🚐 **Total** 34
Acreage 22 **Open** 01-Mar **to** 14-Nov
Access Good **Site** Lev/Slope
Waterfoot Park is located in one of the most beautiful locations within the Lake District National Park. Nestled in the grounds of a Georgian mansion, overlooking Ullswater, the Park is an idyllic location for touring vans, motor homes and privately owned holiday homes. (NB: All holiday homes are privately owned and are not available for hire).
Facilities ♿ ⅃ 🖩 🖩 🛁 ☎ ⊙↵ 🚮 🖾 ☎
🏵 ⊙ 🛁 🏪 🌸 🚮 🖾 🖾 ✂ 🐾 🗖
Nearest Town Penrith
Directions Leave the M6 at junction 40 and take the A66 for approx. 1 mile. Then take the A592 and Waterfoot can be found on the right hand side. Do not leave the A592 until the Park entrance. NB: SatNav is not compatible in this area.
⇥ Penrith

ULVERSTON

Bardsea Leisure, Priory Road, Ulverston, Cumbria, LA12 9QE
Tel: 01229 584712
Email: reception@bardsealeisure.co.uk
www.bardsealeisure.co.uk
Pitches For ⬜ ⬜ ⬜ **Total** 84
Acreage 10 **Open** All Year
Access Good **Site** Lev/Slope
Nearest Bus Stop (Miles) ¼
Ideal for touring.
Facilities ♿ ∮ 🖻 🕍 🚾 🇵 🖙 🛇 🍴 ☺ ♨
🕍 🖸 🍴 ✕ 🖂 ♨ 🚼 🖃 🖸 ✔ ☀
Nearest Town Ulverston
Directions Leave the M6 at junction 36 and take the A590 then the A5087.
🚆 Ulverston

ULVERSTON

Crake Valley Holiday Park, Water Yeat, Blawith, Nr Ulverston, Cumbria, LA12 8DL
Tel: 01229 885203
Email: info@crakevalley.co.uk
www.crakevalley.co.uk
Pitches For ⛺ **Total** 6
Acreage ¼ **Open** May to Sept
Site Level
Nearest Bus Stop (Miles) ½
Opposite Coniston Water. Ideal base for touring the Lakes.
Facilities 🚾 🇵 🖙 ♨ 🖸 ☺♨
Nearest Town Ulverston
Directions Take the A590 Barrow road, turn right at Greenodd onto the A5092. Within 2 miles fork right for Coniston onto the A5084, the Park is 3 miles along on the left hand side.
🚆 Ulverston

WATERMILLOCK

Knotts Hill Caravan Park, Watermillock, Penrith, Cumbria, CA11 0JR
Tel: 017684 86309
Email: holidays@parkfootullswater.co.uk
www.knottshill.co.uk
Pitches For ⬜ ⬜ ⬜ **Total** 6
Acreage 2 **Open** 01-Mar to 14-Jan
Access Good **Site** Sloping
Nearest Bus Stop (Miles) ½
Peaceful location with lovely views of Lake Ullswater. Use of facilities at nearby Park Foot Caravan Park.
Facilities ♿ 🖻 🕍 🚾 🇵 ☺ ♨ 🚼 🖃 🖸
Nearest Town Penrith
Directions Leave the M6 at junction 40 and take the A66 towards Keswick. At the roundabout take the A592 for Ullswater, at the T-Junction turn right for Glenridding. After 3 miles turn right for Patterdale/Glenridding. After 3 miles turn right for Watermillock church park is ½ mile on right.
🚆 Penrith

WINDERMERE

Braithwaite Fold Camping & Caravanning Club Site, Glebe Road, Bowness-on-Windermere, Windermere, Cumbria, LA23 3HB
Tel: 01539 442177
Email: enquires@thefriendlyclub.co.uk
www.campingandcaravanningclub.co.uk/ braithwaitefold
Pitches For ⛺ ⬜ ⬜ **Total** 66
Acreage 4 **Open** 14-Mar to 05-Nov
Access Good
Beattrix Potter Gallery, Lakes Aquarium, Lakeland Motor Museum, Lake District National Park.
Facilities ♿ ∮ 🖻 🕍 🚾 🇵 ☺ ♨ 🖾 🖸 ♨
🖸 🚼 🖃 🖸
Nearest Town Windermere

Directions Turn left onto A592, at roundabout take 1st exit onto A591,turn right onto A593, take left onto Campston Road and keep right.
🚆 Windermere

WINDERMERE

Fallbarrow Park, Rayrigg Road, Windermere, Cumbria, LA23 3DL
Tel: 01539 569835
Email: enquiries@southlakelandparks.co.uk
www.slholidays.co.uk
Pitches For ⬜ ⬜ **Total** 27
Acreage 15 **Open** March to 13-Nov
Access Good **Site** Level
Nearest Bus Stop (Miles) ¼
Beatrix Potter, Windermere lake cruises
Facilities ♿ ∮ 🖻 🕍 🚾 🇵 🖙 ☺ ♨ 🖾 🖸 ♨
🕍 🖸 🖂 ✕ 🖙 🖽 🛋 ♨ 🚼 🖃 🖸 ☀
Nearest Town Bowness on Windermere
Directions Leave the M6 at junction 36 and follow the A591 to Windermere until you reach the town centre. Turn left following signs for Bowness. At Bowness turn right at the mini roundabout signposted Keswick & Steamboat Museum, Park is 300 yards on the left.
🚆 Windermere

WINDERMERE

Hill of Oaks Caravan Estate, Windermere, Cumbria, LA12 8NR
Tel: 015395 31578
Email: enquiries@hillofoaks.co.uk
www.hillofoaks.co.uk
Pitches For ⬜ ⬜ **Total** 43
Acreage 31 **Open** 01-Mar to 14-Nov
Access Good **Site** Lev/Slope
Nearest Bus Stop (Miles) Outside
Nestling on the slopes of ancient woodland, Hill of Oaks offers exclusive lake frontage for more than one kilometre along the shore of Lake Windermere, with well laid out nature walks where intrepid explorers can seek out the wildlife. There is also a natural secure play area for our younger visitors. The park welcomes touring caravans and motorhomes, as well as offering exclusive sites for holiday homes and lodges.Self catering holiday lodge.
Facilities ♿ 🖻 🕍 🚾 🇵 ☺ ♨ 🖾 🖸 ♨
🕍 🖸 🖂 ♨ 🚼 🖃 🖸 ✔ ☀ ☀
Nearest Town Windermere
Directions Leave the M6 at junction 36 and take the A590 to Newby Bridge. Turn right onto the A592 and the site is 3 miles on the left hand side.
🚆 Windermere

WINDERMERE

Park Cliffe Camping & Caravan Estate, Birks Road, Tower Wood, Windermere, Cumbria, LA23 3PG
Tel: 015395 31344
Email: info@parkcliffe.co.uk
www.parkcliffe.co.uk
Pitches For ⛺ ⬜ ⬜ **Total** 170
Acreage 25 **Open** Mar to Mid Nov
Access Good **Site** Lev/Slope
Nearest Bus Stop (Miles) ¼
Near to Lake Windermere with outstanding views of lakes and mountains, ideal touring. AA 5 Pennants, Cumbria Tourism Winner 2011, AA Northwest Campsite of the Year 2009 and England for Excellence Highly comended 2012.
Facilities ♿ ∮ 🖻 🕍 🚾 🇵 🖙 ☺ ♨ 🖾 🖸 ♨
🕍 🖸 🖂 ✕ 🖙 ♨ 🖽 🚼 🖃 🖸 ☀
Nearest Town Windermere
Directions M6 junction 36, A590 to Newby Bridge. Turn right on A592, in 3½ miles turn

---

right into Birks Road. Park is roughly ½ mile on the right.
🚆 Windermere

DERBYSHIRE

ASHBOURNE

Ashbourne Camping & Caravanning Club Site, Belper Road (A517), Bradley, Near Ashbourne, Derbyshire, DE6 3EN
Tel: 01335 370855
Email: ashbourne.site@thefriendlyclub.co.uk
www.campingandcaravanning.co.uk/ ashbourne
Pitches For ⛺ ⬜ ⬜ **Total** 50
Open 15-Mar to 11-Nov
Access Good **Site** Level
Nearest Bus Stop (Miles) Outside
Ideal for exploring the Derbyshire Peaks and Dales. Also Open 9th-26th February 2012. Non members welcome. You can also call us on 0845 130 7633.
Facilities ♿ ∮ 🖻 🕍 🚾 🇵 ☺ ♨ 🖾 🖸 ♨
🕍 🖸 🖂 🚼 🖃 🖸 ☀
Nearest Town Ashbourne
Directions From Ashbourne take the A517 Belper road, pass Bradley and site is signposted ½ a mile on the right.
🚆 Belper

ASHBOURNE

Bank Top Caravan & Camping, Bank Top Farm, Fenny Bentley, Ashbourne, Derbyshire, DE6 1LF
Tel: 01335 350250
Pitches For ⛺ ⬜ ⬜ **Total** 51
Acreage 3 **Open** April to 01-Oct
Access Good **Site** Lev/Slope
Nearest Bus Stop (Miles) ¼
Working farm with scenic views from the site. Ideal for touring Dovedale and other Dales, also pretty little villages.
Facilities ∮ 🚾 🇵 ☺ ♨ 🖾 🖸 🕍 🚼 🖃 ☀
Nearest Town Ashbourne
Directions From Ashbourne take the A515 north, then take the B5056 and the site is 200 yards on the right.
🚆 Derby

ASHBOURNE

Carsington Water Caravan Club Site, Kirk Ireton, Ashbourne, Derbyshire, DE6 3JL
Tel: 01335 370903
www.caravanclub.co.uk
Pitches For ⬜ ⬜ **Total** 130
Acreage 25 **Open** Mar to Nov
Access Good **Site** Level
Set in a beautifully landscaped pine plantation. Adjacent to Carsington Reservoir for fishing and sailing. BBQs allowed with wardens permission. Non members welcome. Booking essential.
Facilities ♿ 🖻 🕍 🚾 🇵 ☺ ♨
🕍 🖸 🖂 🖃
Nearest Town Ashbourne
Directions Take the A517 from Ashbourne, turn left after 4½ miles at signpost Carsington Water, after ¾ miles at crossroads turn right, site is 1 mile on the right.
🚆 Ashbourne

ASHBOURNE

Newton Grange Caravan Site, Newton Grange, Ashbourne, Derbyshire, DE6 1NJ
Tel: 01335 310214
Pitches For ⛺ ⬜ ⬜ **Total** 15
Acreage 1 **Open** Mid March to End Oct
Access Good **Site** Level

Nearest Bus Stop (Miles) ½
Close to Buxton, Matlock and Alton Towers. Tissington Trail adjacent for cycling and walking. Ideal touring.
Facilities ⚲ �ℐ 🖥🚾🖂
Nearest Town Ashbourne
Directions On the A515 4½ miles north of Ashbourne.
⚑ Derby

ASHBOURNE

Peak Gateway Ltd., Moor Lane, Osmaston, Ashbourne, Derbyshire, DE6 1NA
Tel: 01335 344643
Email: info@peakgateway.com
www.peakgateway.com
Pitches For ▲ ⬛ 🚐 🚃≤ **Total** 150
Open 22-Jan to 14-Dec
Access Good **Site** Level
Nearest Bus Stop (Miles) Outside
On the door step of the market town of Ashbourne. Ideal for walking in the Peak District. Only a 20 minute drive to Alton Towers.
Facilities ⚅ ℐ 🖥🆖🏧⌂⊙🍴🖂 🖥
🍴⚑☓🍴🌂🅿🖧🖂 ⚲
Nearest Town Ashbourne
Directions From Derby take the A52 to Ashbourne, turn left at second sign for Osmaston, site entrance is 100 yards on the right.
⚑ Derby

ASHBOURNE

Rivendale Caravan & Leisure Park, Buxton Road, Alsop-en-le-Dale, Ashbourne, Derbyshire, DE6 1QU
Tel: 01335 310311
Email: cades@rivendalecaravanpark.co.uk
www.rivendalecaravanpark.co.uk
Pitches For ▲ ⬛ 🚐 **Total** 80
Acreage 35 **Open** Feb to Jan
Access Good **Site** Level
Nearest Bus Stop (Miles) ¼
Surrounded by scenic countryside, ideal for walking, cycling and outdoor hobbies. Convenient for Chatsworth, Alton Towers and many other attractions. Yurts and Camping Pods for glamping! Holiday caravans/lodges for hire and sale luxurious B&B rooms.
Facilities ⚅ ℐ 🖥🆖🏧⌂⊙🍴🖂 🖥
🍴⚅⊙☓🍴🍴🌂🅿🖧🖂🖂⚓🌂
Nearest Town Hartington
Directions 6½ miles north of Ashbourne, directly accessed from the A515 (Buxton road).
⚑ Buxton

BAKEWELL

Bakewell Camping & Caravanning Club Site, c/o Hopping Farm, Youlgreave, Bakewell, Derbyshire, DE45 1NA
Tel: 01629 636555
Email: bakewell.site@thefriendlyclub.com
www.campingandcaravanningclub.co.uk/bakewell
Pitches For ▲ ⬛ 🚐 **Total** 100
Acreage 14 **Open** 21-Mar to 04-Nov
Site Sloping
Nearest Bus Stop (Miles) 1
Ideally situated for the Peak District. Near to Haddon Hall and Chatsworth Hole. BTB 3 Star Graded and AA 1 Pennant. Non members welcome. You can also call us on 0845 130 7633.
Facilities ℐ 🖥🍴🖂 🍴⊙🏧🆖🖂🌂
⚓🖧
Directions Take the A6 Bakewell to Matlock road, turn onto the B5056 Ashbourne road. After ½ mile take the right hand branch to Youlgreave, turn sharp left after the church

into Bradford Lane opposite The George Hotel. Continue ½ mile to club sign then turn right into Farmers Lane for ¼ mile.
⚑ Matlock

BAKEWELL

Chatsworth Park Caravan Club Site, Chatsworth, Bakewell, Derbyshire, DE45 1PN
Tel: 01246 582226
www.caravanclub.co.uk
Pitches For ⬛ 🚐 **Total** 120
Acreage 6½ **Open** All Year
Access Good **Site** Level
Nearest Bus Stop (Miles) ½
Situated in the old walled garden on the Chatsworth Estate with beautiful countryside views. Visit Chatsworth House, 1000 acre park and farm. Non members welcome. Booking essential.
Facilities ⚅ ℐ 🖥🆖🏧⌂ 🖂 🖥
🍴⊙🖧🖂⚓
Nearest Town Bakewell
Directions From Bakewell take the A619, after 3¼ miles (on the outskirts of Baslow) at the mini roundabout turn right signposted Sheffield. Site is 150 yards on the right.
⚑ Bakewell

BAKEWELL

Greenhills Holiday Park, Crowhill Lane, Bakewell, Derbyshire, DE45 1PX
Tel: 01629 813052/813467
Email: info@greenhillsholidaypark.co.uk
www.greenhillsholidaypark.co.uk
Pitches For ▲ ⬛ 🚐 **Total** 233
Acreage 8 **Open** Mar to Oct
Access Good **Site** Lev/Slope
Nearest Bus Stop (Miles) ¼
In the heart of the Peak District. Close to Chatsworth House and Haddon Hall.
Facilities ⚅ ℐ 🖥🆖🏧⌂⊙🍴🖂 🖥
🍴⚅⊙☓🍴🌂🍴🌂🅿🖧🖂🖂🌂 🛜
Nearest Town Bakewell
Directions 1 mile north west of Bakewell turn left into Crow Hill Lane, turn first right over the cattle grid.
⚑ Matlock

BAKEWELL

Haddon Grove Farm, Bakewell, Derbyshire, DE45 1JF
Tel: 01629 812343
Pitches For ▲ ⬛ 🚐
Acreage 3 **Open** Mar to Oct
Access Good **Site** Level
Nearest Bus Stop (Miles) ½
Close to Lathkil Dale.
Facilities ℐ 🖥🏧⌂⊙🍴🖂 🖂⊙🆖🖂
Nearest Town Bakewell
Directions From Bakewell take the B5055 towards Monyash. Travel for 3 miles then turn left into lane sp Haddon Grove.
⚑ Buxton

BAMFORD

Swallowholme Camping & Caravan Park, Station Road, Bamford, Hope Valley, Derbyshire, S33 0BN
Tel: 01433 650981
Email: swallowholmecamping@btconnect.com
www.swallowholmecampingandcaravanpark.co.uk
Pitches For ▲ ⬛ 🚐 **Total** 65
Acreage 3½ **Open** Mar to Oct
Access Good **Site** Level
Nearest Bus Stop (Miles) Outside
Alongside the River Derwent and close to Derwent Dam. 5 minutes from Hathersage. Outdoor swimming pool nearby. Ideal for walking. Sorry no dogs.

Facilities ℐ 🖥🆖🏧⌂⊙🍴🖂 🍴 🌂
Nearest Town Buxton/Bakewell
Directions On the A6013 on the edge of Bamford Village. 12 miles west of Sheffield off the A525.
⚑ Bamford

BRADWELL

Eden Tree Caravan Park, Eccles Lane, Bradwell, Hope Valley, Derbyshire, S33 9JT
Tel: 01433 623444
Email: edentreecaravanpark@fsmail.net
www.edentreecaravanpark.co.uk
Pitches For ▲ ⬛ 🚐 **Total** 20
Open Mar to Oct
Access Good **Site** Sloping
Nearest Bus Stop (Miles) ¼
In the heart of the Peak District National Park. Close to Chatsworth House, Castleton, Buxton and many other attractions.
Facilities ℐ 🖥🆖🏧⌂⊙🍴🖂 🍴⊙🖧🖂🌂
Nearest Town Bakewell
Directions On the outskirts of the village of Bradwell, 10 miles from Bakewell.
⚑ Hope

BUXTON

Beech Croft Farm, Blackwell in the Peak, Nr Buxton, Derbyshire, SK17 9TQ
Tel: 01298 85330
Email: mail@beechcroftfarm.co.uk
www.beechcroftfarm.co.uk
Pitches For ▲ ⬛ 🚐 **Total** 30
Acreage 3 **Open** All Year
Access Good **Site** Level
Nearest Bus Stop (Miles) ¼
In the centre of a National Park, ideal for walking and touring. Hardstandings have 16 amp hook-up, water tap and TV aerial socket. Hotel and restaurant in 1 mile.
Facilities ⚅⚓ ℐ 🖥🆖🏧⌂⊙🍴🖂 🖥
🍴⊙🖧🖂🛜
Nearest Town Buxton
Directions Turn off the A6 midway between Buxton and Bakewell, signposted.
⚑ Buxton

BUXTON

Buxton Caravan Club Site, Grin Low Road, Ladmanlow, Buxton, Derbyshire, SK17 6UJ
Tel: 01298 77735
www.caravanclub.co.uk
Pitches For ⬛ 🚐 **Total** 117
Acreage 11 **Open** Mar to Nov
Access Good **Site** Level
Situated in the Peak District National Park. Ideal for walking and cycling. Near to many historic houses. No late night arrivals. Non members welcome. Booking essential.
Facilities ⚅ ℐ 🖥🆖🏧⌂ 🖂 🖥
🍴⚅⊙🍴🆖🖂🛜
Nearest Town Buxton
Directions From Buxton take the A53 Leek road, after 1½ miles turn left signposted Grin Low. After 300 yards turn left into site road, entrance is ¼ mile.
⚑ Buxton

BUXTON

Lime Tree Park, Dukes Drive, Buxton, Derbyshire, SK17 9RP
Tel: 01298 22988
Email: info@limetreeparkbuxton.co.uk
Pitches For ▲ ⬛ 🚐 **Total** 100
Acreage 17 **Open** Mar to Nov
Access Good **Site** Lev/slope
Nearest Bus Stop (Miles) ½
Surrounded by farmland with old viaduct backdrop.

DERBYSHIRE

Facilities ⛾ ⏸ 🖥 🏕 ⌂ ☺ ⌿ ♨ ◻ ☎
🍴 🔥 🚽 🔥 🕇 🚻 ⏚ ◻ 🖊 ♨ ⚲
Nearest Town Buxton
Directions From A515 towards Buxton turn right across the carriageway to Dukes Drive, site on right 1 mile from Buxton.
🚲 Buxton

BUXTON

Newhaven Caravan & Camping Park, Newhaven, Nr Buxton, Derbyshire, SK17 0DT
Tel: 01298 84300
Email: newhavencaravanpark@btconnect.com
www.newhavencaravanpark.co.uk
Pitches For ⛺ 🚐 🚍 **Total** 125
Acreage 27 **Open** Mar to Oct
Access Good **Site** Lev/Slope
Ideal centre for touring Peak District, National Park and Derbyshire Dales. Cafe/restaurant opposite site.
Facilities ⏸ 🖥 🏕 ⌂ ☺ ⌿ ♨ ◻ ☎
🍴 🔥 🚽 🔥 🕇 🚻 ⏚ ◻ ♨
Nearest Town Buxton
Directions Midway between Ashbourne and Buxton on A515. At the junction with A5012.
🚲 Buxton

BUXTON

Pomeroy Caravan & Camping Park, Street House Farm, Pomeroy, Nr Flagg, Buxton, Derbyshire, SK17 9QG
Tel: 01298 83259
Email: pomeroycaravanandcamping@hotmail.co.uk
Pitches For ⛺ 🚐 🚍 **Total** 30
Acreage 2 **Open** Apr to Oct
Access Good **Site** Level
Nearest Bus Stop (Miles) 1
Peaceful site adjoining the High Peak Trail. Tarmac road to all pitches. Separate site for campers. 16 miles north of Ashbourne. You can also call us on Mobile: 07980 585545.
Facilities ⏸ 🖥 🏕 ⌂ ☺ ⌿ ♨ ◻ ☎
🔥 🕇 ◻ 🖊
Nearest Town Buxton
Directions 5 miles south of Buxton on the A515, site is on the right opposite corner sign. Go over the cattle grid and up a 200 yard tarmac drive to the site.
🚲 Buxton

BUXTON

Shallow Grange, Chelmorton, Nr Buxton, Derbyshire, SK17 9SG
Tel: 01298 23578
Email: info@shallowgrange.com
www.shallowgrange.com
Pitches For ⛺ 🚐 🚍 **Total** 48
Acreage 3 **Open** Mar to Oct
Access Good **Site** Level
Nearest Bus Stop (Miles) 1
Walking in the SSSI Dale. Chatsworth House, Haddon Hall and Bakewell nearby.
Facilities ⛾ ⏸ 🖥 🏕 ⌂ ☺ ⌿ ♨ ◻ ☎
🕇 ◻ ⌿ ♨ ⚲
Nearest Town Buxton

Directions From Buxton take the A515 Ashbourne road and travel for 2 to 3 miles. Turn left onto the A5270 and Shallow Grange is mile on the left.
🚲 Buxton

BUXTON

Thornheyes Farm Caravan & Camping Site, Longridge Lane, Peak Dale, Buxton, Derbyshire, SK17 8AD
Tel: 01298 26421
Pitches For ⛺ 🚐 🚍 **Total** 18
Acreage 1½ **Open** Easter to Oct
Access Poor **Site** Sloping
Nearest Bus Stop (Miles) ¼
ADULTS ONLY. Ideal for touring the Peak District.
Facilities ⏸ 🖥 ⌂ ☺ ⌿ ♨ 🕇 ◻ A
Nearest Town Buxton
Directions A6 Towards Manchester 2½ miles turn right Batham Gate turn right site on right.
🚲 Buxton

CASTLETON

Castleton Caravan Club Site, Castleton, Hope Valley, Derbyshire, S33 8WB
Tel: 01433 620636
www.caravanclub.co.uk
Pitches For ⛺ 🚐 🚍 **Total** 93
Acreage 6½ **Open** All Year
Access Good **Site** Level
Nearest Bus Stop (Miles) ½
Set in the heart of the Peak National Park with panoramic views. Ideal for outdoor activities such as walking, cycling, potholing, etc.. ½ mile from Peveril Castle. Non members welcome. Booking essential.
Facilities ⛾ ⏸ 🖥 🏕 ⌂ ☺ ⌿ ♨ ☎
🔥 🕇 ◻ 🚽 🕇 ◻ ♨
Directions M1.junc 29 take the A617. In C/field t onto the A619, after 8¾ mls in Baslow t rt at mini r/about onto A623. In Calver t rt onto B6001, in G/ford t lt at sp Hathersage. After 2½ mls t lt onto A6187, site 5 mls on rt.
🚲 Hope

CASTLETON

Rowter Farm, Castleton, Hope Valley, Derbyshire, S33 8WA
Tel: 01433 620271
www.peakdistrictsnationalpark.com
Pitches For ⛺ 🚐 🚍 **Total** 30
Acreage 4 **Open** End March to End Oct
Access Good **Site** Level
One static caravan available for hire.
Facilities 🖥 🏕 ⌂ ☺ 🕇 ◻
Nearest Town Castleton
Directions From Castleton take the B6061 Winnats Pass road, go to the top and continue for 200 yards, turn left through the gate.
🚲 Hope

DERBY

Beechwood Park, Main Road, Elvaston, Thulston, Derby, Derbyshire, DE72 3EQ
Tel: 01332 751938
Email: colinbeech@btconnect.com
www.beechwoodparkleisure.co.uk
Pitches For ⛺ 🚐 🚍 ⏛ **Total** 200
Acreage 25 **Open** All Year
Access Good **Site** Level

Nearest Bus Stop (Miles) ½
On the edge of the Peak District with fishing lakes and a childrens go-karting track. Opposite Elvaston Castle & Country Park. Cafe and tackle shop on site. Pub in the village.
Facilities ⛾ ⏸ 🖥 🏕 ⌂ ☺ ♨ ◻ ☎
🍴 🔥 🚽 🕇 ◻ 🖊
Nearest Town Derby
Directions From Derby take the A6 towards Loughborough and turn left onto the B5010. Beechwood Park is 1 mile on the right hand side.
🚲 Derby

DERBY

Shardlow Marina Caravan Park, London Road, Shardlow, Nr Derby, Derbyshire, DE72 2GL
Tel: 01332 792832
Email: admin@shardlowmarina.co.uk
www.shardlowmarina.co.uk
Pitches For ⛺ 🚐 🚍 **Total** 40
Open March to Jan
Access Good **Site** Level
Near a river and canal.
Facilities ⏸ 🖥 🏕 ⌂ ☺ ⌿ ♨ ◻ ☎
🍴 ⏛ 🔥 🚽 🕇 ◻ 🖊 ♨
Nearest Town Derby
Directions Junction 1 of A6/A50 Derby southern bypass. 5 miles from Derby.
🚲 Derby

EDALE

Fieldhead Campsite, Edale, Hope Valley, Derbyshire, S33 7ZA
Tel: 01433 670386
Email: bookings@fieldhead-campsite.co.uk
www.fieldhead-campsite.co.uk
Pitches For ⛺ **Total** 45
Acreage 3 **Open** All Year
Site Level
Alongside a river, next to Peak District Visitor Centre. 6 fields, 2 of which are by the river. All superb views of Mamtor Ridge and Kinder Scout. At the start of Pennine Way.
Facilities ⛾ 🖥 🏕 ⌂ ☺ ⏛ 🕇
Nearest Town Castleton
Directions 4½ miles from Castleton.
🚲 Edale

EDALE

Highfield Farm, Upper Booth, Edale, Hope Valley, Derbyshire, S33 7ZJ
Tel: 01433 670245
Pitches For ⛺ 🚐 🚍
Acreage 10 **Open** Easter to Oct
Good walking country, near the start of Pennine Way.
Facilities 🖥 ⏛ 🕇 ◻
Nearest Town Buxton
Directions Turn right off the A6187 opposite Hope Church, take minor road to Edale. Follow the road up the valley, pass the turning for Edale Village, at bottom of the hill turn right, go past the viaduct and pass picnic area, round the corner and the house is up ahead.
🚲 Edale

EDALE

Waterside Campsite, Waterside Farm, Barber Booth Road, Edale, Hope Valley, Derbyshire, S33 7ZL
Tel: 01433 670215
Pitches For Å ⊞ ⊞
Open Easter **to** Sept
Access Good **Site** Level
Near to the Pennine Way, Blue John Caverns, Chatsworth House (18 miles) and Bakewell.
Facilities ⊞⊟⌐⊙↵☎⚲⊁⊟⊡
Nearest Town Buxton
⇌ Edale

GLOSSOP

Crowden Camping & Caravanning Club Site, Crowden, Glossop, Derbyshire, SK13 1HZ
Tel: 01457 866057
Email: crowden.site@thefriendlyclub.co.uk
www.campingandcaravanningclub.co.uk/crowden
Pitches For Å ⊞ ⊞ **Total** 45
Acreage 2½ **Open** 21-Mar **to** 04-Nov
Site Level
Nearest Bus Stop (Miles) 100 metres
In the heart of the Peak District National Park, close to the Pennine Way. BTB 3 Star Graded and AA 2 Pennants. Non members welcome. You can also call us on 0845 130 7633.
Facilities ⊞⊞⊟⌐⊙↵☎▯☎⊁⊟⊡
Directions On the A628 Manchester to Barnsley road, in Crowden follow signs for car park, Youth Hostel and camp site. Camp site is approx. 300 yards from the main road.
⇌ Hadfield/Glossop

HARTINGTON

Barracks Farm Caravan & Camping Site, Beresford Dale, Hartington, Buxton, Derbyshire, SK17 0HQ
Tel: 01298 84261
Pitches For Å ⊞ ⊞ **Total** 40
Acreage 5 **Open** Easter **to** End Oct
Access Good **Site** Level
Alongside river, scenic views and ideal touring.
Facilities ⊞⊟⌐⊙☎▯⊁⊟
Nearest Town Buxton
Directions Buxton A515 approx 10 miles. After leaving Buxton go on for 7 miles, turn right for Hartington B5054. Go through village for 1½ miles, turn left for Beresford Dale, continue for ¼ mile then turn left again signposted Beresford Dale. The site is second on the left.
⇌ Buxton

HAYFIELD

Hayfield Camping & Caravanning Club Site, Kinder Road, Hayfield, High Peak, Derbyshire, SK22 2LE
Tel: 01663 745394
Email: hayfield.site@thefriendlyclub.co.uk
www.campingandcaravanningclub.co.uk/hayfield
Pitches For Å ⊞ **Total** 90
Acreage 6 **Open** 21-Mar **to** 01-Nov
Access Difficult **Site** Level
Nearest Bus Stop (Miles) 1
On the banks of the River Sett. Ideal for fell and moorland walkers. 6 miles from a Victorian style swimming pool. 12 miles from Granada Studios. BTB 3 Star Graded and AA 2 Pennants. Non members welcome (no caravans). You can also call us on 0845 130 7633.
Facilities ⊞⊟⌐⊙↵☎
▯☎⚲⊁⊟⊡⊛

Directions On the A624 Glossop to Chapel-en-le-Frith road, the Hayfield by-pass. Well signed to the village, follow wooden carved signs to the site.
⇌ New Mills

HOPE

Hardhurst Farm, Parsons Lane, Hope, Hope Valley, Derbyshire, S33 6RB
Tel: 01433 620001
Email: hardhurstcamping@hotmail.co.uk
Pitches For Å ⊞ ⊞ **Total** 52
Acreage 5 **Open** All Year
Access Good **Site** Level
Nearest Bus Stop (Miles) ¼
Climbing, walking, mountain biking poplar in area.
Facilities ዿ ⨍ ⊞⊞⊟⌐⊙↵☎
✕⊁⊟⊡
Nearest Town Castleton
⇌ Hope

HOPE

Laneside Caravan Park, Laneside Farm, Station Road, Hope, Hope Valley, Derbyshire, S33 6RR
Tel: 01433 620215
Email: laneside@lineone.net
www.lanesidecaravanpark.co.uk
Pitches For Å ⊞ ⊞ **Total** 85
Acreage 5 **Open** March **to** November
Access Good **Site** Level
Nearest Bus Stop (Miles) Outside
Sheltered riverside setting adjacent to to Hope Village. Wonderful central location for walking and touring the Peak District.
Facilities ዿ ⨍ ⊞⊞⊟⌐⊙↵☎▯
☎▯☎⊛⊁⊟⊡⚲⊛
Nearest Town Bakewell
⇌ Hope

HOPE

Pindale Farm Camp Site, Pindale Farm, Pindale Road, Hope, Hope Valley, Derbyshire, S33 6RN
Tel: 01433 620111
Email: pindalefarm@btconnect.com
www.www.pindalefarm.co.uk
Pitches For Å ⊞ **Total** 30
Acreage 2 **Open** March **to** October
Access - **Site** Casual
Pindale farm is situated at the west end of the Hope Valley, the heart of the Derbyshire Peak District
Facilities ⨍ ⊞⊟⌐⊙↵☎▯🅿⊟⊛
Directions Follow signs from church 1 mile.
⇌ Hope

MATLOCK

Birchwood Farm Caravan Park, Wirksworth Road, Whatstandwell, Nr Matlock, Derbyshire, DE4 5HS
Tel: 01629 822280
www.birchwoodfcp.co.uk
Pitches For Å ⊞ ⊞ ⊞≤ **Total** 66
Acreage 4 **Open** 25-Mar **to** Oct
Access Good **Site** Sloping
Nearest Bus Stop (Miles) ½
Situated off Midshires Way which leads to High Peak Trail or the Cromford Canal.
Facilities ዿ⚞⨍ ⊟⊞⊞⊟⌐⊙↵☎
▯☎▯📼⊛⊁⊟⊡⊛
Nearest Town Wirksworth
Directions Leave the A6 at Whatstandwell Bridge (look for our sign near the telephone box) and take the B5035 towards Wirksworth, after 1 mile turn right down our drive.
⇌ Whatstandwell

MATLOCK

Holly Bush Caravan & Camping Site, The Old Toll Bar, Grange Mill, Matlock, Derbyshire, DE4 4HU
Tel: 01629 650809
Pitches For ⊞ ⊞ **Total** 50
Open All Year
Access Good **Site** Level
Ideal for walking.
Facilities ⊞⊟☎☎⚲⊁⊟
Nearest Town Matlock
⇌ Matlock

MATLOCK

Lickpenny Caravan Park, Lickpenny Lane, Tansley, Nr Matlock, Derbyshire, DE4 5GF
Tel: 01629 583040
Email: lickpennycp@btinternet.com
www.lickpennycaravanpark.co.uk
Pitches For ⊞ ⊞ **Total** 100
Acreage 16 **Open** All Year
Nearest Bus Stop (Miles) ¼
Located in the heart of the Peak District. Garden centre and cafe nearby.
Facilities ዿ ⨍ ⊟⊞⊞⊟⌐⊙↵☎▰☎☎
☎▯☎▯☎⊛⊁⊟⊡⊛
Nearest Town Matlock
Directions From Matlock take the A615 towards the M1 for 3 miles, site is signposted on the left. 8 miles from the M1.
⇌ Matlock

MATLOCK

Packhorse Farm Bungalow, Packhorse Farm, Tansley, Matlock, Derbyshire, DE4 5LF
Tel: 01629 582781
Pitches For Å ⊞ ⊞ **Total** 20
Acreage 3 **Open** All Year
Access Good **Site** Level
ADULTS ONLY. Ideal for touring the countryside.
Facilities ⨍ ⊞⊟⌐⊙☎▯☎⊁⊟🅰⊛
Nearest Town Matlock
Directions Take the A615 to Tansley Village, 1½ miles to the site. 4½ miles from Matlock.
⇌ Matlock

MATLOCK

Pinegroves Caravan Park, High Lane, Tansley, Matlock, Derbyshire, DE4 5BG
Tel: 01629 534815
Pitches For ⊞ ⊞ **Total** 20
Acreage 7 **Open** April **to** October
Access Good **Site** Level
Nearest Bus Stop (Miles) ½
Peaceful countryside site. Near to many attractions including Tramway Museum, Chatsworth House, Matlock Bath Cable Cars and Lea Rhododendron Gardens.
Facilities ዿ⚞⨍ ⊞⊟⌐⊙↵☎▯☎
⊁⊟⊡⊛
Nearest Town Matlock
Directions Leave the M1 at junction 28, take the A38 to Alfreton then take the A615 towards Matlock. 2 miles after Wessington turn left at the crossroads into High Lane, site is on the left.
⇌ Matlock

RIPLEY

Golden Valley Caravan & Camping Park, Coach Road, Golden Valley, Derbyshire, DE55 4ES
Tel: 01773 513881
Email: enquiries@goldenvalleycaravanpark.co.uk
www.goldenvalleycaravanpark.co.uk
Pitches For Å ⊞ ⊞ **Total** 120
Acreage 30 **Open** All Year

Access Good **Site** Level
Nearest Bus Stop (Miles) ¼
Near to the Peak District, a canal, the Midland Railway, Matlock and Crich Tramway.
Facilities ⬤ ⓕ 🄵 🄷 ⓌⒸ ⌐ ⊙ ⌐ 🄰 ▣ ♥
🄢 🄻 ⊙ ⓑ ✕ ⓣ 🄰 ⋔ ✦ ⊣ ▣ ⚡ ☀
Nearest Town Ripley
Directions Leave the M1 at junction 26 and take the A610 towards Matlock. When in Codnor turn right at the traffic lights then right again onto Alfreton road, site is 2 miles on the left.
⇌ Alfreton

SWADLINCOTE

Conkers Camping & Caravanning Club Site, Bath Lane, Moira, Swadlincote, Derbyshire, DE12 6BD
Tel: 01283 224925
Email: conkers.site@thefriendlyclub.co.uk
www.campingandcaravanningclub.co.uk/
conkers
Pitches For 🄰 ⬤ 🚐 **Total** 90
Acreage 4 **Open** All Year
Access Good **Site** Level
Nearest Bus Stop (Miles) 1
Close to Corrs Visitor Centre, Donnington Park, Grangewood Zoo, Calke Abbey and Twycross Zoo. Non members welcome. You can also call us on 0845 130 7633.
Facilities ⬤ ⓕ 🄷 ⬤ 🄾 ⬤ ⋔ ▣ 🄲 ☀ ⚡
Nearest Town Swadlincote
Directions From Burton-on-Trent take the A444 towards Overseal. Turn into Moira road and take the fourth exit on the left, site is immediately on the right.
⇌ Burton-on-Trent

DEVON

ASHBURTON

Parkers Farm Holiday Park, Higher Mead Farm, Ashburton, Devon, TQ13 7LJ
Tel: 01364 654869
Email: parkersfarm@btconnect.com
www.parkersfarmholidays.co.uk
Pitches For 🄰 ⬤ 🚐 **Total** 100
Acreage 25 **Open** Easter to Oct
Access Good **Site** Level Terrace
Nearest Bus Stop (Miles) ¼
Friendly, family run, site with spectacular views. Children and pets paradise. Static caravans also for hire. Farm animals to see and feed.
Facilities ⬤ ⓕ 🄷 ⬤ ⌐ ⊙ ⌐ 🄰 ▣ ♥
🄢 🄻 ⊙ ⬤ ✕ ⓣ 🄰 ⋔ ✦ ⊣ ▣ 🄲 ☀ ⚞
Nearest Town Ashburton
Directions Take the A38 to Plymouth, when you see the sign 29 miles Plymouth take second left marked Woodland - Denbury.
⇌ Newton Abbot

AXMINSTER

Andrewshayes Caravan Park, Dalwood, Axminster, Devon, EX13 7DY
Tel: 01404 831225
Email: info@andrewshayes.co.uk
www.andrewshayes.co.uk
Pitches For 🄰 ⬤ 🚐 **Total** 150
Acreage 12 **Open** Easter to Oct
Access Good **Site** Lev/Terraced
Nearest Bus Stop (Miles) ¼
Close to the Jurassic coast. Outdoor heated pool, bar and take-away food.
Facilities ⬤ ⓕ 🄷 ⓌⒸ ⌐ ⊙ ⌐ 🄰 ▣ ♥
🄢 🄻 ⊙ ⓑ ✦ ⓣ 🄰 ⋔ ✦ ⊣ ▣ 🄲 ☀
⚡ ⚞
Nearest Town Axminster
Directions From Axminster take the A35, site is 3 miles on the right.
⇌ Axminster

BARNSTAPLE

Brightlycott Caravan & Camping Site, Brightlycott Barton, Barnstaple, Devon, EX31 4JJ
Tel: 01271 850330
Email: friend.brightlycott@virgin.net
www.brightlycottbarton.co.uk
Pitches For 🄰 ⬤ 🚐 **Total** 20
Acreage 4 **Open** 15-Mar to 15-Oct
Access Good **Site** Sloping
Nearest Bus Stop (Miles) 1
Extremely peaceful, small, friendly, family run site situated on a former dairy farm with panoramic views. 7 miles from nearest beach.
Facilities ⬤ ⓕ ⓌⒸ ⌐ ⊙ ⌐ 🄰 ▣ ♥
🄻 ⊙ 🄰 ⋔ ⊣ ▣ 🄲
Nearest Town Barnstaple
Directions A39 2½ miles north east of Barnstable to Lynyon.
⇌ Barnstaple

BARNSTAPLE

Greenacres Farm Touring Caravan Park, Bratton Fleming, Barnstaple, North Devon, EX31 4SG
Tel: 01598 763334
Pitches For 🄰 ⬤ 🚐 **Total** 30
Acreage 4 **Open** Apr to Oct
Access Good **Site** Level
Nearest Bus Stop (Miles) ¼
Peaceful, secluded park with scenic views. 5 miles from moors and coast, 10 miles from towns. Ideal for touring, walking and cycling.
Facilities ⬤ ⓕ 🄷 ⓌⒸ ⌐ ⊙ ⌐ 🄰 ▣ ♥
🄻 ⊙ 🄰 ⋔ ✦ ⊣ ▣ 🄲 ☀ ⚞
Nearest Town Barnstaple
Directions From North Devon link road (A361), turn right at Northaller roundabout. Take the A399 to Blackmoor Gate, approx 10 miles. Park signed (300yds from the A399).
⇌ Barnstaple

BIDEFORD

Steart Farm Touring Park, Horns Cross, Bideford, Devon, EX39 5DW
Tel: 01237 431836
Email: steartenquiries@btconnect.com
www.steartfarmtouringpark.co.uk
Pitches For 🄰 ⬤ 🚐 **Total** 70
Acreage 10¼ **Open** Easter to Sept
Access Good **Site** Lev/Slope
Nearest Bus Stop (Miles) ½
Set in 17 acres overlooking Bideford Bay, 1 mile from the sea. 2¼ acre dog exercise area. 2 acre childrens play area.
Facilities ⬤ ⓕ ⓌⒸ ⌐ ⊙ ⌐ 🄰 ▣ ♥
🄻 ⊙ 🄰 ⋔ ✦ ⊣ ▣ 🄲 ☀ ⚞
Nearest Town Bideford
Directions From Bideford follow the A39 west (signed Bude). Pass through Fairy Cross and Horns Cross, 2 miles after Horns Cross site will be on the right. 8 miles from Bideford.
⇌ Barnstaple

BRAUNTON

Lobb Fields Caravan & Camping Park, Saunton Road, Braunton, Devon, EX33 1HG
Tel: 01271 812090
Email: info@lobbfields.com
www.lobbfields.com
Pitches For 🄰 ⬤ 🚐 **Total** 180
Acreage 14 **Open** 23-Mar to 28-Oct
Access Good **Site** Gentle Slope
Nearest Bus Stop (Miles) Outside
1½ miles from the beach. 1 mile from the Tarka Trail. Disabled toilet and shower.
Facilities ⬤ ⓕ ⓌⒸ ⌐ ⊙ ⌐ 🄰 ▣ ♥
🄻 ⊙ ⓑ 🄰 ⊣ ▣ 🄲 ⚞

Nearest Town Braunton
Directions Take the A361 to Braunton, then take the B3231. The park entrance is 1 mile from Braunton centre on the right.
⇌ Barnstaple

BRIXHAM

Galmpton Touring Park, Greenway Road, Galmpton, Nr Brixham, Devon, TQ5 0EP
Tel: 01803 842066
Email:
enquiries@galmptontouringpark.co.uk
www.galmptontouringpark.co.uk
Pitches For 🄰 ⬤ 🚐 **Total** 120
Acreage 9 **Open** Easter to Sept
Access Good **Site** Sloping
Nearest Bus Stop (Miles) 1
Superb views of the River Dart. A quiet base for couples and families to explore South Devon. 1½ miles from the beach, boat trips, steam railway, NT gardens, zoo. Beautiful walks nearby.
Facilities ⬤ ⓕ 🄵 🄷 ⓌⒸ ⌐ ⊙ ⌐ 🄰 ▣ ♥
🄢 🄻 ⊙ 🄰 ⬤ ▣ 🄲
Nearest Town Brixham
Directions Follow the A380/A3022 Torbay ring road, on joining the A379 coast road sp Brixham, turn second right sp Galmpton Park. Continue through the village passing the school, park entrance is on the right after approx. 600 yards.
⇌ Paignton

BRIXHAM

Hillhead Caravan Club Site, Hillhead, Brixham, Devon, TQ5 0HH
Tel: 01803 853204
www.caravanclub.co.uk
Pitches For 🄰 ⬤ 🚐 **Total** 239
Acreage 20 **Open** Mar to Jan
Access Good **Site** Lev/Slope
In a great location with many pitches affording stunning views of the sea, South Devon and parts of Dorset. Ideal site for families. Kingswear-Paignton Steam Railway and Paignton Zoo nearby. Non members welcome. Booking essential.
Facilities ⬤ ⓕ 🄷 ⓌⒸ ⌐ ⊙ ⌐ 🄰 ▣ ♥
🄢 🄻 ⊙ ⓑ ✕ ⓣ ⓣ 🄰 ⋔ ✦ ⊣ ▣ 🄲 ⚞
Nearest Town Brixham
Directions From A380 3 miles south of Newton Abbot t rt onto the ring road sp Brixham. After 7 miles at traffic lights t rt onto A3022, just past Churston Golf Course t rt onto A379. At mini r/bout t rt and immediately fork lt onto B3205. Site is ¼ of a mile on the lt.
⇌ Paignton

BUCKFAST

Churchill Farm, Buckfastleigh, Devon, TQ11 0EZ
Tel: 01364 642844/07977113175
Email: apedrick@btinternet.com
www.churchillfarmcampsite.com
Pitches For 🄰 ⬤ 🚐 **Total** 25
Acreage 2 **Open** Apr to Oct
Access Good **Site** Lev/Slope
Nearest Bus Stop (Miles) ½
Stunning views of Dartmoor and Buckfast Abbey, the latter being within easy walking distance as are the Steam Railway, Butterfly Farm, Otter Sanctuary and local inns. Seaside resort 10 miles.
Facilities ⓕ ⓌⒸ ⌐ ⊙ ⌐ 🄰 ▣ ♥
🄻 ⊙ 🄰 ⋔ ⊣ ▣ 🄲 ⚞
Nearest Town Buckfastleigh/Buckfast
Directions Exit A38 at Dartbridge, follow signs for Buckfast Abbey, proceed up hill to crossroads. Turn left into no-through road towards church. Farm entrance is opposite the church 1½ miles from the A38.
⇌ Totnes

BUCKFASTLEIGH

Beara Farm Camping Site, Colston Road, Buckfastleigh, Devon, TQ11 0LW
Tel: 01364 642234
Pitches For Å ⬤ ⬤ **Total** 30
Acreage 3¼ **Open** All Year
Access Good **Site** Level
Quiet, select, sheltered site adjoining River Dart. Within easy reach of sea and moors and 1½ miles southeast of Buckfastleigh.
Facilities ⚒ 🛁 🚿 🚻 ♿ ⊙ ⏬ ⏪ 📻 📼
Nearest Town Buckfastleigh
Directions Coming from Exeter take first left after passing South Devon Steam Railway and Butterfly Centre at Buckfastleigh, signpost marked Beara, fork right at next turning then 1 mile to site, signposted on roadside and junctions.
⇌ Totnes

BUCKFASTLEIGH

Bowden Farm Campsite, Bowden Farm, Buckfastleigh, Devon, TQ11 0JG
Tel: 01364 643955
www.www.holidaydevon.co.uk
Pitches For Å ⬤ ⬤ **Total** 40
Acreage 20 **Open** All Year
Access Good **Site** Level
Magnificent scenic location overlooking Dartmoor & South Devon.
Facilities 📻 🚻
Nearest Town Buckfastleigh
Directions 3 milesfrom Buckfastleigh, A38 Devon Expressway
⇌ Totnes

CHAGFORD

Woodland Springs Adult Touring Park, Venton, Drewsteignton, Devon, EX6 6PG
Tel: 01647 231695
Email: enquiries@woodlandsprings.co.uk
www.woodlandsprings.co.uk
Pitches For Å ⬤ ⬤ **Total** 81
Acreage 4 **Open** All Year
Access Good **Site** Level
ADULTS ONLY. Quiet, secluded site within the Dartmoor National Park, surrounded by wood and farmland. Good access for the larger units and large all-weather pitches. Off season breaks.
Facilities ♿ ✦ 🛁 🚿 ♿ ⊙ ⏬ ⏪ 🗑
🏋 🛒 🚻 📻 🛒 ♿ ⛱ 📶
Nearest Town Okehampton
Directions From Exeter take the A30, after 17 miles turn left at Whiddon Down Junction onto the A382 towards Moretonhampstead, after ½ a mile turn left at the roundabout, site is 1 mile on the left signpost Venton.
⇌ Exeter

CHUDLEIGH

Holmans Wood Holiday Park, Harcombe, Cross, Chudleigh, Devon, TQ13 0DZ
Tel: 01626 853785
Email: enquiries@holmanswood.co.uk
www.holmanswood.co.uk
Pitches For Å ⬤ ⬤ **Total** 100
Acreage 11 **Open** March to End October
Access Good **Site** Level
Picturesque setting. Ideal touring for Dartmoor, Haldon Forest, Exeter and Torbay. Holiday homes for sale.
Facilities ♿ ✦ 📻 🛁 🚿 ♿ ⊙ ⏬ ⏪ 🗑 🛒 📻
🏋 🛒 🚻 ♿ 🛒 📻 ⛱ 📶 📶
Nearest Town Chudleigh
Directions From Exeter take the A38 Towards Plymouth. Go past the racecourse and after 1 mile take the B3344 for Chudleigh. We are on the left at the end of the sliproad.
⇌ Newton Abbot

CLOVELLY

Dyke Green Farm, Camp Site, Dyke Green Farm, Clovelly, Bideford, Devon, EX39 5RU
Tel: 01237 431279
Email: royston.johns@hotmail.co.uk
Pitches For Å ⬤ ⬤ **Total** 25
Acreage 3 **Open** Easter to Oct
Access Good **Site** Level
Ideal stop off for touring the coastal path and visiting Clovelly.
Facilities ✦ 🛁 🚿 ♿ ⊙ 📻 🏋 🛒 🚻 📼 📶
Nearest Town Clovelly
Directions On the A39 Clovelly Cross roundabout.
⇌ Barnstaple

COMBE MARTIN

Newberry Valley Park, Woodlands, Combe Martin, Devon, EX34 0AT
Tel: 01271 882334
Email: relax@newberryvalleypark.co.uk
www.newberryvalleypark.co.uk
Pitches For Å ⬤ ⬤ ⬤< **Total** 110
Acreage 20 **Open** Mar to Oct
Access Good **Site** Level
Near beach and village, adjacent to Wolf Centre.
Facilities ♿ ✦ 📻 🛁 🚿 ♿ ⊙ ⏪ 🗑 📻
🏋 🛒 🛒 🚻 ♿ 📻 🛒 ⛱ 📶
Nearest Town Combe Martin/Ilfracombe
Directions A399 from Aller Cross to Combe Martin. Site at seaside end of village.
⇌ Barnstaple

COMBE MARTIN

Stowford Farm Meadows, Combe Martin, Devon, EX34 0PW
Tel: 01271 882476
Email: enquiries@stowford.co.uk
www.stowford.co.uk
Pitches For Å ⬤ ⬤ **Total** 700
Acreage 140 **Open** All Year
Access Good **Site** Lev/Slope
Nearest Bus Stop (Miles) 1
Set in 450 acres of beautiful countryside. Ideal touring site at the heart of North Devon. Renowned for our extensive range of facilities at excellent value. Horse riding on site. Caravan repair workshop, caravan accessories shop and caravan sales.
Facilities ♿ ✦ 📻 🛁 🚿 ♿ ⊙ ⏪ 🗑 📻 📼
🏋 🛒 🛒 ✗ 🍷 ♿ 🛒 ⚒ 🗑 🛒 🛒 ⛱ 📶 📶
Nearest Town Combe Martin
Directions Situated on the A3123 Combe Martin/Woolacombe road at Berry Down.
⇌ Barnstaple

CREDITON

Yeatheridge Farm Caravan & Camping Park, East Worlington, Crediton, Devon, EX17 4TN
Tel: 01884 860330
Email: yeatheridge@talk21.com
www.yeatheridge.co.uk
Pitches For Å ⬤ ⬤ **Total** 85
Open 01-Apr to 01-Oct
Access Good **Site** Lev/Slope
⇌ Eggesford

CROYDE BAY

Bay View Farm Holidays, Croyde, Devon, EX33 1PN
Tel: 01271 890501
www.bayviewfarm.co.uk
Pitches For Å ⬤ ⬤
Acreage 10 **Open** Easter to Sept
Site Level
Nearest Bus Stop (Miles) Outside
Scenic views. Just a five minute walk to the beach. Ideal touring. Booking is advisable during peak season. Limited statics available. Please send SAE for further information.
Facilities ♿ ✦ 📻 🛁 🚿 ♿ ⊙ ⏪ 🗑 📼 📻
🏋 🛒 🛒 ✗ 📻 🛒 ⛱
Directions At Braunton on A361 turn west on main road B3231 towards Croyde Village
⇌ Barnstaple

CROYDE BAY

Ruda Holiday Park, Croyde Bay, Devon, EX33 1NY
Tel: 0844 335 3732
Email: touringandcamping@parkdeanholidays.com
www.parkdeantouring.com

Pitches For 🏕 🚐 🚐 **Total** 306
Acreage 220 **Open** March **to** Oct
Access Good **Site** Level
Nearest Bus Stop (Miles) Outside
Our own beach, Croyde Bay is immediately adjacent to camping and touring pitches. Excellent surfing and walking. Indoor Tropical Adventure Pool. FREE kids clubs and live family entertainment.
Facilities ♿ ⚡ 🚿 ♨ 🚻 ⛽ ⊙ ↙ 🛒 ▣ 📶
Nearest Town Barnstaple
Directions From Barnstaple take the A361 to Braunton. In the centre of Braunton at the traffic lights turn left onto the B3231 and follow signs to Croyde.
🚏 Barnstaple

DARTMOUTH

Little Cotton Caravan Park, Dartmouth, Devon, TQ6 0LB
Tel: 01803 832558
Email: enquiries@littlecotton.co.uk
www.littlecotton.co.uk
Pitches For 🏕 🚐 🚐 **Total** 117
Acreage 7 **Open** Mid March **to** End Oct
Access Good **Site** Lev/Slope
Nearest Bus Stop (Miles) Outside
River Tripps, Steam Trains, Beaches, ideal touring.

Facilities ♿ ⚡ 🚿 🚻 ⛽ ⊙ ↙ 🛒 ▣ 🛒
♨ 🏕 ⊙ ⚡ 🛒 ⛽ 📶
Nearest Town Dartmouth
Directions Leave A38 onto A384 sign for Dartmouth. Follow directions to Dartmouth we are opposite Sainsburys.
🚏 Totnes

DARTMOUTH

Woodlands Grove Caravan & Camping Park, Blackawton, Totnes, Devon, TQ9 7DQ
Tel: 01803 712598
Email: holiday@woodlandsgrove.com
www.woodlands-caravanpark.com
Pitches For 🏕 🚐 🚐 **Total** 210
Acreage 16 **Open** Easter **to** Oct
Access Good **Site** Mostly Level
Nearest Bus Stop (Miles) Outside
Combining 5 Star facilities with personal supervision. Spacious pitches in beautiful countryside. 4 miles from Dartmouth coast. Excellent bathrooms, laundry and Free hot showers. Two nights stay gives FREE entrance to our 90 acre Leisure Park. 3 watercoasters, 500m Toboggan Run and Arctic Gliders. All weather fun guaranteed - perfect family holiday! Also 'Adults Only Midweek Special', the perfect rural break for adults.
Facilities ♿ ⚡ 🚿 🚻 ⛽ ⊙ ↙ 🛒 ▣ 🛒

♨ 🏕 ⊙ ⚡ 🛒 ✖ 🚻 🏕 🏕 ▣ 🛒 📶
Nearest Town Dartmouth
Directions 4 miles from Dartmouth on main road A3122 (formally B3207).
🚏 Totnes

DAWLISH

Lady's Mile Holiday Park, Exeter Road, Dawlish, -, -, Devon, EX7 0LX
Tel: 01626 863411
Email: info@ladysmile.co.uk
www.ladysmile.co.uk
Pitches For 🏕 🚐 🚐 **Total** 486
Acreage 16 **Open** Mid March **to** End Oct
Access Good **Site** Lev/Slope
Nearest Bus Stop (Miles) Outside
Nearest Town Dawlish
🚏 Dawlish

DAWLISH

Leadstone Camping, Warren Road, Dawlish, Devon, EX7 0NG
Tel: 01626 864411
Email: post@leadstonecamping.co.uk
www.leadstonecamping.co.uk
Pitches For 🏕 🚐 🚐 **Total** 137
Acreage 7 **Open** 07-Jun **to** 01-Sep
Access Good **Site** Lev/Slope
Nearest Bus Stop (Miles) Outside
Rolling grassland in a natural secluded bowl within ½ mile of Dawlish Warrens Blue Flag

Lady's Mile
HOLIDAY PARK

Award winning holidays for all the family

- ◆ TWO FREE Swimming Pools ◆
- ◆ TWO FREE Waterslides ◆
- ◆ "The Mile" family bar ◆ TWO Launderettes ◆
- ◆ Free hot water & showers ◆ Electric Hook-ups ◆
- ◆ Licensed Shop ◆ Adventure Fort & Play Area ◆
- ◆ Multi Sports ◆ Families & Rallies welcome ◆
- ◆ Takeaway, Pizzeria & Cafe ◆ Entertainment ◆
- ◆ Camping Pods ◆ Splash Zone ◆ Gymnasium ◆
- ◆ Themed Soft Play Area ◆ Luxury Holiday Homes ◆

NEW TOURING PITCHES & HOLIDAY HOMES FOR 2013

Send for our FREE colour brochure:
Lady's Mile Holiday Park, Freepost, Dawlish,
South Devon EX7 9YZ

Telephone 01626 863411   www.ladysmile.co.uk

Beach and nature reserve. Ideally situated for discovering Devon.
Facilities
Nearest Town Dawlish
Directions Leave the M5 at junction 30 and take signposted road A379 to Dawlish. As you approach Dawlish, turn left on brow of hill, signposted Dawlish Warren. Our site is ½ mile on the RIGHT.
≠ Dawlish Warren

EXETER
Dartmoor, Barley Meadow Camping & Caravanning Club Site, Crockernwell, Exeter, Devon, EX6 6NR
Tel: 01647 281629
Email: dartmoor.site@thefriendlyclub.co.uk
www.campingandcaravanningclub.co.uk/dartmoor
Pitches For Λ 🚐 🚗 **Total** 63
Acreage 4 **Open** 14-Mar **to** 04-Nov
Access Good **Site** Level
Nearest Bus Stop (Miles) Outside
Set towards the east of the Dartmoor National Park in the heart of Devon. Non members welcome. You can also call us on 0845 130 7633.
Facilities
Nearest Town Okehampton
Directions From Okehampton take the A30. Leave at the A382 and turn onto Hask Lane, Site is on the right before Hopperton Lane.
≠ Exeter

EXETER
Exeter Racecourse Caravan Club Site, Kennford, Exeter, Devon, EX6 7XS
Tel: 01392 832107
www.caravanclub.co.uk
Pitches For Λ 🚐 🚗 **Total** 100
Acreage 10 **Open** Mar **to** Nov
Access Good **Site** Level
Access to racing. Large late night arrivals area. Near to Exeter Cathedral, Dartmoor National Park and Trago Mills Shopping Complex. Non members welcome. Booking essential.
Facilities
Nearest Town Exeter
Directions At the top of Haldon Hill turn left sp Exeter Racecourse then immediately right, follow signs to the site.
≠ Exeter

EXETER
Kennford International Caravan Park, Kennford, Exeter, Devon, EX6 7YN
Tel: 01392 833046
Email: ian@kennfordinternational.com
www.kennfordinternational.co.uk

Pitches For Λ 🚐 🚗 **Total** 96
Acreage 15 **Open** All Year
Access Good **Site** Level
Nearest Bus Stop (Miles) Outside
Kennford International is a family run park close to beaches and the city of Exeter. Fishing and the villages of Kenn and Kennford nearby. 10% discount for the over 50s (not available July & August). 7 Night Special available from Sept to Nov.
Facilities
Nearest Town Exeter
Directions From the M5 join the A38 towards Plymouth and Torquay. Exit at Kennford Services, pass the garage, go over the bridge and we are on the left. Approx. 10 minutes from Exeter.
≠ Exeter

EXETER
Springfield Holiday Park, Tedburn St Mary, Exeter, Devon, EX6 6EW
Tel: 01647 24242
Email:
enquiries@springfieldholidaypark.co.uk
www.springfieldholidaypark.co.uk
Pitches For Λ 🚐 🚗 **Total** 100
Acreage 9 **Open** 15-Mar **to** 15-Nov
Access Good **Site** Lev/Slope
Nearest Bus Stop (Miles) Outside
Central location for the Moors or the coast, north or south Devon. 20 minutes from the seaside.
Facilities
Directions Leave the M5 at junction 31 (Okehampton) and take the A30. Leave at left exit signposted Cheriton Bishop and follow brown tourism signs. For SAT-NAV purposes, please use Postcode EX6 6JN.
≠ Exeter

EXMOUTH
St Johns Caravan & Camping Park, St Johns Road, Exmouth, Devon, EX8 5EG
Tel: 01395 263170
Email: stjohns.farm@virgin.net
www.stjohnsfarm.co.uk
Pitches For Λ 🚐 🚗 **Total** 45
Acreage 6 **Open** Mar **to** Mid Jan
Access Good **Site** Sloping
Nearest Bus Stop (Miles) ¼
Quiet location near lovely common land with ponds and a reservoir for fishing. 2 miles to the town and beach.
Facilities
Directions Heading towards Exmouth go through Woodbury Village and head for Budleigh Salterton and take the B3180, site is a turning off this road.
≠ Exmouth

EXMOUTH
Webbers Park, Castle Lane, Woodbury, Exeter, Devon, EX5 1EA
Tel: 01395 232276
Email: reception@webberspark.co.uk
www.webberspark.co.uk
Pitches For Λ 🚐 🚗 **Total** 150
Acreage 15 **Open** Mid March **to** End Oct
Access Good **Site** Lev/Slope
Nearest Bus Stop (Miles) ¼
Crealy Adventure Park and Exmouths sandy beach nearby.
Facilities
Nearest Town Exmouth
Directions Leave the M5 at junction 30 and take the A376 to Exmouth. Then take the B3179 to Woodbury and follow brown tourism signs.
≠ Exeter

GREAT TORRINGTON
Smytham Manor, Little Torrington, Devon, EX38 8PU
Tel: 01805 622110
Email: info@smytham.co.uk
www.smytham.co.uk
Pitches For Λ 🚐 🚗 **Total** 45
Acreage 25 **Open** Mar **to** Oct
Access Good **Site** Lev/Slope
Nearest Bus Stop (Miles) Outside
Direct access to the Tarka Trail.
Facilities
Nearest Town Great Torrington
Directions 2 miles south of Great Torrington on the A386.
≠ Barnstaple

HARTLAND
Hartland Caravan & Camping Park, South Lane, Hartland, Bideford, North Devon, EX39 6DG
Tel: 01237 441876
Email: info@hartlandcamping.co.uk
www.hartlandcamping.co.uk
Pitches For Λ 🚐 🚗
Open Mar **to** Oct
Access Good **Site** Level
Nearest Bus Stop (Miles) Outside
Within a few minutes walk there are local shops, woodland walks, beaches just 2½ miles away. Well stocked course fishing pond.
Facilities
Nearest Town Bideford/Bude
Directions From Bideford follow A39 towards Bude, just after Clovelly roundabout take right turn B3248 to Hartland. At the Anchor Inn turn right up road past church we are on the right.
≠ Barnstaple

HOLSWORTHY
Hedley Wood Caravan & Camping Park, Bridgerule, Holsworthy, Devon, EX22 7ED
Tel: 01288 381404
Email: alan@hedleywood.co.uk
www.hedleywood.co.uk
Pitches For Ⓐ Ⓟ Ⓦ Ⓦ **Total** 150
Acreage 17½ **Open** All Year
Access Good **Site** Lev/Slope
Nearest Bus Stop (Miles) ½
Very dog friendly,very laid back atmosphere for tourers,campers and motorhomes.
Facilities 🚿 🚻 ⓦ ↑ ℗ ☺ 🍴 ⬛ ◨ 🏪
🕏 ▣ ⬤ ✖ ▽ ⛳ 🎣 ⋀ ↝ ▣ ゔ ⚓
Nearest Town Bude
Directions B3254 to Red Post and A3072 to Bude 5-6 miles.
⚏ Launceston

HOLSWORTHY
Noteworthy Caravan & Campsite, Bude Road, Holsworthy, Devon, EX22 7JB
Tel: 01409 253731
Email: enquiries@noteworthy-devon.co.uk
www.noteworthy-devon.co.uk
Pitches For Ⓐ Ⓟ Ⓦ **Total** 30
Acreage 5 **Open** All Year
Access Good **Site** Slight Slope
Nearest Bus Stop (Miles) Outside
Set on a working Angora goat farm on the Devon/Cornwall border.
Facilities 🚿 ⓦ ↑ ℗ ☺ 🍴 🏪 ⋀ ↝ ▣
Nearest Town Holsworthy/Bude
Directions From Holsworthy take the A3072 towards Bude. The site is 2.7 miles on the right hand side.
⚏ Barnstaple

ILFRACOMBE
Hele Valley Holiday Park, Hele Bay, Ilfracombe, North Devon, EX34 9RD
Tel: 01271 862460
Email: holidays@helevalley.co.uk
www.helevalley.co.uk
Pitches For Ⓐ Ⓟ Ⓦ **Total** 50
Acreage 7 **Open** Easter **to** Oct
Access Good **Site** Level
Nearest Bus Stop (Miles) ¼
Set within a tranquil secluded valley. Just a few minutes walk to the beach, pubs, shop and coastal path. The only campsite in Ilfracombe.
Facilities 🚿 🚿 ▣ 🚻 ⓦ ↑ ℗ ☺ 🍴 ⬛ ◨ 🏪
🏵 ℗ ⬤ ⋀ ↝ ▣ ◨
Nearest Town Ilfracombe
Directions From the A399 in Hele Bay follow signs to turn off main road to a T-Junction. Take a right turn to Hele Valley.
⚏ Barnstaple

ILFRACOMBE
Hidden Valley Touring & Camping Park, West Down, Nr Ilfracombe, North Devon, EX34 8NU
Tel: 01271 813837
Email: relax@hiddenvalleypark.com
www.hiddenvalleypark.com
Pitches For Ⓐ Ⓟ Ⓦ Ⓦ **Total** 115
Acreage 27 **Open** All Year **to** -
Access Good **Site** Level
Nearest Bus Stop (Miles) Outside
Nearest Town Ilfracombe
⚏ Barnstaple

ILFRACOMBE
IlfrcombeCaravan Club Site, West Down, Ilfracombe, Devon, EX34 8NE
Tel: 01271 862848
www.caravanclub.co.uk
Pitches For Ⓟ Ⓦ **Total** 103
Acreage 9 **Open** Mar **to** Oct
Access Good **Site** Lev/Slope
Nearest Bus Stop (Miles) ½
Elevated position with superb views and a woodland walkway. 5 miles from a sandy beach and near to Exmoor National Park and Tarka Trail Cycle Track. Own sanitation required. Non members welcome. Booking essential.
Facilities 🚿 🏪 ℗℣ ▣ ☺ ⬛ ↝ ▣ ◨ ゔ ⚓
Nearest Town Ilfracombe
Directions From Barnstaple take the A361, to Mullacott Cross roundabout turn right onto the A3123. Turn right at caravan sign signposted West Down, site is 1 mile on the left.
⚏ Ilfracombe

ILFRACOMBE
Napps Touring Holidays, Napps, Old Coast Road, Berrynarbor, Ilfracombe, Devon, EX34 9SW
Tel: 01271 882557
Email: enquiries@napps.fsnet.co.uk
www.napps.co.uk
Pitches For Ⓐ Ⓟ Ⓦ **Total** 250
Acreage 11 **Open** March **to** November
Access Good **Site** Level
Nearest Bus Stop (Miles) Outside
Probably the most beautiful coastal setting you will see. 200 yards from the beach. Popular family site with woodland and coastal walks. Heated swimming pool, tennis, coffee shop, breakfasts, Devon cream teas and your own local pub on site.
Facilities 🚿 🚻 ⓦ ↑ ℗ ☺ 🍴 ⬛ ◨ 🏪
🕏 ℗ ⬤ ⬤ ✖ ▽ ⛳ 🎣 ⋀ ↝ ▣ ◨ ゔ ⚓
Nearest Town Ilfracombe
Directions On A399, 1¼ miles west of Combe Martin, turn right onto Old Coast Road (signposted). Site 400yds along Old Coast Road.
⚏ Barnstaple

ILFRACOMBE
Watermouth Cove Holiday Park, Berrynarbor, Nr Ilfracombe, North Devon, EX34 9SJ
Tel: 01271 862504
Email: info@watermouthcoveholidays.co.uk
www.watermouthcoveholidays.co.uk
Pitches For Ⓐ Ⓟ Ⓦ **Total** 90
Acreage 27 **Open** Apr **to** Oct
Access Good **Site** Lev/Slope
Nearest Bus Stop (Miles) Outside
On the headlands with stunning views across the Channel. Own cove with rock pools and caves. Adjacent to Watermouth Harbour.
Facilities 🚿 🚻 ⓦ ↑ ℗ ☺ 🍴 ⬛ ◨ 🏪
🕏 ▣ ⬤ ✖ ▽ ⛳ 🎣 ⋀ ↝ ▣ ◨ 🚲 ゔ ⚓ 🛜
Nearest Town Ilfracombe
Directions From Barnstaple tale the A361 through to Ilfracombe and on to Watermouth Cove.
⚏ Barnstaple

ILFRACOMBE
Watermouth Valley Camping Park, Watermouth, Ilfracombe, North Devon, EX34 9SJ
Tel: 01271 862282
Email: watermouthvalley@hotmail.co.uk
www.watermouthpark.co.uk
Pitches For Ⓐ Ⓟ Ⓦ **Total** 155
Acreage 30 **Open** Easter **to** Mid Sept
Access Good **Site** Level
Nearest Bus Stop (Miles) Outside
Just a 5 minute walk to Watermouth Castle and harbour. Near beaches, Ilfracombe, Combe Martin and Woolacombe.
Facilities 🚿 🚿 🚻 ⓦ ↑ ℗ ☺ 🍴 ⬛ ◨ 🏪
🕏 ℗ ⬤ ⬤ ✖ ▽ ⛳ ⋀ ↝ ▣ ◨
Nearest Town Ilfracombe
Directions Situated on the A399 Ilfracombe to Combe Martin road, near to Watermouth Harbour.
⚏ Barnstaple

IVYBRIDGE
Cheston Caravan & Camping Park, Folly Cross, Wrangaton Road, South Brent, Devon, TQ10 9HF
Tel: 01364 72586
Email: enquiries@chestoncaravanpark.co.uk
www.chestoncaravanpark.co.uk
Pitches For Ⓐ Ⓟ Ⓦ **Total** 24
Acreage 1¾ **Open** 15-Mar **to** 31-Oct
Access Good **Site** Level
Nearest Bus Stop (Miles) ¼
Set in Dartmoor National Park. Close to lots of major attractions located in Torquay, Paignton and Plymouth. Ideal for a family holiday, perfect for walking and sightseeing.
Facilities 🚿 🚿 🚻 ⓦ ↑ ℗ ☺ 🍴 ⬛ ◨ 🏪 ℗ ↝ ▣ 🚲
Nearest Town Ivybridge

Directions From Exeter, after by-passing South Brent, turn left at Wrangaton Cross slip road then right A38. From Plymouth take South Brent (Woodpecker) turn, at end of slip road turn right, go under A38 and rejoin A38 and follow directions from Exeter.

KINGSBRIDGE

Parkland, Sorley Green Cross, Kingsbridge, Devon, TQ7 4AF
Tel: 01548 852723
Email: enquiries@parklandsite.co.uk
www.parklandsite.co.uk
Pitches For 🛆 🚐 🚎 ≷ **Total** 50
Acreage 3 **Open** All Year
Access Good **Site** Level
Nearest Bus Stop (Miles) ¼
PARKLAND is a high quality traditional site set in 3 acres of level grounds, located 1 mile north of Kingsbridge. Just a short distance from Bantham Beach with panoramic views of Salcombe and Dartmoor. FREE electric hook-ups. Full modern heated facilities, family and disabled suites. Large children's playground. Free Wi-Fi. Course fishing ½ mile and leisure centre 1 mile. Special breaks available. All enquiries welcome.
Facilities ⚹ ⨍ ⊟ 🖾 ⚇ ⅌ ⌒ ⊙ ⅃ ▰ ⊡ ♥
⍾ ⩗ ⌖ ⊟ ▱ ⩘ ⟆
Nearest Town Kingsbridge/Salcombe
Directions From Totnes follow the A381, main Kingsbridge road, to Sorley Green Cross. Go straight ahead and the site is 100 yards on the left.

KINGSBRIDGE

Slapton Sands Camping & Caravanning Club Site, Middle Grounds, Slapton, Kingsbridge, Devon, TQ7 2QW
Tel: 01548 580538
Email:
slapton.sandssite@thefriendlyclub.co.uk
www.campingandcaravanningclub.co.uk/
slaptonsands
Pitches For 🛆 🚐 🚎 **Total** 115
Acreage 5½ **Open** 21-Mar to 04-Nov
Nearest Bus Stop (Miles) ¼
Overlooking Start Bay, just a few minutes from the beach. BTB 4 Star Graded and AA 3 Pennants. Club Member Caravans Only. Non members welcome. You can also call us on 0845 130 7633.
Facilities ⚹ ⨍ 🖾 ⚇ ⌒ ⊙ ⅃ ▰ ⊡ ♥
⊙ ⊟ ⩙ ⊟ ⊡ ⟆
Nearest Town Dartmouth
Directions From Kingsbridge take the A379, site entrance is ¼ mile from the A379, beyond the brow of the hill approaching Slapton Village.
⚏ Totnes

LYDFORD

Lydford Caravan & Camping Park, Lydford, Nr Okehampton, Devon, EX20 4BE
Tel: 01822 820497
Email: info@lydfordsite.co.uk
www.lydfordsite.co.uk
Pitches For 🛆 🚐 🚎 **Total** 80
Acreage 7 **Open** 23-Mar to 29-Oct
Access Good **Site** Level
Nearest Bus Stop (Miles) ¼
ADULTS ONLY PARK in Dartmoor National Park with beautiful views. Lydford has the deepest gorge in the South West. Ideal for visiting National Trust properties.
Facilities ⚹ ⨍ 🖾 ⚇ ⌒ ⊙ ⅃ ▰ ⊡ ♥
⍾ ⊙ ⊟ ⩙ ⊟ ⊡ ⩘ ⟆
Nearest Town Okehampton
Directions From the A30 (DO NOT follow SatNav) take the A386 sp Tavistock and Plymouth. After 5 miles turn right to Lydford. At the war memorial turn right, right fork, site is on the left.
⚏ Gunnislake

LYNTON

Channel View Caravan & Camping Park, Manor Farm, Barbrook, Lynton, Devon, EX35 6LD
Tel: 01598 753349
Email: relax@channel-view.co.uk
www.channel-view.co.uk
Pitches For 🛆 🚐 🚎 **Total** 70
Acreage 6 **Open** 15-Mar to 15-Nov
Access Good **Site** Lev/Slope
Nearest Bus Stop (Miles) ½
On the edge of Exmoor overlooking Lynton and Lynmouth for panoramic views.
Facilities ⚹ ⨍ ⊟ 🖾 ⚇ ⌒ ⊙ ⅃ ▰ ⊡ ♥
⍾ ⊙ ⩗ ⌖ ⋈ ▱ ⩙ ⊟ ⊡ ⟆
Nearest Town Lynton/Lynmouth
Directions On the A39 ½ a mile from Barbrook.
⚏ Barnstaple

LYNTON

Lynton Camping & Caravanning Club Site, Caffyns Cross, Lynton, Devon, EX35 6JS
Tel: 01598 752379
Email: lynton.site@thefriendlyclub.co.uk
www.campingandcaravanningclub.co.uk/
lynton
Pitches For 🛆 🚐 🚎 **Total** 105
Acreage 5½ **Open** 21-Mar to 30-Sep
Access Good **Site** Lev/Slope
Nearest Bus Stop (Miles) ½
Overlooking the Bristol Channel. 2 miles from Lynton and Lynmouth. ETB 4 Star Graded and AA 3 Pennants. Non members welcome. You can also call us on 0845 130 7633.
Facilities ⚹ ⨍ 🖾 ⚇ ⌒ ⊙ ⅃ ▰ ⊡ ♥
⊙ ⩙ ⊟ ⩘ ⟆
Nearest Town Lynton
Directions Leave the M5 and take the A361 to Barnstaple. At South Molton turn right to Blackmoor Gate sp Lynmouth and Lynton. After 5 miles turn left at the bus shelter, turn first left then first right to camp site.
⚏ Barnstaple

MODBURY

California Cross Camping & Caravanning Club Site, California Cross, Modbury, Ivybridge, Devon, PL21 0SG
Tel: 01548 821297
Email:
california.crosssite@thefriendlyclub.co.uk
www.campingandcaravanningclub.co.uk/
californiacross
Pitches For 🛆 🚐 🚎 **Total** 80
Acreage 2.9 **Open** 30-Mar to 30-Sep
Access Good **Site** Lev/Slope
Nearest Bus Stop (Miles) 3
Rural setting centrally situated in the South Hams. Close to the beaches of Salcombe and Torbay. Take-away food available two nights a week. 5 miles from Sorley Tunnel Childrens Adventure Park. Chocks needed on some pitches. BTB 4 Star Graded and AA 3 Pennants. Non members welcome. You can also call us on 0845 130 7633.
Facilities ⚹ ⨍ 🖾 ⚇ ⌒ ⊙ ⅃ ▰ ⊡ ♥
⍾ ⊙ ⩗ ⩙ ⊟ ⊡ ⟆
Nearest Town Ivybridge
Directions On the A38 travelling south west take the A3121 to the crossroads, straight across to the B3196 to California Cross Hamlet. Turn left after California Cross Hamlet sign but before the petrol station, site is on the right.
⚏ Ivybridge

MODBURY

Modbury Caravan Club Site, Higher East Leigh, Modbury, Ivybridge, Devon, PL21 0SH
Tel: 01548 830714
www.caravanclub.co.uk
Pitches For 🚐 🚎 **Total** 113
Open Nov to Nov **Access** Poor **Site** Level
Situated between moors and sea, this makes a splendid base from which to explore South Devon. Main attractions include Dart Valley Steamer Trips, Dartmoor Wildlife Park and Miniature Pony Centre. Non members welcome. Booking essential.
Facilities ⚹ ⨍ ⊟ 🖾 ⚇ ⌒ ⊙ ⅃ ▰ ⊡ ♥
⍾ ⊙ ⊟ ⩙ ⊟ ⊡ ⟆
Nearest Town Ivybridge
Directions From Exeter SW on A38, after 30 miles pass the Woodpecker Inn and after ½ a mile take the A3121. At the top of the slip road t lt following Broad Park sign, at Xroads go straight across, after 2½ miles continue rt just past California Cross onto B3207. Site on lt in 1 mile.
⚏ Ivybridge

MORTEHOE

Easewell Farm Holiday Village & Golf Club Mortehoe Station Road, Mortehoe, Devon, EX34 7EH
Tel: 0844 7700 367
Email: goodtimes@woolacombe.com
www.woolacombe.com/cades
Pitches For 🛆 🚐 🚎 **Total** 302
Open 23-Mar to 02-Nov
Access Good **Site** Level
Nearest Bus Stop (Miles) Outside
Close to 3 miles of golden sandy beaches Woolacombe and spectacular coastal walks. Choice of 4 Parks and their facilities and entertainment. Fishing nearby. Golf on Park.
Facilities ⚹ ⨍ 🖾 ⚇ ⌒ ⊙ ⅃ ▰ ⊡ ♥
⍾ ⍦ ⍾ ⊙ ⩗ ⌖ ⋈ ▱ ⋔ ⩙ ⊟ ⊡ ⩘ ⟆
Nearest Town Woolacombe
Directions From Barnstaple take the A361 Ilfracombe road to the junction with the B3343 at Mullacott Cross. Turn first left signposted Woolacombe, after 1¾ miles turn right to Mortehoe. Park is 1¼ miles on the right.
⚏ Barnstaple

MORTEHOE

North Morte Farm Caravan & Camping Park, North Morte Road, Mortehoe, Woolacombe, Devon, EX34 7EG
Tel: 01271 870381
Email: info@northmortefarm.co.uk
www.northmortefarm.co.uk
Pitches For 🛆 🚐 🚎 **Total** 175
Open April to End Oct
Access Narrow **Site** Lev/Slope
Nearest Bus Stop (Miles) ¼
500 yards from Rockham Beach. Adjoining National Trust. Ideal walking country.
Facilities ⚹ ⨍ 🖾 ⚇ ⌒ ⊙ ⅃ ▰ ⊡ ♥
⍾ ⊙ ⩗ ▱ ⩙ ⊟ ⊡ ⩘ ⟆
Nearest Town Woolacombe
Directions 14 miles from Barnstaple on the A361 take the B3343 and follow signs to Mortehoe. In the village turn right at the Post Office, park is 500 yards on the left.
⚏ Barnstaple

MORTEHOE

Twitchen House Holiday Village, Mortehoe, Woolacombe, North Devon, EX34 7ES
Tel: 0844 7700 367
Email: goodtimes@woolacombe.com
www.woolacombe.com/cades
Pitches For 🛆 🚐 🚎 ≷ **Total** 339

Pitches from £9

"We left feeling a part of the family"

Hidden Valley
Quality family holidays

Hidden Valley Park, West Down,
Nr. Ilfracombe, North Devon
EX34 8NU

info@hiddenvalleypark.com

01271 813 837

• Luxury 5 star facilities
• Woodland walks & dog exercise areas
• 4 miles from Woolacombe Beach
• Wi-Fi across the park
• Children's play areas
• Coffee shop

www.hiddenvalleypark.com

Acreage 20 **Open** 23-Mar **to** 02-Nov
Access Good **Site** Sloping
Nearest Bus Stop (Miles) Outside
Rural, scenic setting, close to 3 miles of golden sandy beaches and spectacular coastal walks.
Facilities [icons]

Nearest Town Woolacombe
Directions From Barnstaple/Ilfracombe road (A361) to junction with B3343 at Mullacott Cross, first left signposted Woolacombe for 1¾ miles, then right signposted Mortehoe. Park is 1¼ miles on left.
⇥ Barnstaple

MORTEHOE

Warcombe Farm Camping Park,
Mortehoe, Nr Woolacombe, North Devon, EX34 7EJ
Tel: 01271 870690
Email: info@warcombefarm.co.uk
www.warcombefarm.co.uk
Pitches For ▲ ⌂ ⌂ **Total** 200
Acreage 19 **Open** 15-Mar **to** Oct
Access Good **Site** Mostly Level
Nearest Bus Stop (Miles) Outside
Family run, landscaped site with a beautiful lake and panoramic sea views. Excellent facilities. 1¼ miles to Woolacombe beach.
Facilities [icons]

Nearest Town Barnstaple
Directions Turn left off the A361, Barnstaple to Ilfracombe road at Mullacott Cross roundabout signposted Woolacombe. After 2 miles turn right towards Mortehoe. Site is first on the right in less than a mile.
⇥ Barnstaple

NEWTON ABBOT

Dornafield Touring Park, Two Mile Oak, Newton Abbot, Devon, TQ12 6DD
Tel: 01803 812732
Email: enquiries@dornafield.com
www.dornafield.com
Pitches For ▲ ⌂ ⌂ **Total** 135
Acreage 30 **Open** 15-Mar **to** 02-Jan
Access Good **Site** Level
Nearest Bus Stop (Miles) ½
Beautiful 14th Century farmhouse location with superb facilities to suit discerning caravanners and campers. Tennis court on site. Booking essential.
Facilities [icons]

Nearest Town Newton Abbot
Directions Take the A381 (Newton Abbott to Totnes), in 2 miles at Two Mile Oak Inn turn right. In ½ mile turn first left, site is 200 yards on the right.
⇥ Newton Abbot

NEWTON ABBOT

Lemonford Caravan Park, Bickington, Newton Abbot, Devon, TQ12 6JR
Tel: 01626 821242
Email: info@lemonford.co.uk
www.lemonford.co.uk
Pitches For ▲ ⌂ ⌂ ⌂ **Total** 85
Acreage 7 **Open** All Year
Access Good **Site** Level
Nearest Bus Stop (Miles) Outside
In a beautiful setting and scrupulously clean. Close to Torbay and the Dartmoor National Park.
Facilities [icons]

Nearest Town Ashburton
Directions From Exeter along A38 take A382

turnoff, on roundabout take 3rd exit and follow site signs to Bickington. From Plymouth take A383 turnoff, follow road for ¼ mile and turn left into site.
⇥ Newton Abbot

NEWTON ABBOT

Ross Park Caravan Park, Park Hill Farm, Moor Road, Ipplepen, Newton Abbot, Devon, TQ12 5TT
Tel: 01803 812983
Email:
enquiries@rossparkcaravanpark.co.uk
www.rossparkcaravanpark.co.uk
Pitches For ▲ ⌂ ⌂ **Total** 110
Acreage 32 **Open** 01-Mar **to** 01-Jan
Access Good **Site** Level
Nearest Bus Stop (Miles) 150 yards
Tranquil and friendly atmosphere in beautiful surroundings. Excellent range of facilities including a bar and restaurant, Tropical Conservatory, play and conservation areas, centrally heated amenities block and a snooker room. Ideal for touring the South Hams area. 6 miles from Torbay and Dartmoor National Park within a 15 minute drive.
Facilities [icons]

Directions 3 miles from Newton Abbot and 6 miles from Totnes on the A381. At Park Hill crossroads and Texaco Filling Station take the road signposted Woodland and brown tourism sign to Ross Park.
⇥ Newton Abbot

NEWTON ABBOT

Twelveoaks Farm Caravan Park,
Twelveoaks Farm, Teigngrace, Newton Abbot, Devon, TQ12 6QT
Tel: 01626 335015

Email: info@twelveoaksfarm.co.uk
www.twelveoaksfarm.co.uk
Pitches For ▲ ⊕ ⊜≾ **Total** 60
Acreage 4 **Open** All Year
Access Good **Site** Sloping
Nearest Bus Stop (Miles) 1
7 miles to beach or moors.
Facilities ⚏ ⨍ ⌧ ⬚ ⊡⬚ ┍ ⊙⌐ ◢ ▣ ☎
ẞ ⅋ ◐ ⊜ ⤢✝ ⊬ ⊟ ⊟ ⊿ ⊰ ⊷ ⟨⟨
Nearest Town Newton Abbot
Directions 2 miles from A38 Drumbridges
roundabout.
⚏ Newton Abbot

OKEHAMPTON
Bridestowe Caravan Park, Bridestowe, Nr
Okehampton, Devon, EX20 4ER
Tel: 01837 861261
Pitches For ▲ ⊕ ⊜ **Total** 53
Open Mar to Dec
Access Good **Site** Level
Nearest Bus Stop (Miles) ½
Dartmoor National Park 2 miles, ideal for
walking, cycling, horse riding, fishing and
touring Devon and Cornwall. Within easy
reach of coastal resorts.
Facilities ⚏ ⨍ ⌧ ⬚ ◐ ⊡⬚ ┍ ⊙⌐ ◢ ▣ ☎
ẞ ⅋ ◐ ⊜ ⤢ ⊟ ⊟ ⊬
Nearest Town Bude
Directions Leave M5 for A30 to Okehampton
3 miles west of Okehampton turn off A30 to
Bridestowe village, follow camping signs to site.

OKEHAMPTON
Bundu Camping & Caravan Park,
Sourton Down, Okehampton, Devon, EX20
4HT
Tel: 01837 861747
Email: bundu@btconect.com
www.bundu.co.uk
Pitches For ▲ ⊕ ⊜ **Total** 38
Acreage 4½ **Open** All Year
Access Good **Site** Level

Nearest Bus Stop (Miles) ¼
Situated with access to Dartmoor and
adjacent to National Cycleway Route 27.
Ideal for touring Devon and Cornwall.
Facilities ⚏ ⨍ ⌧ ⬚ ⊡⬚ ┍ ⊙⌐ ◢ ▣ ☎
ẞ ⅋ ◐ ⌧ ⤢⊟ ⊟ ⊜ ⊰
Nearest Town Okehampton
Directions On the A30 west, turn off at first
slip road taking the A386 to Tavistock. Take
first turn left to Sourton Down, site is at the
end of the lane.
⚏ Okehampton

PAIGNTON
Beverley Park Holiday Centre,
Goodrington Road, Paignton, Devon, TQ4
7JE
Tel: 01803 661973
Email: info@beverley-holidays.co.uk
www.beverley-holidays.co.uk
Pitches For ▲ ⊕ ⊜ ⊜≾ **Total** 180
Acreage 9½ **Open** Feb to Dec
Access Good **Site** Level
Nearest Bus Stop (Miles) ¼
Views across Torbay. Indoor heated
swimming pool, tennis court and sauna on
site.
Facilities ⚏ ⨍ ⊟ ⌧ ⬚ ┍ ⊙⌐ ◢ ▣ ☎
ẞ ⅋ ◐ ⊜ ⤢✕ ⊟ ◢ ⊰ ⊶ ⊟ ⊟ ⊬
⟨⟨
Nearest Town Paignton
Directions 2 miles south of Paignton (ring
road) A3022. Turn left into Goodrington
Road.
⚏ Paignton

PAIGNTON
Higher Well Farm Holiday Park, Stoke
Gabriel, Totnes, Devon, TQ9 6RN
Tel: 01803 782289
www.higherwellfarmholidaypark.co.uk
Pitches For ▲ ⊕ ⊜ **Total** 80
Acreage 8 **Open** Easter to October

Access Good **Site** Lev/Slope
Nearest Bus Stop (Miles) ¼
Within 4 miles of Torbays beaches, 1 mile
from Stoke Gabriel and the River Dart.
Facilities ⚏≾ ⨍ ⌧ ⬚ ┍ ⊙⌐ ◢ ▣ ☎
ẞ ⅋ ◐ ⊜ ⤢ ⊟ ⊟
Directions From Paignton take A385
towards Totnes, turn off left at Parkers Arms.
Go 1½ miles then turn left again, site is 200
yards down road.
⚏ Paignton

PAIGNTON
Hoburne Torbay, Grange Road,
Goodrington, Paignton, -, Devon, TQ4 7JP
Tel: 01803 558010
Email: enquiries@hoburne.com
www.hoburne.com
Pitches For ⊕ ⊜ **Total** 139
Acreage 65 **Open** 26-Feb to 30-Jan
Access Good **Site** Lev/Slope
Nearest Bus Stop (Miles) 0.25

PLYMOUTH
Plymouth Sound Caravan Club Site,
Bovisand Lane, Down Thomas, Plymouth,
Devon, PL9 0AE
Tel: 01752 862325
www.caravanclub.co.uk
Pitches For ⊕ ⊜ **Total** 58
Acreage 6 **Open** Mar to Oct
Access Good **Site** Lev/Slope
Nearest Bus Stop (Miles) ½
¾ miles from a sandy beach. Plenty to see
and do in the local area. Near a dry ski slope
centre, Tamar Valley Railway, Lydford Gorge,
Dartington Crystal and National Marine
Aquarium. Own sanitation required. Non
members welcome. Booking essential.
Facilities ⨍ ☎ ⅋ ◐ ⊜ ⤢✝ ⊟ ⊟
Nearest Town Plymouth

Panoramic views across the English Riviera, with Dartmoor and all the attractions of South Devon on your doorstep. Our striking clubhouse includes all the leisure and entertainment you could wish for!

Call: **0844 288 1935**
or visit **hoburne.com/cadest**
Celebrating 100 years of happy holidays

Directions From east on A38 turn off at Marsh Mills flyover at roundabout turn left onto A374 sp Plymouth City Centre. After 1¾ miles move to offside lane and follow signs for A379 Kingsbridge. Follow signs to Down Thomas.
⇌ Plymouth

PLYMOUTH

Riverside Caravan Park, Leigham Manor Drive, Marsh Mills, Plymouth, Devon, PL6 8LL
Tel: 01752 344122
Email: office@riversidecaravanpark.com
www.riversidecaravanpark.com
Pitches For 🏕 🚐 🚐 🚐 **Total** 259
Acreage 11 **Open** All Year
Access Good **Site** Level
Nearest Bus Stop (Miles) ¼
Adjacent to the River Plym. Perfect base for exploring the South Hams coastline, Dartmoor and South East Cornwall.
Facilities 🚿 ⊘ 🖃 🔟 🚰 ♿ ☉ 🍴 ▣ ◳
🔊 🎮 🏐 ✗ ▽ 🛒 ♨ 🏇 🐕 🖃 🗋 🖃
Nearest Town Plymouth
Directions From Plymouth city centre follow signs for A38 Saltash. After approx. 3 miles you will reach Marsh Mills roundabout, take the exit for Plympton and follow brown tourism signs.
⇌ Plymouth

PUTSBOROUGH

Putsborough Sands Caravan Park, Manor Farm, Putsborough, Braunton, North Devon, EX33 1LB
Tel: 01271 890230
Email: rob@putsborough.com
www.putsborough.com
Pitches For 🚐 **Total** 25
Acreage 2 **Open** 01-Apr **to** 10-Oct
Access Poor **Site** Level
Nearest Bus Stop (Miles) 1
Adjacent to the multi award winning Putsborough Sands. Unrivalled views over the Atlantic. Booking is essential.
Facilities 🚿 ⊘ 🔟 🚰 ♿ ☉ 🍴 ▣
🔊🎮✗♿🖃🖃✎🛰
Nearest Town Croyde
Directions From Braunton take the B3231 Croyde road and follow signs.
⇌ Barnstaple

SALCOMBE

Alston Farm Camping & Caravan Site, Nr Salcombe, Kingsbridge, Devon, TQ7 3BJ
Tel: 01548 561260
Email: info@alstoncampsite.co.uk
www.alstoncampsite.co.uk
Pitches For 🏕 🚐 🚐 **Total** 200

Acreage 15 **Open** Easter **to** October
Access Good **Site** Level
Nearest Bus Stop (Miles) 1
Secluded, sheltered site. Dish washing facilities. You can also contact us on Mobile: 07808 030921.
Facilities 🚿 ⊘ 🔟 🚰 ♿ ☉ 🍴 ▣ ◳ 🖃
🔊 ⊘ 🏐 🚰 🖃 🛰
Nearest Town Salcombe
Directions Signposted on left of A381 between Kingsbridge and Salcombe towards Salcombe.
⇌ Totnes

SALCOMBE

Higher Rew Touring Caravan & Camping Park, Rew, Malborough, Kingsbridge, South Devon, TQ7 3BW
Tel: 01548 842681
Email: enquiries@higherrew.co.uk
www.higherrew.co.uk
Pitches For 🏕 🚐 🚐 **Total** 90
Acreage 6 **Open** Easter **to** Oct
Access Fair **Site** Lev/Slope
Sloping Park with level pitches. Only 1 mile from the coastal path and Salcombe Estuary.
Facilities 🚿 ⊘ 🔟 🚰 ♿ ☉ 🍴 ▣ ◳ 🖃
🔊 ⊘ 🏐 🚰 🛰
Nearest Town Salcombe
Directions From Kingsbridge take the A381 towards Salcombe. Im Malborough turn sharp right through the village towards Soar, after 1 mile turn left.
⇌ Totnes

SEATON

Ashdown Caravan Park, Colyton Hill, Colyton, Devon, EX24 6HY
Tel: 01297 20292
Email: ashdowncaravanpark@btinternet.com
Pitches For 🚐 🚐 **Total** 80
Acreage 7 **Open** Apr **to** Nov
Access Good **Site** Level
Nearest Bus Stop (Miles) 1
Pecorama, beach, Seaton Tramway.
Facilities ✗ ⊘ 🔟 🚰 ♿ ☉ 🍴 ▣ 🖃
🔊 ⊘ 🚰 🖃 🛰
Nearest Town Seaton
Directions A3052 north of Seaton.
⇌ Axminster

SEATON

Berry Barton Caravan & Camping Park, Berry Barton, Branscombe, Seaton, Devon, EX12 3BD
Tel: 01297 680208
Email: tmandaewhite@btconnect.com
www.berrybarton.co.uk
Pitches For 🏕 🚐 🚐
Acreage 16 **Open** 15-Mar **to** 15-Nov

Access Good **Site** Level
Nearest Bus Stop (Miles) ¼
Situated on a farm in an area of outstanding natural beauty, with our land finishing at the top of the pebble beach at Littlecombe Shute. 1 mile of coastline and the Jurassic Coast for good walks. New washing up room built for this year.
Facilities ⊘ 🔟 🚰 ♿ ☉ 🍴 ▣ ◳ 🖃🖃
Nearest Town Seaton/Sidmouth
Directions From the M5 at Exeter take the A3052 to Branscombe turning and turn off right following brown tourism signs. At the T-Junction turn left, after 10 metres turn right, at the next T-Junction turn left and the site is on the right after ½ a mile, Berry Barton.
⇌ Honiton

SEATON

Leacroft Touring Park, Colyton Hill, Colyton, Devon, EX24 6HY
Tel: 01297 552823
www.leacrofttouringpark.co.uk
Pitches For 🏕 🚐 🚐 **Total** 138
Acreage 10 **Open** April **to** September
Access Good **Site** Sloping
Nearest Bus Stop (Miles) 2
Quiet, peaceful site in open countryside. Picturesque villages to explore and woodland walks nearby.
Facilities 🚿 ⊘ 🔟 🚰 ♿ ☉ 🍴 ▣ ◳ 🖃
🔊 ⊘ 🏐 🚰 🖃 🛰 ✎ 🛰
Nearest Town Colyton
Directions A3052 Sidmouth to Lyme Regis road, 2 miles west of Seaton. Turn left at Stafford Cross international caravan sign, site is 1 mile on the right.
⇌ Axminster

SIDMOUTH

Oakdown Country Holiday Park, Weston, Sidmouth, Devon, EX10 0PT
Tel: 01297 680387
Email: enquiries@oakdown.co.uk
www.oakdown.co.uk
Pitches For 🏕 🚐 🚐 🚐 **Total** 150
Acreage 16 **Open** Apr **to** Oct
Access Good **Site** Level
Nearest Bus Stop (Miles) ¼
Welcome to Oakdown, a Caravan Holiday Park of the Year Winner - SIDMOUTHS MULTI AWARD WINNING PARK near the Jurassic Coast World Heritage Site and beautiful Weston Valley - lovely cliff walks. Oakmead Par 3 Golf Course. Field trail to nearby world famous Donkey Sanctuary. Luxurious Holiday Caravans to let. Awards for 2011/12: ETB 5 Star Grading, AA 5 Pennant De-Luxe Park, David Bellamy Gold and Loo of the Year.
Facilities 🚿 ⊘ 🖃 🔟 🚰 ♿ ☉ 🍴 ▣ ◳ 🖃
🔊 ⊘ 🏐 ✗ 🛒 🚰 🏇 🖃 🖃 🛰 ✎ 🛰

Directions 1½ miles east of Sidford on A3052, take the second Weston turning at the Oakdown sign. Site 50 yards on left. Also sp with international Caravan/Camping signs.
⚑ Honiton

SIDMOUTH
Putts Corner Caravan Club Site, Sidbury, Sidmouth, Devon, EX10 0QQ
Tel: 01404 42875
www.caravanclub.co.uk
Pitches For ⛺ 🚐 **Total** 118
Acreage 7 **Open** Mar to Nov
Access Good **Site** Lev/Slope
Nearest Bus Stop (Miles) ¼
Quiet site in pretty surroundings where wildlife and flowers abound. Plenty of walks from the site. Boules pitch, water softening plant and water supply from borehole. 200 yards from a pub. Near the Donkey Sanctuary. Non members welcome. Booking essential.
Facilities ⚹ ...
Nearest Town Sidmouth
Directions From east on A30 Honiton bypass, turn off via slip road at sp Sidmouth A375, at end of slip road turn left then 100 yards and turn left again, after 350 yards turn right onto A375. At Hare & Hounds Inn turn right onto B3174, site is ¼ mile on the right.
⚑ Sidmouth

SIDMOUTH
Salcombe Regis Camping & Caravan Park, Salcombe Regis, Sidmouth, Devon, EX10 0JH
Tel: 01395 514303
Email: contact@salcombe-regis.co.uk
www.salcombe-regis.co.uk
Pitches For ⛺ 🚐 🚐 **Total** 100
Acreage 16 **Open** 11-Mar to 02-Nov
Access Good **Site** Level
A park with peace and quiet. Just a 5 minute walk from the Jurassic Coastal Path, and a 5-10 minute drive from Select Sidmouth. Ideally based for touring East Devon.
Facilities ...
Nearest Town Sidmouth
Directions From Exeter M5 take the A3052 through Sidford towards Lyme Regis. Take second turning to Salcombe Regis, on the left after Golf Range.
⚑ Honiton or Exeter

SLAPTON
Sea View Campsite, Newlands Farm, Slapton, Nr Dartmouth, Devon, TQ7 2RB
Tel: 01548 580366
Email: cades@devon-camping.com
www.camping-devon.com
Pitches For ⛺ 🚐 🚐 **Total** 45
Acreage 10 **Open** 23-May to September
Access Good **Site** Level
Nearest Bus Stop (Miles) ½
We have a friendly, uncommercialised, quiet site overlooking beautiful countryside and sea. Within 1 mile of glorious beaches, cliff walks and a nature reserve. Woodlands Leisure Centre is close by with fun for all the family.

Facilities ⚹ ...
Nearest Town Dartmouth
Directions From Totnes take the A381 towards Kingsbridge, after Halwell Village take the fourth signposted Slapton. Go 4 miles to Buckland Cross, proceed for ¼ mile, site is on the left hand side.

SOUTH MOLTON
Riverside Caravan & Camping Park, Marsh Lane, North Molton Road, South Molton, EX36 3HQ
Tel: 01769 579269
Email: relax@exmoorriverside.co.uk
www.www.exmoorriverside.co.uk
Pitches For ⛺ 🚐 🚐 **Total** 100
Acreage 40 **Open** All Year
Access Good **Site** Level
Nearest Bus Stop (Miles) Outside
Lakes - rivers on site, woodland - valley walks on and from site, ideal touring.
Facilities ...
Nearest Town South Molton
⚑ Barnstaple

SOUTH MOLTON
Romansleigh Holiday Park, Odam Hill, South Molton, Devon, EX36 4NB
Tel: 01769 550259
Email: romhols@btconnect.com
www.romansleigh.com
Pitches For ⛺ 🚐 🚐 **Total** 20
Acreage 14 **Open** 15-Mar to 31-Oct
Access poor **Site** Lev/slope
Nearest Bus Stop (Miles) outside
Ideal for touring,countryside site 35 minites from the North Devon Coast.
Facilities ...
Nearest Town South Moulton
Directions Take the B3137 South Molton to Witheridge road. Site is signposted right approximately 4 miles.
⚑ Kings Nympton

SOUTH MOLTON
Yeo Valley Holiday Park, The Blackcock Inn, Molland, South Molton, North Devon, EX36 3NW
Tel: 01769 550297
Email: info@yeovalleyholidays.co.uk
www.yeovalleyholidays.co.uk
Pitches For ⛺ 🚐 🚐 **Total** 65
Open 15-Mar to 15-Nov
Access Good **Site** Level
Nearest Bus Stop (Miles) 1
Close to Exmoor. Heated indoor swimming pool and The Blackcock Inn on site.
Facilities ...
Nearest Town South Molton
Directions Leave the M5 at junction 27 and take the A361 to South Molton, follow brown tourism signs to Blackcock Inn.
⚑ Tiverton

STOKENHAM
Old Cotmore Farm, Stokenham, Kingsbridge, Devon, TQ7 2LR
Tel: 01548 580240
Email: info@holiday-in-devon.com
www.holiday-in-devon.com
Pitches For ⛺ 🚐 🚐 🚐 **Total** 30
Acreage 22 **Open** 15-Mar to Oct
Access Good **Site** Level
Nearest Bus Stop (Miles) ½
Small, family run, picturesque, peaceful site with views over farms and fields. Cliff walks, beaches, fishing and bird watching. Excellent pubs.
Facilities ...
Nearest Town Kingsbridge
Directions From Kingsbridge take the A379 towards Dartmouth, go through Frogmore and at the mini roundabout at Stokenham turn right signposted Beesands. The farm is 1 mile on the right.
⚑ Totnes

TAVISTOCK
Harford Bridge Holiday Park, Peter Tavy, Tavistock, Devon, PL19 9LS
Tel: 01822 810349
Email: stay@harfordbridge.co.uk
www.harfordbridge.co.uk
Pitches For ⛺ 🚐 🚐 **Total** 120
Acreage 15 **Open** All Year
Access Good **Site** Level
Nearest Bus Stop (Miles) ¼
Select family run park set in Dartmoor beside the River Tavy.   Ideal for exploring Devon and Cornwall.
Facilities ...
Nearest Town Tavistock
Directions Leave Tavistock on Okehampton road 2½ miles turn right to Peter Tavy park is approx 100yds on right
⚑ Plymouth

TAVISTOCK
Langstone Manor Caravan & Camping Park, Langstone Manor, Moortown, Tavistock, Devon, PL19 9JZ
Tel: 01822 613371
Email: web@langstone-manor.co.uk
www.langstone-manor.co.uk
Pitches For ⛺ 🚐 🚐 **Total** 40
Acreage 5½ **Open** 15-Mar to Oct
Access Good **Site** Level
Nearest Bus Stop (Miles) 1½
Direct access onto Dartmoor. Quiet, friendly park with views over moor and farmland. Bar and evening meals. Dogs welcome. ETB 4 Star Graded and AA 4 Pennants.
Facilities ...
Directions Take the B3357 from Tavistock towards Princetown, after approx. 2 miles turn right at crossroads, pass over the cattle grid, continue up the hill then turn left following signs for Langstone Manor. We are ½ mile on the right.
⚑ Plymouth

TAVISTOCK

Tavistock Camping & Caravanning Club Site, Higher Longford, Moorshop, Tavistock, Devon, PL19 9LQ
Tel: 01822 618672
Email: tavistock.site@thefriendlyclub.co.uk
www.campingandcaravanningclub.co.uk/tavistock
Pitches For ▲ ⚐ ⛺ **Total** 90
Acreage 6 **Open** All Year
Access Good **Site** Level
Nearest Bus Stop (Miles) Outside
Lying on the west side of the Dartmoor National Park, ideal for walkers and cyclists. Non members welcome. You can also call us on 0845 130 7633.
Facilities ⚏ ∮ ⊞ ⎙ ⍟ ⌂ ⊙ ⌟ ⚐ ☎
♨ ⍾ ⟐ ✻ ♿ ⇥ ⬚ ⚒ ⟲ ⬗
Nearest Town Tavistock
Directions From Tavistock take the B3357 towards the National Park, site is approx. 2 miles on the right, signposted.
⇥ Plymouth

TAVISTOCK

Woodovis Park, Gulworthy, Tavistock, Devon, PL19 8NY
Tel: 01822 832968
Email: info@woodovis.com
www.woodovis.com
Pitches For ▲ ⚐ ⛺ **Total** 50
Acreage 14 **Open** Apr to Oct
Access Good **Site** Level
Nearest Bus Stop (Miles) ½
5 Star BTB Graded Park. Quiet, rural site with outstanding views. Near to Dartmoor, coasts and Cornwall. Excellent facilities, free showers, laundry/washing-up room. Shop, off-license, farm produce, bread/croissants baked on site. Heated indoor pool, Infrared therapy, sauna and jacuzzi. Petanque court. Outdoor table tennis
Facilities ⚏ ∮ ⊞ ⎙ ⍟ ⌂ ⊙ ⌟ ⚐ ⬚ ☎
♨ ⟐ ⬚ ♠ ⏃ ✻ ⇥ ⬚ ⟲ ⬗ ✻ ♿
Nearest Town Tavistock
Directions Take A390 Liskeard road from Tavistock, after 3 miles turn right at the roundabout.
⇥ Plymouth/Gunnislake

TEIGNMOUTH

Coast View Holiday Park, Torquay Road, Shaldon, Teignmouth, South Devon, TQ14 0BG
Tel: 01626 818350
Email: holidays@coastview.co.uk
www.coastview.co.uk
Pitches For ▲ ⚐ ⛺ **Total** 250
Acreage 18 **Open** 18-Mar
Access Good **Site** Lev/Slope
Nearest Bus Stop (Miles) Outside
Near the beach with fantastic views.
Facilities ∮ ⊞ ⍟ ⌂ ⊙ ⌟ ⚐ ☎
♨ ⟐ ⬚ ✕ ⟐ ⬚ ♿ ⇥ ⬚ ⟲
Nearest Town Teignmouth
Directions On the A379 between Teignmouth and Torquay.
⇥ Teignmouth

TIVERTON

Minnows Touring Park, Sampford Peverell, Tiverton, Devon, EX16 7EN
Tel: 01884 821770
www.ukparks.co.uk/minnows
Pitches For ▲ ⚐ ⛺ ⍧ **Total** 60
Acreage 5½ **Open** 05-Mar to 29-Oct
Access Good **Site** Level
Nearest Bus Stop (Miles) ¼
Alongside the Grand Western Canal and National Cycle Way, ideal for walking, cycling, fishing, canoeing and bird watching. Centrally placed for coasts, Exmoor and Dartmoor.
Facilities ⚏ ⚒ ∮ ⊞ ⍟ ⌂ ⌟ ⚐
⍾ ⟐ ♨ ⟐ ⊙ ⚒ ⍾ ⇥ ⬚ ⟲ ✻ ♿
Nearest Town Tiverton
Directions Leave the M5 at junction 27 and take the A361 signposted Tiverton and Barnstaple. After 500 yards take the slip road signposted Sampford Peverell, turn right at the mini roundabout, site is ¼ of a mile ahead.
⇥ Tiverton Parkway

TIVERTON

West Middlewick Farm Caravans & Camping, West Middlewick Farm, Nomansland, Tiverton, Devon, EX16 8NP
Tel: 01884 861235
Email: stay@westmiddlewick.co.uk
www.westmiddlewick.co.uk
Pitches For ▲ ⚐ ⛺ **Total** 25
Acreage 3½ **Open** All Year
Access Good **Site** Level
Nearest Bus Stop (Miles) Outside
Working family farm with lovely walks. Fishing ½ mile. Ideal touring. Log cabins B&B.
Facilities ⚏ ∮ ⊞ ⍟ ⌂ ⌟ ⊙ ⚐ ☎
♿ ⇥ ⬚ ⟐ ⍾
Nearest Town Tiverton
Directions Leave the A361 at junction 27 for Tiverton, then take the B3137 to Witheridge. 9 miles from Tiverton.
⇥ Tiverton Parkway

TIVERTON

Zeacombe House Caravan Park, East Anstey, Nr Tiverton, Devon, EX16 9JU
Tel: 01398 341279
Email: enquiries@zeacombeadultretreat.co.uk
www.zeacombeadultretreat.co.uk
Pitches For ▲ ⚐ ⛺ **Total** 50
Acreage 4½ **Open** 31-Mar to Oct
Access Good **Site** Level
ADULTS ONLY site near to Exmoor, Tarr Steps, National Trust properties, Tarka Trail and Rosemoor Gardens. Ideal for walking. Evening meal system. TV is now digital, FreeView Box required for standard TV. AA 4 Pennants.
Facilities ∮ ⊞ ⍟ ⌂ ⌟ ⊙ ⌟ ⚐ ⬚ ☎
♨ ⟐ ⇥ ⬚ ⬚ ♿ ⍾
Nearest Town Tiverton
Directions Leave the M5 at junc 27 and take A361 to Tiverton. At the roundabout turn right sp A396 to Minehead and Dulverton. After 5 miles turn left at the Exeter Inn, after 1¾ miles turn left at the Black Cat onto the B3227, 5 miles to Knowstone and the site is on the left.
⇥ Tiverton

TORQUAY

Widdicombe Farm Touring Park, Widdicombe Lane, Marldon, Paignton, Torquay, Devon, TQ3 1ST
Tel: 01803 558325
Email: info@widdicombefarm.co.uk
www.widdicombefarm.co.uk
Pitches For ▲ ⚐ ⛺ ⍧ **Total** 198
Acreage 8 **Open** Mid Mar to Mid Oct
Access Good **Site** Level
Nearest Bus Stop (Miles) ½
ADULTS ONLY PARK ideal for Torquay, Paignton and Dartmouth. Easy access with no narrow country lanes. Bus service from the Park (according to demand). Bargain Breaks available.
Facilities ⚏ ∮ ⊞ ⍟ ⌂ ⌟ ⊙ ⌟ ⚐ ⬚ ☎
♨ ⟐ ⟐ ✕ ⇥ ⬚ ⬚ ♿ ✻ ⟲
Nearest Town Torquay/Paignton
Directions From the A380 Torquay to Paignton ring road, from Newton Abbot turn right at the roundabout at Kerswell Gardens, go to the top of the hill to the roundabout and go straight on, see Widdicombe Farm on the right, double back at the next roundabout.
⇥ Paignton

TOTNES

Steamer Quay Caravan Club Site, Steamer Quay Road, Totnes, Devon, TQ9 5AL
Tel: 01803 862738
www.caravanclub.co.uk
Pitches For ⚐ ⛺ **Total** 40
Acreage 3 **Open** Mar to Oct
Access Good **Site** Level
Nearest Bus Stop (Miles) Outside
Quiet site with lovely views, just a short walk from Totnes centre. Close to Paignton Zoo, Dart River Cruises and South Devon Railway. Non members welcome. Booking essential.
Facilities ⍟ ⌂ ⌟ ⊙ ⌟ ⚐ ☎ ♨ ⟐ ⇥ ⬚ ⬚
Nearest Town Totnes
Directions From A38 take either A384 or A385 at South Brent, both roads become A385 at Dartington. In Totnes cross the railway bridge and turn right at r/about, in 300 yds t lt over the bridge, turn right into Seymour Road, turn rightt into Steamer Quay Road, site is on left.
⇥ Totnes

UFFCULME

Waterloo Cross Caravan Park, Uffculme, Devon, EX15 3ES
Tel: 01884 841342
Pitches For ▲ ⚐ ⛺ **Total** 50
Acreage 50 **Open** March to Feb
Access Good **Site** Level
Nearest Bus Stop (Miles) Outside
Ideal for touring.
Facilities ∮ ⊞ ⍟ ⌂ ⌟ ⊙ ⌟ ⚐
♨ ✕ ⟐ ✻ ⇥ ⬚ ⟲ ✻
Nearest Town Tiverton
Directions 6 miles from Tiverton and Cullompton.
⇥ Tiverton Parkway

DEVON

UMBERLEIGH

Umberleigh Camping & Caravanning Club Site, Over Weir, Umberleigh, Devon, EX37 9DU
Tel: 01769 560009
Email: umberleigh.site@thefriendlyclub.co.uk
www.campingandcaravanningclub.co.uk/umberleigh
Pitches For Å ⊕ ➡ **Total** 60
Acreage 3 **Open** 21-Mar **to** 04-Nov
Access Good **Site** Lev/Slope
Nearest Bus Stop (Miles) Entrance
The site enjoys a peaceful and relaxing atmosphere, situated between Exmoor and Dartmoor National Park. Superb golden beaches nearby. BTB 4 Star Graded and AA 3 Pennants. Non members welcome. You can also call us on 0845 130 7633.
Facilities & ⨍ ☐ ⬚⬚ ⌂ ⌐ ⊙ ↵ ⬛ ◻ ☎
⌘ ⌘ ☐ ⬚ 🔥 ⬛ ⊡ ⊡ ◢ ⚡ 🛜
Nearest Town Barnstaple
Directions From Barnstaple take the A377 and turn right at Umberleigh nameplate.
⇥ Umberleigh

WOOLACOMBE

Damage Barton, Mortehoe, Woolacombe, Devon, EX34 7EJ
Tel: 01271 870502
Email: info@damagebarton.co.uk
www.damagebarton.co.uk
Pitches For Å ⊕ ➡ **Total** 155
Acreage 16 **Open** 15-Mar **to** 05-Nov
Access Good **Site** Lev/Slope
Nearest Bus Stop (Miles) Outside
Peaceful site with good views, wild flowers and birds. Access to a network of footpaths including the coastal path.
Facilities & ⨍ ☐ ⊞ ⬚⬚ ⌂ ⌐ ⊙ ↵ ⬛ ◻ ☎
⌘ ⌘ ☐ ⊙ ⬛ ⬛ ⊡ ⊡

Nearest Town Woolacombe
Directions Take the A361 from Barnstaple and turn left at the Mullacott Cross roundabout onto the B3343 signposted Woolacombe and Mortehoe. After 1¾ miles turn right signposted Mortehoe, site is on the right after approx. 1 mile.
⇥ Barnstaple

WOOLACOMBE

Golden Coast Holiday Village, Woolacombe, Devon, EX34 7HW
Tel: 0844 7700 367
Email: goodtimes@woolacombe.com
www.woolacombe.com/cades
Pitches For Å ⊕ ➡ ⛺⊰ **Total** 125
Open Feb **to** Nov
Access Good **Site** Lev/Slope
Nearest Bus Stop (Miles) Outside
Close to 3 miles of golden sandy beaches bus service to the beach. Choice of four parks and their facilities, entertainment and accommodation.
Facilities & ⨍ ☐ ⬚⬚ ⌂ ⌐ ⊙ ↵ ⬛ ◻ ☎
⌘ ⌘ ☐ ⬚ 🔥 ⬛ ⊡ ⊡ ◢ 🛜
Directions Take the A361 to Barnstaple and follow signs for Ilfracombe, take the Woolacombe junction from Mullacott Cross.
⇥ Barnstaple

WOOLACOMBE

Little Roadway Farm, Woolacombe, Devon, EX34 7HL
Tel: 01271 870313
Email: enquiries@littleroadway.co.uk
www.littleroadway.co.uk
Pitches For Å ⊕ ➡ ⛺⊰ **Total** 180
Acreage 15 **Open** Mar **to** 01-Nov
Access Good **Site** Level
Nearest Bus Stop (Miles) 1

Within 1 mile of Woolacombe beach, which is perfect for families and surfing.
Facilities & ⨍ ⬚⬚ ⌂ ⌐ ⊙ ☎
⌘ ⌘ ☐ ⬚ ✕ ⬛ ⬛ 🔥 ⬛ ⊡ ⊡ ⊡ ⚡
Nearest Town Woolacombe
Directions Woolacombe is off the main road to Ilfracombe via Braunton.
⇥ Barnstaple

WOOLACOMBE

Woolacombe Bay Holiday Village, Sandy Lane, Woolacombe, Devon, EX34 7AH
Tel: 0844 7700 367
Email: goodtimes@woolacombe.com
www.woolacombe.com/cades
Pitches For Å **Total** 150
Open 23-Mar **to** 02-Nov
Nearest Bus Stop (Miles) Outside
Close to 3 miles of golden sandy beaches of Woolacombe and spectacular coastal walks. Choice of 4 Parks and their facilities and entertainment. Fishing nearby. Golf and tennis on Park.
Facilities & ⨍ ☐ ⬚⬚ ⌂ ⌐ ⊙ ↵ ⬛ ◻ ☎
⌘ ⌘ ☐ ⬚ 🔥 ⬛ ⊡ ⊡ ◢ 🛜
Nearest Town Woolacombe
Directions From Barnstaple take the A361 Ilfracombe road to the junction of the B3343 at Mullacott Cross. Turn first left signposted Woolacombe, after 1¾ miles turn right to Mortehoe, Park is 1 mile on the left.
⇥ Barnstaple

WOOLACOMBE

Woolacombe Sands Holiday Park, Beach Road, Woolacombe, Devon, EX34 7AF
Tel: 01271 870569
Email: lifesabeach@woolacombe-sands.co.uk
www.woolacombe-sands.co.uk
Pitches For Å ⊕ ➡ ⛺⊰ **Total** 147

Escape to North Devon...

WOOLACOMBE BAY
HOLIDAY PARKS

Set within North Devon's breathtaking countryside next to Woolacombe's three miles of golden sandy beach

PITCHES
NOW FROM JUST **£9**
per pitch, per night

LEVEL PITCHES & EASY ACCESS

400 ALL WEATHER PITCHES

16 AMP ELECTRIC HOOKUPS

- Four award winning Holiday Parks
- Grass and hard standing pitches
- Outstanding leisure facilities
- Sea view touring & super pitches
- Modern amenity blocks
- Activities for all ages

We're here

Call **0844 7700 367**
or visit **woolacombe.com/cct**

Open Mar **to** Nov
Access Good **Site** Lev/Slope
Nearest Bus Stop (Miles) Outside
Woolacombes beach.
Facilities ⬚⬚⬚⬚⬚⬚⬚⬚⬚⬚⬚⬚⬚⬚⬚
⬚⬚⬚⬚⬚⬚⬚⬚⬚⬚⬚⬚
⬚⬚
Nearest Town Woolacombe
Directions On main A361 road.
⬚ Barnstaple

DORSET

BERE REGIS

Rowlands Wait Touring Park, Rye Hill,
Bere Regis, Dorset, BH20 7LP
Tel: 01929 472727
Email: enquiries@rowlandswait.co.uk
www.rowlandswait.co.uk
Pitches For ⬚ ⬚ ⬚ **Total** 71
Acreage 8½ **Open** 15-Mar **to** 31-Oct
Access Good **Site** Lev/Slope
Nearest Bus Stop (Miles) ½
The Tank Museum and Monkey World
nearby. Poole 10 miles Weymouth 11 miles.
Facilities ⬚⬚⬚⬚⬚⬚⬚⬚⬚⬚⬚⬚⬚⬚
⬚⬚⬚⬚⬚⬚⬚⬚⬚⬚⬚
Nearest Town Wareham
Directions From Bere Regis follow signs for
the Tank Museum, Park is ¾ miles from the
village on the right hand side at the top of
the hill.
⬚ Wool

BLANDFORD

The Inside Park, Blandford, Dorset, DT11
9AD
Tel: 01258 453719
Email: mail@theinsidepark.co.uk
www.theinsidepark.co.uk
Pitches For ⬚ ⬚ ⬚ **Total** 100
Acreage 13 **Open** Easter **to** October
Access Good **Site** Lev/Slope
Rural environment with extensive wildlife.
Ideal for touring.
Facilities ⬚⬚⬚⬚⬚⬚⬚⬚⬚⬚⬚⬚⬚
⬚⬚⬚⬚⬚⬚⬚⬚⬚⬚
Nearest Town Blandford Forum
Directions 1¼ miles south west of Blandford
on the road to Winterborne Stickland.
Signposted from junction of A350 and A354
on Blandford bypass.

BOURNEMOUTH

Charris Camping & Caravan Park,
Candys lane, Corfe Mullen, Wimborne,
Dorset, BH21 3EF
Tel: 01202 885970
Email: bookings@charris.co.uk
www.charris.co.uk
Pitches For ⬚ ⬚ ⬚ **Total** 45
Acreage 3 **Open** All Year
Access Good **Site** Lev/Slope
Nearest Bus Stop (Miles) ¼
AA 3 Pennants and Caravan & Camping Club
listed. Good central site convienient for the
coast and New Forest. Poole 7½ miles and
Bournemouth 8¼ miles. Cafe/restaurant
close by.
Facilities ⬚⬚⬚⬚⬚⬚⬚⬚⬚⬚⬚⬚
⬚⬚⬚⬚⬚⬚⬚
Nearest Town Wimborne
Directions A31 Wimborne bypass 1 mile
west of Wimborne. Signs for entrance.
⬚ Poole

BOURNEMOUTH

St Leonards Farm, Ringwood Road, West
Moors, Ferndown, Dorset, BH22 0AQ
Tel: 01202 872637
Email: enquiries_stleonards@yahoo.co.uk
www.stleonardsfarm.biz
Pitches For ⬚ ⬚ ⬚ **Total** 120
Acreage 12 **Open** April **to** October
Access Good **Site** Level
Nearest Bus Stop (Miles) Outside
AA 3 Pennants.
Facilities ⬚⬚⬚⬚⬚⬚⬚⬚⬚⬚⬚⬚
⬚⬚⬚⬚⬚⬚⬚⬚⬚⬚⬚
Nearest Town Bournemouth
Directions On the A31 4 miles west of
Ringwood, opposite the Murco Garage.
⬚ Bournemouth Central

BRIDPORT

Bingham Grange Touring Camping Park,
Binghams Farm, Melplash, Bridport,
Dorset, DT6 3TT
Tel: 01308 488234
Email: enquiries@binghamgrange.co.uk
www.binghamgrange.co.uk
Pitches For ⬚ ⬚ ⬚ ⬚ **Total** 111
Acreage 5 **Open** Mar **to** Nov
Access Good **Site** Lev/Slope
Nearest Bus Stop (Miles) Outside
EXCLUSIVELY FOR ADULTS. An Award
Winning Park set in an area of outstanding
natural beauty yet only 4½ miles from the
coast. An ideal base to explore Dorset. All
modern heated facilities.
Facilities ⬚⬚⬚⬚⬚⬚⬚⬚⬚⬚⬚⬚⬚⬚
⬚⬚⬚⬚⬚⬚⬚⬚⬚⬚⬚⬚⬚⬚
Nearest Town West Bay/Bridport
Directions Turn off A35 in Bridport at the
roundabout onto A3066, signposted
Beaminster. In 1¼ miles turn left into Farm
Road.
⬚ Dorchester/Crewkerne

BRIDPORT

Britt Valley Campground, West Bay,
Bridport, Dorset, DT6 4SU
Tel: 01308 897232
Email: enq@brittvalley.co.uk
www.brittvalley.co.uk
Pitches For ⬚ ⬚ **Total** 100
Acreage 13 **Open** 06-Jul **to** 03-Sep
Access Good **Site** Level
Nearest Bus Stop (Miles) ¼
Alongside the River Britt and near the beach.
Facilities ⬚⬚⬚⬚⬚⬚⬚⬚⬚⬚⬚⬚⬚
Nearest Town Bridport
Directions From Bridport Crown roundabout
on the A35, take the exit for West Bay and
the entrance is approx 1 mile on the right
hand side.
⬚ Dorchester

BRIDPORT

Eype House Caravan Park, Eype,
Bridport, Dorset, DT6 6AL
Tel: 01308 424903
Email: enquiries@eypehouse.co.uk
www.eypehouse.co.uk
Pitches For ⬚ ⬚ **Total** 20
Acreage 4 **Open** Easter **to** 30-Sep
On the Dorset coastal path and only 200
yards from the beach. Pitches are levelled
into hill. NO electric hook-ups. Sorry, NO
touring caravans.
Facilities ⬚⬚⬚⬚⬚⬚⬚⬚⬚⬚⬚
⬚⬚⬚⬚⬚⬚
Directions Signposted Eype off the A35,
follow signs to the sea.
⬚ Dorchester/Crewkerne

BRIDPORT

Freshwater Beach Holiday Park, Burton
Bradstock, Bridport, Dorset, DT6 4PT
Tel: 01308 897317
Email: office@freshwaterbeach.co.uk
www.freshwaterbeach.co.uk
Pitches For ⬚ ⬚ ⬚ **Total** 500
Acreage 40 **Open** Mid Mar **to** Mid Nov
Access Good **Site** Level
Nearest Bus Stop (Miles) Outside
Own private beach. Free family
entertainment (SBH to Mid Sept). Good cliff
walks. NEW leisure complex with 10 pin
bowling, indoor water play, sauna, steam
room and hot tub. Golf course adjoining park.
Pitch price includes 6 people and free club
membership.
Facilities ⬚⬚⬚⬚⬚⬚⬚⬚⬚⬚⬚⬚⬚⬚
⬚⬚⬚⬚⬚⬚⬚⬚⬚⬚⬚⬚⬚⬚⬚
Nearest Town Bridport
Directions From Bridport take B3157
towards Weymouth, Park is 2 miles on the
right.
⬚ Dorchester

BRIDPORT

Graston Copse Holiday Park, Annings
Lane, Burton Bradstock, Bridport, Dorset,
DT6 4QP
Tel: 01308 426947
Email: enquiries@wdlh.co.uk
www.wdlh.co.uk
Pitches For ⬚ ⬚ **Total** 48
Open 27-Apr **to** 09-Sep
Access Average **Site** Level
Nearest Bus Stop (Miles) ½
Peaceful location in the Dorset countryside.
25 minutes walk to the beach. Online booking
available or call our Bookings Hotline: 01308
426947.
Facilities ⬚⬚⬚⬚⬚⬚⬚⬚⬚⬚
⬚⬚⬚⬚⬚⬚
Nearest Town Bridport
Directions From Bridport take the B3157
coastal road towards Weymouth. When in
Burton Bradstock turn left at the Anchor Pub,
then turn second right into Annings Lane.
⬚ Dorchester

BRIDPORT

Highlands End Holiday Park, Eype,
Bridport, Dorset, DT6 6AR
Tel: 01308 422139
Email: holidays@wdlh.co.uk
www.wdlh.co.uk
Pitches For ⬚ ⬚ ⬚ **Total** 195
Acreage 8 **Open** 15th Mar **to** 03-Nov
Access Good **Site** Level
Nearest Bus Stop (Miles) ½
Exceptional views across Lyme Bay, 500
metres from the beach. Heated swimming
pool, steam room and sauna. Tennis and
Pitch & Putt on site. All weather awning
areas. Online booking available or call our
Bookings Hotline: 01308 426947.
Facilities ⬚⬚⬚⬚⬚⬚⬚⬚⬚⬚⬚⬚⬚⬚
⬚⬚⬚⬚⬚⬚⬚⬚⬚⬚⬚⬚⬚⬚⬚
Nearest Town Bridport
Directions On approach to Bridport from
east (Dorchester) on A35 turn left at
roundabout, follow Bridport By-pass. Second
roundabout take third exit signposted A35
West 1 mile turn left to Eype and follow
signposts.
⬚ Axminster

FreshwaterBeach
HOLIDAY PARK

Wi Fi

- Exclusive Private Beach
- Jurassic Fun Centre including:
  Indoor Family Pools, Water Slides, Hot Tub,
  Sauna & Steam Room, Restaurants.
- Fabulous Entertainment*
- Outdoor Family Pool
- Children's Activities
- Large Touring and Camping Field and much more....

Great family holidays on Dorset's World Heritage Coast.

Facilities will be reduced outside the main holiday periods
* Spring Bank Holiday to mid September

01308 897 317 • freshwaterbeach.co.uk

BRIDPORT

Home Farm Caravan & Campsite,
Rectory Lane, Puncknowle, Nr Dorchester, Dorset, DT2 9BW
Tel: 01308 897258
www.homefarmcaravanand
campingsite.co.uk
Pitches For 🏕 ⛺ 🚐 **Total** 42
Acreage 5 **Open** 01-Apr **to** 05-Oct
Access Good **Site** Lev/Slope
Nearest Bus Stop (Miles) ¼
In a beautiful area, 1½ miles from the Heritage Coast. Ideal touring.
Facilities 🏕🚿🚽♿🅿️⛱🍴⛺🛒🔥🚮⚡
Nearest Town Weymouth/Bridport
Directions Directions for carvavans from Dorchester take the A35 towards Bridport, then take the B3157 to Burton Bradstock. Turn off at Swyre and follow the road to Puncknowle. Continue past Rectory Lane. and take next left turn into Hazel Lane, at the T-Junction turn left, turn left again at the red phone box into Rectory Lane. 12 miles from Dorchester.
🚉 Weymouth/Dorchester

BRIDPORT

West Bay Holiday Park, West Bay, Bridport, Dorset, DT6 4HB
Tel: 0844 335 3732
Email:
touringandcamping@parkdeanholidays.com
www.parkdeantouring.com
Pitches For 🏕 ⛺ 🚐 **Total** 131
Acreage 30 **Open** March **to** Oct
Access Good **Site** Level
Nearest Bus Stop (Miles) Outside
Situated in the heart of West Bay, beside the beach, harbour and picturesque village. Indoor pool. FREE kids clubs and live family entertainment.
Facilities 🏕🚿🚽♿🅿️⛱🍴⛺🛒
🏪🎮🎯🍺🍴🛒🔥🚮⚡📶
Nearest Town Bridport
Directions Take the M3 towards Winchester, then follow the M27 then the A31. Join the A35 to Dorchester and head west to Bridport, then head into West Bay.
🚉 Dorchester

CHARMOUTH

Charmouth Camping & Caravanning Club Site, Monkton Wylde Farm, Nr. Charmouth, Dorset, DT6 6DB
Tel: 01297 32965
Email:
charmouth.site@thefriendlyclub.co.uk
www.campingandcaravanningclub.co.uk/charmouth
Pitches For 🏕 ⛺ 🚐 **Total** 150

Acreage 12 **Open** 08-Mar **to** 04-Nov
Access Good **Site** Level
Nearest Bus Stop (Miles) 1
5 miles from Forde Abbey and Charmouths fossil beach. 7 miles from Cricket St. Thomas Wildlife Park. Motorhome service point. ETB 5 Star Graded, AA 4 Pennants and David Bellamy Gold Award. Non members welcome. You can also call us on 0845 130 7633.
Facilities 🚿🚽♿🅿️⛱🍴⛺🛒
🏪🎮🎯🍺🛒🔥🚮⚡
Nearest Town Charmouth
Directions From Dorchester take the A35, turn right onto the B3165 signposted Hawkchurch, site is on the left within ¼ of a mile.
🚉 Axminster

CHARMOUTH

Manor Farm Holiday Centre, Manor Farm, Charmouth, Bridport, Dorset, DT6 6QL
Tel: 01297 560226
Email:
enquiries@manorfarmholidaycentre.co.uk
www.manorfarmholidaycentre.co.uk
Pitches For 🏕 ⛺ 🚐 🚐≤ **Total** 345
Acreage 30 **Open** All Year
Access Good **Site** Lev/Slope
Nearest Bus Stop (Miles) Outside
Ten minutes level walk to beach, alongside river. In area of outstanding natural beauty. Ideal touring.
Facilities 🚿🚽♿🅿️⛱🍴⛺🛒
🏪🎮🎯🍺🍴🎯🍴⛺🔥🚮⚡📶
Nearest Town Charmouth
Directions Come off the Charmouth bypass at east end Manor Farm is ¾ miles on the right, in Charmouth.
🚉 Axminster

CHARMOUTH

Monkton Wyld Farm, Charmouth, Dorset, DT6 6DB
Tel: 01297 631131
Email: holidays@monktonwyld.co.uk
www.www.monktonwyld.co.uk
Pitches For 🏕 ⛺ 🚐 **Total** 130
Acreage 20 **Open** Mid March **to** End Oct
Access Good **Site** Level
Nearest Bus Stop (Miles) 1
Beautifully landscaped pitches with room to relax, and space for children to play. Friendly, helpful wardens offer every assistance. Spotless shower block. Self catering houses sleeping 2-10 persons available to rent on farm.
Facilities 🚿🚽♿🅿️⛱🍴⛺🛒
🏪🏪🎮🎯🍴⛺🔥🚮⚡

Directions Take the A35 from Axminster towards Charmouth, cross the county boundary into Dorset and almost immediately turn left down an unmarked lane. Brown tourist sign only.
🚉 Axminster

CHARMOUTH

Newlands Holiday Park, Charmouth, Nr. Bridport, Dorset, DT6 6RB
Tel: 01297 560259
Email: enq@newlandsholidays.co.uk
www.www.newlandsholidays.co.uk
Pitches For 🏕 ⛺ 🚐 **Total** 200
Acreage 23
Access Good **Site** Terraced
Nearest Bus Stop (Miles) Outside
Nearest Town Lyme Regis
🚉 Axminster

CHIDEOCK

Golden Cap Holiday Park, Seatown, Chideock, Nr Bridport, Dorset, DT6 6JX
Tel: 01308 426947
Email: enquiries@wdlh.co.uk
www.wdlh.co.uk
Pitches For 🏕 ⛺ 🚐 **Total** 260
Acreage 12 **Open** 15-Mar **to** 03-Nov
Site Level/Sloping
Nearest Bus Stop (Miles) ¼
100 metres from beach, overlooked by the famous Golden Cap cliff top. All weather awning areas. Unique location on the Jurassic Coast, ideal for Lyme Regis and Weymouth. Online booking available or call our Bookings Hotline: 01308 426947.
Facilities 🚿🚽♿🅿️⛱🍴⛺🛒
🏪🎮🎯🍴⛺🔥🚮⚡📶
Nearest Town Bridport
Directions Follow the A35 to Chideock, once in the village turn opposite the church into Duck Street signposted Seatown. Follow the lane to the beach and turn left.
🚉 Axminster/Dorchester

CHRISTCHURCH

Longfield Caravan Park, Matchams Lane, Hurn, Christchurch, Dorset, BH23 6AW
Tel: 01202 485214
www.longfieldcaravanpark.co.uk
Pitches For ⛺ 🚐 **Total** 20
Acreage 2½ **Open** All Year
Access Good **Site** Level
Dry ski slope within walking distance, with bar and food available. Swimming pool on site. Near to the New Forest and within easy reach of Christchurch and Bournemouth.
Facilities 🚿🚽♿🅿️⛱🍴⛺
⛱🛒🔥
Nearest Town Christchurch

Directions From the A338 follow signs for Bournemouth International Airport. At Hurn bare right and then left into Matchams Lane. After approx 3 miles Longfield is on the left.
⇌ Christchurch

CORFE CASTLE

Burnbake Campsite, Rempstone, Corfe Castle, Wareham, Dorset, BH20 5JH
Tel: 01929 480570
Email: info@burnbake.com
www.burnbake.com
Pitches For Å ⇌ **Total** 130
Acreage 12 **Open** Apr **to** Oct **Site** Level
A quiet, secluded site in woodlands with a stream. 4 miles from Studland with its three miles of sandy beach and excellent safe bathing. 4 miles from Swanage.
Facilities ƒ 🏠 🛱 🏪 ⊙ ⌨ 🍴 🐶
🆘 🏕 🔥 👶 🛒 ⊕ 🚻 🔲
Nearest Town Swanage
Directions From Wareham take the A351 to Corfe Castle, turn left under the castle onto the B3351 Studland road, through the old railway arches, and take the third turning left signposted Rempstone and follow signs.
⇌ Wareham

CORFE CASTLE

Corfe Castle Camping & Caravanning Club Site, Bucknowle, Wareham, Dorset, BH20 5PQ
Tel: 01929 480280
www.campingandcaravanningclub.co.uk/corfecastle
Pitches For Å ⇌ ⇌ **Total** 80
Open 01-Mar **to** 31-Oct
Access Good **Site** Lev/Slope
Nearest Bus Stop (Miles) ½
Very close to the historic thousand year old Corfe Castle, which survived the English Civil

War, rising above the Isle of Purbeck. Chocks may be required on some pitches. You can also call us on 0845 130 7633.
Facilities 🔥 ƒ 🏠 🛱 🏪 ⊙ ⌨ 🍴 🔲 🐶
🆘 🏕 🔥 🛱 🔲
Nearest Town Wareham
Directions From Wareham head south along A351, turn right at foot of castle, after ¾ mile turn right at first brown camping sign.
⇌ Wareham

CORFE CASTLE

Knitson Farm Tourers Site, Knitson Farm, Corfe Castle, Dorset, BH20 5JB
Tel: 01929 425121
www.knitsonfarm.co.uk
Pitches For Å ⇌ ⇌ **Total** 60
Acreage 5½ **Open** See web site
Site Lev/Slope
Set in very beautiful countryside with many walks radiating from the field, including Swanage and Studland beaches.
Facilities 🐶 🔥 👶 🛱 🔲 ⋇
Directions Take the A351 to Swanage outskirts, turn first left into Wash Pond Lane. Continue until the lane finishes at a T-Junction turn left. Site is approx. ½ mile further on, on the left hand side.
⇌ Wareham

DORCHESTER

Crossways Caravan Club Site, Crossways, Dorchester, Dorset, DT2 8BE
Tel: 01305 852032
www.caravanclub.co.uk
Pitches For ⇌ ⇌ **Total** 113
Acreage 35 **Open** Apr **to** Oct
Access Good **Site** Level
Nearest Bus Stop (Miles) ½
Landscaped site set in 35 acres of woodland. So much to see and do in the local area. 8½

miles from Weymouth beach and attractions. Non members welcome. Booking essential.
Facilities 🔥 ƒ 🏠 🛱 🏪 ⊙ 🔲 🐶
🅿 🏕 👶 🔲 🛒
Nearest Town Dorchester
Directions From NE on A31, at the roundabout on the outskirts of Bere Regis turn right onto A35. At Tolpuddle Ball junction turn left onto slip road sp Warmwell, at T-junction turn left, at next T-junction turn right, site is 4 miles on the left.
⇌ Dorchester

DORCHESTER

Giants Head Caravan & Camping Park, Old Sherborne Road, Dorchester, Dorset, DT2 7TR
Tel: 01300 341242
Email: holidays@giantshead.co.uk
www.giantshead.co.uk
Pitches For Å ⇌ ⇌ ⇌ **Total** 50
Acreage 3½ **Open** Easter **to** Oct
Access Good **Site** Lev/Slope
Nearest Bus Stop (Miles) 1
Rural, Beautiful countryside, peaceful surroundings.
Facilities ƒ 🏠 🛱 🏪 ⊙ ⌨ 🍴 🔲 🐶
🅿 🏕 👶 🔲 🛒 ⋇
Nearest Town Dorchester
Directions 8 miles from Dorchester, 10 miles from Sherborne, 2 miles from Cern Abbas.
⇌ Dorchester

DORCHESTER

Lyons Gate Caravan Park, Lyons Gate, Dorchester, Dorset, DT2 7AZ
Tel: 01300 345260
Email: info@lyons-gate.co.uk
www.lyons-gate.co.uk
Pitches For Å ⇌ ⇌ ⇌ **Total** 90
Acreage 10 **Open** All Year

Access Good **Site** Level
Nearest Bus Stop (Miles) Outside
Four coarse fishing lakes on site.
Facilities 🚿 ♿ 🅿 ⛽ 🅿 ⊙ 🍴 🛒 ☎ 🔥 🛁 🏪 🅿 🛒 ✂ ☀ 📶
Nearest Town Dorchester
Directions On the A352 between Dorchester and Sherborne.
🚂 Dorchester

DORCHESTER

Moreton Camping & Caravanning Club Site, Station Road, Moreton, Nr Dorchester, Dorset, DT2 8BB
Tel: 01305 853801
Email: moreton.site@thefriendlyclub.co.uk
www.campingandcaravanningclub.co.uk/moreton
Pitches For 🔺 ⛺ 🚐 **Total** 120
Acreage 7 **Open** 15-Mar **to** 06-Jan
Access Good **Site** Sloping
Nearest Bus Stop (Miles) ½
A lovely, leafy site on the outskirts of Dorchester. One holiday bungalow to let. BTB 5 Star Graded, AA 3 Pennants and Loo of the Year Award. Non members welcome. You can also call us on 0845 130 7633.
Facilities ☎ ♿ 🅿 ⛽ 🅿 ⊙ 🍴 🛒 ☎ 🔥 🛁 🏪 🅿 🛒 📶
Nearest Town Dorchester
Directions Take the A35 from Poole, continue past Bere Regis then turn left onto the B3390 signposted Alfpuddle. After approx. 2 miles the site is on the left before Moreton Station, adjacent to the Frampton Arms public house.
🚂 Moreton

LULWORTH COVE

Durdle Door Holiday Park, Lulworth Cove, Wareham, Dorset, BH20 5PU
Tel: 01929 400200
Email: durdle.door@lulworth.com
www.lulworth.com
Pitches For 🔺 ⛺ 🚐 **Total** 104
Acreage 45 **Open** Mar **to** Oct
Access Good **Site** Lev/Slope
Unique cliff top position overlooking the famous landmark of Durdle Door. Sea view hook-ups for motor homes and touring caravans only, and pitches for tents with electric hook-ups.
Facilities ☎ 🅿 ⛽ 🅿 ⊙ 🍴 ✖ 🛒 ♀ 🏪 🅿 🛒
Nearest Town Wareham
Directions Take the B3077 Wool to West Lulworth road, fork right in West Lulworth Village, entrance is at the top of the hill.
🚂 Wool

LYME REGIS

Cummins Farm, Penn Cross, Charmouth, Bridport, Dorset, DT6 6BX
Tel: 01297 560898
www.cumminsfarmcampsitelymeregis.co.uk
Pitches For 🔺 ⛺ 🚐 **Total** 30
Acreage 5½ **Open** Easter **to** End Sept
Access Good **Site** Level
Nearest Bus Stop (Miles) ¼
Quiet farm site in a rural setting.
Facilities ☎ 🅿 ⛽ 🅿 ⊙ 🍴 🏪 🅿
Nearest Town Lyme Regis
Directions Midway between Charmouth and Lyme Regis, 200 metres from the A3052.
🚂 Axminster

LYME REGIS

Hook Farm Camping & Caravan Park, Gore Lane, Uplyme, Lyme Regis, Dorset, DT7 3UU
Tel: 01297 442801
Email: information@hookfarm-uplyme.co.uk
www.hookfarm-uplyme.co.uk
Pitches For 🔺 🚐 **Total** 100
Acreage 5¾ **Open** 01-Mar **to** 15-Nov
Access Good **Site** Level/Terraced
Nearest Bus Stop (Miles) ¼
The closest campsite to Lyme Regis (1 mile). Peaceful, tranquil site in an area of outstanding natural beauty. Many national footpaths are accessible from the park.
Facilities 🚿 ♿ 🅿 ⛽ 🅿 ⊙ 🍴 🛒 ☎ 🔥 🛁 🏪 🅿 🛒
Directions From the centre of Lyme Regis take the B3165 to Uplyme (1 mile). In Uplyme turn left opposite the Talbot Arms Pub into Gore Lane. The Park is 400 yards on the right hand side.
🚂 Axminster

LYME REGIS

Shrubbery Touring Park, Rousdon, Lyme Regis, Dorset, DT7 3XW
Tel: 01297 442227
Email: info@shrubberypark.co.uk
www.shrubberypark.co.uk
Pitches For 🔺 ⛺ 🚐 **Total** 120
Acreage 10 **Open** 22-Mar **to** Oct
Access Good **Site** Level
Nearest Bus Stop (Miles) Outside
Ideal base for fossil hunters.
Facilities 🚿 ♿ 🅿 ⛽ 🅿 ⊙ 🍴 🛒 ☎ 🔥 🛁 🏪 🅿 🛒
Nearest Town Lyme Regis
Directions 3 miles west of Lyme Regis on the A3052 coast road.
🚂 Axminster

OWERMOIGNE

Sandyholme Holiday Park, Moreton Road, Owermoigne, Dorchester, Dorset, DT2 8HZ
Tel: 01308 426947
Email: holidays@wdlh.co.uk
www.wdlh.co.uk
Pitches For Å 😊 😊 **Total** 143
Acreage 6 **Open** 15-Mar **to** 03-Nov
Access Good **Site** Level
Nearest Bus Stop (Miles) ½
Near to Lulworth Cove, Durdle Door and Ringstead Bay. The nearby towns of Dorchester and Weymouth provide plenty of attractions and sights. Online booking available or call our Bookings Hotline: 01308 426947.
Facilities ⚅ ✆ 🖰🖧🖚🏧 ⊙🞨 🚿 🖵 🍴
🏵 🖸 🛝 🖾 ☂🖨🖼 ⛆
Nearest Town Dorchester/Weymouth
Directions Take the A35 to Dorchester then take the A352 to Broadmayne. Continue for 4 miles, at the roundabout take second exit, take left hand turning onto Moreton Road, Park can be found on the left hand side.
🚆 Moreton

POOLE

Huntick Farm Caravan Park, Huntick Road, Lytchett Matravers, Poole, Dorset, BH16 6BB
Tel: 01202 622222
Email: huntickcaravans@btconnect.com
www.huntick.co.uk
Pitches For Å 😊 😊 **Total** 30
Acreage 4 **Open** Apr **to** Oct
Access Good **Site** Level
Nearest Bus Stop (Miles) ½
Very spacious site which is quiet and friendly.
Facilities ✆ 🖰🖧🖚🏧 ⊙🞨 🍴
🗽 🖸 🛝 ☂🖨🖼 🖼 🕭

Nearest Town Poole
Directions Turn right off the A350 or left off the A35 and follow signs to Lytchett Matravers. At the Rose & Crown turn into Huntick Road.
🚆 Poole

POOLE

Sandford Holiday Park, Holton Heath, Poole, Dorset, BH16 6JZ
Tel: 0844 335 3732
Email: touringandcamping@parkdeanholidays.com
www.parkdeantouring.com
Pitches For Å 😊 😊 **Total** 354
Acreage 22 **Open** 02-Mar **to** 02-Nov
Access Good **Site** Level
Nearest Bus Stop (Miles) Outside
Tucked away in a beautiful countryside setting. Spacious, level, private, serviced or Star pitches. Standard pitches also available. Free modern showers and toilets. Heated indoor and outdoor pools. FREE kids clubs and live family entertainment.
Facilities ⚅ ✆ 🖰🖧🖚🏧 ⊙🞨 🚿 🖵 🍴
🏵 🖸 🛝 ✗ 🍴 🎏 🛝 🗽 ☂🖨🖼 ⛆
🖼
Nearest Town Poole
Directions Located on the A351 (signposted Wareham) which branches off the A35 approx. 5 miles west of Poole. Turn right at Holton Heath traffic lights, park is on the left.
🚆 Wareham

POOLE

South Lytchett Manor Caravan & Camping Park, Dorchester Road, Lytchett Minster, Poole, Dorset, BH16 6JB
Tel: 01202 622577
Email: info@southlytchettmanor.co.uk

www.southlytchettmanor.co.uk
Pitches For Å 😊 😊 **Total** 150
Acreage 22 **Open** Mar **to** 02-Jan
Access Good **Site** Level
Nearest Bus Stop (Miles) Outside
Close to Sandbanks, Poole and Bournemouth, set in 22 acres of parkland.
Facilities ⚅ ✆ 🖰🖧🖚🏧 ⊙🞨 🚿 🖵 🍴
🏵 🖸 🛝 🍴 🛝 ☂🖨🖼 ⛆ 🕭
Nearest Town Poole
Directions From Poole take A35 dual carriageway. At Bakers Arms Island take the third exit to Lytchett Minster, go through Lytchett Minster and the site is situated on the left 400 yards out of the village.
🚆 Hamworthy

SHAFTESBURY

Blackmore Vale Caravan & Camping Park, Sherborne Causeway, Shaftesbury, Dorset, SP7 9PX
Tel: 01747 851523
Email: mike_farrow@btconnect.com
www.blackmorevalecaravanpark.co.uk
Pitches For Å 😊 😊 😊 ≈
Acreage 5 **Open** All Year
Access Good **Site** Level
Friendly, family run Park in the heart of Hardy country. Gym and a lake for fishing. Touring caravan hire, sales and accessories. Self catering also available.
Facilities ✆ 🖰🖧🖚🏧 ⊙🞨 🖵 🍴
🏵 🗽 🖸 🛝 ☂🖨🖼 ✒
Nearest Town Shaftesbury
Directions 2 miles west of Shaftesbury on the A30.
🚆 Gillingham

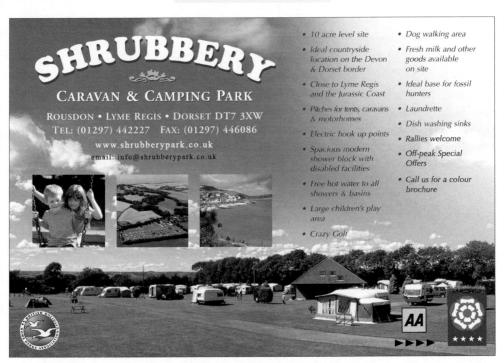

ST. LEONARDS

Back-of-Beyond Touring Park, 234 Ringwood Road, St Leonards, Dorset, BH24 2SB
Tel: 01202 876968
Email: melandsuepike@aol.com
www.backofbeyondtouringpark.co.uk
Pitches For Å ⊞ ₩ **Total** 80
Acreage 28 **Open** 01-Mar **to** 31-Oct
Access Good **Site** Level
Nearest Bus Stop (Miles) ½
Quiet 4 Star ADULTS ONLY country and woodland site with good facilities. Golf and fishing on site. Central for the New Forest, Bournemouth and the World Heritage coast.
Facilities ⅙ ∮ ⊞ ↑ ⊙ ⌒ ♨ ☐ ☎
℠ ⊙ ╌ ⊟ ☐ ✐ A ♒ ✦
Nearest Town Ringwood
Directions Off the A31 at Boundary Lane roundabout in St. Leonards.
⇥ Bournemouth

SWANAGE

Downshay Farm, Haycrafts Lane, Swanage, Dorset, BH19 3EB
Tel: 01929 480316
Email: downshayfarm@tiscali.co.uk
www.downshayfarm.co.uk
Pitches For Å ⊞ ₩ **Total** 12
Open Easter **to** 01-Nov
Access Good **Site** Level
Nearest Bus Stop (Miles) ½
Close to Corfe Castle and the Jurassic Coast. Steam rail service.
Facilities ∮ ⊞ ↑ ⊙ ╌ ☎ ℠ ⋈ ⊟
Nearest Town Swanage
Directions From Wareham take the A351 to Swanage, at Harmans Cross crossroads turn right, site is ½ a mile up the hill on the right.
⇥ Wareham

SWANAGE

Haycraft Caravan Club Site, Haycrafts Lane, Swanage, Dorset, BH19 3EB
Tel: 01929 480572
www.caravanclub.co.uk
Pitches For ⊞ ₩ **Total** 53
Acreage 6 **Open** Mar **to** Nov
Access Good **Site** Level
Nearest Bus Stop (Miles) ½
Tranquil site set in the heart of Purbeck countryside, 5 miles from the beach. Ideal for walkers. Just a few minutes walk from the Swanage Light Railway. Non members welcome. Booking essential.
Facilities ⅙ ∮ ⊞ ⊞ ↑ ⌒ ╌ ☐ ☎
⅛ ⊙ ☐ ╌ ⊟ ☎
Nearest Town Swanage
Directions From A352, at the mini roundabout on the outskirts of Wareham turn onto A351 sp Swanage. After 6¾ miles at Harmans Cross, just before the petrol station, turn right into Haycrafts Lane, site is ½ mile on the left.
⇥ Swanage

SWANAGE

Tom's Field Camping & Shop, Tom's Field Road, Langton Matravers, Swanage, Dorset, BH19 3HN
Tel: 01929 427110
Email: tomsfield@hotmail.com
www.tomsfieldcamping.co.uk
Pitches For Å ₩ **Total** 100
Acreage 4½ **Open** Mid Mar **to** End Oct
Site Lev/Slope
Nearest Bus Stop (Miles) ¼
Set in beautiful countryside, an area of outstanding natural beauty. Coastal walk can be reached in 20 minutes.
Facilities ∮ ⊞ ↑ ⊙ ╌ ☎ ℠ ⊟ ⊟
Nearest Town Swanage

Directions A351 from Swanage, then B3069 to Langton Matravers, campsite at end of Tom's Field
Road.
⇥ Wareham

SWANAGE

Ulwell Cottage Caravan Park, Ulwell, Swanage, Dorset, BH19 3DG
Tel: 01929 422823
Email: enq@ulwellcottagepark.co.uk
www.ulwellcottagepark.co.uk
Pitches For Å ⊞ ₩ **Total** 77
Acreage 13 **Open** 01-Mar **to** 07-Jan
Access Good **Site** Lev/Slope
Nearest Bus Stop (Miles) Outside
⇥ Wareham

THREE LEGGED CROSS

Woolsbridge Manor Farm Caravan Park, Three Legged Cross, Wimborne, Dorset, BH21 6RA
Tel: 01202 826369
Email: woolsbridge@btconnect.com
www.woolsbridgemanorcaravanpark.co.uk
Pitches For Å ⊞ ₩ ₩⁵ **Total** 100
Acreage 6¾ **Open** Mar **to** Oct
Access Good **Site** Level
Nearest Bus Stop (Miles) ½
Just a short walk to Moors Valley Country Park, and a 10 minute drive to Bournemouth. AA 4 Pennant grading, David Bellamy Gold Award.
Facilities ⅙ ∮ ⊞ ↑ ⊙ ╌ ☎ ☐ ☎
℠ ⊙ ☎ ⋈ ⊟ ⊟ ✐ ✂
Nearest Town Ringwood
Directions Take the A31 west, Ringwood on the left, stay in left hand lane and automatically go into slip road. At the roundabout turn right (third exit) signposted Three Legged Cross, site is 2 miles along this road on the right hand side.
⇥ Bournemouth

WAREHAM

East Creech Caravan & Camping Site,
East Creech Farm, East Creech,
Wareham, Dorset, BH20 5AP
Tel: 01929 480519/481312
Email: east.creech@virgin.net
www.eastcreechfarm.co.uk
Pitches For Å ⊕ ⊞ **Total** 80
Acreage 5 **Open** April **to** October
Access Good **Site** Lev/Slope
Nearest Bus Stop (Miles) 2
Free fishing at the Farm.
Facilities ∮ ⌨⌂⌐⊙◎ ♥ ⋔⊁⊟ ✦
Nearest Town Wareham
Directions From Wareham bypass A351,
turn right at the roundabout signposted Blue
Pool. Site is on the right ½ a miles past Blue
Pool.
⇌ Wareham

WAREHAM

Lookout Holiday Park, Stoborough,
Wareham, Dorset, BH20 5AZ
Tel: 01929 552546
Email: enquiries@caravan-sites.co.uk
www.caravan-sites.co.uk
Pitches For Å ⊕ ⊞ **Total** 150
Acreage 15 **Open** 22-Mar **to** Dec
Access Good **Site** Level
Nearest Bus Stop (Miles) Outside
Ideal for touring the Purbecks and Studland
Bay. Static caravans available all year.
Facilities ♿ ∮ ⌨⌂⌐⊙◎ ⊟⊒ ♥
⌞⌟ ⊙ ⊛ ◪ ⊟ ⊞ ⛄ ✦ ⟨⟩
Nearest Town Wareham
Directions 1 mile south of Wareham on the
Swanage road.
⇌ Wareham

WAREHAM

Luckford Caravan & Camping Park,
Holme Lane, East Stoke, Wareham,
Dorset, BH20 6AP
Tel: 01929 463098
Email: luckfordleisure@hotmail.co.uk
www.luckfordleisure.co.uk
Pitches For Å ⊕ ⊞ ⊟⌇ **Total** 30
Acreage 4 **Open** Mar **to** Oct
Access Good **Site** Level
Near Tank Museum, Monkey World and
Lulworth, Jurasic Coast,Swanage, Studland .
Facilities ∮ ⌨⌂⌐ ♥ ⌞⌟⌐⊟ ⛄ ✦
Nearest Town Wareham
Directions From Wareham take the A352,
after 1½ miles turn left onto the B3070 to
Lulworth. At crossroads turn right into Holme
Lane (sp East Stoke), site is 1½ miles on the
right after a sharp left hand bend.
⇌ Wool

WAREHAM

Manor Farm Caravan & Camping Park,
Church Lane, East Stoke, Wareham,
Dorset, BH20 6AW
Tel: 01929 462870
Email: info@manorfarmcp.co.uk
www.manorfarmcp.co.uk
Pitches For Å ⊕ ⊞ **Total** 60
Acreage 2½ **Open** All Year
Access Good **Site** Level
Flat, grass touring park in a rural area of
outstanding natural beauty, central for most
of Dorset. Family run park with clean
facilities. Good walking area near beaches.
Close to Monkey World, Bovington Tank
Museum and the World Heritage Coast on
Pierbeck Cycle Way. RAC Appointed. Winter
storage available. No rallies, No groups and
No commercial vans.
Facilities ♿⚿∮ ⌨⌂⌐⊙◡ ♥
⌞⌟⊙⊛◪⊟⊞⛄✦⟨⟩

Nearest Town Wareham/Lulworth Cove
Directions From Wareham take A352 then
B3070. Turn into Holme Lane, at the
crossroads turn right sp Manor Farm CP. Or
from Wool sp down Bindon Lane, at the
crossroads turn left sp Manor Farm CP, site
is 300 yards on the left.
⇌ Wool/Wareham

WAREHAM

Ridge Farm Camping & Caravan Park,
Barnhill Road, Ridge, Wareham, Dorset,
BH20 5BG
Tel: 01929 556444
Email: info@ridgefarm.co.uk
www.ridgefarm.co.uk
Pitches For Å ⊕ ⊞ **Total** 60
Acreage 3½ **Open** Easter **to** Sept
Access Good **Site** Level
Peaceful, family run site in a rural setting
close to the Arne RSPB Reserve. In an area
of outstanding natural beauty and ideally
situated for the Purbeck Hills, Poole Harbour
and the coast. Boat launching nearby.
Facilities ∮ ⌨⌂⌐⊙◡◎ ⌞⌟ ⊙ ⊛ ⊟ ⛄
✦ **Nearest Town** Wareham
Directions Approx. 1½ miles south of
Wareham turn left in the village of
Stoborough towards Ridge. Follow signs
down Barnhill Road to Ridge Farm at the end
of the lane.
⇌ Wareham

WAREHAM

Wareham Forest Tourist Park, North
Trigon, Wareham, Dorset, BH20 7NZ
Tel: 01929 551393
Email: holiday@warehamforest.co.uk
www.warehamforest.co.uk
Pitches For Å ⊕ ⊞ ⊟⌇ **Total** 200
Acreage 40 **Open** All Year
Access Good **Site** Level

Tranquil, family owned park set in the forest. Ideal for relaxing and walking. Central location for exploring East Dorset and the Purbeck coastline.
Facilities ⬤ ⏚ 🛢 🍴 🏪 ⛽ 🔌 ☕ 🚿 🛁 🗑 🚻 ⚿ 🚗 ✕ 🏊 🎣 ⚓ 🌳 ⛔ 🔥 🚻 🚲 💧 ♿ 🛜
Nearest Town Wareham
Directions Located midway between Wareham and Bere Regis in Wareham Forest.
⚞ Wareham

WEYMOUTH
Bagwell Farm Touring Park, Knights in the Bottom, Chickerell, Weymouth, Dorset, DT3 4EA
Tel: 01305 782575
Email: cab@bagwellfarm.co.uk
www.bagwellfarm.co.uk
Pitches For ⛺ ⛘ 🚐 🚍 **Total** 320
Acreage 14 **Open** All Year
Access Good **Site** Level
Nearest Bus Stop (Miles) ¼
A friendly welcome awaits you. 5 miles from Weymouths sandy beach. Close to The Fleet Lagoon and the World Heritage Coast. Access to the coastal path. Seasonal bar, restaurant and take-away on the Park. Ideal location for discovering Dorset and exploring Dorsets Jurassic Coastline. Wheelchair friend
Facilities ⬤ ⏚ 🛢 🍴 🏪 ⛽ 🔌 ☕ 🚿 🛁 🗑 🚻 ⚿ 🚗 ✕ 🏊 🎣 ⚓ 🌳 🚲 💧 ♿ 🛜
Nearest Town Weymouth
Directions From A354 follow signs for Weymouth town centre and Portland until you see signs for Chickerell, Abbotsbury B3157 We are 1 mile west of Chickerell.
⚞ Weymouth

WEYMOUTH
East Fleet Farm Touring Park, East Fleet Farm, Chickerell, Weymouth, Dorset, DT3 4DW
Tel: 01305 785768
Email: enquiries@eastfleet.co.uk
www.eastfleet.co.uk
Pitches For ⛺ ⛘ 🚐 **Total** 400
Acreage 21 **Open** 16-Mar to Oct
Access Good **Site** Lev/Slope
Nearest Bus Stop (Miles) Outside
Peaceful countryside location, on the edge of Fleet Water, in the midst of organic farmland, yet only 3 miles from Weymouth with its golden beach and attractions. Large camping and caravan accessories and spares shop.
Facilities ⬤ ⏚ 🛢 🍴 ✕ 🍷 ⚓ 🌳 🚻 🚲 💧 🛜
Nearest Town Weymouth
Directions 3 miles west of Weymouth on the B3157, go straight over the lights into Fleet Lane.
⚞ Weymouth

WEYMOUTH
Portesham Dairy Farm Camp Site, Bramdon Lane, Portesham, Weymouth, Dorset, DT3 4HG
Tel: 01305 871297
Email: info@porteshamdairyfarm.co.uk
www.porteshamdairyfarm.co.uk
Pitches For ⛺ ⛘ 🚐 **Total** 80
Acreage 7 **Open** April to Sept
Access Good **Site** Level
Nearest Bus Stop (Miles) Outside
Ideal touring for Chesil area. Local pub 230 yards. AA 4 Pennant graded.
Facilities ⏚ 🛢 🍴 🏪 ⛽ 🔌 ☕ 🗑 🚻 🚗 🌳 🚲 💧 ⚓
Nearest Town Weymouth
Directions 7 miles from Weymouth on B3157 Coast road.
⚞ Weymouth

WEYMOUTH
Sea Barn Farm Camping Park, Fleet, Weymouth, Dorset, DT3 4ED
Tel: 01305 782218
Email: enquiries@seabarnfarm.co.uk
www.seabarnfarm.co.uk
Pitches For ⛺ 🚐 **Total** 250
Acreage 12 **Open** 16-Mar to Oct
Access - **Site** Lev/slope
Nearest Bus Stop (Miles) 1
Fabulous views of the coast and Dorset countrtyside. Access to a coastal footpath. Ideal location for discovering Dorset.
Facilities ⬤ ⏚ 🛢 🍴 🏪 🔌 ☕ 🗑 🚻 ⚿ 🚗 🌳 🚲 💧
Nearest Town Weymouth
Directions From Weymouth take the B3157 towards Abbotsbury. After 2½ miles at the mini roundabout turn left to Fleet, site is 1 mile on the left.
⚞ Weymouth

WEYMOUTH
West Fleet Holiday Farm, Fleet, Weymouth, Dorset, DT3 4EF
Tel: 01305 782218
Email: ca@westfleetholidays.co.uk
www.westfleetholidays.co.uk
Pitches For ⛺ 🚐 **Total** 250
Acreage 12 **Open** Easter to Sept
Site Level
Nearest Bus Stop (Miles) Outside
Kids love camping at West Fleet. Outdoor pool, family clubhouse and lots of space to play. New facilities in 2007. Bus service during main season only.
Facilities ⬤ ⏚ 🛢 🍴 🏪 ⛽ 🔌 ☕ 🗑 🚻 ⚿ 🚗 ✕ 🍷 ⚓ 🌳 🚲 💧 🛜
Nearest Town Weymouth
Directions From Weymouth take the B3157 towards Abbotsbury. After 2½ miles at the mini roundabout turn left to Fleet, site is 1 mile on the right.
⚞ Weymouth

WIMBORNE
Gundrys Farm Caravan & Camping Park, School Lane, Three Legged Cross, Wimborne, Dorset, BH21 6RU
Tel: 01202 826322
Email: gundrysfarm@gmail.com
Pitches For ⛺ ⛘ 🚐 **Total** 50
Acreage 8 **Open** March to October
Access Good **Site** Level
Nearest Bus Stop (Miles) ¼
Friendly, family run park in a beautiful secluded location. All pitches are flat and level. 5 mins from a country park for fishing, golf and walking. 15 mins from Bournemouth and Poole with their sandy beaches, and the New Forest. 15 minute off-road walk to Moors Valley Country Park.
Facilities ⏚ 🛢 🍴 ☕ 🗑 🚻 ⚿ 🌳 🚲 💧 ⚓
Nearest Town Ringwood
Directions Take the A31 west 1 mile past Ringwood, follow the slip road and turn right at the roundabout signposted Three Legged Cross and Moors Valley Country Park, site is 1½ miles past Moors Valley on the left (brown tourism sign).
⚞ Bournemouth

WIMBORNE
Springfield Touring Park, Candys Lane, Corfe Mullen, Wimborne, Dorset, BH21 3EF
Tel: 01202 881719
Email: john.clark18@btconnect.com
www.springfieldtouringpark.co.uk
Pitches For ⛺ ⛘ 🚐 **Total** 45
Acreage 3½ **Open** April to October
Access Good **Site** Lev/Slope
Nearest Bus Stop (Miles) ¼
Family run park, overlooking the Stour Valley. Free showers and awnings. Convenient for the coast, New Forest, also ferry. Low Season Offers - £80, any 7 days for 2 adults including electric. Practical Caravan Top 100 Parks 2008/09/10/11.
Facilities ⬤ ⏚ 🛢 🍴 🔌 ☕ 🗑 🚻 🚗 🌳 🚲 💧
Nearest Town Wimborne
Directions 1¼ miles west of Wimborne just off main A31.
⚞ Poole

WIMBORNE

Verwood Camping & Caravanning Club Site, Sutton Hill, Woodlands, Wimborne, Dorset, BH21 8NQ
Tel: 01202 822763
Email: verwood.site@thefriendlyclub.co.uk
www.campingandcaravanningclub.co.uk/verwood
Pitches For ▲ ⚑ ⛟ **Total** 150
Acreage 12 **Open** 15-Mar **to** 04-Nov
Access Good **Site** Gentle Slope
Beautifully situated next to Ringwood Forest. Miles of safe, sandy beaches at Poole and Bournemouth are a reasonable distance. BTB 4 Star Graded and AA 3 Pennants. Non members welcome. You can also call us on 0845 130 7633.
Facilities ⚿ ✆ 🅷 ⊞⛉🏳 ⊙⌔ 🍴 ⛒ 🖾 🚻
🎱 🕯 🛒 🔥 ⚓ 🔠🐾 🖿 🖾 🌙 🛜
Nearest Town Ringwood
Directions From Salisbury take the A354, after 13 miles turn left onto the B3081, site is 1½ miles west of Verwood.
⚏ Bournemouth

WOOL

Whitemead Caravan Park, East Burton Road, Wool, Dorset, BH20 6HG
Tel: 01929 462241
Email: whitemeadcp@aol.com
www.whitemeadcaravanpark.co.uk
Pitches For ▲ ⚑ ⛟ **Total** 95
Acreage 5 **Open** Mid March **to** End Oct
Access Good **Site** Level
Nearest Bus Stop (Miles) ¼
Woodland site with several secluded pitches. Off licence on site.
Facilities ✆ ⊞⛉🏳 ⊙⌔ 🍴 🖾 🚻
🎱 🕯 🔥 ⚓ 🔠🖿 🖾 🌙 🛜
Nearest Town Wareham
Directions Off the A352 Wareham to Weymouth road. 5 miles west of Wareham and 5 miles north of Lulworth Cove.
⚏ Wool

DURHAM

BARNARD CASTLE

Barnard castle Camping & Caravanning Club Site, Dockenflatts Lane, Lartington, Barnard Castle, Durham, DL12 9DG
Tel: 01833 630228
Email:
barnard.castlesite@thefriendlyclub.co.uk
www.campingandcaravanningclub.co.uk/barnardcastle
Pitches For ▲ ⚑ ⛟ **Total** 90
Acreage 10 **Open** 21-Mar **to** 04-Nov
Site Level
Nearest Bus Stop (Miles) ½
Well placed for exploring the Pennines and the city of Durham. BTB 5 Star Graded, AA 4 Pennants and Loo of the Year Award. Non members welcome. You can also call us on 0845 130 7633.
Facilities ⚿ ✆ 🅷 ⊞⛉🏳 ⊙⌔ 🍴 ⛒ 🖾 🖾
🕯 🍴 ⚓ 🔠🖿 🖾 🌙 🛜
Directions On approach from Scotch Corner take the second turn right for Middleton in Teesdale and Barnard Castle. On approach from Penrith take the B6277 to Middleton in Teesdale. In approx 1 mile take turn off left signposted Raygill Riding Stables. The site is 500 metres on the left.
⚏ Darlington

BARNARD CASTLE

Hetherick Caravan Park, Marwood, Barnard Castle, Durham, DL12 8QX
Tel: 01388 488384
Email: info@hetherickcaravanpark.co.uk
www.hetherickcaravanpark.co.uk
Pitches For ▲ ⚑ ⛟ **Total** 41

Acreage 15 **Open** March **to** October
Access Good **Site** Level
Nearest Bus Stop (Miles) ½
Pleasant park situated on a working farm in open countryside, in the heart of beautiful Teesdale. 3 miles from the pretty market town of Barnard Castle.
Facilities ⚿ ✆ 🅷 ⊞⛉🏳 ⊙⌔ 🖾 🖾 🍴
🎱 🕯 🔥 ⚓ 🔠🖿
Nearest Town Barnard Castle
Directions Take the B6278 from Barnard Castle towards Eggleston, once past the golf course take the second right turn towards Kinninvie and Woodland.
⚏ Darlington

BARNARD CASTLE

Pecknell Farm Caravan Site, Pecknell Farm, Lartington, Barnard Castle, Co. Durham, DL12 9DF
Tel: 01833 638357
Pitches For ⚑ ⛟ **Total** 20
Acreage 1½ **Open** April **to** October
Access Good **Site** Level
Nearest Bus Stop (Miles) ¼
Ideal walking area, very attractive walk into historic Barnard Castle. Within easy reach of many attractions.
Facilities ✆ 🅷 ⊞⛉🏳 ⊙⌔ 🖾 🖾 🍴
Nearest Town Barnard Castle
Directions 1½ miles from Barnard Castle on the B6277 to Lartington, we are the first farm on the right.
⚏ Darlington

BARNARD CASTLE

Winston Caravan Park, The Old Forge, Winston, Darlington, Durham, DL2 3RH
Tel: 01325 730228
Email: m.willetts@ic24.net
www.touristnetuk.com/ne/winston
Pitches For ▲ ⚑ ⛟ **Total** 21
Open Mar **to** Oct
Access Good **Site** Level
Nearest Bus Stop (Miles) Outside
Ideally situated for exploring the many attractions in County Durham. Caravan for the disabled available for hire.
Facilities ✆ 🅷 ⊞⛉🏳 ⊙⌔ ⛒ 🖾 🔠🖿 🖾
Nearest Town Darlington
Directions From Darlington take the A67 west for 10 miles, turn left onto the B6274 into Winston Village, site is 400 yards on the right hand side.
⚏ Darlington

CONSETT

Manor Park Caravan & Camping Park, Manor Park Limited, Broadmeadows, Near Castleside, Consett, Durham, DH8 9HD
Tel: 01207 501000
Pitches For ⚑ ⛟ **Total** 20
Open May **to** Aug
Access Good **Site** Sloping
Ideal base for visiting Durham with its cathedral and castle, Northumberland, Beamish Museum and the Angel of the North.
Facilities ⊞⛉🏳 ⊙ 🖾 🔥
Nearest Town Consett
Directions From A68, Castleside - Tow Law turn east onto Eliza Lane site ¾ mile on right.
⚏ Durham

DURHAM

Durham Grange Caravan Club Site, Meadow Lane, Durham, Co. Durham, DH1 1TL
Tel: 0191 384 4778
www.caravanclub.co.uk
Pitches For ▲ ⚑ ⛟ **Total** 76
Acreage 12 **Open** All Year
Access Good **Site** Level

Nearest Bus Stop (Miles) ½
Only 3 miles from the city of Durham with its castle and cathedral. Beamish Open Air Museum nearby. Non members welcome. Booking essential.
Facilities ✆ 🅴 🅷 ⊞⛉🏳 ⊙ 🖾 🍴 🖿 🖾 🛜
Nearest Town Durham
Directions Leave the A1(M) via slip road onto the A690 signposted Durham. Immediately move to the outside lane to turn right in 50 yards at brown caravan sign into Meadow Lane, site entrance is ahead.
⚏ Durham

DURHAM

Finchale Abbey Caravan Park, Finchale Abbey Farm, Durham, DH1 5SH
Tel: 0191 386 6528
Email: godricawatson@hotmail.com
www.finchaleabbey.co.uk
Pitches For ⚑ ⛟ ⚑ **Total** 40
Acreage 6 **Open** All Year
Access Good **Site** Level
Nearest Bus Stop (Miles) 1
ADULTS ONLY PARK set in the meander of the River Wear. Ideally situated to visit most of the North Easts highlights.
Facilities ⚿ ✆ 🅴 🅷 ⊞⛉🏳 ⊙⌔ 🖾
🎱 🕯 🔥 ⚓ 🔠🖿 🖾 🍴 A
Nearest Town Durham City
Directions Leave the A1M at junction 63 and head south on the A167. At Arnson roundabout follow signs for Finchale Priory, site is at the same place.
⚏ Durham City

DURHAM

Strawberry Hill Farm Caravan & Camping Park, Old Cassop, Durham, DH6 4QA
Tel: 0191 372 3457
Email: info@strawberryhf.co.uk
www.strawberry-hill-farm.co.uk
Pitches For ▲ ⚑ ⛟ **Total** 45
Acreage 6 **Open** March **to** Dec
Access Good **Site** Terraced
Nearest Bus Stop (Miles) ¼
Approx. 4 miles from Durham City, World Heritage Site, Castle and Cathedral. Caravan holiday homes for hire.
Facilities ⚿ ✆ 🅷 ⊞⛉🏳 ⊙⌔ 🖾 🖾 🖾
🎱 🔥 🔠🖿 🖾
Nearest Town Durham City
Directions From junction 61 of the A1M take exit sp Bowburn A177. Travel to the second set of traffic lights (2.6 miles) and turn right sp A19 Peterlee and Hartlepool. The Park is 3½ miles on the left.
⚏ Durham City

MIDDLETON-IN-TEESDALE

Mickleton Mill Caravan Park, The Mill, Mickleton, Barnard Castle, Durham, DL12 0LS
Tel: 01833 640317
Email: mickletonmill@aol.com
www.mickletonmill.co.uk
Pitches For ⚑ ⛟ **Total** 4
Acreage 7½ **Open** March **to** October
Access Fair **Site** Level
Nearest Bus Stop (Miles) ½
Set on the banks of the River Lune.
Facilities ✆ 🅷 ⊞⛉🏳 ⊙⌔ 🖾 🖾 🖾
🎱 🕯 🖿 🖾 🍴 🌙 🛜
Nearest Town Barnard Castle
Directions From Barnard Castle take the B6277. In Mickleton take the first turn right past Blacksmiths Arms, go down the bank and bear left at the bottom of the hill.
⚏ Darlington

WOLSINGHAM

Bradley Burn Caravan Park,
Wolsingham, Bishop Auckland, Co.
Durham, DL13 3JH
Tel: 01388 527285
Email: stay@bradleyburn.co.uk
www.bradleyburn.co.uk
Pitches For ⊞ ⊞ **Total** 5
Open March **to** October
Access Good **Site** Lev/Slope
Nearest Bus Stop (Miles) Outside
Peaceful Park set in beautiful scenery in the
heart of the Durham Dales and on the edge
of the Pennines. Farm shop and cafe.
Facilities ⨍ ⌂ ⊙ ⊠ Ⓧ Ⓜ ⊬ ⊟ ⚲
Nearest Town Wolsingham
Directions 2 miles east of Wolsingham on
the A689 and 2 miles west of the A68/A689
junction.
⇝ Bishop Auckland

ESSEX

BRENTWOOD

**Kelvedon Hatch Camping & Caravanning
Club Site,** Warren Lane, Doddinghurst,
Brentwood, Essex, CM15 0JG
Tel: 01277 372773
Email:
kelvedon.hatch@thefriendlyclub.co.uk
www.campingandcaravanningclub.co.uk/
kelvedonhatch
Pitches For Å ⊞ ⊞ **Total** 90
Acreage 12 **Open** 21-Mar **to** 04-Nov
Access Fair **Site** Level
Nearest Bus Stop (Miles) ½
Peaceful site, good for country walks. 20
miles from the centre of London. Plenty of
sporting activities within easy reach. BTB 3
Star Graded and AA 3 Pennants. Non
members welcome. You can also call us on
0845 130 7633.
Facilities ⅊ ⨍ ⊞ ⎈ ⌂ ⊙ ⇗ ⌁ ⌂ ⊟ ⚎
Ⓡ ⊙ ⊠ ⋔ ⊬ ⊟ ⊡ ⚲ ⚲ ⚲
Directions Leave the M25 at junction 28 and
take the A1023 towards Brentwood. Turn left
onto the A128 to Ongar, the site is 3 miles
on the right, signposted.
⇝ Brentwood

CLACTON-ON-SEA

Orchards Holiday Village, St Osyth,
Clacton-on-Sea, Essex, CO16 8LJ
Tel: 01255 820651
Email: theorchards@haven.com
www.haventouring.com/totheorchards
Pitches For Å ⊞ ⊞ **Total** 69
Acreage 140 **Open** Mid March **to** End Oct
Access Good **Site** Level
Nearest Bus Stop (Miles) Outside
Nearest Town St Osyth
⇝ Clacton-on-Sea

CLACTON-ON-SEA

Silver Dawn Touring Park, Jaywick Lane,
Clacton-on-Sea, Essex, CO16 8BB
Tel: 01255 421856
www.silverdawntouringpark.co.uk
Pitches For ⊞ ⊞ **Total** 38
Acreage 3 **Open** April **to** October

Access Good **Site** Level
Sky TV. David Bellamy Silver Award for
Conservation. You can also contact us on
Mobile: 07906 222353.
Facilities ⨍ ⌂ ⌂ ⌂ ⊙ ⚎
Ⓡ ⊙ ⊠ ⚲ ⋔ ⚲ ⚎
Nearest Town Clacton-on-Sea
Directions Take the A12 then A120 to Clacton.
⇝ Clacton-on-Sea

COLCHESTER

Colchester Holiday Park Ltd., Cymbeline
Way, Colchester, Essex, CO3 4AG
Tel: 01206 545551
Email: enquiries@colchestercamping.co.uk
www.col.camping park.
Pitches For Å ⊞ ⊞ **Total** 150
Open All Year **Access** Good **Site** Level
Nearest Bus Stop (Miles) ½
10 miles from beaches, ideal touring for the
Essex countryside.
Facilities ⨍ ⊞ ⎈ ⌂ ⌂ ⊙ ⇗ ⌁ ⌂ ⊟ ⚎
Ⓡ ⊙ ⊠ ⊬ ⊟ ⊡ ⚲ ⚲ ⚲
Nearest Town Colchester
Directions From London take the A12 to
junction 27 and follow brown tourism signs.
⇝ Colchester North

HALSTEAD

Gosfield Lake Resort, Church Road,
Gosfield, Essex, CO9 1UD
Tel: 01787 475043
Email: turps@gosfieldlake.co.uk
www.gosfieldlake.co.uk
Pitches For Å ⊞ ⊞ **Total** 30
Acreage 5 **Open** Apr **to** Oct
Access Good **Site** Level
Nearest Bus Stop (Miles) ¼
Lakeside pitches. Fishing and waterskiing
available. Booking and availability online.
Facilities ⨍ ⎈ ⌂ ⌂ ⊙ ⇗ ⌂ ⊠ Ⓧ ⋔ ⚎ ⚲
Nearest Town Halstead
Directions From Braintree take the A131
towards Halstead. Turn left at High Garrett
traffic lights to Gosfield. Follow brown tourism
signs from the A120.
⇝ Braintree

MANNINGTREE

**The Strangers Home Inn Caravan &
Camping Park,** The Street, Bradfield,
Manningtree, Essex, CO11 2US
Tel: 01255 870304
Email: enquiries@strangershome.co.uk
www.stargladeleisure.co.uk
Pitches For Å ⊞ ⊞ **Total** 53
Acreage 4 **Open** Mar **to** Oct
Access Good **Site** Level
Nearest Bus Stop (Miles) Outside
The nearest campsite to Harwich Port and
in an area of outstanding natural beauty, this
family run Park has full facilities and more!
Pub, Bed & Breakfast, entertainment and
kids play area on site.
Facilities ⨍ ⊞ ⊙ ⊠ Ⓧ ⚲ ⊞ ⋔ ⚲ ⚎
Ⓡ ⊙ ⊠ ⚲ ⋔ ⋔ ⊞ ⊡ ⚲ ⚲ ⚲
Directions Leave the A12 at junction 29 then
merge onto the A120. Continue on the A120
and at the roundabout take the first exit onto
the B1035 Clacton road. Turn right into Heath
Road and continue onto The Street.
⇝ Histley

MERSEA ISLAND

Fen Farm Caravan & Camping Site,
Moore Lane, East Mersea, Colchester,
Essex, CO5 8FE
Tel: 01206 383275
Email: fenfarm@talk21.com
www.fenfarm.co.uk
Pitches For Å ⊞ ⊞ ⊞ **Total** 90
Acreage 5 **Open** Mid March **to** End Oct
Access Good **Site** Level
Quiet, rural, family run site just a 2 minute
walk to the beach and on an estuary. Close
to a country park.
Facilities ⚲ ⨍ ⊞ ⎈ ⌂ ⌂ ⊙ ⇗ ⌂ ⊟ ⚎
Ⓢ Ⓡ ⊙ ⊠ Ⓜ ⊬ ⊟ ⊡ ⚲ ⚲ ⚲ ⚲
Nearest Town Colchester
Directions Take the B1025 from Colchester
to Mersea, take the left fork to East Mersea.
Moore Lane is the first left turn after the Dog
& Pheasant Public House.
⇝ Colchester

MERSEA ISLAND

Seaview Holiday Park, Seaview Avenue,
West Mersea, Colchester, Essex, CO5
8DA
Tel: 01206 382534
Email: info@westmersea.com
www.westmersea.com
Pitches For ⊞ ⊞ **Total** 66
Acreage 18 **Open** Apr **to** Oct
Access Good **Site** Level
Nearest Bus Stop (Miles) ¼
Situated alongside out own private sandy
beach. Coastal walks and a country park.
Facilities ⨍ ⊞ ⎈ ⌂ ⌂ ⊙ ⇗ ⌂ ⊟ ⚎
Ⓢ Ⓡ ⊙ ⊠ Ⓧ ⚲ ⊞ ⋔ ⊟ ⊡ ⚲
Nearest Town Colchester
Directions Take the A12 to Colchester then
join the B1025 to West Mersea. Cross the
Strood Channel via 'The Causeway', take the
left fork and follow brown tourism signs.
⇝ Colchester

MERSEA ISLAND

Waldegraves Holiday & Leisure Park,
Mersea Island, Colchester, Essex, CO5
8SE
Tel: 01206 382898
Email: holidays@waldegraves.co.uk
www.waldegraves.co.uk
Pitches For Å ⊞ ⊞ **Total** 60
Acreage 45 **Open** Mar **to** Nov
Access Good **Site** Level
Nearest Bus Stop (Miles) ½
Ideal family park, surrounded by trees and
lakes. Safe private beach. Licensed bar and
restaurant, swimming pool, undercover golf
driving range, pitch & putt, Family
entertainment, play areas and games room,
fishing and boating lake. Luxury holiday
homes for hire and sale.
Facilities ⚲ ⨍ ⊞ ⎈ ⌂ ⌂ ⊙ ⇗ ⌂ ⊟ ⚎
Ⓢ Ⓡ ⊙ ⊠ Ⓧ ⚲ ⊞ ⋔ ⚲ ⋔ ⊞ ⊡ ⊡ ⚲ ⚎
⚲ ⚲
Nearest Town Colchester
Directions From Colchester take B1025, 10
miles to West Mersea. Take left fork to East
Mersea, second road to right.
⇝ Colchester

SOUTHEND-ON-SEA
Riverside Village Holiday Park, Creeksea Ferry Road, Wallasea Island, Rochford, Essex, SS4 2EY
Tel: 01702 258297
Email: riversidevillage@tiscali.co.uk
www.riversidevillageholidaypark.co.uk
Pitches For Å ♙ ♙ **Total** 60
Acreage 25 **Open** Mar to 01-Nov
Access Good **Site** Level
Nearest Bus Stop (Miles) Outside
Open countryside walks,cycling,wildlife (RSPB) top notch pubs/resturants. Easy access to London.
Facilities ⚊ ⚊ ⚊ ⚊ ⚊ ⚊
Nearest Town Southend-on-Sea
Directions A127 to Tesco roundabout to B1013 Rochford follow signs for Wallasea Island.
⚊ Rochford

SOUTHMINSTER
Waterside Holiday Park, Main Road, St Lawrence Bay, Southminster, Essex, CM0 7LY
Tel: 01621 779248
Email: lisabacon@park-resorts.com
www.park-resorts.com
Pitches For Å ♙ ♙
Open Apr to Oct
Access Good **Site** Level
Near the coast and not far from the town centre.
Facilities ⚊ ⚊ ⚊ ⚊ ⚊
Nearest Town Maldon/Colchester
Directions Follow the A12 towards Chelmsford and take the A414 sp Maldon. Take the B1010 and follow signs for St Lawrence, turn left off the main road and the Park is on the right.
⚊ Maldon/Colchester

WEELEY
Homestead Lake Park, Thorpe Road (B1033), Weeley, Clacton-on-Sea, Essex, CO16 9JN
Tel: 01255 833492
Email: lakepark@homesteadcaravans.co.uk

www.homesteadlake.co.uk
Pitches For ♙ ♙ ♙ **Total** 50
Acreage 4 **Open** March to October
Access Good **Site** Sloping
Nearest Bus Stop (Miles) ¼
Quiet and relaxing site with a fishing lake. Caravan accessory shop on site,very clean.
Facilities ⚊ ⚊ ⚊ ⚊ ⚊
Nearest Town Clacton-on-Sea
Directions From the A12 take the A120/A133 towards Clacton then the B1033 towards Frinton and Walton on the Naze.
⚊ Weeley

GLOUCESTERSHIRE
CHELTENHAM
Briarfields Motel & Touring Park, Gloucester Road, Cheltenham, Gloucestershire, GL51 0SX
Tel: 01242 235324
Email: briarfields@hotmail.co.uk
www.briarfields.net
Pitches For Å ♙ ♙ ♙ **Total** 72
Acreage 6 **Open** All Year
Access Good **Site** Level
Nearest Bus Stop (Miles) Outside
Excellent bus service to Cheltenham and Gloucester from outside our park.
Facilities ⚊ ⚊ ⚊ ⚊ ⚊
Nearest Town Cheltenham
Directions Leave the M5 at junction 11 and take the A40 for Cheltenham. At the first roundabout take the first exit onto the B4063, Briarfields is 200 metres on the left.
⚊ Cheltenham Spa

CHELTENHAM
Cheltenham Racecourse Caravan Club Site, Prestbury Park, Cheltenham, Gloucestershire, GL50 4SH
Tel: 01242 523102
www.caravanclub.co.uk
Pitches For ♙ ♙ **Total** 75
Acreage 7 **Open** Apr to Oct
Access Good **Site** Lev/Slope
Nearest Bus Stop (Miles) ¼
Set on the edge of elegant Cheltenham with panoramic views of the Cleeve Hills. Free

racing, putting course adjacent (small charge). Non members welcome. Booking essential.
Facilities ⚊ ⚊ ⚊ ⚊ ⚊ ⚊
Nearest Town Cheltenham
Directions From west on the A40, 1½ miles past M5 junc at Benhall r/about t lt into Princess Elizabeth Way. At the r/about continue straight into Kingsditch Industrial Estate, after ½ mile turn right, at r/about turn left into racecourse and follow signs.
⚊ Cheltenham

CIRENCESTER
Hoburne Cotswold, Broadway Lane, South Cerney, Cirencester, Gloucestershire, GL7 5UQ
Tel: 01285 860216
Email: enquiries@hoburne.com
www.hoburne.com
Pitches For Å ♙ ♙ **Total** 189
Acreage 70 **Open** March to October
Access Good **Site** Level
Nearest Bus Stop (Miles) 0.25
Nearest Town South Cerney

CIRENCESTER
Mayfield Touring Park, Cheltenham Road, Perrotts Brook, Cirencester, Gloucestershire, GL7 7BH
Tel: 01285 831301
Email: mayfield-park@cirencester.fsbusiness.co.uk
www.mayfieldpark.co.uk
Pitches For Å ♙ ♙ **Total** 76
Acreage 10 **Open** All Year
Access Good **Site** Lev/Slope
Nearest Bus Stop (Miles) Outside
In a position central to the Cotswolds with pleasant views and a warm welcome. This site benefits from having a variety of pitch types with something to suit every need. Disabled toilet/shower and baby changing facilities.
Facilities ⚊ ⚊ ⚊ ⚊ ⚊ ⚊
Directions On A435, 13 miles from Cheltenham and 2 miles from Cirencester. From Cirencester by-pass A419/A417 take the Burford Road exit then follow camping and caravan signs.
⚊ Kemble

GLOUCESTERSHIRE

CIRENCESTER

Second Chance Caravan Park, Nr Marston Meysey, Wiltshire, SN6 6SZ
Tel: 01285 810675/810939
www.secondchancetouring.co.uk
Pitches For ▲ ⊞ ⊞ **Total** 26
Acreage 2 **Open** March **to** November
Access Good **Site** Level
Nearest Bus Stop (Miles) ¼
Riverside location with private fishing and access for your own small person kyack. The first camping/caravan park on the Thames Path, great for exploring the upper reaches of the Thames. Excellent opportunity to visit the old Roman capital of Cirencester and the many attractions of the Cotswolds. AA 2 Pennants.
Facilities ∮ ⊞ ⊞ ⋒ ⌐ ⊙ ⊣ ⊞ ☎
⊟ ⊞ ⊿ ※
Nearest Town Castle Eaton/Fairford
Directions Between Swindon and Cirencester on the A419. Turn off at the Fairford/Marston Meysey exit and follow the caravan park signs. Proceed approx. 3 miles then turn right at the brown caravan/camping signpost. We are on the right.
⚐ Swindon

COLEFORD

Greenacres Campsite, Scowles Road, Coleford, Gloucestershire, GL16 8QS
Tel: 01594 837753
Email: greenacres2@btinternet.com
www.greenacrescampsite.co.uk
Pitches For ▲ ⊞ ⊞ **Total** 12
Acreage 1½ **Open** April **to** October
Access Good **Site** Level
Nearest Bus Stop (Miles) ½
Situated in the Forest of Dean near Symonds Yat, in an Area of Outstanding Natural Beauty near a river.
Facilities ∮ ⊞ ⋒ ⌐ ⊣ ☎ ⅛ ⊮ ⊞ ⋇

Nearest Town Coleford
Directions From Coleford take the main road for Staunton, just out of Coleford turn left towards The Scowles, site is ½ a mile.
⚐ Lydney

DURSLEY

Hogsdown Farm Caravan & Camping, Hogsdown Farm, Lower Wick, Dursley, Gloucestershire, GL11 6DD
Tel: 01453 810224
www.hogsdownfarm.co.uk
Pitches For ▲ ⊞ ⊞
Acreage 5 **Open** All Year
Access Good **Site** Level
Nearest Bus Stop (Miles) 1
Great for visiting Berkeley Castle, Jenner Museum, Wild Fowl Trust, Weston Birt Arboretum, and the hills and valleys of the Cotswolds.
Facilities ∮ ⊞ ⊞ ⋒ ⌐ ⊙ ⊣ ⊞ ⊡ ☎
⊟ ⊕ ❋ ⊮ ⊞ ⋇ ⚶
Nearest Town Berkeley
Directions Between junctions 13 and 14 of the M5, off the A38.
⚐ Cam

GLOUCESTER

The Red Lion Inn Caravan & Camping Park, Wainlode Hill, Norton, Gloucestershire, GL2 9LW
Tel: 01452 730251
www.redlioninn-caravancampingpark.co.uk
Pitches For ▲ ⊞ ⊞ ⊞⊱ **Total** 109
Acreage 10 **Open** All Year
Access Good **Site** Level
Nearest Bus Stop (Miles) ½
On the banks of the River Severn with a riverside pub.
Facilities ⅊ ∮ ⊞ ⊞ ⋒ ⌐ ⊙ ⊣ ⊞ ⊡ ☎
⅛ ⊕ ✕ ⋒ ⊮ ⊞ ⊿ ⋇ ⚶
Nearest Town Gloucester/Tewkesbury

Directions From Tewkesbury take the A38 south for 3 miles, turn right onto the B4213. After 3 miles turn left to Wainlode Hill, 350 yards alongside the River Severn, park is on the left.
⚐ Gloucester

LECHLADE

Bridge House Campsite, Bridge House, Thames Street, Lechlade, Gloucestershire, GL7 3AG
Tel: 01367 252348
Pitches For ▲ ⊞ ⊞ **Total** 75
Acreage 3½ **Open** Apr **to** Oct
Access Good **Site** Level
Nearest Bus Stop (Miles) ¼
Set on the edge of the Cotswolds, near to Lechlade with its local shops, pubs and resturants.
Facilities ⅋ ∮ ⊞ ⋒ ⌐ ⊙ ⊣ ⊞ ☎ ⅛ ⊮ ⊞ ⋇
Nearest Town Lechlade
Directions Site is on the A361 to Swindon, approximately 500yds from River Thames. r
⚐ Swindon

MORETON VALENCE

Gables Farm Caravan & Camping Site, Moreton Valence, Gloucestershire, GL2 7ND
Tel: 01452 720331
Pitches For ▲ ⊞ ⊞ **Total** 30
Acreage 3 **Open** March **to** Nov
Access Good **Site** Level
Nearest Bus Stop (Miles) Outside
Facilities ∮ ⊞ ⋒ ⌐ ⊙ ⊣ ☎ ⅛ ⊕ ⊮ ⊞
Nearest Town Gloucester
Directions Leave the M5 at junction 13 and take the A38 north for 2 miles. Or leave the M5 at junction 12 and take the A38 south for 1½ miles.
⚐ Gloucester

MORETON-IN-MARSH

Moreton-In-Marsh Caravan Club Site,
Bourton Road, Moreton-in-Marsh,
Gloucestershire, GL56 0BT
Tel: 01608 650519
www.caravanclub.co.uk
Pitches For ⊡ ⛺ **Total** 183
Acreage 21 **Open** All Year
Access Good **Site** Level
Nearest Bus Stop (Miles) ¼
Attractive, wooded site offering crazy golf, 5-a-side football, volleyball and a boules pitch. Near Batsford Arboretum & Falconry Centre and Sleepy Hollow Farm Park. Non members welcome. Booking essential.
Facilities ♿ ⏷ 🚻 🚿 🖥️ ☈ ⊡ ⛺
🏪 🛒 🔥 ⚡ 🚮 🖃 🐕 ⛱
Nearest Town Moreton-in-Marsh
Directions Leave Evesham on the A44, site entrance is on the left approx. 1¼ miles past Bourton-on-the-Hill and 150 yards before Moreton-in-Marsh sign. NB: No arrivals before 1pm at weekends and in peak periods.

SLIMBRIDGE

Tudor Caravanning & Camping Park,
Shepherds Patch, Slimbridge,
Gloucestershire, GL2 7BP
Tel: 01453 890483
Email: cades@tudorcaravanpark.co.uk
www.tudorcaravanpark.com
Pitches For ⋏ ⊡ ⛺ 🚐 **Total** 75
Acreage 7¼ **Open** All Year
Access Good **Site** Level
Sharpness Canal alongside, Slimbridge Wetlands Centre 800 metres, Cotswold Way 5 miles. Pub on our doorstep. NEW toilet and shower block. AA 4 Pennants.
Facilities ♿ ⏷ 🚻 🚿 🖥️ ☈ 🚮 🖃 ⊡ ⛺
🏪 🛒 🗙 🖃 🖃 ⛱ ⛱
Nearest Town Dursley/Gloucester
Directions Leave the M5 at junction 13 and follow signs for WWT Wetlands Centre, Slimbridge. 1½ miles off the A38 at the rear of the Tudor Arms Pub.
🚉 Dursley

TEWKESBURY

Croft Farm Leisure & Water Park,
Bredons Hardwick, Tewkesbury,
Gloucestershire, GL20 7EE
Tel: 01684 772321
Email: alan@croftfarmleisure.co.uk
www.croftfarmleisure.co.uk
Pitches For ⋏ ⊡ ⛺ 🚐 **Total** 60
Acreage 10 **Open** Mar to Oct
Access Good **Site** Level
Nearest Bus Stop (Miles) ¼
Lakeside location with own watersports centre and lake for sailing, windsurfing and canoeing. River Avon close by. Gym and Clubhouse on site.
Facilities ♿ ⏷ 🚻 🚿 🖥️ ☈ 🚮 🖃 ⊡ ⛺
🏪 🛒 🗙 ⛾ 🛒 🔥 🖃 🖃 🥾 ⛱ ⛱
Nearest Town Tewkesbury
Directions 1½ miles north-east of Tewkesbury on the B4080.
🚉 Ashchurch

TEWKESBURY

Dawleys Caravan Park, Owls Lane,
Shuthonger, Tewkesbury, Gloucestershire,
GL20 6EQ
Tel: 01684 292622
Email:
enquiries@dawleyscaravanpark.co.uk
www.ukparks.co.uk/dawleys
Pitches For ⋏ ⊡ ⛺ **Total** 20
Acreage 3 **Open** April to Sept
Access Fair **Site** Sloping
Nearest Bus Stop (Miles) ½
Secluded rural site, near a river. Close to the M5 and M50.
Facilities ⏷ 🚻 🖥️ ☈ 🚮 ⊙ ⊡ ⛺
🏪 🛒 🖃 🖃 🥾
Nearest Town Cheltenham/Gloucester
Directions A38 north from Tewkesbury, approximately 2 miles on the left hand side. Or 1¼ miles south on A38 from M50 junction 1.
🚉 Tewkesbury

TEWKESBURY

Mill Avon Holiday Park, Gloucester Road,
Tewkesbury, Gloucestershire, GL20 5SW
Tel: 01684 296876
Email: millavon@btconnect.com
www.millavon.com

Pitches For ⊡ ⛺ **Total** 24
Open Mar to Dec
Access Good **Site** Level
Nearest Bus Stop (Miles) ¼
Alongside river, close to town centre.
Facilities ⚒ ⏷ 🚻 🖥️ ☈ ⊙ 🚮 ⚡ ⊡ ⛺
🏪 🛒 🖃 🖃 🖃 ⛱
Nearest Town Tewkesbury
Directions ¼ of a mile from the town centre.
🚉 Ashchurch

TEWKESBURY

Tewkesbury Abbey Caravan Club Site,
Gander Lane, Tewkesbury,
Gloucestershire, GL20 5PG
Tel: 01684 294035
www.caravanclub.co.uk
Pitches For ⋏ ⊡ **Total** 145
Acreage 9 **Open** Apr to Nov
Access Good **Site** Lev/Slope
Nearest Bus Stop (Miles) ½
Situated adjacent to the ancient Abbey. Many interesting walks, historic buildings and museums locally. Near the Battle Trail and Royal Worcester Factory. Non members welcome. Booking essential.
Facilities ♿ ⏷ 🖥️ ☈ 🚮 ⊡ ⛺
🏪 🛒 ⚡ 🖃 🖃 ⛱
Nearest Town Tewkesbury
Directions Leave the M5 at junc 9 and take the A438 sp Tewkesbury. At the traffic lights by Morrisons go straight on, at the town centre crossroads keep left and after 200 yards turn left into Gander Lane, site is on the left.
🚉 Tewkesbury

TEWKESBURY

Winchcombe Camping & Caravanning Club Site, Brooklands Farm, Alderton, Nr Tewkesbury, Gloucestershire, GL20 8NX
Tel: 01242 620259
Email:
winchcombe.site@thefriendlyclub.co.uk
www.campingandcaravanning.co.uk/winchcombe
Pitches For ⋏ ⊡ ⛺ **Total** 80
Acreage 20 **Open** 11-Mar to 15-Jan
Access Good **Site** Level
Nearest Bus Stop (Miles) 1

Set amidst the lovely Cotswold countryside, with its own fishing lake. Lodges available for hire. BTB 4 Star Graded and AA 3 Pennants. Non members welcome. You can also call us on 0845 130 7633.
Facilities ⬤ ∮ ⬚ ⬚ ⬚ ⬚ ⬚ ⬚ ⬚ ⬚
⬚ ⬚ ⬚ ⬚ ⬚ ⬚ ⬚ ⬚ ⬚ ⬚ ⬚ ⬚
Nearest Town Tewkesbury
Directions From Tewkesbury take the A46, at the roundabout go straight over then take the B4077 to Stow-on-the-Wold, site is on the right in 3 miles.
⬥ Tewkesbury

HAMPSHIRE
ANDOVER
Wyke Down Touring Caravan & Camping Park, Picket Piece, Andover, Hants., SP11 6LX
Tel: 01264 352048
Email: p.read@wykedown.co.uk
www.wykedown.co.uk

Pitches For ⬤ ⬚ ⬚ ⬚ ⬚ **Total** 69
Acreage 3 **Open** All Year
Access Good **Site** Level
Nearest Bus Stop (Miles) ½
Ideal touring centre. Country pub and restaurant with golf driving range.
Facilities ∮ ⬚ ⬚ ⬚ ⬚ ⬚ ⬚ ⬚ ⬚
⬚ ⬚ ⬚ ⬚ ⬚ ⬚ ⬚ ⬚ ⬚
Nearest Town Andover
Directions Follow camping/caravan park signs from the A303, go through the village of Picket Piece and site is on the left in approx. 1 mile.
⬥ Andover

BRANSGORE
Harrow Wood Farm Caravan Park,
Poplar Lane, Bransgore, Nr Christchurch, Hampshire, BH23 8JE
Tel: 01425 672487
Email: harrowwood@caravan-sites.co.uk
www.caravan-sites.co.uk
Pitches For ⬤ ⬚ **Total** 60

Open Mar to 06-Jan
Access Good **Site** Level
Nearest Bus Stop (Miles) ½
Set in 80 acres of farmland. Within easy reach of the New Forest and the sea.

Facilities ⬤ ∮ ⬚ ⬚ ⬚ ⬚ ⬚ ⬚ ⬚ ⬚

⬚ ⬚ ⬚ ⬚ ⬚

Nearest Town Christchurch
Directions 4 miles from Christchurch on the A35, in Bransgore turn first right after the school into Poplar Lane.

⬥ Hinton Admiral

FAREHAM
Dibles Park, Dibles Road, Warsash, Southampton, Hampshire, SO31 9SA
Tel: 01489 575232
Email: dibles.park@btconnect.com
www.diblespark.co.uk

Pitches For Å ⚑ ⛺ ⛺⚡ Total 14
Open All Year **Access** Good **Site** Level
Nearest Bus Stop (Miles) ½
Ideal for touring, walking and cycling. Excellent location for cross Channel ferries. Near Hamble Estuary and nature reserves.
Facilities ∮ 🚿🚽⚡🏧🛒⚷🔒⛽🔌🛒
Nearest Town Fareham/Southampton
Directions Leave the M27 at junc 9 and take the A27 for Fareham. At the next roundabout exit sp Park Gate A27. At the third roundabout take the exit onto Brook Lane. Continue along this road going across 3 roundabouts, at 4th roundabout (mini) take second exit into Dibles Road, Park entrance is 500 yards on the left.

HAMBLE

Riverside Holidays, Satchell Lane, Hamble, Hampshire, SO31 4HR
Tel: 023 8045 3220
Email: enquiries@riversideholidays.co.uk
www.riversideholidays.co.uk
Pitches For Å ⚑ ⛺ ⛺ Total 77
Acreage 2 **Open** March to October
Access Good **Site** Lev/Slight Slope
Nearest Bus Stop (Miles) 0.5
Nearest Town Southampton
⚏ Hamble

FORDINGBRIDGE

Hill Cottage Farm Camping & Caravan Park, Sandleheath Road, Alderholt, Fordingbridge, Hampshire, SP6 3EG
Tel: 01425 650513
Email:
hillcottagefarmcaravansite@supanet.com
www.hillcottagefarmcampingandcaravanpark.co.uk
Pitches For Å ⚑ ⛺ ⛺⚡ Total 90
Acreage 12 **Open** Mar to Oct
Access Good **Site** Level
Nearest Bus Stop (Miles) ½
Situated on the edge of the New Forest. Listed in Practical Caravans Top 100 Parks.

Facilities ⚷ ∮ 🚿🚽⚡🏧🔌⛽⚷🔒⛽🔌🛒
♨ 🏧⚽🛒⚷🔌🔒⚙🔌⚷✦✦
Directions 2 miles from Fordingbridge on the B3078.
⚏ Salisbury

HAYLING ISLAND

Oven Camping Site, Manor Road, Hayling Island, Hampshire, PO11 0QX
Tel: 02392 464695
Email: theovencampsite@talktalk.net
www.haylingcampsites.co.uk
Pitches For Å ⚑ ⛺ Total 330
Acreage 10 **Open** March to Dec Incl.
Access Good **Site** Level
Nearest Bus Stop (Miles) Outside
Heated swimming pool. Excellent touring area for Portsmouth, Chichester, New Forest etc. Safe, clean, Blue Flag beaches, excellent for water sports. Excellent Rally site at discount prices.3 nights for the price in off peak times
Facilities ⚷ ∮ 🚿⚡🔌⚷🔒⚙🔌⛽
♨ 🏧⚽🛒⚷🔌🔒⚙✦✦
Nearest Town Havant
Directions Exit M27 or the A37 at Havant. Take the A3023 from Havant, approx 3 miles after crossing bridge onto Hayling Island bear right at the roundabout. Site is on the left in 450yds.
⚏ Havant

NEW MILTON

Hoburne Bashley, Sway Road, New Milton, Hampshire, BH25 5QR
Tel: 01425 612340
Email: hoburnebashley@hoburne.com
www.hoburne.com
Pitches For ⚑ ⛺ Total 289
Open 05-Feb to 30-Oct
Access Good **Site** Lev/Slope
Nearest Bus Stop (Miles) 0.75
⚏ New Milton

OWER

Green Pastures Park Ower, Romsey, Hampshire, SO51 6AJ
Tel: 023 8081 4444
Email: enquiries@greenpasturesfarm.com
www.greenpasturesfarm.com
Pitches For Å ⚑ ⛺ ⛺⚡ Total 45
Acreage 5 **Open** 15-Mar to 31-Oct
Access Good **Site** Level
A grassy site on family run farm, within easy reach of the New Forest. Pub with good food only a 20 minute walk. Paultons Park 1 mile. Convenient for ferries. Ample space for children to play in full view of units. Separate toilet/shower room for the disabled. Day kennelling available. Emergency telephone only.
Facilities ⚷ ∮ 🚿🚽⚡🔌⚷🔒⚙⛽
♨ 🏧🔌⛽🔌🛒
Directions Leave the M27 at junction 2 and follow signposts for Salisbury for ½ a mile. Then start to follow our own signs. Also signposted from the A36 and the A3090 at Ower.
⚏ Romsey

RINGWOOD

Oakdene Forest Park, St Leonards, Ringwood, Hampshire, BH24 2RZ
Tel: 01590 648331
Email: holidays@shorefield.co.uk
www.shorefield.co.uk
Pitches For Å Total 14
Acreage 55 **Open** 10-Feb to 02-Jan
Access Good **Site** Level
Nearest Bus Stop (Miles) ½
Bordering Avon Forest, surrounded by parkland and Forestry Commission land. 9 miles from Bournemouth beaches.
Facilities 🏧🔌⚷🔒⚙
🔌♨🏹⚽🛒🎱🏧⚷🔌🔒⚙🔌⛽⚷✦
Nearest Town Ringwood
Directions 3 miles west of Ringwood off the A31 just past St Leonards Hospital.
⚏ Bournemouth

ROMSEY

Hill Farm Caravan Park, Branches Lane, Sherfield English, Romsey, Hampshire, SO51 6FH
Tel: 01794 340402
Email: joe@hillfarmpark.com
www.hillfarmpark.com
Pitches For ▲ ⚏ ⚏ ⚏
Acreage 11 **Open** Mar to Oct
Access Good **Site** Level
Nearest Bus Stop (Miles) ¼
Close to Poultons Park, also central for Southampton, Winchester, Salisbury & coast.
Facilities ⚏ ⚏ ⚏ ⚏ ⚏ ⚏ ⚏ ⚏ ⚏ ⚏ ⚏ ⚏ ⚏ ⚏ ⚏ ⚏
Nearest Town Romsey
⚏ Romsey

RINGWOOD

The Red Shoot Camping Park, Linwood, Nr Ringwood, Hampshire, BH24 3QT
Tel: 01425 473789
Email: enquiries@redshoot-campingpark.com
www.redshoot-campingpark.com
Pitches For ▲ ⚏ ⚏ **Total** 130
Acreage 4 **Open** March to October
Access Good **Site** Lev/Slope
Nearest Town Ringwood
⚏ Brockenhurst

SOUTHSEA

Southsea Leisure Park, Melville Road, Southsea, Hampshire, PO4 9TB
Tel: 02392 735070
Email: info@southsealeisurepark.com
www.southsealeisurepark.com
Pitches For ▲ ⚏ ⚏ **Total** 188
Acreage 12 **Open** All Year
Access Good **Site** Level
Direct beach access, ideal base to explore Portsmouth and Southsea.Ideal for

continental ferries.
Facilities ⚏
Nearest Town Southsea
Directions Follow seafront towards Eastney, as main road bends to the leftSouthsea leisure Park is first right.
⚏ Fratton

ST. LEONARDS

Shamba Holidays, 230 Ringwood Road, St Leonards, Ringwood, Hants., BH24 2SB
Tel: 01202 873302
Email: enquiries@shambaholidays.co.uk
www.shambaholidays.co.uk
Pitches For ▲ ⚏ ⚏ **Total** 150
Acreage 7 **Open** March to October
Access Good **Site** Level
Nearest Bus Stop (Miles) 0.5
Nearest Town Ringwood
⚏ Bournemouth

WINCHESTER

Morn Hill Caravan Club Site, Morn Hill, Winchester, Hampshire, SO21 1HL
Tel: 01962 869877
www.caravanclub.co.uk
Pitches For ▲ ⚏ ⚏ **Total** 139
Acreage 9 **Open** Mar to Nov
Access Good **Site** Level
Nearest Bus Stop (Miles) ¼
Large site. Near Paultons Leisure Park, Marwell Zoo, Beaulieu, New Forest, Broadlands and Watercress Railway Line. Non members welcome. Booking essential.
Facilities ⚏ ⚏ ⚏ ⚏ ⚏ ⚏ ⚏ ⚏ ⚏ ⚏ ⚏ ⚏
Directions Leave the M3 onto A31. In 2½ miles at r/about continue on road sp Easton. Immediately turn right at Neptune Homes, site entrance in 100 yards.
⚏ Winchester

HEREFORDSHIRE

BROMYARD

Bromyard Downs Caravan Club Site, Brockhampton, Bringsty, Worcestershire, WR6 5TE
Tel: 01885 482607
www.caravanclub.co.uk
Pitches For ⚏ ⚏ **Total** 40
Acreage 4 **Open** Mar to Oct
Access Good **Site** Lev/Slope
Rural, woodland site situated in beautiful countryside. Ideal for walkers. Many historic houses, museums and steam railways nearby. Own sanitation required. Non members welcome. Booking essential.
Facilities ⚏ ⚏ ⚏ ⚏ ⚏ ⚏ ⚏
Nearest Town Bromyard
Directions Site on the left of A44 (Worcester-Bromyard) 300 yards past Brockhampton NT entrance immed before sp Bromyard Down.

HAY-ON-WYE

Penlan Caravan & Campsite, Penlan, Brilley, Hay-on-Wye, Herefordshire, HR3 6JW
Tel: 01497 831485
Email: peter@penlan.org.uk
www.penlancampsite.co.uk
Pitches For ▲ ⚏ ⚏ **Total** 20
Acreage 2½ **Open** Easter to Oct
Site Level
Peaceful and relaxing site. Ideal for exploring Mid Wales and the black and white villages of Herefordshire. National Trust small holding. Advance booking essential.
Facilities ⚏ ⚏ ⚏ ⚏ ⚏ ⚏ ⚏
Nearest Town Hay-on-Wye
Directions From Kington Church follow the Brilley to Whitney-on-Wye road for 4 miles. Look for National Trust signs on the left, turn sharp left into Apostles Lane, Penlan is first on the right.
⚏ Hereford

HEREFORD

Cuckoos Corner, Moreton-on-Lugg, Herefordshire, HR4 8AH
Tel: 01432 760234
Email: cuckooscorner@gmail.com
www.cuckooscorner.com
Pitches For Å ₽ ₩ ₩≤ **Total** 20
Acreage 1½ **Open** All Year
Access Good **Site** Level
Nearest Bus Stop (Miles) Outside
ADULTS ONLY. Friendly site with pleasant views. 15 hard standings: 5' x 45' feet long. Free broadband. Good touring area. Shop and chip shop nearby. 3 miles north of Hereford. Very reasonable rates.
Facilities ₺ ₣ ⊞⊞≠₽ ⊙ ☎ ◲ ☎
₧₤♠⊞◪☂
Nearest Town Hereford
Directions 4 miles north of Hereford on the A49, 100 yards beyond signpost Village Centre and Marden. Or 10 miles south of Leominster opposite advance sign Village Centre and Marden.
₹ Hereford

HEREFORD

Hereford Camping & Caravanning Club Site, The Millpond, Little Tarrington, Hereford, Herefordshire, HR1 4JA
Tel: 01432 890243
Email: hereford.site@thefriendlyclub.c.uk
www.campingandcaravanningclub.co.uk/hereford
Pitches For Å ₽ ₩ **Total** 55
Acreage 24 **Open** 01-Mar to 03-Nov
Access Good **Site** Level
Nearest Bus Stop (Miles) ½
Idyllic rural location next to The Millpond. A perfect spot for fishing, walking, exploring the Malvern Hills and the Wye Valley, or for simply relaxing. Four berth caravan available for hire. Non members welcome. You can also call us on 0845 130 7633.
Facilities ₺ ₣ ⊞⊞≠₽ ⊙ ⊿ ☎ ☎
₧ ⊙ ⊞ ♠ ⊞⊡ ⊿ ⊛ ☂
Nearest Town Hereford
Directions From Hereford take the A438 and turn left at the A438/Ledbury Road. Follow the A438 and go over one roundabout, then turn left.
₹ Ledbury

HEREFORD

Lucksall Caravan & Camping Park, Mordiford, Hereford, Herefordshire, HR1 4LP
Tel: 01432 870213
Email: enquires@lucksallpark.co.uk
www.lucksallpark.co.uk
Pitches For Å ₽ ₩ ₩≤ **Total** 120
Acreage 17 **Open** 01-Mar to 30-Nov
Access Good **Site** Level
Nearest Bus Stop (Miles) Outside
On the banks of the River Wye, ideal for canoeing and walking. ETC 5 Star Graded.
Facilities ₺ ₣ ⊞⊞≠₽ ⊙ ⊿ ☎ ☎
₧ ⊙ ⊞ ✕ ⊞ ⊞⊡ ⊿ ⊛
Nearest Town Hereford
Directions On the B4224 between Hereford (5 miles) and Ross-on-Wye (9 miles).
₹ Hereford

LEOMINSTER

Home Farm Caravan Site, Home Farm, Bircher, Leominster, Here., HR6 0AX
Tel: 01568 780525
Email: dawnhomefarmbb@aol.com
www.homefarmaccommodation.co.uk
Pitches For Å ₽ ₩ **Total** 36
Acreage 20 **Open** All Year
Access Good **Site** Level

Nearest Bus Stop (Miles) Outside
Set amongst green pastures and surrounded by stunning scenery. Near to National Trust properties and the historic town of Ludlow. You can also contact us on Mobile: 07905 212605. Holiday lets available from autumn 2012.
Facilities ₺ ₣ ⊞⊞≠₽ ⊙ ⊿ ☎ ₫₩↞
Directions 5 miles north of Leominster on the B4362, follow signs for Croft Castle (NT).
₹ Leominster

LEOMINSTER

Pearl Lake Leisure Park, Shobdon, Leominster, Herefordshire, HR6 9NQ
Tel: 01568 708326
Email: info@pearllake.co.uk
www.pearllake.co.uk
Pitches For Å ₽ ₩ ₩≤ **Total** 15
Acreage 80 **Open** March to November
Access Good **Site** Level
Nearest Bus Stop (Miles) Outside
Outstanding park in a beautiful setting with a 15 acre fishing lake, 9 hole golf course, Crown bowls and woodland walks.
Facilities ₺ ₣ ⊞⊞≠₽ ⊙ ⊿ ☎ ☎
₧ ⊙ ⊞ ♀ ♠ ⊞⊞⊡ ⊿
Nearest Town Leominster
Directions Situated on the B4362 in the village of Shobdon.
₹ Leominster

PETERCHURCH

Poston Mill Park, Peterchurch, Golden Valley, Herefordshire, HR2 0SF
Tel: 01981 550225
Email: info@poston-mill.co.uk
www.postonmill.co.uk
Pitches For Å ₽ ₩ **Total** 64
Acreage 35 **Open** All Year
Access Good **Site** Level
Nearest Bus Stop (Miles) Outside
Highly recommended, beautiful, well maintained park with electric, water and TV (cable) connections on fully serviced pitches. Set on the banks of the River Dore. Shop and Mill Restaurant alongside the Park.
Facilities ₺ ₣ ⊞⊞≠₽ ⊙ ⊿ ☎ ◲ ☎
₧ ⊙ ⊞ ✕ ♠ ⊞ ✿⊞⊞⊡ ⊿ ⊛ ♠ ☂
Nearest Town Hereford
Directions On the B4348, 11 miles from Hereford and 11 miles from Hay on Wye.
₹ Hereford

ROSS-ON-WYE

Broadmeadow Caravan Park, Broadmeadows, Ross-on-Wye, Herefordshire, HR9 7BW
Tel: 01989 768076
Email: broadm4811@aol.com
www.broadmeadow.info
Pitches For Å ₽ ₩ **Total** 150
Acreage 16 **Open** Easter/1st Apr to Sept
Access Good **Site** Level
Nearest Bus Stop (Miles) ¼
Lake walks. Fishing on site. Only 10 minutes to the centre of Ross-on-Wye. Ideal touring and walking in the Wye Valley. ETB 5 Star.
Facilities ₺ ₣ ⊞⊞≠₽ ⊙ ⊿ ☎ ◲ ☎
₧ ⊙ ⊞ ♪ ✿⊞⊞⊡ ⊿ ⊛ ☂
Nearest Town Ross-on-Wye
Directions Adjacent to the A40 Ross relief road. Access from Pancake roundabout off relief road turning into Ross. Take the first turning right into Ashburton Estate Road, then turn right by Morrisons Supermarket.
₹ Gloucester

ROSS-ON-WYE

Lower Ruxton Farm, Kings Caple, Herefordshire, HR1 4TX
Tel: 01432 840223
Pitches For Å ₩ **Total** 20

Acreage 8 **Open** Mid July to End Aug only
Site Level
Nearest Bus Stop (Miles) ½
Alongside a river.
Facilities ₳ ☎ ₩⊡
Nearest Town Ross-on-Wye
Directions A49 from Ross-on-Wye, 1 mile turn right follow signs for Hoarwithy (Kings Caple 4 miles) across river bridge ½ mile sign to Ruxton second farm on right.
₹ Hereford

SYMONDS YAT WEST

Doward Park Camp Site, Great Doward, Symonds Yat West, Nr Ross-on-Wye, Herefordshire, HR9 6BP
Tel: 01600 890438
Email: enquiries@dowardpark.co.uk
www.dowardpark.co.uk
Pitches For Å ₩ **Total** 27
Acreage 4 **Open** March to Oct
Access Good **Site** Level
Very scenic and peaceful site with excellent, clean facilities. Close to the River Wye with woodland and river walks. Ideal base for touring the Wye Valley and the Forest of Dean.
Facilities ₣ ⊞⊞≠₽ ⊙ ☎ ◲ ☎ ⊛
Nearest Town Monmouth
Directions On the A40 between Ross-on-Wye and Monmouth. Turn off at Symonds Yat West and follow signs for The Doward.
₹ Hereford

SYMONDS YAT WEST

Sterretts Caravan Park, Symonds Yat (West), Nr Ross-on-Wye, Herefordshire, HR9 6BY
Tel: 01594 832888/833162
www.ukparks.co.uk/sterretts
Pitches For Å ₽ ₩ **Total** 8
Acreage 9 **Open** Feb to Nov
Access Good **Site** Level
Nearest Bus Stop (Miles) ½
Near a river. Ideal for walking, fishing, canoeing, rock climbing and touring the Forest of Dean. Pets welcome with tourers.Static holiday caravans for hire.
Facilities ₣ ⊞⊞≠₽ ⊙ ⊿ ◲ ⋔₩⊡
Nearest Town Ross-on-Wye
Directions Take the A40 from Ross-on-Wye or Monmouth to Whitchurch, turn off and go over a small roundabout by the school, after 200 yards you will come to a large car park, drive through.
₹ Hereford

HERTFORDSHIRE

BALDOCK

Radwell Mill Lake, Radwell Mill, Baldock, Hertfordshire, SG7 5ET
Tel: 01462 730242
Email: camping@radwellmill.com
www.radwellmill.com
Pitches For Å ₽ ₩ **Total** 20
Acreage 3 **Open** Apr to Nov
Access Good **Site** Level
Nearest Bus Stop (Miles) ½
Quiet site with a lake and orchard. Good for bird watching. New Motorway Services (½ mile away) with cafe/restaurant, shops and take-away food.
Facilities ⊞⊡⊣ ☎ ⋔♠

Nearest Town Baldock
Directions Junction 10 A1(M) then the A507, ½ mile towards Baldock take a lane signed Radwell Only to the lake and site.
⏟ Baldock

HERTFORD

Hertford Camping & Caravanning Club Site, Mangrove Road (Not Ball Park), Hertford, Hertfordshire, SG13 8AJ
Tel: 01992 586696
Email: hertford.site@thefriendlyclub.co.uk
www.campingandcaravanningclub.co.uk/hertford
Pitches For ⋀ ⊕ ⊟ **Total** 250
Open All Year **Site** Level
Set in acres of meadowland. 5 miles from Hatfield House and 20 miles from London. BTB 4 Star Graded, AA 4 Pennants and David Bellamy Gold Award. Non members welcome. You can also call us on 0845 130 7633.
Facilities 🏃 ⨍ 🏠 🎖 🅿 🄲 ⊙ 🍽 🍴 🔟 🝊
🝊 🄾 🄱 🄰 ♣ ➕ 🄷 🄳 🄿 �*/ ↖ 🔍 ☎
Directions From the A10 follow the A414 Hertford signs to the next roundabout (Foxholes) and go straight across, after 200 yards turn left signposted Balls Park and Hertford University. Turn left at the T-Junction into Mangrove Road, go past Simon Balle School, University and Cricket Ground, site is 400 yards past the cricket club on the left.
⏟ North & East Hertford

HODDESDON

Lee Valley Caravan Park Dobbs Weir, Charlton Meadows, Essex Road, Hoddesdon, Herts, EN11 0AS
Tel: 08456 770609
Email: dobbsweircampsite@leevalley.org.uk
www.visitleevalley.org.uk
Pitches For ⋀ ⊕ ⊟ ≶ **Total** 70
Open Mar to Nov
Access Good **Site** Level
Nearest Bus Stop (Miles) ¼
Lee Valley White Water Centre and other Lee Valley attractions.
Facilities ⅙ 🏃 🏠 🎖 🅿 🄲 ⊙ 🍽 🍴 🔟 🝊
🝊 🄾 🄱 🄷 🄳 ✒ 🔍
Nearest Town Hoddesdon
⏟ Broxbourne

WALTHAM CROSS

Theobalds Park Camping & Caravanning Club Site, Bulls Cross Ride, Waltham Cross, Hertfordshire, EN7 5HS
Tel: 01992 620604
Email: theobalds.park@thefriendlyclub.co.uk
www.campingandcaravanningclub.co.uk/theobaldspark
Pitches For ⋀ ⊕ ⊟ **Total** 90
Acreage 14 **Open** 21-Mar to 04-Nov
Access Good **Site** Level
Leafy site just 13 miles from London. Plenty of wildlife to see on the site including birds, foxes, deer and rabbits. Lee Valley nearby which is ideal for boating, sailing and swimming. BTB 3 Star Graded and AA 2 Pennants. Non members welcome. You can also call us on 0845 130 7633.
Facilities 🏃 🏠 🎖 🅿 🄲 ⊙ 🍽 🍴 🔟 🝊
🝊 🄾 🄱 🄰 ♣ ➕ 🄷 🄳 🄿 🌙 🔍 ☎
Nearest Town Waltham Cross
Directions Leave the M25 at junction 25, take the A10 towards London keeping to the right hand lane, turn right at the first set of traffic lights signposted Crews Hill. Turn right at the T-Junction (opposite Pied Bull), turn right behind the dog kennels, site is towards the top of the lane on the right.
⏟ Waltham Cross

78

ISLE OF MAN
UNION MILLS

Glenlough Campsite, Union Mills, Isle Of Man, IM4 4AT
Tel: 01624 822372/852057
Email: glenloughcampsite@manx.net
www.glenloughcampsite.com
Pitches For ⋀ ⊟ **Total** 350
Acreage 15 **Open** April to Sept
Site Level
Nearest Bus Stop (Miles) Outside
Family run, sheltered site on the TT Course. Located in the scenic central valley. 3 Camping Pods available for the outdoor camping experience with a cosy and peaceful nights sleep! Everyone welcome.
Facilities 🏃 🏠 🎖 🅿 🄲 ⊙ 🍽 🔟 🝊
Nearest Town Douglas
Directions 3 miles from Douglas on the A1 Douglas to Peel road.
⏟ Douglas

ISLE OF WIGHT
ATHERFIELD

Chine Farm Camping Site, Military Road, Atherfield Bay, Nr Chale, Ventnor, Isle Of Wight, PO38 2JH
Tel: 01983 740901
Email: jill@chine-farm.co.uk
www.chine-farm.co.uk
Pitches For ⋀ ⊕ ⊟ ⊟≶ **Total** 80
Acreage 10 **Open** Easter to Sept
Access Good **Site** Level
Nearest Bus Stop (Miles) Outside
Footpath from the Site to the beach. Spacious pitches with wonderful views of the sea, coast and countryside.
Facilities 🏃 🎖 🅿 🄲 ⊙ 🍽 🔟 🝊
🝊 🄾 🄱 ➕ 🄷 🄳 🌙
Nearest Town Freshwater
Directions Situated on the A3055 coast road, halfway between Freshwater Bay and Ventnor.
⏟ Sandown

BRIGHSTONE BAY

Grange Farm Caravan & Camping Site, Military Road, Brighstone Bay, Isle Of Wight, PO30 4DA
Tel: 01983 740296
Email: grangefarmholiday@googlemail.com
www.grangefarmholidays.com
Pitches For ⋀ ⊕ ⊟ **Total** 60
Open Mar to Oct
Access Good **Site** Level
Nearest Bus Stop (Miles) Outside
We have direct access to Brighstone Beach, in an area of outstanding beauty with great views.
Facilities ⅙ 🏃 🎖 🅿 🄲 ⊙ 🍽 🔟 🝊
🝊 🔟 🄾 🄱 🄰 ➕ 🄷 🄳 🄿 🔍
Nearest Town Freshwater
Directions From Freshwater Bay take the A3055 towards Ventnor we are approx 7 miles, on the right.
⏟ Shanklin

FRESHWATER

Compton Farm, Brook, Newport, Isle Of Wight, PO30 4HF
Tel: 01983 740215
www.comptonfarm.co.uk
Pitches For ⋀ ⊟ **Total** 28
Acreage 17 **Open** May to September
Site Level
Nearest Bus Stop (Miles) ¼
A working farm near the beach and chalk downland. Wonderful walks locally. Booking

essential. Sorry, No Touring Caravans.
Facilities 🔟 🏃 🎖 🅿 🄲 ⊙ 🍽 🔟 🝊 🄻 🄰 🄿 🌙
Nearest Town Freshwater
Directions From Freshwater Bay take the A3055 (Military Road), after 1½ miles turn left at NT car park.

FRESHWATER

Heathfield Farm Camping, Heathfield Road, Freshwater, Isle Of Wight, PO40 9SH
Tel: 01983 407822
Email: web@heathfieldcamping.co.uk
www.heathfieldcamping.co.uk
Pitches For ⋀ ⊕ ⊟ **Total** 60
Acreage 5 **Open** May to Sept
Site Level
Nearest Bus Stop (Miles) Outside
Facilities 🏃 🎖 🅿 🄲 ⊙ 🍽 🔟 🝊
🄾 🄱 🄰 ♣ ➕ 🄷 🄳 🔍
Nearest Town Freshwater
Directions 2 miles from Yarmouth ferry port, head towards Freshwater
⏟ Shanklin

RYDE

Beaper Farm Camping & Caravan Park, Nr Ryde, Isle Of Wight, PO33 1QJ
Tel: 01983 615210/875184
Email: beaper@btinternet.com
www.beaperfarm.com
Pitches For ⋀ ⊕ ⊟ **Total** 150
Acreage 13 **Open** May to September
Access Good **Site** Level
Nearest Bus Stop (Miles) ¼
Near to beaches, golf, water sports, fishing trips, horse riding, ice skating, ten pin bowling and nightclubs, plus Isle of Wight Steam Railway.
Facilities ⅙ 🏃 🎖 🅿 🄲 ⊙ 🍽 🔟 🝊
🄾 🄷 🄳 🔍
Nearest Town Ryde
Directions On the main A3055 Ryde to Sandown road, go past Tesco roundabout for ½ mile, Beaper Farm is second on the left.
⏟ Ryde

RYDE

Whitefield Forest Touring Park, Brading Road, Ryde, Isle Of Wight, PO33 1QL
Tel: 01983 617069
Email: pat&louise@whitefieldforest.co.uk
www.whitefieldforest.co.uk
Pitches For ⋀ ⊕ ⊟ **Total** 75
Acreage 23 **Open** Easter to October
Access Good **Site** Level
Nearest Bus Stop (Miles) Outside
Set in the ancient woodland of Whitefield Forest. We provide ideal holidays for families, couples and individuals.
Facilities ⅙ 🏃 🎖 🅿 🄲 ⊙ 🍽 🔟 🝊
🝊 🄾 🄱 🄷 🄳
Directions From Ryde take the A3055 to Brading, at Tescos roundabout go straight over and the Park is ½ a mile on the left.
⏟ Smallbrook

SANDOWN

Adgestone Camping & Caravanning Club Site, Lower Adgestone Road, Adgestone, Isle Of Wight, PO36 0HL
Tel: 01983 403432
Email: adgestone.site@thefriendlyclub.co.uk
www.campingandcaravanningclub.co.uk/adgestone
Pitches For ⋀ ⊕ ⊟ **Total** 270
Acreage 22 **Open** 30-Apr to 30-Sep
Access Difficult **Site** Level
Nearest Bus Stop (Miles) 1

One of the best locations on the Isle of Wight, 1 mile from Sandown. Adjacent to the River Yar and nestled in the valley beneath Brading Downs, an area of natural beauty. BTB 4 Star Graded and AA 4 Pennants. Non members welcome. You can also call us on 0845 130 7633.
Facilities ⚡ ✆ 🅿 🔌 ⊙ ⬅ ▬ ▢ ☎
💵 ⊙ 🏢 ✕ ♦ 🔥 ⟶ 🎣 🌳 ♿ 🛈 ✿
Nearest Town Sandown
Directions Turn off the A3055 Sandown to Shanklin road at Manor House Pub in Lake. Go past the school and golf course on the left and turn right at the T-Junction, park is 200 yards on the right.
🚢 Sandown

SANDOWN

Old Barn Touring Park, Cheverton Farm, Newport Road, Sandown, Isle Of Wight, PO36 9PJ
Tel: 01983 866414
Email: oldbarn@weltinet.com
www.oldbarntouring.co.uk
Pitches For 🛆 🏕 🚐 **Total** 60
Acreage 5 **Open** 01-May to 25-Sep
Access Good **Site** Level
Nearest Bus Stop (Miles) ¼
1½ miles from the seaside towns of Sandown and Shanklin. Grade II Listed Barn used as a TV and games room.
Facilities ⚡ ✆ 🅿 🔌 ⓤ 🔌 ⊙ ⬅ ▬ ▢ ☎
💵 ⊙ 🏢 ♦ 🔥 ⟶ 🎣 ▢ ☎
Nearest Town Sandown
Directions From Newport take the A3056, Park is on the right ½ mile after Apse Heath mini roundabout.
🚢 Lake

SANDOWN

Queen Bower Dairy Caravan Park, Alverstone Road, Queen Bower, Sandown, Isle Of Wight, PO36 0NZ
Tel: 01983 403840
Email: queenbowerdairy@btconnect.com
www.queenbowerdairy.co.uk
Pitches For 🛆 🏕 🚐 **Total** 20
Acreage 2¼ **Open** May to October
Access Good **Site** Level
Nearest Bus Stop (Miles) ¼
Scenic views, ideal touring. Sell our own produced Dairy products (milk and cream). Public telephone ¼ mile.
Facilities ✗ ✆ 🅿 ☎ 💵 🔌 ⟶ 🔌 ▢
Nearest Town Sandown
Directions On the A3056 Newport to Sandown road, turn into Alverstone Road at Apse Heath crossroads. Park is 1 mile on the left.
🚢 Sandown

SANDOWN

Village Way Caravan & Camping Park, Newport Road, Apse Heath, Sandown, Isle Of Wight, PO36 9PJ
Tel: 01983 863279
Email: norma.smith@btconnect.com
www.villagewaypark.co.uk
Pitches For 🛆 🏕 🚐 **Total** 14
Open All Year
Access Good **Site** Level
Nearest Bus Stop (Miles) ¼
Near the beach. Free carp fishing on site. Beautiful country walks to the woods and within walking distance of a garden centre and Morrisons. The Heights Leisure Centre is only a mile away.
Facilities ✆ 🅿 🔌 ⊙ ⬅ ▬ ▢ ☎
💵 ⊙ 🔌 ✔
Nearest Town Sandown
Directions From Newport take the A22 to Blackwater then the A3056 to Apse Heath. We are on the main A3056.

SHANKLIN

Ninham Country Holidays, Shanklin, Isle Of Wight, PO37 7PL
Tel: 01983 864243
Email: office@ninham-holidays.co.uk
www.ninham-holidays.co.uk
Pitches For 🛆 🏕 🚐 **Total** 98
Acreage 10 **Open** 01-May to 30-Sep
Access Very Good **Site** Level
Nearest Bus Stop (Miles) ¼
Country park setting close to Islands premier seaside resort. Outdoor heated swimming pool, on-site carp fishing and bike hire. Great walking and cycling. Ferry tickets issued. On-line booking available.
Facilities ✗ ✆ 🅿 🔌 ⊙ ⬅ ▬ ▢ ☎
💵 ⊙ 🏢 ♦ 🔥 ⟶ 🔌 ▢ ☎ ✗ ✿ ⚓
Nearest Town Shanklin
Directions Signposted off Newport/Sandown road (A3056). Site entrance is ¼ mile west of Morrisons on the left.
🚢 Shanklin

VENTNOR

Appuldurcombe Gardens Holiday Park, Wroxall, Ventnor, Isle Of Wight, PO38 3EP
Tel: 01983 852597
Email: info@appuldurcombe.co.uk
www.appuldurcombegardens.co.uk
Pitches For 🛆 🏕 🚐 🚐≒ **Total** 130
Acreage 14 **Open** Mar to Nov
Access Good **Site** Lev/Slope
Nearest Bus Stop (Miles) ¼
Countryside location, ideal for walkers and cyclists
Facilities ⚡ ✆ 🅿 🔌 ⓤ 🔌 ⊙ ⬅ ▬ ▢ ☎
💵 💵 🔌 ⊙ 🏢 ✕ 🛈 ♦ 🔥 ⟶ 🔌 ▢ 🏢 ☎
Nearest Town Ventnor

Directions From Newport take the A3020 and turn off towards Shanklin. Go through Godshill, turn right at Whiteley Bank roundabout towards Wroxall.
🚢 Shanklin

YARMOUTH

The Orchards Holiday Caravan & Camping Park, Newbridge, Yarmouth, Isle Of Wight, PO41 0TS
Tel: 01983 531331
Email: admin@orchards-holiday-park.co.uk
www.orchards-holiday-park.co.uk
Pitches For 🛆 🏕 🚐 **Total** 175
Acreage 8 **Open** 20-Feb to 02-Jan
Access Good **Site** Lev/Slope
Nearest Bus Stop (Miles) Outside
Excellent multi award winning family park in a peaceful village setting amid downs and meadowland with glorious views. Luxury Facilities Centre has excellent touring facilities. Also take-away food, shop, pool table, table tennis, play areas and dog walk. Excellent walking and cycling. WiFi available. Booking essential.
Facilities ⚡ ✆ 🅿 🔌 ⓤ 🔌 ⊙ ⬅ ▬ ▢ ☎
💵 💵 🔌 ⊙ 🏢 ✕ 🛈 ♦ 🔥 ⟶ 🔌 ▢ 🏢 ⚓
Nearest Town Yarmouth
Directions 4 miles east of Yarmouth and 6 miles west of Newport on B3401. Entrance opposite Newbridge Post Office.
🚢 Lymington

KENT
ASHFORD

Broadhembury Caravan & Camping Park, Steeds Lane, Kingsnorth, Ashford, Kent, TN26 1NQ
Tel: 01233 620859
Email: holidaypark@broadhembury.co.uk
www.broadhembury.co.uk
Pitches For 🛆 🏕 🚐 🚐≒ **Total** 80
Acreage 8 **Open** All Year
Access Good **Site** Level
Nearest Bus Stop (Miles) ½
Open all year with centrally heated toilets and showers, en-suite facilities, wheelchair access, playgrounds, games room and every amenity for families. Also adults meadows, the ideal place for those who like things a little quieter! Picturesque villages, sandy beaches, Channel crossings, Canterbury, castles and gardens all within easy reach.
Facilities ⚡ ✆ 🅿 🔌 ⓤ 🔌 ⊙ ⬅ ▬ ▢ ☎
💵 💵 🔌 ⊙ 🏢 🛈 ♦ ⟶ 🔌 ▢ 🏢 ✗ ⚓
Nearest Town Ashford
Directions Leave the M20 at junction 10, take the A2070 following signs for Kingsnorth. Turn left at the second crossroads in the village.
🚢 Ashford

BIRCHINGTON
Quex Caravan Park, Park Road, Birchington, Kent, CT7 0BL
Tel: 01843 841273
Email: quex@keatfarm.co.uk
www.keatfarm.co.uk
Pitches For ⬛ 🚐 🚙 **Total** 50
Acreage 3 **Open** 07-Mar **to** 07-Nov
Access Good **Site** Level
Ideal base for touring the areas around Thanet and Canterbury.
Facilities 🚿 ⚡
Nearest Town Margate/Ramsgate
Directions Follow road signs to Margate. When in Birchington turn right at mini roundabout (sp Margate). Approximately 100yds after roundabout take the first turning on the right and then right again, left into park road, Park approx ¼ on right.
🚃 Birchington

BIRCHINGTON
St. Nicholas Camping Site, Court Road, St Nicholas-at-Wade, Birchington, Kent, CT7 0NH
Tel: 01843 847245
Pitches For ⛺ ⬛ 🚐 **Total** 75
Acreage 3 **Open** March **to** Oct
Access Good **Site** Level
Nearest Bus Stop (Miles) ¼
On the edge of the village with two Pubs serving food and a Post Office.
Facilities 🚿 ⚡
Nearest Town Birchington
Directions Turn off the A28 9½ miles north east of Canterbury to St. Nicholas. Or take the A299 from Herne Bay and turn left signposted St. Nicholas-at-Wade, go over the bridge and into Court Road.
🚃 Birchington

BIRCHINGTON
Two Chimneys Holiday Park, Shottendane Road, Birchington, Kent, CT7 0HD
Tel: 01843 841068/843157
Email: info@twochimneys.co.uk
www.twochimneys.co.uk
Pitches For ⛺ ⬛ 🚐 **Total** 200
Acreage 30 **Open** March **to** October
Access Good **Site** Level
Nearest Bus Stop (Miles) ¼
Country site near lovely beaches. Swimming pool with retractable roof, adventure play area and tennis court on site. Sorry, No dogs. Holiday Caravans available for hire. Storage.
Facilities 🚿 ⚡
Nearest Town Margate
Directions 1½ miles from Birchington, turn right into park lane at Birchington Church, left fork "RAF Manston". First left onto B2048 site is ½ a mile on right.
🚃 Birchington

CANTERBURY
Canterbury Camping & Caravanning Club Site, Bekesbourne Lane, Canterbury, Kent, CT3 4AB
Tel: 01227 463216
Email:
canterbury.site@thefriendlyclub.co.uk
www.campingandcaravanningclub.co.uk/ canterbury
Pitches For ⛺ ⬛ 🚐 **Total** 200
Acreage 20 **Open** All Year
Site Lev/Slope
Nearest Bus Stop (Miles) ¼
Close to Canterbury and within easy reach of the Channel ports. 2 miles from Canterbury Cathedral and Howletts Wildlife Park. Local

produce sold in the site shop. BTB 4 Star Graded, AA 3 Pennants and David Bellamy Gold Award. Non members welcome. You can also call us on 0845 130 7633.
Facilities 🚿 ⚡
Directions From Canterbury follow the A257 towards Sandwich, turn right opposite the golf course.
🚃 Canterbury

CANTERBURY
Yew Tree Park, Stone Street, Petham, Canterbury, Kent, CT4 5PL
Tel: 01227 700306
Email: info@yewtreepark.com
www.yewtreepark.com
Pitches For ⛺ ⬛ 🚐 **Total** 45
Acreage 2 **Open** Mar **to** Oct
Access Good **Site** Lev/Slope
Nearest Bus Stop (Miles) Outside
30 minutes drive from the coast. Ideal touring.
Facilities 🚿 ⚡
Nearest Town Canterbury
Directions 4 miles south of Canterbury on the B2068, turn right by the Chequers Public House, park entrance is on the left hand side.
🚃 Canterbury

DOVER
Hawthorn Farm, Martin Mill, Dover, Kent, CT15 5LA
Tel: 01304 852658
Email: hawthorn@keatfarm.co.uk
www.keatfarm.co.uk
Pitches For ⛺ ⬛ 🚐 **Total** 250
Acreage 27 **Open** March **to** Oct
Access Good **Site** Level
Beautiful Award Winning park in a quiet and peaceful location. Superb toilet and shower facilities.
Facilities 🚿 ⚡
Nearest Town Dover
Directions Martin Mill is approx. 3 miles from Dover, signposted along the main A258 towards Deal.
🚃 Martin Mill

FOLKESTONE
Black Horse Farm Caravan Club Site, 385 Canterbury Road, Densole, Folkestone, Kent, CT18 7BG
Tel: 01303 892665
www.caravanclub.co.uk
Pitches For ⛺ ⬛ 🚐 **Total** 140
Acreage 11 **Open** All Year
Access Good **Site** Level
Nearest Bus Stop (Miles) ¼
Situated in the heart of farming country. Limited hard standings available March to October only. Close to Canterbury, Dover Castle and the Channel Tunnel. Non members welcome. Booking essential.
Facilities 🚿 ⚡
Nearest Town Folkestone
Directions Leave the M20 at junc 13 (at end) and continue onto the A20. Pass the end of the tunnel turn off via slip road and roundabout onto the A260 sp Canterbury, go through Hawkinge into Densole. Site is on the left 200 yards past the Black Horse Inn.
🚃 Folkestone

FOLKESTONE
Folkestone Camping & Caravanning Club Site, The Warren, Folkestone, Kent, CT19 6NQ
Tel: 01303 255093
Email: folkestone.site@thefriendlyclub.co.uk
www.campingandcaravanningclub.co.uk/ folkestone

Pitches For ⛺ 🚐 **Total** 80
Open 21-Mar **to** 04-Nov
Access Difficult **Site** Lev/Slope
Nearest Bus Stop (Miles) ½
Just a short walk to the beach. On a clear day you can see France. Fishing off the site on the sea front, 50 yards. BTB 5 Star Graded, AA 3 Pennants and Loo of the Year Award. Non members welcome. You can also call us on 0845 130 7633.
Facilities 🚿 ⚡
Directions From the M2 and Canterbury on the A260 take a left turn at the roundabout into Hill Road, Folkestone. Go straight over the crossroads into Wear Bay Road, turn second left past Martello Tower, site is ½ mile on the right.
🚃 Folkestone

FOLKESTONE
Little Satmar Holiday Park, Winehouse Lane, Capel-le-Ferne, Nr Folkestone, Kent, CT18 7JF
Tel: 01303 251188
Email: satmar@keatfarm.co.uk
www.keatfarm.co.uk
Pitches For ⛺ ⬛ 🚐 **Total** 60
Acreage 6 **Open** March **to** October
Access Good
Quiet, secluded park. Convenient for Channel ports and Tunnel.
Facilities 🚿 ⚡
Nearest Town Folkestone
Directions Travelling towards Folkestone on the A20 from Dover, exit left signposted Capel-le-Ferne onto the B2011. After 1 mile turn right into Winehouse Lane.
🚃 Folkestone

FOLKESTONE
Little Switzerland Caravan & Camping Park, Little Switzerland, Wear Bay Road, Folkestone, Kent, CT19 6PS
Tel: 01303 252168
Email: btony328@aol.com
www.caravancampingsites.co.uk
Pitches For ⛺ ⬛ 🚐 🚙
Open Mar **to** Oct
Access Good **Site** Level
Nearest Bus Stop (Miles) Outside
Facilities 🚿 ⚡
Nearest Town Folkestone
Directions From Dover follow Folkestone signs then Country Park signs.
🚃 Folkestone

HERNE BAY
Southview Camping, Southview, Maypole Lane, Hoath, Canterbury, Kent, CT3 4LL
Tel: 01227 860280
Email: southviewcamping@aol.com
www.southviewcamping.co.uk
Pitches For ⛺ ⬛ 🚐 **Total** 45
Acreage 3 **Open** Apr **to** Sept
Access Good **Site** Level
Nearest Bus Stop (Miles) ¼
Peaceful country setting. Excellent local pub and restaurant. Central location for Canterbury and the beautiful beaches of Thanet.
Facilities 🚿 ⚡
Nearest Town Canterbury
Directions Well signed from the A299 at Herne Bay or the A28 near Canterbury.
🚃 Herne Bay

The Hop Farm Camping and Touring Park

In the heart of the Kent countryside

A family run touring park in a beautiful setting within open fields and woodlands, with 500 acres of natural landscape to explore.
Over 300 pitches · Electric hook ups · Hard standings · Newly refurbished toilet/shower block · Close to a major attraction · Dogs welcome
The Hop Farm, Beltring, Paddock Wood, Kent TN12 6PY. 01622 870838. touring@thehopfarm.co.uk. Visit us online at www.thehopfarm.co.uk

MAIDSTONE

Bearsted Caravan Club Site, Ashford Road, Hollingbourne, Maidstone, Kent, ME17 1XH
Tel: 01622 730018
www.caravanclub.co.uk
Pitches For ⚏ ⚏ **Total** 69
Acreage 6 **Open** Mar to Jan
Access Good **Site** Lev/Slope
Peaceful stop-off point (for ferries). Near to Leeds Castle. Non members welcome. Booking essential.
Facilities ⚒ ⚐ 🔲 📷 🍴 ⏚ ⊙ 🍳 🔲 🛒
🏧 🎣 📞 🔌 🛜
Nearest Town Maidstone
Directions Leave the M20 at junction 8, at the roundabout turn into road sp Bearsted and Maidstone, site is ½ mile on the left.
🚂 Maidstone

MARDEN

Tanner Farm Touring Caravan & Camping Park, Tanner Farm, Goudhurst Road, Marden, Kent, TN12 9ND
Tel: 01622 832399
Email: enquiries@tannerfarmpark.co.uk
www.tannerfarmpark.co.uk
Pitches For Å ⚏ ⚏ **Total** 100
Acreage 15 **Open** All Year
Access Good **Site** Level
Nearest Bus Stop (Miles) Outside
Peaceful, secluded park in the centre of a 150 acre farm, shire horses kept. QIT 5 Star Graded Park and David Bellamy Gold Award. Booking essential.
Facilities ⚒ ⚐ 🔲 🔲 📷 🍴 ⏚ ⊙ 🍳 🔲 🛒
🏧 🎣 ⊙ 🏪 🎣 🛒 📞 🔌 🛒 🛜
Nearest Town Maidstone/Tunbridge Wells
Directions From the A262 or A229 onto the B2079. Midway between the village of Marden and Goudhurst.
🚂 Marden

RAMSGATE

Nethercourt Touring Park, Nethercourt Hill, Ramsgate, Kent, CT11 0RX
Tel: 01843 595485
Email: nethercourtcamp@aol.com
www.campsite-in-kent.co.uk
Pitches For Å ⚏ ⚏ **Total** 50
Acreage 2 **Open** All Year
Access Good **Site** Level
Nearest Bus Stop (Miles) Outside
1¼ miles from the beach and harbour. Sea fishing 1 mile. Indoor swimming pool nearby. 3 star site.
Facilities ⚒ ⚐ 🔲 📷 🍴 ⏚ ⊙ 🍳 ⏚ 🔲 🛒
🏧 🎣 ⏚ 🏪 🔌 📞 🔌 🔲 🛒
Directions Off Nethercourt Hill on the outskirts of the town.
🚂 Ramsgate

ROCHESTER

Woolmans Wood Tourist Caravan Park, Rochester Road (B2097), Chatham, Kent, ME5 9SB
Tel: 01634 867685
Email: johnbedrock@aol.com
www.woolmans-wood.co.uk
Pitches For ⚏ ⚏ **Total** 40
Acreage 6 **Open** All Year
Access Good **Site** Level

Nearest Bus Stop (Miles) ¼
ADULTS ONLY SITE. Rochester Castle and Cathedral, Chatham Hitoric Dockyard, Leesd Castle Dickens world, Royal engineers Museum.
Facilities ⚐ 🔲 🔲 📷 🍴 ⏚ ⊙ 🍳 ⏚ 🔲 🛒
🏧 ⏚ ⊙ 🏪 📞 🔌 🛒
Directions Take the A229 from the M2 junction 3 or the M20 junction 6. Follow caravan signs to the B2097. Park is ¼ mile on the right hand side.
🚂 Rochester

SEVENOAKS

East Hill Farm Park, East Hill Road, Nr Kemsing, Sevenoaks, Kent, TN15 6YD
Tel: 01959 522347
Pitches For Å **Total** 30
Acreage 6 **Open** Apr to Oct
Site Level
Facilities 🔲 📞 🛒
Directions Off the A225. Please telephone for directions.
🚂 Otford

SEVENOAKS

Oldbury Hill Camping & Caravanning Club Site, Styants Bottom, Seal, Sevenoaks, Kent, TN15 0ET
Tel: 01732 762728
Email: oldbury.hillsite@thefriendlyclub.co.uk
www.campingandcaravanningclub.co.uk/oldburyhill
Pitches For Å ⚏ ⚏ **Total** 60
Acreage 6 **Open** 21-Mar to 04-Nov
Access Difficult **Site** Sloping
Nearest Bus Stop (Miles) ½
Set in a quiet countryside location, close to a number of National Trust properties. BTB 4 Star Graded and AA 3 Pennants. Non members welcome. You can also call us on 0845 130 7633.
Facilities ⚒ ⚐ 🔲 📷 🍴 ⏚ ⊙ 🍳 ⏚ 🔲 🛒
🏧 ⏚ ⊙ 🏪 🔌 📞 🔌 🔲 🛜
Nearest Town Sevenoaks
Directions From Sevenoaks take the A25 towards Borough Green, turn left just after the Crown Point Inn, go down the lane to Styants Bottom, site is on the left.
🚂 Borough Green

TONBRIDGE

The Hop Farm Touring & Camping Park, Maidstone Road, Beltring, Nr Tonbridge, Paddock Wood, Kent, TN12 6PY
Tel: 01622 870838
Email: touring@thehopfarm.co.uk
www.thehopfarm.co.uk/touring
Pitches For Å ⚏ ⚏ **Total** 300
Acreage 400 **Open** March to October
Access Good **Site** Level
Nearest Bus Stop (Miles) Outside
Nearest Town Paddock Wood
🚂 Paddock Wood

WHITSTABLE

Primrose Cottage Caravan Park, Golden Hill, Whitstable, Kent, CT5 3AR
Tel: 01227 273694
Email: campbell_brian@btconnect.com

Pitches For Å ⚏ ⚏
Acreage 1 **Open** Mar to Oct
Access Good **Site** Level
Nearest Bus Stop (Miles) ¼
Views of the sea and nearby Whitstable. Superstore nearby. 1 mile to the town centre, 15 minutes to Canterbury and within easy reach by road or rail of Herne Bay, Margate and Dover.
Facilities ⚒ ⚐ 🔲 📷 🍴 ⊙ 🔲 🛒 🏧 ⏚ 🔌 🛒 🔌
Nearest Town Whitstable
🚂 Whitstable

WHITSTABLE

Seaview Holiday Park, St Johns Road, Swalecliffe, Whitstable, Kent, CT5 2RY
Tel: 01227 792246
Email: seaview@parkholidaysuk.com
www.parkholidaysuk.com/cades
Pitches For Å ⚏ ⚏ **Total** 34
Open March to Oct
Access Good **Site** Level
Nearest Bus Stop (Miles) ¼
Just a 5 minute stroll from Swalecliffe beach. Ideal spot for camping and touring.
Facilities
⚒ ⚐ 🔲 📷 🍴 ⏚ ⊙ 🍳 🏧 🎣 ⏚ 🏪 🔌 📞 🔌 🛜
Nearest Town Whitstable
Directions Off the A299, at the double roundabout turn left and go under the railway bridge, at the mini roundabout turn right, after 600 yards turn left down lane to the park (signposted).
🚂 Whitstable

LANCASHIRE

BENTHAM

Lowther Hill Caravan Park, Bentham, Nr Lancaster, Lancashire, LA2 7AN
Tel: 01524 261657
www.caravancampingsites.co.uk/northyorkshire/lowtherhi
Pitches For Å ⚏ ⚏ **Total** 9
Acreage 1¼ **Open** March to Nov
Access Good **Site** Sloping
A quiet site (once a farm) with lovely panoramic views. Caravan rallies welcome (up to 25 caravans, function barn available). You wont want to leave! Dog walking area.
Facilities ⚒ 🔲 📷 🍴 ⊙ 🔌 📞 🔌 🛒
Nearest Town High Bentham
Directions Leave the M6 at junction 34 and take the A683 signposted Kirkby Lonsdale. After 6 miles turn right onto the B6480 signposted Bentham. Site is on the left hand side 2 miles east of High Bentham.
🚂 Bentham

BENTHAM

Riverside Caravan Park, High Bentham, Lancaster, Lancashire, LA2 7FJ
Tel: 015242 61272
Email: info@riversidecaravanpark.co.uk
www.riversidecaravanpark.co.uk
Pitches For ⚏ ⚏ ⚏ **Total** 61
Open 01-Mar to 02-Jan
Access Good **Site** Level
Nearest Bus Stop (Miles) ½

81

Alongside a river, just a short walk to the town for shops and pubs. Close to the famous Yorkshire Three Peaks for walking.
Facilities
Nearest Town High Bentham
Directions Follow signs from the B6480 in the middle of High Bentham, turn south at the Black Bull Pub.
High Bentham

BLACKPOOL

Clifton Fields Caravan Park, Peel Road, Nr Blackpool, Lancashire, FY4 5JU
Tel: 01253 761676
www.clifton-fields.co.uk
Pitches For 🚐 🚙 **Total** 46
Open Mar **to** Oct
Access Good **Site** Slightly Sloping
Nearest Bus Stop (Miles) ¼
Semi rural
Facilities
Nearest Town Blackpool
Directions Blackpool junction 4 on M55 turn left to Kirkham 400yds, straight on at the roundabout to traffic lights. Turn right and immediate left into Peel Road. 350yds second site on the right.
Blackpool

BLACKPOOL

Redleigh Orchard Touring Caravan Park, Cropper Road, Blackpool, Lancashire, FY4 5LB
Tel: 01253 691459
Email: mdwilky@btinternet.com
www.redleighorchard.co.uk
Pitches For 🚐 🚙 **Total** 29
Acreage 2 **Open** Mar **to** Oct
Access Good **Site** Level
Nearest Bus Stop (Miles) ½
2 miles from Blackpools promenade and pleasure beach. Lytham St Annes within easy reach. Garden centre opposite.
Facilities
Nearest Town Blackpool
Directions Leave the M55 at junction 4, at the roundabout turn left, at the next roundabout turn right, go straight across the mini roundabout, at next roundabout turn right, Park is 100 yards.
Blackpool South

CARNFORTH

Hollins Farm, Far Arnside, Off Cove Road, Silverdale, Carnforth, Lancashire, LA5 0SL
Tel: 01524 701508
Email: reception@holgates.co.uk
www.holgates.co.uk
Pitches For 🏕 🚐 🚙
Acreage 5 **Open** Mar **to** Oct
Access Good **Site** Lev/Slope
Nearest Bus Stop (Miles) ¼
Situated in an area of outstanding natural beauty, near the shore and a bird reserve.
Facilities
Nearest Town Arnside

Directions Leave the M6 at junction 35 into Carnforth, follow signs for Silverdale. Go over the level crossing and bear right, after ¾ miles bear left and after ¼ of a mile fork right into Cove Road.
Arnside/Silverdale

CARNFORTH

Old Hall Caravan Park, Capernwray, Carnforth, Lancashire, LA6 1AD
Tel: 01524 733276
Email: info@oldhallcaravanpark.co.uk
www.oldhallcaravanpark.co.uk
Pitches For 🚐 🚙 **Total** 38
Open 01-Mar **to** 10-Jan
Access Good **Site** Level
Quiet, peaceful, woodland retreat.
Facilities
Nearest Town Carnforth
Directions Leave the M6 at junction 35, go to Over Kellet. Turn left in the village of Over Kellet and the park is 1½ miles on the right.
Carnforth

CLITHEROE

Clitheroe Camping & Caravanning Club Site, Edisford Road, Clitheroe, Lancashire, BB7 3LA
Tel: 01200 425294
Email: clitheroe.site@thefriendlyclub.co.uk
www.campingandcaravanningclub.co.uk/clitheroe
Pitches For 🏕 🚐 🚙 **Total** 80
Acreage 6 **Open** 07-Mar **to** 04-Nov
Site Lev/Slope
Nearest Bus Stop (Miles) ½
In the Ribble Valley, on the banks of a river. Local ghost walks on a weekly basis. Near Clitheroe Castle. Near a swimming pool and a dog walk. BTB 4 Star Graded and AA 3 Pennants. Non members welcome. You can also call us on 0845 130 7633.
Facilities
Directions Nearest main road is the A59. From the west follow the A671 into Clitheroe. Look for the signpost indicating a left turn to Longridge/Sports Centre, turn into Greenacre Road approx 25 metres beyond the pelican crossing. Continue until the T-Junction at Edisford Road, turn left and continue past the church on the right, look for the Sports Centre on the right and car park opposite.
Clitheroe

CLITHEROE

Rimington Caravan Park, Hardhouse Farm, Hardacre Lane, Rimington, Clitheroe, Lancashire, BB7 4EE
Tel: 01200 445355
Email: rimingtoncaravanpark@btinternet.com
www.rimingtoncaravanpark.co.uk
Pitches For 🚐 🚙 **Total** 4
Open Mid-Mar **to** MidNov
Access Good **Site** Level
Nearest Bus Stop (Miles) 1
ADULTS ONLY PARK.
Facilities
Nearest Town Clitheroe

Directions Follow A59 to Gisburn, turn right on A682 park on right after 1 mile.
Clitheroe

GARSTANG

Claylands Caravan Park, Weavers Lane, Cabus, Garstang, Nr Preston, Lancashire, PR3 1AJ
Tel: 01524 791242
www.wyreparks.co.uk
Pitches For 🏕 🚐 🚙 **Total** 36
Acreage 10 **Open** Mar **to** Jan
Access Good **Site** Level
Nearest Bus Stop (Miles) Outside
On the doorstep to the Trough of Bowland. 20 miles from Blackpool and 40 minutes drive to the Lake District.
Facilities
Nearest Town Blackpool
Directions Leave the M6 at junction 33, 6 miles to Garstang. Drive past Quattro's and two garages on the left, then turn left into Weavers Lane.
Lancaster

GARSTANG

Fell View Park Sykes Farm, Scorton, Preston, Lancs, PR3 1DA
Tel: 01524 791283
Email: susan_atkingsin@btconnect.com
www.fellviewparkandfishing.co.uk
Pitches For 🏕 🚐 🚙 **Total** 40
Acreage 4 **Open** Mar **to** Oct
Access Good **Site** Level
Nearest Bus Stop (Miles) 4
Lovely walks, 7 miles from Lancaster 5 miles from Garstang 20 miles from Blackpool.
Facilities
Nearest Town Garstang
Directions From J33 M6 take 1st lt off the r/ about on A6 south t immediately lt into Hampson Lane ar T Junc t rt.After ½ mile straight on at Xrds at Fleece Inn. Followroad for 1½ miles t rt at xrds sp Scorton,long lane. take 1st lane on lt sp Fell View Park and Ford site on rt.
Lancaster

GARSTANG

Six Arches Caravan Park, Scorton, Garstang, Nr Preston, Lancashire, PR3 1AL
Tel: 01524 791683
Email:
bookings@sixarchescaravanpark.co.uk
www.sixarchescaravanpark.co.uk
Pitches For 🚐 🚙 **Total** 12
Open Mar **to** Oct
Access Good **Site** Level
Nearest Bus Stop (Miles) ¼
On the banks of the River Wyre.
Facilities
Nearest Town garstang
Directions Follow the main A6 to 2½ miles north of Garstang.
Lancaster

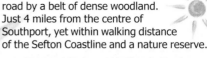
GARSTANG
Wyreside Farm Park, Allotment Lane, St Michaels-on-Wyre, Garstang, Lancashire, PR3 0TZ
Tel: 01995 679797
Email: penny.wyresidefarm@talktalk.net
www.wyresidefarmpark.co.uk
Pitches For 🅰 🚐 🚥 **Total** 16
Acreage 7 **Open** Mar **to** Oct
Access Good **Site** Level
Nearest Bus Stop (Miles) Outside
On the banks of the River Wyre. Mowed field to play in. Central for Blackpool, the Lakes and the Trough of Bowland.
Facilities ⨍ 🛁♿🚻🕭 ☎⛽🕭🔒 🖂 🖭
Nearest Town Garstang/Blackpool
Directions From South, leave M6 at junc 32 and take A6 north to Garstang. In village of Billsborrow turn immediately left, after 4 miles at mini roundabout turn right, go past church, over bridge, past The Grapes Pub, right hand bend, bus stop on left, Allotment Lane is on the right hand side.
🚆 Preston

LANCASTER
New Parkside Farm Caravan Park, Denny Beck, Caton Road, Lancaster, Lancashire, LA2 9HH
Tel: 01524 770723
www.ukparks.co.uk/newparkside
Pitches For 🅰 🚐 🚥 **Total** 40
Acreage 4 **Open** Mar **to** Oct
Access Good **Site** Level
Nearest Bus Stop (Miles) ¼
A working farm with beautiful views of Lune Valley. On the edge of Forest of Bowland and close to historic Lancaster and Morecambe Bay. Central for lakes and dales.
Facilities ⨍ 🛁🕭🖂⊙⛽🕭🔒 🖭
Directions Leave the M6 at junction 34 and take the A683 towards Kirkby Lonsdale. Park is situated 1 mile on the right.
🚆 Lancaster

LANCASTER
Wyreside Lakes Fishery, Sunnyside Farmhouse, Bay Horse, Lancaster, Lancashire, LA2 9DG
Tel: 01524 792093
Email: wyresidelakes@btconnect.com
www.wyresidelakes.co.uk
Pitches For 🅰 🚐 🚥 **Total** 100
Acreage 120 **Open** All Year
Access Good **Site** Lev/Slope
Set in the beautiful Wyreside Valley with views of the Bowland Fells. 7 lakes to walk around and the beautiful Foxes Wood.
Facilities ⨍ 🛁🕭🖂♿⊙⛽🕭🔒 🖂 🖭 ☎
Ⓢ🅿♿✗ ♑ 🚼🎣🕭🖂 🖋 🕭
Nearest Town Garstang

Directions Leave the M6 at junction 33, turn left towards Garstang and follow brown tourism signs.
🚆 Lancaster

MORECAMBE
Glen Caravan Park, Westgate, Morecambe, Lancashire, LA3 3EL
Tel: 01524 423896
Pitches For 🚐 🚥 **Total** 10
Acreage ½ **Open** March **to** October
Access Good **Site** Level
Nearest Bus Stop (Miles) ¼
15 minutes walk Morecambe Promenade.
Facilities ⨍ 🛁🕭🖂⊙🖂🔒 🖭
🕭🖂🕭 🕭
Nearest Town Morecambe
Directions In Morecambe itself close to promenade, Regent Road and Westgate.

MORECAMBE
Greendales Farm & Bowland View Holiday Park, Greendales Farm, Carr Lane, Middleton, Morecambe, Lancashire, LA3 3LH
Tel: 01524 852616
Email: greendalesfarm@tiscali.co.uk
www.greendalesfarmcaravanpark.co.uk
Pitches For 🚐 🚥 **Total** 24
Acreage 2 **Open** 01-Mar **to** 14-Jan
Access Good **Site** Level
Nearest Bus Stop (Miles) ¼
Close to the beach. Ideal for the Lake District, Blackpool and Morecambe.
Facilities ⨍ 🛁🕭🖂🖂⊙
🕭🖂🖂🕭 🕭
Nearest Town Morecambe
Directions Leave the M6 at junction 34 and follow signs to Middleton and Overton, turn left into Carr Lane, then turn left at the Greendales Farm sign.
🚆 Morecambe

MORECAMBE
Melbreak Caravan Park, Carr Lane, Middleton, Morecambe, Lancashire, LA3 3LH
Tel: 01524 852430
Pitches For 🅰 🚐 🚥 **Total** 40
Acreage 1½ **Open** March **to** October
Access Good **Site** Lev/Slope
Nearest Bus Stop (Miles) ½
Near the beach and some of the oldest churches in England. Lovely walking area.
Facilities ⨍ 🛁🕭🖂⊙🖂 🖂 🖭
Ⓢ 🕭🖂🖂 🕭
Nearest Town Morecambe
Directions Take the B5274 from Morecambe to the roundabout, go straight across until you get to Middleton, signposted from the junction.
🚆 Morecambe

MORECAMBE
Morecambe Lodge Caravan Park, Shore Lane, Bolton-le-Sands, Carnforth, Lancashire, LA5 8JP
Tel: 01524 824361
Email: andrew@morecambe-lodge.co.uk
www.morecambe-lodge.co.uk
Pitches For 🚐 🚥 ⛺ **Total** 25
Acreage 2 **Open** March **to** Oct
Access Good **Site** Level
Nearest Bus Stop (Miles) ½
Direct access to the beach. Excellent views over the bay across to the Lake Hills. Good for walking, fishing and cycling. US RVs welcome with 16 or 32 amp supply.
Facilities ⨍ 🛁🕭🖂🖂⊙🖂 ☎
🕭⊙🕭🖂🖂 🕭🖂 📶
Nearest Town Morecambe
Directions Take the A6 north from Lancaster to Bolton-le-Sands, turn left at the traffic lights onto the A5105. After 200yds turn right by the first house, travel down towards the beach and over the bridge, Park is on the left hand side.
🚆 Carnforth

MORECAMBE
Venture Caravan Park, Langridge Way, Westgate, Morecambe, Lancashire, LA4 4TQ
Tel: 01524 412986
Email: mark@venturecaravanpark.co.uk
www.venturecaravanpark.co.uk
Pitches For 🅰 🚐 🚥 **Total** 75
Acreage 17 **Open** All Year
Access Good **Site** Level
Beautifully landscaped Park offering a relaxing family holiday experience. Ideal for the Lake District and the Yorkshire Dales.
Facilities ♿ ⨍ 🛁🕭🖂⊙🖂 🖂 🖭
Ⓢ ☎✗ ♑ 🍴♑🕭 ♑🚼🕭🖂🖂 🕭
Nearest Town Morecambe
Directions Leave the M6 at junction 34 and take the A683 to Morecambe. At the roundabout go straight across onto the A589, at 3rd roundabout take 1st left onto Westgate (sp West Promenade, West End and Sandylands). Go over the bridge and straight across the traffic lights, after ¾ miles turn right after the Fire Station into Langridge Way, the Park is at the end of Langridge Way.
🚆 Morecambe

SOUTHPORT
Willowbank Holiday Home & Touring Park, Coastal Road, Ainsdale, Southport, Merseyside, PR8 3ST
Tel: 01704 571566
Email: info@willowbankcp.co.uk
www.willowbankcp.co.uk

Pitches For ⚏ 🚐 **Total** 87
Acreage 10 **Open** March **to** Jan
Access Good **Site** Level
Nearest Bus Stop (Miles) ¼
Ideal for woodland walks and all of Southports attractions. Close to the Trans-Penine Cycle Way. Motorhome service bay and dog walk area. Ideal touring.
Facilities ♿ ⚡ ♻ 🔟 ♨ ⌐ ⊙ ⤴ 🔋 ▣ 🍴
🔟 ⊙ ≊ ⌐ 🅟 ▣ ⊙
Nearest Town Southport
Directions From South M6-M57/M58 onto the A5036, then take the A5207 onto the A565 for Southport. After RAF Woodvale at traffic lights turn left, park is 150 metres on the left.
🚐 Ainsdale

THORNTON

Kneps Farm Holiday Park, River Road, Stanah, Thornton-Cleveleys, Blackpool, Lancashire, FY5 5LR
Tel: 01253 823632
Email: enquiries@knepsfarm.co.uk
www.www.knepsfarm.co.uk
Pitches For ⚏ 🚐 **Total** 60
Acreage 3½ **Open** Mar **to** Mid Nov
Access Good **Site** Level
Nearest Bus Stop (Miles) Outside
Situated adjacent to the Stanah Amenity and Picnic Area, forming part of the River Wyre Estuary Country Park. A rural retreat close to Blackpool. Camping Pods for hire. We are proud to have been voted Regional Winner for North-West England and Overall Winner in the Practical Caravan Top 100 Sites 2011 Awards.
Facilities ♿ ⚡ ⚡ ♻ 🔟 ♨ ⌐ 🅟 ⊙ ⤴ 🔋
▣ ⊙ ≊ ⊙ ⤴ 🅟 ▣ ⊙ ≊ 📶
Nearest Town Blackpool

Directions 5 mls, NNE of B/pool. From the M55 junc 3 take the A585 F/wood rd, to the River Wyre Hotel on lt, turn Rt at the r/about onto the B5412 sp Little Thornton. Turn Rt at the mini r/about after the school onto Stanah Road, go straight over the next r/ about leading to River Road.
🚐 Poulton-le-Fylde

LEICESTERSHIRE
LEICESTER

Hill Top Caravan Park, Hill Top, 67 Old Gate Rd, Thrussington, Leicestershire, LE7 4TL
Tel: 01664 424357
Email: mjandstarry@googlemail.com
www.caravancampingsites.co.uk/ leicestershire
Pitches For ⚏ 🚐 🚐 **Total** 10
Acreage 1 **Open** All Year
Access Good **Site** Level
Nearest Bus Stop (Miles) ½
ADULTS ONLY SITE. Within walking distance of two country pubs. 5 minutes drive to two golf courses. Close to Belvoir Castle, Rutland Water, Ragdale Hall Health Spa, National Space Centre and much more. Site Fees from £9 per night.
Facilities ⚡ ♻ 🔟 🍴 🔟 ⊙ ⤴ ▣ A
Nearest Town Leicester
Directions 9 miles north of Leicester on the A46 Newark road. At Thrussington Rearsby sign turn right, on entering Thrussington turn sharp left at 30mph sign into Old Gate Road, site is 500 yards on the right.
🚐 Syston

LUTTERWORTH

Stanford Hall Caravan Park, Stanford Road, Swinford, Leicestershire, LE17 6DH
Tel: 01788 860387

Email: stanfordpark@yahoo.co.uk
www.stanfordhallcaravanpark.co.uk
Pitches For ⚏ 🚐 **Total** 120
Acreage 10½ **Open** All Year
Access Good **Site** Level
Nearest Bus Stop (Miles) ½
Ideal for Stanford Hall, the Grand Union Canal, Silverstone and the NEC.
Facilities ⚡ 🔟 ♨ ≊ ⊙ ⤴ ▣ ⊙ 🌿
Nearest Town Lutterworth
Directions Only 5 miles from Lutterworth. 10 minutes from Rugby by car.
🚐 Rugby

MARKET BOSWORTH

Bosworth Water Trust, Far Cotton Lane, Market Bosworth, Leicestershire, CV13 6PD
Tel: 01455 291876
Email: info@bosworthwatertrust.co.uk
www.bosworthwatertrust.co.uk
Pitches For 🛆 ⚏ 🚐 🚐 **Total** 70
Acreage 4 **Open** All Year
Access Good **Site** Level
Nearest Bus Stop (Miles) ¼
Own man made beach, water front pitches, kids play area, boat hire, crazy golf.
Facilities ♿ ⚡ 🔟 ♨ ⌐ ⊙ ⤴ 🍴
≊ 🔟 ⊙ ≊ ✕ ♀ ♨ ✿ ⤴ ▣ ⊙ ✏ 🌿
Nearest Town Market Bosworth
Directions Located on the B585, half a mile west of Market Bosworth.
🚐 Hinckley/Nuneaton

LINCOLNSHIRE
ALFORD

Woodthorpe Hall Leisure Park,
Woodthorpe Hall, Woodthorpe, Alford, Lincolnshire, LN13 0DD
Tel: 01507 450294

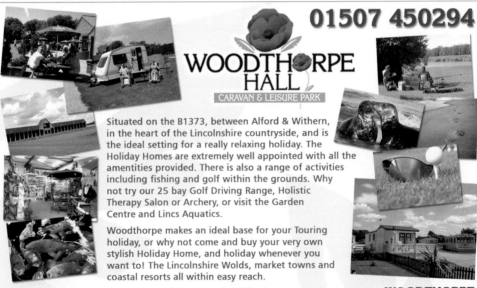

Email:
enquiries@woodthorpehallleisure.co.uk
www.woodthorpehallleisure.co.uk
Pitches For ▲ ⌂ ⇔ **Total** 60
Open Mar **to** 03-Jan
Access Good **Site** Level
Golf course, golf driving range and fishing lakes on site. 6 miles from the beach and 10 miles from the Georgian market town of Louth.
Facilities ⚹ ⅃ 🏠 🎾 ☂ ⌂ ⊿ ⚐ ◻ ☎
🏧 🍴 🛒 ✕ 🍸 🍺 🔥 ❄ 🌙 🛒 ⊿ ☀ 🚿 📶
Nearest Town Alford
Directions Just off the B1373, 1½ miles from Withern Village and 3½ miles from the market town of Alford.
⇌ Skegness

BOSTON
Long Acres (Adult Only) Caravan Park,
Station Road, Old Leake, Boston,
Lincolnshire, PE22 9RF
Tel: 01205 871555
Email: enquiries@longacres-caravanpark.co.uk
www.longacres-caravanpark.co.uk
Pitches For ▲ ⌂ ⇔ **Total** 40
Acreage 2 **Open** March **to** October
Access Good **Site** Level
Nearest Bus Stop (Miles) 3
ADULTS ONLY PARK with peace and tranquillity. Ideal starting point for exploring Lincolnshires many attractions.
Facilities ⚹ ⅃ 🏠 🎾 ☂ ⌂ ⊿ ⚐ ☎ ◻ 🏧 📶
Nearest Town Boston
Directions From the A16 take the B1184 (Station Road) at Sibsey. After approx 1 mile at the T-Junction turn left, then after approx 1½ miles turn right into Station Road.
⇌ Boston

BOSTON
Orchard Park, Frampton Lane, Hubberts Bridge, Boston, Lincolnshire, PE20 3QU
Tel: 01205 290328
Email: info@orchardpark.co.uk
www.orchardpark.co.uk
Pitches For ▲ ⌂ ⇔ **Total** 87
Acreage 61 **Open** All Year
Access Good **Site** Level
Nearest Bus Stop (Miles) Outside
ADULTS ONLY. ETB 3 Star Graded, AA 4 Pennants and David Bellamy Gold Award.
Facilities ⚹ ⅃ 🏠 🎾 ☂ ⌂ ⊿ ⚐ ◻ ☎
🏧 🍴 🛒 ✕ 🍸 ⇔ 🍺 ⚐ ◻ ⊿ 🌙 🛒 🍺 📶
Nearest Town Boston
Directions Take the A52 from Boston towards Grantham. After approx. 3½ miles turn right at Four Cross Roads Pub onto the B1192, Park is ¼ of a mile.
⇌ Hubberts Bridge

BOSTON
Pilgrims Way Caravan & Camping Park,
Church Green Road, Fishtoft, Boston,
Lincolnshire, PE21 0QY
Tel: 01205 366646
Email: pilgrimsway@caravanandcampingpark.com
www.pilgrimsway-caravanandcamping.com
Pitches For ▲ ⌂ ⇔ 🚿 **Total** 22
Acreage 2.5 **Open** All Year
Access Good **Site** Level
Nearest Bus Stop (Miles) Outside
Close to town & RSPB Reserves, easy drive to Skegness.
Facilities ⚹ ⅃ 🏠 🎾 ☂ ⌂ ⊿ ⚐ ◻ ☎
🏧 🏠 🍺 ⏚ ⌂ ◻ 📶
Nearest Town Boston/Skegness
Directions Take the A52 east from Boston, in 1 mile, after the junction with the A16 at

The Ball Public House, turn right and follow international signs to the Park.
⇌ Boston

BOSTON
The Moorings, Station Road, Swineshead Bridge, Boston, Lincolnshire, PE20 3PS
Tel: 01205 820184
Email: di.mccormack@yahoo.co.uk
www.themoorings.org
Pitches For ▲ ⌂ ⇔ 🚿 **Total** 5
Acreage 10 **Open** Apr **to** Sept
Access Good **Site** Level
Nearest Bus Stop (Miles) ½
Alongside a river for fishing.
Facilities ⅃ 🏠 🎾 ☂ ⌂ ⊿ ⚐ ☎ ✕ 🛒 ⊿ 📶
Nearest Town Boston
Directions From the A1121 signed Sleaford, turn left onto the A17 and immediately left over the railway.
⇌ Swineshead Bridge

BOSTON
Walnut Lake Lodges & Camping, Main Road, Algarkirk, Boston, Lincolnshire, PE20 2LQ
Tel: 01205 460482
Email: mariawalnutlakes@yahoo.co.uk
Pitches For ⌂ ⇔ 🚿 **Total** 10
Acreage 4 **Open** Mar **to** Oct
Access Good **Site** Level
Nearest Bus Stop (Miles) 1
ADULTS ONLY PARK with fishing on site.
Facilities ⚹ ⅃ 🏠 🎾 ☂ ⌂ ◻ ☎ 🛒 🌙 🛒 ⊿ ⏚
Nearest Town Boston/Spalding
Directions From the A17/A16 roundabout heading towards Kings Lynn, site is 30 metres on the left.
⇌ Boston/Spalding

LINCOLNSHIRE

CLEETHORPES

Thorpe Park Holiday Centre, Thorpe Park, Cleethorpes, Lincolnshire, DN35 0PW
Tel: 01472 813395
Email: thorpepark@haven.com
www.haventouring.com/tothorpepark
Pitches For ▲ ⊞ ⊟ **Total** 141
Open Mid March **to** End Oct
Access Good **Site** Level
Nearest Bus Stop (Miles) Outside
Nearest Town Cleethorpes
≠ Cleethorpes

HORNCASTLE

Ashby Park, West Ashby, Nr Horncastle, Lincolnshire, LN9 5PP
Tel: 01507 527966
Email: ashbypark@btconnect.com
www.ukparks.co.uk/ashby
Pitches For ▲ ⊞ ⊟ **Total** 130
Acreage 70 **Open** 01-Mar **to** 06-Jan
Access Good **Site** Level
Nearest Bus Stop (Miles) 1
Lincoln Castle and Cathedral 20 miles, East coast beach 25 miles 7 fishing lakes on site,David Bellamy Gold award Park.
Facilities ₺ ⨍ 🖥 📵 ⌐ ⊙ ⌐ 🛒
🏧 🞊 🖭 🗚🖭 ⊟ ✐ ⛇ ⚲
Nearest Town Horncastle
Directions 1½ miles north of Horncastle between the A153 and the A158.
≠ Lincoln

HORNCASTLE

Greetham Retreat Holidays (CL Site)
Greetham Lodge, Tetford Road, Greetham, Horncastle, Lincolnshire, LN9 6PT
Tel: 01507 588640
Email: holidays@greethamretreat.co.uk
www.greethamretreat.co.uk
Pitches For ⊞ ⊟ ⊟< **Total** 5
Acreage 4 **Open** All Year
Access Sloping **Site** 5
Nearest Bus Stop (Miles) Outside
Facilities ₺ ⨍ 🖥 🖭 ⌐ ⊙ ⌐ 🖭 📵 🛒
🗚🖭 📶
Nearest Town Horncastle
Directions A158 from Horncastle. Turn left in village of Toynton. Continue for 2¼ miles. Greetham Retreat Holidays is on the left.
≠ Lincoln, Boston or Skegness

HUTTOFT

Jolly Common Adult Only Caravan Park, Jolly Common, Sea Lane, Huttoft, Alford, Lincolnshire, LN13 9RW
Tel: 01507 490236
www.jollycommoncaravanpark.co.uk
Pitches For ⊞ ⊟
Acreage 9 **Open** 15-Mar **to** 15-Oct
Access Good **Site** Level
Nearest Bus Stop (Miles) ½
ADULTS ONLY SITE set in peaceful countryside. 1 mile from a sandy beach.
Facilities ⨍ 🖥 🖭 ⌐ ⊙ 🖥 🛒 🗚🖭 ✐ ⚠
Nearest Town Sutton-on-Sea
Directions From Sutton-on-Sea head south on the A52 for 4 miles. In the village of Huttoft turn first left, after ¾ miles turn first right and the site is 200 yards on the left.
≠ Skegness

INGOLDMELLS

Bridge End Touring Site, Boltons Lane, Ingoldmells, Skegness, Lincolnshire, PE25 1JJ
Tel: 01754 872456
Email: bridgeendsite@hotmail.co.uk
www.bridgendsite.co.uk
Pitches For ⊞ ⊟ **Total** 40

Open Easter **to** Oct
Access Good **Site** Level
Nearest Bus Stop (Miles) ¼
Beach, fishing ,market.
Facilities ₺ ⨍ 🖥 🖭 ⌐ ⊙ 🖥 🛒 🖭
Nearest Town Ingoldmells
Directions Situated 3 miles north of Skegness at the junction of the main Ingoldmells to Skegness road (A52) and Boltons Lane.
≠ Skegness

INGOLDMELLS

Hardy's Touring Site, Sea Lane, Ingoldmells, Skegness, Lincolnshire, PE25 1PG
Tel: 01754 874071
Pitches For ⊞ ⊟ **Total** 112
Acreage 5 **Open** Easter **to** October
Access Good **Site** Level
Nearest Bus Stop (Miles) ¼
5 minutes walk from the beach. Next to Fantasy Island and 10 minutes from an animal farm.
Facilities ⨍ 🖥 🖭 ⌐ ⊙ 🖥 🛒
🏧 🞊 🞊 🗚 🗚🖭 ✐
Nearest Town Skegness/Ingoldmells
Directions Take the A52 north from Skegness to Ingoldmells. At the Ship Inn in Ingoldmells turn right down Sea Lane, towards the sea. Site is ½ mile on the right.
≠ Skegness

INGOLDMELLS

Valetta Farm Caravan Site, Mill Lane, Addlethorpe, Skegness, Lincolnshire, PE24 4TB
Tel: 01754 763758
Email: leeman22@btinternet.com
Pitches For ▲ ⊞ ⊟ **Total** 55
Acreage 2 **Open** 25-Mar **to** 20-Oct
Access Good **Site** Level
Nearest Bus Stop (Miles) 1
Quite a pretty site in the country, 1 mile from the beach.
Facilities ✐ ⨍ 🖥 ⌐ ⊙ 🖥 🛒 🗚🖭 ⛇ ⚲
Nearest Town Skegness
Directions Turn left off the A158 (Horncastle to Skegness road) on Burgh-le-Marsh bypass at the signpost Ingoldmells and Addlethorpe. Follow signposts for Ingoldmells for 3 miles, turn right by disused mill into Mill Lane. Site is on the left in 150yds.
≠ Skegness

LINCOLN

Hartsholme Country Park, Skellingthorpe Road, Lincoln, Lincolnshire, LN6 0EY
Tel: 01522 873578
Email: hartsholmecp@lincoln.gov.uk
www.lincoln.gov.uk
Pitches For ▲ ⊞ ⊟ **Total** 32
Acreage 2½ **Open** Mar **to** Oct
Access Good **Site** Level
Nearest Bus Stop (Miles) ¼
Set amongst mature woodland with a large picturesque lake, as well as open grassland. Adjacent to Swanholme Lakes local nature reserve. theres a frequent bus service to city centre use the convenient cycly path.
Facilities ₺ ⨍ 🖥 🖭 ⌐ ⊙ 🖥 🛒
🞊 ✕ 🞊 🗚 🗚🖭 ✐
Nearest Town Lincoln
Directions 2½ miles south west of Lincoln city centre. Hartsholme country Park Signposted on the A46, we are on the B1378.
≠ Lincoln Central

LINCOLN

Oakhill Leisure, Swinderby Road, Norton Disney, Lincoln, Lincolnshire, LN6 9QG
Tel: 01522 868771
Email: ron@oakhill-leisure.co.uk
www.oakhill-leisure.co.uk
Pitches For ▲ ⊞ ⊟ ⊟< **Total** 60
Acreage 10 **Open** All Year
Access Good **Site** Level
Nearest Bus Stop (Miles) 1
Peaceful woodland site with open fields and a fishing lake.
Facilities ₺ ⨍ 🖥 🖭 ⌐ ⊙ 🖥 🛒
🗚 🗚🖭 ✐ ⛇ ⚲
Nearest Town Lincoln
Directions A46 from A1 follow brown caravan signs.
≠ Lincoln

LINCOLN

Shortferry Caravan Park, Ferry Road, Fiskerton, Lincoln, Lincolnshire, LN3 4HU
Tel: 01526 398021
Email: kay@shortferry.co.uk
www.shortferry.co.uk
Pitches For ⊞ ⊟ **Total** 75
Acreage 80 **Open** All Year
Access Good **Site** Level
Nearest Bus Stop (Miles) Outside
Situated by a river with 2 fishing ponds. Fishing tackle and bait shop. Entertainment most weekends. Bar meals and take-away in our public house. Seasonal outdoor heated swimming pool.
Facilities ₺ ⨍ 🖥 🖭 ⌐ ⊙ 🖥 🛒
🏧 🞊 🞊 ✕ 🞒 ♦ 🗚 ⌑ 🞊 🗚🖭 ✐ ⛇ 📶
Nearest Town Lincoln
Directions From the A46 Lincoln ring road take the A158 towards Skegness. After approx. 5 miles turn right at Shortferry sign, continue to follow signs for approx. 5 miles.
≠ Lincoln

MABLETHORPE

Mablethorpe Camping & Caravanning Club Site, Highfield, 120 Church Lane, Mablethorpe, Lincolnshire, LN12 2NU
Tel: 01507 472374
Email:
mablethorpe.site@thefriendlyclub.co.uk
www.campingandcaravanningclub.co.uk/
mablethorpe
Pitches For ▲ ⊞ ⊟ **Total** 105
Acreage 11 **Open** 21-Mar **to** 04-Nov
Access Difficult **Site** Level
Nearest Bus Stop (Miles) 1
Just 1 mile from the sea and award winning beaches. Ideal for cyclists. Near the Lincolnshire Wolds. Swimming pool, play area, bicycle hire, horse racing and dog walk nearby. BTB 4 Star Graded and AA 3 Pennants. Non members welcome. You can also call us on 0845 130 7633.
Facilities ₺ ⨍ 🖥 🖭 ⌐ ⊙ 🖥 🛒
🗚 🞊 🞊 🗚 🗚🖭 📶
Nearest Town Mablethorpe
Directions On the outskirts of Mablethorpe, on the A1104. Turn into Church Lane after the petrol station on the right, site is 800 yards along the lane on the right hand side.
≠ Cleethorpes

MABLETHORPE

Trusthorpe Springs Leisure Park, Mile Lane, Trusthorpe, Mablethorpe, Lincolnshire, LN12 2QQ
Tel: 01507 441384
Pitches For ⊞ ⊟ **Total** 125
Acreage 6 **Open** Mar **to** Sept
Access Good **Site** Level
Nearest Bus Stop (Miles) 1

Facilities ♿ ✠ 🔲📷🏧🎣 ☉🍴🍺🛒🛁 ⛱ 📶📻🍴🛒🛁 ⛱ 📶
Nearest Town Mablethorpe
Directions A52 from Mablethorpe follow brown signs.
⚆ Skegness

MARKET DEEPING
The Deepings Caravan Park, Outgang Road, Towngate East, Market Deeping, Lincolnshire, PE6 8LQ
Tel: 01778 344335
Email: info@thedeepings.com
www.thedeepings.com
Pitches For ⚑ 🚐 🚌 **Total** 60
Acreage 9 **Open** All Year
Access Good **Site** Level
Family run and owned park with a clubhouse and childrens play area. Fishing on site.
Facilities ♿ ✠ 🔲📷🏧🎣 ☉ 🛒🛁
Nearest Town Market Deeping
Directions From Peterborough take the A15 to Market Deeping. At the roundabout take second exit, turn right at the Towngate Inn, Park is 2 miles on the left.
⚆ Peterborough

MARKET RASEN
Lincolnshire Lanes Caravan & Camping Site, Manor Farm, East Firsby, Market Rasen, Lincolnshire, LN8 2DB
Tel: 01673 878258
Email: robert@lincolnshire-lanes.com
www.lincolnshire-lanes.com
Pitches For ⚑ 🚐 🚌 ⛺ **Total** 21
Acreage 3 **Open** All Year
Access Good **Site** Level
Nearest Bus Stop (Miles) Outside
Small site shop. Disabled toilet. ETB 3 Star Graded and Welcome Host.
Facilities ✠ 🔲📷🏧🎣 ☉🛒🛁
Nearest Town Market Rasen/Lincoln
Directions Take the A15 north from Lincoln, 2½ miles past RAF Scampton turn right and follow brown tourism signs to the site entrance.
⚆ Market Rasen/Lincoln

SCUNTHORPE
Brookside Caravan & Camping Park, Stather Road, Burton-Upon-Stather, Scunthorpe, Lincolnshire, DN15 9DH
Tel: 01724 721369
Email: brooksidecp@aol.com
www.brooksidecaravanpark.co.uk
Pitches For ⚑ 🚐 🚌 **Total** 70
Acreage 10 **Open** All Year
Access Good **Site** Level
Nearest Bus Stop (Miles) Outside

Our family run, superbly equipped park, set in an area of outstanding beauty, is the ideal location for visiting North Lincolnshire. 4½ miles from Scunthorpe town centre. Bank Holidays - Adults only. ETB 5 Star Graded.
Facilities ♿ ✠ 🔲📷🏧🎣 ☉🛒🛁 🍴🛒🛁 📶
Nearest Town Scunthorpe
Directions B1430 from Scunthorpe town centre to Burton-Upon-Stather (4 miles) turn left in front of Sheffield Arms public house. From the bottom of the hill travel 250 yards, entrance to Brookside is on the right.
⚆ Scunthorpe

SKEGNESS
Homelands Caravan Park, Sea Road, Anderby, Skegness, Lincolnshire, PE24 5YB
Tel: 01507 490511
Email: homelandspark@gmail.com
www.ukcampsite.co.uk
Pitches For ⚑ 🚐 🚌 **Total** 10
Acreage 1 **Open** Nov **to** Nov
Access Good **Site** Level
Quiet, friendly site in the countryside. Within walking distance of a sandy beach. 4 Berth Static Van also available for hire.
Facilities ⚒ ✠ 🔲📷🏧🎣 ☉🍴🛒🛁
Nearest Town Skegness/Mablethorpe
Directions Take the A52 Skegness to Mablethorpe road, approx. ¾ miles past Mumby (½ a mile past the B1449 junction) turn right on a sharp bend signposted Anderby, site is on the left in 1¼ miles.
⚆ Skegness/Mablethorpe

SKEGNESS
North Shore Holiday Centre, Elmhirst Avenue, Roman Bank, Skegness, Lincolnshire, PE25 1SL
Tel: 01754 763815
Email: reception@northshore-skegness.co.uk
www.northshore-skegness.co.uk
Pitches For 🚐 🚌 **Total** 133
Open 01-Mar **to** 30-Nov
Access Good **Site** Level
Nearest Bus Stop (Miles) Outside
Just a short walk to both the beach and Skegness centre. Set well back from the main road, ideal family holiday base. Pitch & Putt and Miniature Golf on site. Camping Pods and all weather touring pitches now available. SORRY NO TENTS.
Facilities ♿ ✠ 🔲📷🏧🎣 ☉🛒🛁
Nearest Town Skegness
Directions A52 towards Mablethorpe, 500yds from the A158 junction.
⚆ Skegness

SKEGNESS
Pine Trees Leisure Park, Croft Bank, Skegness, Lincolnshire, PE24 4RE
Tel: 01754 762949
Email: enquiries@pinetreesholidays.co.uk
www.pinetreesholidays.co.uk
Pitches For ⚑ 🚐 🚌 ⛺ **Total** 150
Acreage 8 **Open** March **to** Nov
Access Good **Site** Level
Nearest Bus Stop (Miles) Outside
Landscaped fishing lakes and a 180 acre wetland conservation project with bird hides.
Facilities ♿ ✠ 🔲📷🏧🎣 ☉🍴🛒🛁
Nearest Town Skegness
Directions Take the A52 from Skegness (signposted Boston) for 1½ miles, turn right at right hand turning lane.
⚆ Skegness

SKEGNESS
Richmond Holiday Centre, Richmond Drive, Skegness, Lincolnshire, PE25 3TQ
Tel: 01754 762097
Email: sales@richmondholidays.com
www.richmondholidays.com
Pitches For 🚐 🚌 **Total** 70
Open March **to** Nov
Access Good **Site** Level
Nearest Bus Stop (Miles) Outside
A short walk to the bustling resort of Skegness with funfairs, sandy beaches and donkey rides. Just a short drive from the Wolds or the wild open scenery of Gibraltar Point Nature Reserve.
Facilities ♿ ✠ 🔲📷🏧🎣 ☉🍴🛒🛁
Nearest Town Skegness
Directions Follow signs to the coach park on Richmond Drive, we are located approx. ½ a mile past the coach park on the right hand side.
⚆ Skegness

SKEGNESS
Riverside Caravan Park, Wainfleet Bank, Wainfleet, Skegness, Lincolnshire, PE24 4ND
Tel: 01754 880205
Pitches For ⚑ 🚐 🚌 **Total** 30
Acreage 1¼ **Open** 15-Mar **to** 31-Oct
Access Good **Site** Level
Nearest Bus Stop (Miles) Entrance
Alongside a river. Golf 1 mile.
Facilities ✠ 🔲📷🏧🎣 ☉🛒🛁 🍴
Nearest Town Skegness
Directions From the A52 Boston to Skegness road, take the B1195 to Wainfleet All Saints by-pass, Site is 1 mile from the by-pass turn off.
⚆ Wainfleet

LINCOLNSHIRE

SKEGNESS

Ronam Cottage, Sea Road, Anderby, Skegness, Lincolnshire, PE24 5YA
Tel: 01507 490750
Pitches For 🏕 ⛺ 🚐
Acreage 1½ **Open** All Year
Access Good **Site** Level
Near to Anderby Creek and beach. Countryside walks. 2 hard standings available. Rally Field available. Trailer tents welcome. Camping & Caravanning Club site, non members welcome.
Facilities ✦ 🏪 🖤 ↿ 🎇⚓
Nearest Town Skegness/Mablethorpe
Directions From Alford take the A1104 and turn onto the A1111 to Bilsby. Turn right onto the B1449 then left onto the A52, turn first right to Anderby. After 1½ miles turn left on the bend, site entrance is 50 yards on the right.
⚵ Skegness

SKEGNESS

Skegness Water Leisure Park, Walls Lane, Ingoldmells, Skegness, Lincolnshire, PE25 1JF
Tel: 01754 899400
Email:
enquiries@skegnesswaterleisurepark.co.uk
www.skegnesswaterleisurepark.co.uk
Pitches For 🏕 ⛺ 🚐
Acreage 133 **Open** Mar to Oct
Access Good **Site** Level
Nearest Bus Stop (Miles) ¼
A rural setting with on site fishing and a water ski centre. Close to Butlins (day visitors allowed) and Fantasy Island. Near to beaches.
Facilities ✦ ✦ 🖤 ↿ ⊙ ↘ 🛒 🔲 🍴
🎇 🛢 🗙 🍷 🔟 🔥 ↾ 🌳 ⚓
Nearest Town Skegness
Directions From Skegness follow the A52 north (sp Mablethorpe) for 3 miles, turn left into Walls Lane at Cheers Pub, Park is ½ a mile on the left.
⚵ Skegness

SKEGNESS

Southview Holiday Park, Burgh Road, Skegness, Lincolnshire, PE25 2LA
Tel: 01754 896001
Email: southview@park-resorts.com
www.www.park-resorts.com
Pitches For ⛺ 🚐 **Total** 96
Open Apr to Oct
Nearest Bus Stop (Miles) Entrance
5 minute drive to beach
Facilities ✦ ✦ 🖤 ↿ ⊙ ↘ 🛒 🔲 🍴
🎇 🛢 🗙 🍷 🔟 🔥 🌳 ↾ ✖🛒 🔲 🍴 🌳 ⚓
Nearest Town Skegness
⚵ Skegness

SLEAFORD

Low Farm Touring & Camping Park, Spring Lane, Folkingham, Sleaford, Lincolnshire, NG34 0SJ
Tel: 01529 497322
Email: lowfarmpark@sky.com
www.lowfarmpark.co.uk
Pitches For 🏕 ⛺ 🚐 **Total** 36
Acreage 2¼ **Open** Easter to End Sept
Access Good **Site** Lev/Slope
Nearest Bus Stop (Miles) ¼
Facilities ✦ 🖤 ↿ ⊙ 🔲 🌳 ⚓
🎇 🛢 🌳 🔲 🌳 ⚓
Nearest Town Sleaford
Directions 9 miles south of Sleaford on the A15. Go through village, turn right by the Village Hall.
⚵ Sleaford

SPALDING

Ashleigh Caravan Park, Ashleigh House, 45 Broadgate, Whaplode Drove, Spalding, Lincolnshire, PE12 0TN
Tel: 01406 330666
Email: ashleighcaravans@aol.com
Pitches For 🏕 ⛺ 🚐 **Total** 12
Acreage ¾ **Open** Mar to Nov
Access Good **Site** Level
Nearest Bus Stop (Miles) Outside
Quiet Camping & Caravan Club Site with two fishing lakes stocked with nine species. Convenient for Fenland attractions including the Spalding Flower Parade.
Facilities ✦ 🖤 ↿ ⊙ ↘ 🌳 🎇🛒 🔲 🍴
Nearest Town Spalding
Directions From Spalding take the A16 towards Peterborough. 6 miles after A16/A1175 roundabout turn left onto the B1166, after approx 4 miles turn left into Broadgate. Site is ¾ miles on the right. From Peterborough take A16 to Spalding after 7 miles turn right onto B1166 then as above.
⚵ Spalding

SPALDING

Delph Bank Touring Caravan Park, Old Main Road, Fleet Hargate, Holbeach, Nr Spalding, Lincolnshire, PE12 8LL
Tel: 01406 422910
Email: enquiries@delphbank.co.uk
www.delphbank.co.uk
Pitches For ⛺ 🚐 **Total** 45
Acreage 3
Access Good **Site** Level
Nearest Bus Stop (Miles) ¼
ADULTS ONLY PARK. An attractive, quiet, tree lined site, convenient for touring the Fens and Lincolnshire/Norfolk coastal resorts. Pubs and eating places within walking distance. BH&HPA Member. ETB 5 Stars and David Bellamy Gold Award.
Facilities ✦ 🖤 ↿ ⊙ ↘ 🛒 🔲 🍴
🎇 🛢 🌳 🔲 🌳 ⚓
Nearest Town Holbeach
Directions From Kings Lynn take the A17, Turn left in the village of Fleet Hargate then right, site is on the left. From Spalding take the A151 to Holbeach, continue a further 3 miles to Fleet Hargate, turn right into the village and look for our sign on the right.
⚵ Spalding

SPILSBY

Meadowlands, Monksthorpe, Great Steeping, Spilsby, Lincolnshire, PE23 5PP
Tel: 01754 830794
www.meadowlandslodgepark.co.uk
Pitches For 🏕 ⛺ 🚐 🚐 **Total** 20
Acreage 5 **Open** All Year
Access Good **Site** Level
Nearest Bus Stop (Miles) ½
Quiet ADULTS ONLY site in a rural setting. Ideal for walking and cycling. Handy for Skegness and the beautiful Wolds. 3 miles from Spilsby.
Facilities ✦ 🖤 ↿ ⊙ ↘ 🔲 🍴
🔲 🌳 🔲 🌳 ⚓
Nearest Town Skegness
Directions Take the A16 into Spilsby town then take the Wainfleet road, pass The Bell Inn and after approx. 1 mile turn left signposted Gunby and Heavy Horse Centre, Park is on the right after ¾ miles.
⚵ Wainfleet

SUTTON-ON-SEA

Cherry Tree Site, Huttoft Road, Sutton-on-Sea, Lincolnshire, LN12 2RU
Tel: 01507 441626
Email: info@cherrytreesite.co.uk
www.cherrytreesite.co.uk

Pitches For ⛺ 🚐 **Total** 60
Acreage 3 **Open** March to October
Access Good **Site** Level
Nearest Bus Stop (Miles) Outside
ADULTS ONLY SITE. Beach, golf course and Lincolnshire Wolds. ETB 5 Star Graded.
Facilities ✦ ✦ 🖤 ↿ ⊙ ↘ 🛒 🔲 🍴
🎇 🛢 🗙 🔲 🍴 🌳 ⚓
Nearest Town Sutton-on-Sea
Directions Take the A52 south from Sutton-on-Sea, 1½ miles on the left hand side. Entrance via a lay-by. Tourist Board signs on road.
⚵ Skegness

SUTTON-ON-SEA

Kirkstead Holiday Park, North Road, Trusthorpe, Sutton-on-Sea, Lincolnshire, LN12 2QD
Tel: 01507 441483
Email: mark@kirkstead.co.uk
www.kirkstead.co.uk
Pitches For 🏕 ⛺ 🚐 **Total** 60
Acreage 6 **Open** March to 01-Dec
Access Good **Site** Level
Nearest Bus Stop (Miles) ¼
10 minute walk to the beach. Clubhouse, new shower block. Familys welcome.
Facilities ✦ ✦ 🖤 ↿ ⊙ ↘ 🛒 🔲 🍴
🎇 🛢 🗙 🍷 🔟 🔥 🔲 🌳 ⚓
Nearest Town Sutton-on-Sea
Directions Take the A52 coast road from Sutton to Mablethorpe, turn off left at Trusthorpe. Signposted from the A52.
⚵ Skegness

WAINFLEET

Holly Tree Pub & Caravan Park, Little Steeping Road, Thorpe Culvert, Wainfleet, Skegness, Lincolnshire, PE24 4QT
Tel: 01754 880490
Pitches For 🏕 ⛺ 🚐 **Total** 70
Acreage 6 **Open** March to Nov
Access Good **Site** Level
Set in the heart of rural Lincolnshire alongside the River Steeping. Excellent fishing on and off site. Ideal for touring, 15 minutes from the coast. Family Pub on site.
Facilities ✦ 🖤 ↿ ⊙ ↘ 🛒 🔲 🍴
🔲 🛢 🍷 🔥 ✖🛒 🔲 🌳 ⚓
Nearest Town Skegness
Directions Go from Wainfleet All Saints to Thorpe St. Peter, then to Thorpe Culvert Railway Station, Little Steeping Road go over the river and onto Holly Tree.
⚵ Wainfleet

WOODHALL SPA

Glen Lodge Touring Park, Glen Lodge, Edlington Moor, Woodhall Spa, Lincolnshire, LN10 6UL
Tel: 01526 353523
www.glenlodgetouringpark.com
Pitches For ⛺ 🚐 🚐 **Total** 35
Acreage 3 **Open** Mar to Nov
Access Good **Site** Level
Nearest Bus Stop (Miles) 1
Ideal for the woods, the Battle of Britain Memorial Flight, Tattershall Castle and Horncastle (with its antiques).
Facilities ✦ ✦ 🖤 ↿ ⊙ ↘ 🔲 🍴
🔲 🛢 🔲 🌳 ⚓
Nearest Town Woodhall Spa
Directions From the mini roundabout in the village turn northeast towards Bardney, after 1 mile turn left, turn right after the bend and the site is 300 yards on the left.
⚵ Metheringham

WOODHALL SPA

Woodhall Spa Camping & Caravanning Club Site, Wellsyke Lane, Kirkby-on-Bain, Woodhall Spa, Lincolnshire, LN10 6YU
Tel: 01526 352911
Email:
woodhall.spasite@thefriendlyclub.co.uk
www.campingandcaravanningclub.co.uk/woodhallspa
Pitches For A 🚐 🚙 **Total** 90
Acreage 6½ **Open** 21-Mar **to** 04-Nov
Access Good **Site** Level
Nearest Bus Stop (Miles) 1
A nature lovers dream with many varieties of birds seen on site. Dish washing facilities. BTB 5 Star Graded, David Bellamy Gold Award and AA 3 Pennants. Non members welcome. You can also call us on 0845 130 7633.
Facilities 🚻 ♿ 🏪 🔥 🚿 ⊙ 🛒 🚮 💷 🍴
🏧 🅿 🔌 ✉ 🏪 📞
Nearest Town Horncastle
Directions From Sleaford or Horncastle take the A153 to Haltham. At the garage turn left towards Kirkby-on-Bain. At the Ebrington Arms turn right, site is 1 mile.
🚊 Metheringham

LONDON

ABBEY WOOD

Abbey Wood Caravan Club Site,
Federation Road, Abbey Wood, London, SE2 0LS
Tel: 020 8311 7708
www.caravanclub.co.uk
Pitches For A 🚐 🚙 **Total** 220
Acreage 9 **Open** All Year
Access Good **Site** Lev/Slope
Nearest Bus Stop (Miles) ½
Spacious site screened by mature trees. Within walking distance of railway link to central London for its attractions. Near the London Eye, Thames Barrier and Splash World at Woolwich. Non members welcome. Booking essential.
Facilities 🚻 ♿ 🏪 🔥 🚿 ⊙ 🅿 🏧 🛒 🚮 💷 📞 🛜
Directions From central London on A2 turn off at A221 junc into Danson Rd, follow signs for Bexleyheath to Crook Log (A207 junc). At lights turn right and immediately left into Brampton Rd. After 1½ miles at lights turn left into Bostal Rd (A206), at lights turn right into Basildon Rd (B213). In 300yds turn right into McLeod Rd, at roundabout turn right into Knee Hill, turn second right into Federation Rd, site is 50yds on the left.
🚊 Abbey Wood

CHINGFORD

Lee Valley Campsite, Sewardstone Road, Chingford, London, E4 7RA
Tel: 020 8529 5689
Email:
sewardstonecampsite@leevalleypark.org.uk
www.visitleevalley.org.uk
Pitches For A 🚐 🚙 🚗 ≈ **Total** 200
Acreage 14 **Open** 01-Mar **to** 31-Jan
Access Good **Site** Lev/Slope
Nearest Bus Stop (Miles) Outside
Very close to London and historical Waltham Abbey.
Facilities 🚻 ♿ 🏪 🔥 🚿 ⊙ 🛒 🚮 💷 📞
🏧 🅿 🔌 🚮 🏪 📞
Nearest Town Chingford
Directions From Chingford take the A379.
🚊 Chingford

CRYSTAL PALACE

Crystal Palace Caravan Club Site,
Crystal Palace Parade, London, SE19 1UF
Tel: 020 8778 7155
www.caravanclub.co.uk

Pitches For A 🚐 🚙 **Total** 126
Acreage 6 **Open** All year
Access Good **Site** Level
Nearest Bus Stop (Miles) ¼
On the edge of a pleasant park. Ideal for the sights of central London which is easily accessible by public transport (Travelcards sold on site April to November). Non members welcome. Booking essential.
Facilities ♿ 🚻 🏪 🔥 🚿 ⊙ 🛒 🚮 💷 📞
🏧 🅿 🚮 🔌 🏪 📞 🛜
Nearest Town London
Directions Site entrance is off the A212 at the junction of Crystal Palace Parade and Westwood Hill.
🚊 Crystal Palace

EDMONTON

Lee Valley Camping & Caravan Park,
Meridian Way, Edmonton, London, N9 0AS
Tel: 020 8803 6900
Email:
edmontoncampsit@leevalleypark.org.uk
www.visitleevalleypark.org.uk
Pitches For A 🚐 🚙 🚗 ≈ **Total**
Direct buses, trains and tubes to London and the West End. Golf course and athletics centre on site, plus a cinema.
Facilities 🚻 ♿ 🏪 🔥 🚿 ⊙ 🛒 🚮 💷 📞
🏧 🅿 🏪 ✕ 🚮 🔌 💷 📞 🛜
Nearest Town London
Directions Exit the M25 at junction 25 and follow signs to the city on the A10. Follow signs to Freezywater A1055. Continue for 6 miles and follow signs to Lee Valley Leisure Complex.
🚊 Edmonton Green

MANCHESTER

LITTLEBOROUGH

Hollingworth Lake Caravan Park, Round House Farm, Rakewood, Littleborough, Manchester, OL15 0AS
Tel: 01706 378661
Pitches For A 🚐 🚙 **Total** 45
Acreage 3 **Open** All Year
Access Good **Site** Level
Nearest Bus Stop (Miles) 1
Near a large lake that covers 120 acres. Cafe/Restaurant nearby.
Facilities 🚻 ♿ 🏪 🔥 🚿 ⊙ 🛒 💷 🏧 🔌 🏪 🅿
Nearest Town Rochdale
Directions Leave the M62 at junction 21, Milnrow B6255. Follow Hollingworth Lake Country Park signs to The Fishermans Inn/The Wine Press. Take Rakewood Road, then the second on the right.
🚊 Littleborough

NORFOLK

BURGH ST. PETER

Waveney River Centre, Staithe Road, Burgh St Peter, Norfolk, NR34 0BT
Tel: 01502 677343
Email: info@waveneyrivercentre.co.uk
www.waveneyrivercentre.co.uk
Pitches For A 🚐 🚙 **Total** 48
Open All Year
Access Poor **Site** Lev/Slope
Nearest Bus Stop (Miles) ¾
Alongside the River Waveney. Heated showers and toilet blocks.
Facilities 🚻 ♿ 🏪 🔥 🚿 ⊙ 🛒 🚮 💷 📞
🏧 🅿 🏪 ✕ 🍴 🚮 ♨ 🚮 🔌 💷 🏪 🛜
Nearest Town Beccles
Directions From the A143 at Haddiscoe, turn into Wiggs Road following brown tourism signs. After 2 miles turn left into Burgh Road and the site is 2½ miles.
🚊 Haddiscoe

CAISTER-ON-SEA

Grasmere Caravan Park, Bultitudes Loke, Yarmouth Road, Caister-on-Sea, Great Yarmouth, Norfolk, NR30 5DH
Tel: 01493 720382
www.grasmere-wentworth.co.uk
Pitches For 🚐 🚙 **Total** 46
Acreage 2 **Open** April **to** Mid October
Access Good **Site** Level
Nearest Bus Stop (Miles) ¼
½ a mile from the beach, 3 miles to centre of Great Yarmouth. Advance bookings taken for touring site pitches. Each pitch with its own electric, water tap and foul water drain. Some hard standings.
Facilities ♿ 🚻 🏪 🔥 🚿 ⊙ 🛒 🚮 💷 📞
🏧 🅿 🏪 🚮 🔌 💷
Nearest Town Great Yarmouth
Directions Enter Caister from roundabout near Yarmouth Stadium at Yarmouth end of bypass. After ½ mile turn sharp left just before the bus stop.
🚊 Great Yarmouth

CROMER

Forest Park Caravan Site Ltd., Northrepps Road, Cromer, Norfolk, NR27 0JR
Tel: 01263 513290
Email: info@forestpark.co.uk
www.forestpark.co.uk
Pitches For A 🚐 🚙 **Total** 355
Acreage 90 **Open** 15-Mar **to** 15-Jan
Access Good **Site** Sloping
🚊 Cromer

CROMER

Manor Farm Caravan & Camping Site,
Manor Farm, East Runton, Cromer, Norfolk, NR27 9PR
Tel: 01263 512858
Email: manor-farm@ukf.net
www.manorfarmcaravansite.co.uk
Pitches For A 🚐 🚙 **Total** 230
Acreage 16 **Open** Easter **to** Oct
Access Good **Site** Lev/Slope
Panoramic sea and woodland views. Spacious, quiet, family run farm site. Ideal for families. Separate field for dog owners.
Facilities ♿ ♿ 🔥 🏪 🔥 🚿 ⊙ 🛒 💷 📞
🏧 🚮 🔌
Nearest Town Cromer
Directions Signposted Manor Farm from the A148 and the A149. The A149 is the preferable route if towing.
🚊 Cromer

CROMER

West Runton Camping & Caravanning Club Site, Holgate Lane, West Runton, Cromer, Norfolk, NR27 9NW
Tel: 01263 837544
Email:
west.runtonsite@thefrindlyclub.co.uk
www.campingandcaravanningclub.co.uk/westrunton
Pitches For A 🚐 🚙 **Total** 200
Acreage 15 **Open** 21-Mar **to** 04-Nov
Access Difficult **Site** Lev/Slope
Nearest Bus Stop (Miles) ¾
Panoramic view of the countryside. Just 1 mile from the sea. Boules pitch on site. BTB 4 Star Graded and AA 4 Pennants. Non members welcome. You can also call us on 0845 130 7633.
Facilities 🚻 ♿ 🏪 🔥 🚿 ⊙ 🛒 🚮 💷 📞
🏧 🅿 🏪 🚮 🔌 💷 📞 🔌
Nearest Town Cromer
Directions Take the A148 from Kings Lynn, on approaching West Runton turn left at the Roman Camp Inn, ½ a mile along the track, on the crest of the hill, is the site entrance.
🚊 West Runton

CROMER

Woodhill Park, Cromer Road, East Runton, Cromer, Norfolk, NR27 9PX
Tel: 01263 512242
Email: info@woodhill-park.com
www.woodhill-park.com
Pitches For ▲ ⬜ ⬜ ⬜⛌ **Total** 300
Acreage 32 **Open** Mar **to** Oct
Access Good **Site** Lev/Slope
Nearest Bus Stop (Miles) Outside
Peace and tranquillity with views of the sea and surrounding countryside. A choice of pitch styles and excellent amenity buildings. Rose Award.
Facilities ⬚ ⬚ ⬚⬚⬚⬚⬚⬚⬚⬚⬚
⬚⬚⬚⬚⬚⬚⬚⬚⬚⬚⬚
Nearest Town Cromer
Directions Set between East and West Runton on the seaside of the A149 Cromer to Sheringham road.
⇌ West Runton

DISS

The Willows Camping & Caravan Park, Diss Road, Scole, Diss, Norfolk, IP21 4DH
Tel: 01379 740271
Pitches For ▲ ⬜ ⬜ **Total** 32
Acreage 8 **Open** Easter **to** Mid Oct
Access Good **Site** Level
Nearest Bus Stop (Miles) ¼
Alongside the River Waveney.
Facilities ⬚ ⬚⬚⬚⬚⬚⬚⬚⬚
⬚⬚⬚⬚⬚⬚⬚
Nearest Town Diss
Directions 1½ miles east of Diss on the A1066.
⇌ Diss

DISS

Waveney Valley Holiday Park, Airstation Farm, Airstation Lane, Rushall, Diss, Norfolk, IP21 4QF
Tel: 01379 741690/741228
Email: waveneyvalleyhp@aol.com
www.caravanparksnorfolk.co.uk
Pitches For ▲ ⬜ ⬜ ⬜⛌ **Total** 45
Acreage 4 **Open** April **to** October
Access Good **Site** Level
Nearest Bus Stop (Miles) ¼
Family run site in a rural position. Horse riding for all ages and abilities on site. Good fishing locally.
Facilities ⬚ ⬚⬚⬚⬚⬚⬚⬚⬚
⬚⬚⬚⬚⬚⬚⬚⬚⬚⬚
Nearest Town Harleston
Directions From Diss take the A140, at Dickleburgh in Rushall turn at telephone box towards Pulham, turn into Airstation Lane and site is on the right.
⇌ Diss

DOCKING

The Garden Caravan Site, Barmer Hall Farm, Syderstone, Kings Lynn, Norfolk, PE31 8SR
Tel: 01485 578220/178
Email: nigel@mason96.fsnet.co.uk
www.gardencaravansite.co.uk
Pitches For ▲ ⬜ ⬜ **Total** 30
Open March **to** November
Access Good **Site** Lev/Slope
A lovely secluded and sheltered site in a walled garden. Close to the famous North Norfolk coast.
Facilities ⬚ ⬚ ⬚⬚⬚⬚⬚⬚⬚
⬚⬚⬚⬚⬚
Nearest Town Fakenham
Directions From Fakenham or Kings Lynn take the A148, then take the B1454 towards Hunstanton, 4 miles on the right hand side.

DOWNHAM MARKET

Grange Farm Touring Park, Whittington Hill, Whittington, Kings Lynn, Norfolk, PE33 9TF
Tel: 01366 500075
Email:
relax@grangefarmtouringpark.co.uk
www.grangefarmtouringpark.co.uk
Pitches For ⬜ ⬜ **Total** 25
Open Feb **to** Dec
Access Good **Site** Level
Nearest Bus Stop (Miles) Outside
Alongside a river for fishing and boating. Only suitable for adults. Within 1 hours drive of Hunstanton, Sheringham and Cromer.
Facilities ⬚ ⬚ ⬚⬚⬚ ⬚⬚⬚⬚⬚A
Nearest Town Downham Market
Directions Just off the A134.
⇌ Downham Market

FAKENHAM

Crossways Caravan & Camping Park, Crossways, Holt Road, Little Snoring, Norfolk, NR21 0AX
Tel: 01328 878335
Email:
joyholland@crosswayscaravanpark.co.uk
Pitches For ▲ ⬜ ⬜ **Total** 26
Acreage 2½ **Open** All Year
Access Good **Site** Level
Nearest Bus Stop (Miles) ½
Central location in North Norfolk. Easy access.
Facilities ⬚ ⬚ ⬚⬚⬚⬚⬚⬚⬚⬚⬚
⬚⬚⬚⬚⬚⬚⬚⬚
Nearest Town Fakenham
Directions On the A148, 3 miles past Fakenham towards Cromer.
⇌ Kings Lynn

FAKENHAM

Greenwoods Campsite, Old Fakenham Road, Tattersett, Kings Lynn, Norfolk, PE31 8RS
Tel: 07917 842371
Email: info@greenwoodscampsite.co.uk
www.greenwoodscampsite.co.uk
Pitches For ⅄ ⊞ ⊟ **Total** 25
Open Mar to Oct **Access** Good **Site** Sloping
Nearest Bus Stop (Miles) ¼
Beaches 12 miles from the campsite.
Facilities ⬩⬩⬩⬩⬩⬩⬩⬩
Nearest Town Fakenham
Directions From Fakenham take the A148 west for 4 miles, turn left at the Coxford sign, turn left again onto Old Fakenham Road and the site entrance is on the right.
⚏ Kings Lynn

FAKENHAM

The Old Brick Kilns, Little Barney Lane, Barney, Fakenham, Norfolk, NR21 0NL
Tel: 01328 878305
Email: enquiries@old-brick-kilns.co.uk
www.old-brick-kilns.co.uk
Pitches For ⅄ ⊞ ⊟ **Total** 65
Acreage 13 **Open** 12-Mar to 04-Jan
Access Good **Site** Level
Nearest Bus Stop (Miles) 1
Beaches within 20 minutes drive. Near to Sandringham, Blicking Hall, Pensthorpe Nature Reserve, Thursford, Walsingham and Norwich. Strictly no arrivals til after 1.30pm due to narrow access lane. NB: Money Off Vouchers will NOT be accepted on Bank Holidays.
Facilities ⬩⬩⬩⬩⬩⬩⬩⬩⬩⬩⬩⬩⬩⬩⬩⬩⬩
Nearest Town Fakenham
Directions From the A148 Fakenham to Cromer road, take the B1354 to Melton Constable. After 300 yards turn right to Barney, then turn first left down Little Barney Lane, Park is at the end in ¾ miles.
⚏ Kings Lynn

GREAT HOCKHAM

Thetford Forest Camping & Caravanning Club Site, Puddledock Farm, Great Hockham, Thetford, Norfolk, IP24 1PA
Tel: 01953 498455
Email: thetford@thefriendlyclub.co.uk
www.campingandcaravanningclub.co.uk/thetfordforest
Pitches For ⅄ ⊞ ⊟ ⌁ **Total** 160
Acreage 12 **Open** All Year
Access Good **Site** Level
Nearest Bus Stop (Miles) ½
Very quiet site backing onto the forest, with a network of paths and picnic areas which provide an abundance of birds and wildlife. Camping Pods available for hire. Dog exercise area. Non members welcome. You can also call us on 0845 130 7633.
Facilities ⬩⬩⬩⬩⬩⬩⬩⬩⬩⬩⬩⬩⬩⬩⬩⬩⬩⬩
Nearest Town Watton
Directions Midway between Thetford and Watton on the A1075. Turn left at 83 post Forestry Commission picnic site, no roadside sign.
⚏ Thetford

GREAT YARMOUTH

Bureside Holiday Park, Boundary Farm, Oby, Great Yarmouth, Norfolk, NR29 3BW
Tel: 01493 369233
www.www.bureside.com
Pitches For ⅄ ⊞ ⊟ **Total** 170
Acreage 10 **Open** End May Bank Hol to Mid Sept
Access Good **Site** Level
⚏ Acle

GREAT YARMOUTH

Burgh Castle Marina, Butt Lane, Burgh Castle, Norfolk, NR31 9PZ
Tel: 01493 780331
Email: stuart@burghcastlemarina.co.uk
www.burghcastlemarina.co.uk
Pitches For ⅄ ⊞ ⊟ **Total** 45
Acreage 19 **Open** Mar to Oct
Access Good **Site** Level
Nearest Bus Stop (Miles) Outside
Spectacular Broads views, Fishermans Inn 2 mins walk,good food.
Facilities ⬩⬩⬩⬩⬩⬩⬩⬩⬩⬩⬩⬩⬩
Directions A12 bypass from Gt Yarmouth A143 to Beccles, then follow signs to Belton and Burgh Castle.
⚏ Great Yarmouth

GREAT YARMOUTH

Drewery Caravan Park, California Road, California, Great Yarmouth, Norfolk, NR29 3QW
Tel: 01493 730845
Email: drewerycp@btinternet.com
www.drewerycaravanpark.co.uk
Pitches For ⅄ ⊞ ⊟ **Total** 135
Acreage 4 **Open** Easter to Oct
Access Good **Site** Level
Nearest Bus Stop (Miles) ¼
Near the beach. Ideal for Norfolk Broads and Great Yarmouth.
Facilities ⬩⬩⬩⬩⬩⬩⬩⬩⬩⬩⬩
Directions Take the A149 from Great Yarmouth, at the Greyhound Stadium roundabout turn left, at next roundabout take the second exit onto the B1159. Go to roundabout and take the second exit, after ¼ mile turn right into California Road and follow to the end. Site is opposite California Tavern. 6 miles from Great Yarmouth.
⚏ Great Yarmouth

GREAT YARMOUTH

Great Yarmouth Racecourse Caravan Club Site, Jellicoe Road, Great Yarmouth, Norfolk, NR30 4AU
Tel: 01493 855223
www.caravanclub.co.uk
Pitches For ⊞ ⊟ **Total** 115
Acreage 5¼ **Open** Mar to Nov
Access Good **Site** Level
Nearest Bus Stop (Miles) Outside
300yds from the lively seafront. Adjacent to a racecourse and golf course. Near the Norfolk Broads and Pleasurewood Hills. Dogs on leads at all times. Non members welcome. Booking essential.

Facilities ⬩⬩⬩⬩⬩⬩⬩⬩⬩
Nearest Town Great Yarmouth
Directions From north on the A149, at the traffic lights on the south outskirts of Caister turn left into Jellicoe Road. After ¼ mile turn left into the Racecourse entrance (BEWARE of blind turning), go across the racetrack to the site.
⚏ Great Yarmouth

GREAT YARMOUTH

Pampas Lodge Holiday Park, The Street (A143), Haddiscoe, Norfolk, NR14 6AA
Tel: 01502 677265
Email: colinshirley@btinternet.com
Pitches For ⊞ ⊟ **Total** 54
Acreage 4 **Open** Apr to Oct
Access Good **Site** Level
Nearest Bus Stop (Miles) Outside
Near rivers and sae.
Facilities ⬩⬩⬩⬩⬩⬩⬩⬩⬩⬩⬩
Nearest Town Great Yarmouth
Directions On the A143 between Beccles and Great Yarmouth.
⚏ Haddiscoe

GREAT YARMOUTH

Rose Farm Touring & Camping Park, Stepshort, Belton, Great Yarmouth, Norfolk, NR31 9JS
Tel: 01493 780896
Email: myhra@rosefarmtouringpark.co.uk
www.rosefarmtouringpark.co.uk
Pitches For ⅄ ⊞ ⊟ **Total** 120
Acreage 10 **Open** All Year
Access Good **Site** Level
Nearest Bus Stop (Miles) ¼
A clean site in peaceful surroundings. Special offers.
Facilities ⬩⬩⬩⬩⬩⬩⬩⬩⬩⬩⬩⬩
Nearest Town Gorleston
Directions From Great Yarmouth on the bypass take the A143 to Beccles, through Bradwell up to the small dual carriageway. Turn right into new road signposted Belton and Burgh Castle. Down New Road first right at Stepshort, site is first on right.
⚏ Great Yarmouth

GREAT YARMOUTH

The Grange Touring Park, Yarmouth Road, Ormesby St Margaret, Great Yarmouth, Norfolk, NR29 3QG
Tel: 01493 730306
Email: info@grangetouring.co.uk
www.grangetouring.co.uk
Pitches For ⅄ ⊞ ⊟ **Total** 70
Acreage 3½ **Open** Easter to End Sept
Access Good **Site** Level
Nearest Bus Stop (Miles) ¼
Rural, sheltered site, very convenient for Great Yarmouth and the Norfolk Broads.
Facilities ⬩⬩⬩⬩⬩⬩⬩⬩⬩⬩⬩
Nearest Town Great Yarmouth
Directions 2 miles north of Great Yarmouth, by the roundabout on the B1159 at the north end of Caister bypass.
⚏ Great Yarmouth

Discover the Norfolk Broads

Bureside
Holiday Park

Open Spring Bank Holiday to Mid-September

A spacious site for Touring Caravans & Tents, with the tranquillity of the Broadland. Relax with your family and enjoy the swimming pool, or take an evening stroll along the quiet country lanes and riverbanks spotting wildlife. Newly created Wildlife Conservation Area.

Adult only fishing is available on our private lake stocked with Mirror and Common Carp & Tench, or you can cast your line into our Bure River frontage. Trekking stables, wildlife parks, beaches and the beautiful cathedral city of Norwich are all within easy reach. Excellent standards of cleanliness and hygiene maintained at all times. No all male parties please.

On site launching for boats (slipway), directly into the most popular river network for sailing and cruising on the Norfolk Broads

Boundary Farm, Oby, Great Yarmouth, Norfolk NR29 3BW
01493 369233   www.bureside.com

GREAT YARMOUTH AND THE NORFOLK BROADS

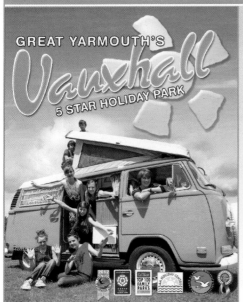

GREAT YARMOUTH'S Vauxhall 5 STAR HOLIDAY PARK

FOR THE BEST TOURING AND CAMPING HOLIDAYS

- Over 220 all electric sites ● Free car parking
- Hair dryers ● Grass & hard standings
- Baby changing facilities ● Awnings FREE
- Gas cylinder refills on site
- Heated shower & toilet blocks
- Night security for late arrivals

SUPER PITCH: Full mains service pitch with hedged, landscaped and awning areas

FREE WITH YOUR HOLIDAY
★ Star Studded Entertainment ★ Electricity
★ Kid's Club ★ Indoor Tropical Waterworld
★ Sport & Fitness Fun
★ Louie's Adventure Playground
★ TV selected Freeview channels (super pitch only)

PUTTING SMILES ON FACES
Call Now For a Free Colour Brochure
01493 857231
Vauxhall Holiday Park, 8 Acle New Road, Great Yarmouth, Norfolk NR30 1TB Ref: 8

great touring savers at **www.vauxhall-holiday-park.co.uk**

93

GREAT YARMOUTH
Vauxhall Holiday Park, Acle New Road, Great Yarmouth, Norfolk, NR30 1TB
Tel: 01493 857231
Email: info@vauxhallholidays.co.uk
www.vauxhall-holiday-park.co.uk
Pitches For Å ⊕ ⊕ **Total** 213
Acreage 48 **Open** Easter then Mid May **to** Sept
Access Good **Site** Level
Nearest Bus Stop (Miles) Outside
Nearest Town Great Yarmouth
⇌ Great Yarmouth

GREAT YARMOUTH
Willowcroft Camping & Caravan Park, Staithe Road, Repps-with-Bastwick, Norfolk Broads, Norfolk, NR29 5JU
Tel: 01692 670380
Email: willowcroftsite@btinternet.com
www.willowcroft.net
Pitches For Å ⊕ ⊕ **Total** 32
Acreage 2 **Open** Mar **to** Oct
Access Good **Site** Level
Nearest Bus Stop (Miles) ½
Beautiful, tranquil site, just a two minute walk to a river for fishing. Safe footpath along the river which leads to Potter Heigham. Excellent new ladies toilets for 2009.
Facilities ∮ ⊞ ♿ ⌐ ⊙ ╝ ⊕ ⊡
Nearest Town Wroxham
Directions From Great Yarmouth take the A149 to Stalham, in Repps turn left into Church Road, then turn right into Staithe Road. Or from Acle take the B1152 to Caister, then take the A149 and follow as above.
⇌ Acle

HARLESTON
Little Lakeland Caravan Park, Wortwell, Harleston, Norfolk, IP20 0EL
Tel: 01986 788646
Email: info@littlelakeland.co.uk
www.littlelakeland.co.uk
Pitches For ⊕ ⊕ **Total** 40
Acreage 4 **Open** Mar **to** Oct
Access Good **Site** Level
Nearest Bus Stop (Miles) ¼
Half acre fishing lake, site library.
Facilities ⊕ ∮ ⊞ ♿ ⌐ ⊙ ╝ ⊿ ⊡ ⊕
ℒℒ ⊙ ⊠ ⦿ ⌂ ⊕ ⊡ ⊿ ⋇ ⊞
Nearest Town Harleston
Directions Turn off A143 (Diss to Lowestoft) at roundabout signposted Wortwell. In village turn right about 300 yards after Bell P.H. at bottom of lane turn right into site.
⇌ Diss

HEMSBY
Long Beach Caravan Park, Hemsby, Great Yarmouth, Norfolk, NR29 4JD
Tel: 01493 730023
Email: info@long-beach.co.uk
www.long-beach.co.uk
Pitches For Å ⊕ ⊕ **Total** 100
Acreage 5 **Open** Mid March **to** End Oct
Access Good **Site** Level
Nearest Bus Stop (Miles) ¼
Park adjoins its own private sandy beach and dunes. Sea fishing on site.
Facilities ∮ ⊞ ♿ ⌐ ⊙ ╝ ⊕ ⊡ ⊕
ℒℒ ⊙ ⊠ ⌸ ♿ ⦿ ⊙ ⋇ ⋇ ⊞
Nearest Town Great Yarmouth
Directions 5 miles north of Great Yarmouth, turn east from the B1159 at Hemsby.
⇌ Great Yarmouth

HOLT
Kelling Heath Holiday Park, Weybourne, Holt, Norfolk, NR25 7HW
Tel: 01263 588181
Email: info@kellingheath.co.uk
www.kellingheath.co.uk
Pitches For Å ⊕ ⊕ ⊕⫶ **Total** 300
Acreage 250 **Open** Mid Feb **to** Dec
Access Good **Site** Level
A 250 acre estate of woodland and heather, with magnificent views of the Weybourne coastline. Rose Award.
Facilities ⊕ ∮ ⊞ ♿ ⌐ ⊙ ╝ ⊕ ⊡ ⊕
ℒℒ ⊙ ⊠ ⊗ ⦿ ⌂ ⚐ ⋇ ⋇ ⊞ ⊕ ⊡ ⊿ ⊞
Nearest Town Sheringham
Directions Turn north at site sign at Bodham on the A148 or turn south off the A149 at Weybourne Church.
⇌ Sheringham

HORSEY
Waxham Sands Holiday Park, Warren Farm, Horsey, Norfolk, NR29 4EJ
Tel: 01692 598325
www.waxhamsandsholidaypark.co.uk
Pitches For Å ⊕ ⊕ ⊕⫶ **Total** 200
Acreage 22 **Open** 20-May **to** 30-Sep
Access Good **Site** Level
Adjacent to the beach, ideal for sea fishing.
Facilities ⊕ ∮ ⊞ ♿ ⌐ ⊙ ╝ ⊕ ⊡ ⊕
ℒℒ ⊙ ⊠ ⌸ ⦿ ⊿ ⋇ ⋇
Nearest Town Great Yarmouth
Directions Situated on the B1159 main coast road, 12 miles north of Great Yarmouth.
⇌ Great Yarmouth

KINGS LYNN
Kings Lynn Caravan & Camping Park, Parkside House, New Road, North Runcton, Kings Lynn, Norfolk, PE33 0RA
Tel: 01553 840004
Email: klcc@btconnect.com
www.kl-cc.co.uk

Pitches For Å ⊕ ⊕ ⊕⫶ **Total** 150
Acreage 9 **Open** All Year
Access Good **Site** Level
Nearest Bus Stop (Miles) Outside
Situated in a beautiful parkland setting with mature trees. Well situated for Kings Lynn, inland market towns, the North Norfolk coast, watersports and good pubs. Tescos nearby. Rallies welcome.
Facilities ⊕ ∮ ⊞ ♿ ⌐ ⊙ ╝ ⊕ ⊡ ⊕
ℒℒ ⊙ ⌸ ⊞ ⊡ ⊕ ⋇ ⊞
Nearest Town Kings Lynn
Directions 1½ miles from the A17, A47, A10 and A149 main Kings Lynn Hardwick roundabout. Take the A47 towards Swaffham and take the first right at North Runcton.
⇌ Kings Lynn

KINGS LYNN
Narborough Trout & Coarse Lakes, Main Road, Narborough, Kings Lynn, Norfolk, PE32 1TE
Tel: 01760 338005
Email: narfish@supanet.com
www.narfish.co.uk
Pitches For ⊕ ⊕ ⊕⫶ **Total** 15
Open All Year **Access** Good **Site** Level
Nearest Bus Stop (Miles) ½
ADULTS ONLY Site. Ideal for the historic towns of Swaffham, Kings Lynn and Royal Sandringham, plus the Norfolk coast, Thetford Forest, Oxborough Hall, Holkam Hall and the bird reserves at Welney and Titchwell.
Facilities ⊕ ⊞ ♿ ⌐ ⊙ ╝ ⊕ ⊡ ⊕ ⊿ A
Nearest Town Swaffham
Directions A47 from Kings Lynn or Swaffham turn off for Marborough follow main road to site.
⇌ Kings Lynn

KINGS LYNN
Pentney Park, Main Road, Pentney, Kings Lynn, Norfolk, PE32 1HU
Tel: 01760 337479
Email: holidays@pentney-park.co.uk
www.pentney-park.co.uk
Pitches For Å ⊕ ⊕ ⊕⫶ **Total** 170
Acreage 16 **Open** All Year
Access Good **Site** Level
Nearest Bus Stop (Miles) 1
Near the River Nar Valley Walk, linking to Peddars Way Walk. Ideal base for visiting beautiful Norfolk. Washing up facilities.
Facilities ⊕ ∮ ⊞ ♿ ⌐ ⊙ ╝ ⊕ ⊡ ⊕
ℒℒ ⊙ ⊠ ✕ ⌂ ⋇ ⋇ ⊞ ⊡ ⊕ ⋇ ⊞
Nearest Town Kings Lynn
Directions Situated on the A47 9 miles east of Kings Lynn and 7 miles west of Swaffham. Turn onto the B1153 to Gayton, entrance is 200 yards.
⇌ Kings Lynn

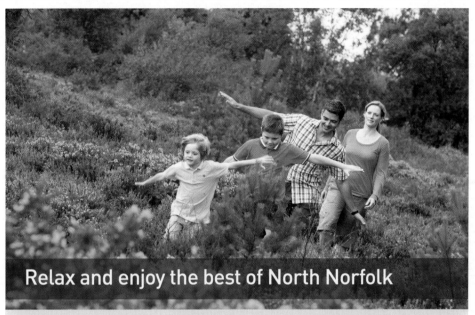

Relax and enjoy the best of North Norfolk

Award-winning Kelling Heath offers a beautiful, natural environment with pitches set amongst rare open heathland with a backdrop of native woodland and pine. Connect with nature... come to Kelling.

Activities
- Woodland walks & nature trails
- Guided walks & events
- Cycle Routes on & off park
- Trim trail, orienteering, petanque and adventure play

Relax
- Health & Fitness Club with indoor pool
- Free outdoor leisure pool
- The Forge: bars, restaurants, take-away
- Village Store
- The Folly open air jazz, folk

We also offer lodges and luxurious holiday homes.

Bookings or brochure 01263 588181
or online www.kellingheath.co.uk
Kelling Heath, Weybourne, Holt,
Norfolk NR25 7HW

KELLING HEATH
THE NATURAL ESCAPE

NORFOLK

METHWOLD

Warren House Caravan Park, Warren House, Brandon Road, Methwold, Thetford, Norfolk, IP26 4RL
Tel: 01366 728238
Email: janescarrott@btinternet.com
Pitches For 🏕 🚐 🚍 **Total** 40
Acreage 4 **Open** March **to** Oct
Access Good **Site** Level
Situated in Thetford Forest and close to Lakenheath Fen RSPB site and NNT Weeting Heath. Good central location for touring East Anglia. Good cycling area.
Facilities 🔟 🚻 🚽 ➰ 🔌 🔥 ⚲ ⚲
Nearest Town Thetford
Directions 5 miles from Brandon on the B1112.
🚆 Thetford

MUNDESLEY

Sandy Gulls Cliff Top Touring Park, Cromer Road, Mundesley, Norfolk, NR11 8DF
Tel: 01263 720513
Email: info@sandygulls.co.uk
www.sandygulls.co.uk
Pitches For 🚐 🚍 **Total** 40
Acreage 2½ **Open** Easter **to** October
Access Good **Site** Level
ADULTS ONLY TOURING PARK on a cliff top location, overlooking the beach. Near to the Broads National Park. TV Hook-ups. ETB 3 Star Graded Park.
Facilities 🚿 ⚡ 🔟 🍴 ➰ ⊙ 🍽 🍺 🚻
🔌 🔥 🚽 🔌 🍴 🔌 A
Nearest Town Cromer
Directions South along the coast road for 4 miles.
🚆 Cromer

NORTH WALSHAM

Two Mills Touring Park, Yarmouth Road, North Walsham, Norfolk, NR28 9NA
Tel: 01692 405829
Email: enquiries@twomills.co.uk
www.twomills.co.uk
Pitches For 🏕 🚐 🚍 **Total** 81
Acreage 8 **Open** 01-Mar **to** 03-Jan
Access Good **Site** Level
Nearest Bus Stop (Miles) Outside
ADULTS ONLY. Ideally situated for visiting North Norfolks many attractions.
Facilities 🚿 ⚡ 🔟 🍴 ➰ ⊙ 🍽 🍺 🚻
🔌 🔥 🔌 🚽 🔌 A 🔌 ⚲ 🛜
Nearest Town North Walsham
Directions Follow Hospital signs passing the Police Station on route. 1 mile on the left from the town centre.
🚆 North Walsham

NORWICH

Norwich Camping & Caravanning Club Site, Martineau Lane, Norwich, Norfolk, NR1 2HX
Tel: 01603 620060
Email: norwich.site@thefriendlyclub.co.uk
www.campingandcaravanningclub.co.uk/norwich
Pitches For 🏕 🚐 🚍 **Total** 50
Acreage 2½ **Open** 21-Mar **to** 04-Nov
Access Good **Site** Level
Nearest Bus Stop (Miles) ¼
A rural location close to the city of Norwich. Near to the Norfolk Broads. BTB 3 Star Graded and AA 3 Pennants. Non members welcome. You can also call us on 0845 130 7633.
Facilities 🚿 ⚡ 🔟 ➰ ⊙ 🍽 🚻
🔌 🔥 🔌 🚽 🔌 ⚲ 🛜
Nearest Town Norwich

Directions From the A47 join the A146 towards Norwich city centre. At the traffic lights turn left, then left again at the Cock Public House. Site is 150 yards on the right.
🚆 Thorpe

NORWICH

Swans Harbour Caravan & Camping Park, Barford Road, Marlingford, Norwich, Norfolk, NR9 5HU
Tel: 01603 759658
Email: info@swansharbour.co.uk
www.swansharbour.co.uk
Pitches For 🏕 🚐 🚍 **Total** 30
Acreage 4 **Open** All Year
Access Good **Site** Level
Nearest Bus Stop (Miles) ½
Alongside a river with own fishing rights. Hard standing available.
Facilities 🚿 ⚡ 🔟 🔟 ➰ ⊙ 🍽 🍺 🚻
🍺 🔌 🍴 🛜
Nearest Town Norwich
Directions Turn off the B1108 (Norwich to Watton road). 3 miles past Southern Bypass turn right signposted Marlingford. Follow brown tourist signs to the site.
🚆 Wymondham

NORWICH

The Willows, The Willows, Stratton Strawless Hall, Stratton Strawless, Norwich, Norfolk, NR10 5LT
Pitches For 🚐 🚍 **Total** 5
Open All Year
Access Good **Site** sloping
Nearest Bus Stop (Miles) Outside
15 miles from coast, 7 milesfrom Broads.
Facilities ⚡ 🔟 ➰ ⊙ 🍽 🍺 🔌 ⚲
Nearest Town Cromer
Directions 7 miles from Norwich Airport on the A140 entrance on main road on right.
🚆 Norwich

POTTER HEIGHAM

Causeway Cottage Caravan Park, Bridge Road, Potter Heigham, Nr Great Yarmouth, Norfolk, NR29 5JB
Tel: 01692 670238
Email: sue324@btinternet.com
www.causewaycottage.webs.com
Pitches For 🏕 🚐 🚍
Access Good **Site** Level
Nearest Bus Stop (Miles) ¼
Static caravans for hire. Restaurant nearby.
Facilities ⚡ 🔟 ➰ ⊙ 🍽
🔌 🔥 🔌 🚽 🔌
Nearest Town Great Yarmouth
Directions Potter Heigham is between Great Yarmouth and Norwich. Turn off the A149 at Potter Heigham, we are 250yds from the river and old bridge.
🚆 Acle

REEDHAM

Reedham Ferry Complex Ltd., Ferry Road, Reedham, Norwich, Norfolk, NR13 3HA
Tel: 01493 700999
Email: reedhamferry@aol.com
www.reedhamferry.co.uk
Pitches For 🏕 🚐 🚍 **Total** 30
Acreage 4 **Open** March **to** Oct
Access Good **Site** Level
Nearest Bus Stop (Miles) ¼
Tranquil site alongside a river. Ideal touring.
Facilities ⚡ 🔟 🔟 ➰ ⊙ 🍽 🚻
🍺 ✕ 🍴 🚽 🔌 🔌
Nearest Town Norwich/Great Yarmouth
Directions From Acle follow signs for Reedham Ferry.
🚆 Reedham

SANDRINGHAM

Sandringham Camping & Caravanning Club Site, The Sandringham Estate, Double Lodges, Sandringham, Norfolk, PE35 6EA
Tel: 01485 542555
Email: sandringham.site@thefriendlyclub.co.uk
www.campingandcaravanning.club.c
Pitches For 🏕 🚐 🚍 **Total** 275
Acreage 28 **Open** 14-Feb **to** 18-Nov
Access Good **Site** Lev/Slope
Nearest Bus Stop (Miles) 1
In the grounds of the Royal Estate. Motorhome stop-off. Ice pack and freezing facilities. BTB 5 Star Graded, David Bellamy Gold Award and AA 4 Pennants. Non members welcome. You can also call us on 0845 130 7633.
Facilities 🚿 ⚡ 🔟 ➰ ⊙ 🍽 🍺 🔌 ⊙ 🚻
🔌 🔥 🔌 🚽 🔌 ⚲ 🛜
Nearest Town Kings Lynn
Directions From the A148 Kings Lynn to Cromer road, turn left onto the B1440 sp West Newton. Follow signs indicating tents and caravans to reach the site.
🚆 Kings Lynn

SANDRINGHAM

Sandringham Estate Caravan Club Site, Glucksburg Woods, Sandringham, Norfolk, PE35 6EZ
Tel: 01553 631614
www.caravanclub.co.uk
Pitches For 🚐 🚍 **Total** 136
Acreage 13 **Open** All Year
Access Good **Site** Lev/Slope
Nearest Bus Stop (Miles) ¼
Set in the heart of the Royal estate, with Sandringham House, museum and grounds on the doorstep. Then theres the Country Park with nature trails, train ride, Visitor Centre, tea room, gift shop and flower stall. Non members welcome. Booking essential.
Facilities 🚿 ⚡ 🔟 ➰ ⊙ 🍽 🚻
🔌 🔥 🔌 A 🔌 🔌 🛜
Nearest Town Sandringham
Directions From north on the A149, at the end of Dersingham bypass turn left onto the B1439 at signpost for West Newton, site is within ½ a mile on the left at rustic signpost SECC.

SCRATBY

Green Farm Caravan Park, 100 Beach Road, Scratby, Great Yarmouth, Norfolk, NR29 3NW
Tel: 01493 730440
Email: contact@greenfarmcaravanpark.com
www.greenfarmcaravanpark.com
Pitches For 🚐 🚍 **Total** 25
Open 26-Mar **to** 31-Oct
Access Good **Site** Level
Nearest Bus Stop (Miles) Outside
Near the beach.
Facilities ⚡ 🔟 ➰ 🔌 🚽 🔌 🚻
🔌 🔥 ✕ 🍴 🔌 🔌 🚽 🔌
Nearest Town Great Yarmouth
Directions 5 miles north of Great Yarmouth along the coast road between Caister and Hemsby.
🚆 Great Yarmouth

SCRATBY

Scratby Hall Caravan Park, Thoroughfare

Lane, Scratby, Great Yarmouth, Norfolk, NR29 3SR
Tel: 01493 730283
Email: scratbyhall@aol.com
www.scratbyhall.co.uk
Pitches For A ⊕ ⊜ **Total** 85
Acreage 5 **Open** Easter **to** End Sept
Access Good **Site** Level
Nearest Bus Stop (Miles) ½
Set in countryside and off the main road. Ideal for visiting the Norfolk Broads and only ½ a mile from the coast.
Facilities ⑥ ∮ ⑫ ⌐ ⨀ ⌣ ◿ ⊿ ◻ ⬤
𝄪 ⨀ ⓐ ⚏ ⋈ ⬜ ⬤ ⬛ ⬤
Nearest Town Great Yarmouth
Directions Approx. 5 miles north of Great Yarmouth. Take the A149 then the B1159, signposted.
⇌ Great Yarmouth

SHERINGHAM
Beeston Regis Caravan Park, Cromer Road, West Runton, Nr Sheringham, Norfolk, NR27 9QZ
Tel: 01263 823614
Email: info@beestonregis.co.uk
www.beestonregis.co.uk
Pitches For A ⊕ ⊜ **Total** 45
Acreage 60 **Open** 24-Mar **to** Oct
Access Good **Site** Level
Nearest Bus Stop (Miles) Outside
Cliff top setting with stunning views and direct access to the beach via steps. Within walking distance of Sheringham and Cromer. Woodland walks in an area of natural beauty.
Facilities ⑥ ∮ ⑫ ⌐ ⨀ ⌣ ◿ ⊿ ◻ ⬤
𝄪 ⓘ ⓐ ⓧ ⚏ ⋈ ⬜ ◿ ⋇ ⬤ ⬤
Nearest Town Sheringham
Directions On the A149 coast road between Sheringham and Cromer, at Beeston Regis opposite the school.
⇌ West Runton

SHERINGHAM
Woodlands Caravan Park, Holt Road, Upper Sheringham, Norfolk, NR26 8TU
Tel: 01263 823802
Email: info@woodlandcaravanpark.co.uk
www.woodlandcaravanpark.co.uk
Pitches For ⊕ ⊜ ⊜≤ **Total** 216
Acreage 5 **Open** 20-Mar **to** Nov
Access Good **Site** Lev/Slope
Nearest Bus Stop (Miles) Outside
Situated in an area of outstanding natural beauty. Beaches, National Park, walkers paradise.
Facilities ⑥ ✗ ∮ ⑫ ⨀ ⌣ ◻ ⬤
𝄪 ⓘⓔ ⓐ ⓧ ⚏ ⬜ ⓜ ⚏ ⋈ ⬜ ◿ ⋇⬤
Nearest Town Sheringham
Directions From Sheringham take the A148 towards Holt, site is situated 1 mile from Sheringham.
⇌ Sheringham

SNETTISHAM
Diglea Caravan & Camping Park, 32 Beach Road, Snettisham, Kings Lynn, Norfolk, PE31 7RA
Tel: 01485 541367
Email: diglea@hotmail.co.uk
Pitches For A ⊕ ⊜ ⊜≤
Acreage 10 **Open** Apr **to** Sept

Access Good **Site** Level
Nearest Bus Stop (Miles) 1
Friendly, family run Park in a rural setting.
Facilities ⑥ ∮ ⑤ ⑫ ⌐ ⨀ ⌣ ◿ ⊿ ◻ ⬤
⓲ ⓐ ⓔ ⚏ ⬜ ◿ ⬤ ⋇ ⬤
Nearest Town Hunstanton
Directions Take the A149 from Kings Lynn towards Hunstanton to Snettisham. After approx 10½ miles turn left signposted Snettisham Beach, Park is on the left after 1½ miles.
⇌ Kings Lynn

STANHOE
The Rickels Caravan & Camping Park, Bircham Road, Stanhoe, Kings Lynn, Norfolk, PE31 8PU
Tel: 01485 518671
Pitches For A ⊕ ⊜ **Total** 30
Acreage 2¼ **Open** March **to** October
Access Good **Site** Lev/Slope
ADULTS ONLY PARK. Close to local beaches, stately homes, Sandringham and market towns. Dogs £1 per night, short dog walk. Static caravan available for hire.
Facilities ∮ ⑫ ⌐ ⨀ ⬤ ⓘ ⬤ ⬤⚏A
Nearest Town Hunstanton
Directions From Kings Lynn take the A148 to Hillington, turn left onto the B1153 to Great Bircham. Fork right onto the B1155 to the crossroads, straight over. Park is 100yds on the left.
⇌ Kings Lynn

SWAFFHAM
Breckland Meadows Touring Park, Lynn Road, Swaffham, Norfolk, PE37 7PT
Tel: 01760 721246
Email: info@brecklandmeadows.co.uk
www.brecklandmeadows.co.uk
Pitches For A ⊕ ⊜ ⊜≤ **Total** 45
Acreage 3 **Open** All Year
Access Good **Site** Level
Nearest Bus Stop (Miles) ½
ADULTS ONLY. Small, friendly and very clean park. Within walking distance of the town centre for shops, pubs, restaurants, etc.. Dog walk adjacent to the park. Central for touring Norfolk. Ideal for walking and cycling.
Facilities ⑥ ∮ ⑫ ⌐ ⨀ ⌣ ◻ ⬤
⓲ ⓐ ⚏ ⬜ ⓐ ⋇ ⬤ ⬤
Nearest Town Swaffham/Hunstanton
Directions Take the A47 from Kings Lynn to Swaffham, approx 15 miles. Take the first exit off the dual carriageway, site is ¾ miles before Swaffham town centre.
⇌ Kings Lynn

THETFORD
Lowe Caravan Park, Ashdale, 134 Hills Road, Saham Hills (Nr Watton), Thetford, Norfolk, IP25 7EZ
Tel: 01953 881051
www.lowecaravanpark.co.uk
Pitches For A ⊕ ⊜ **Total** 20
Acreage 2 **Open** All Year
Access Good **Site** Lev/Slope
Quiet, relaxing site in the countryside. Only closed for Christmas and New Year.
Facilities ∮ ⑤ ⑫ ⌐ ⨀ ⬤ ⓐ ⚏ ⬜

Nearest Town Watton
Directions Take the A11 from Thetford then take the road to Watton. Go through the high street and take second turn into Saham Road (past the golf club). Take the second turning right, turn right at the T-Junction and the Park is the first drive on the right.
⇌ Thetford

THETFORD
The Dower House Touring Park, Thetford Forest, East Harling, Norwich, Norfolk, NR16 2SE
Tel: 01953 717314
Email: info@dowerhouse.co.uk
www.dowerhouse.co.uk
Pitches For A ⊕ ⊜ **Total** 140
Acreage 20 **Open** 18-Mar **to** 02-Oct
Access Good **Site** Level
Set in Thetford Forest, the site is spacious and peaceful. Although we have a bar, we have no amusement arcade or gaming machines.
Facilities ⑥ ∮ ⑫ ⌐ ⨀ ⌣ ◿ ◻ ⬤
𝄪 ⨀ ✗ ⚏ ⑫ ⓜ ⚏ ⋈ ⬜ ◿ ⋇
Nearest Town Thetford
Directions From Thetford take A1066 East for 5 miles, fork left at camping sign onto unclassified road, site on left after 2 miles, signposted.
⇌ Harling Road

THETFORD
Thetford Forest Caravan Club Site, High Ash, Hilborough, Thetford, Norfolk, IP26 5BZ
Tel: 01842 878356
www.caravanclub.co.uk
Pitches For ⊕ ⊜ **Total** 103
Acreage 9½ **Open** Mar **to** Nov
Access Good **Site** Level
Quiet, secluded site set in Forestry Commission woodland. Ideal for wildlife lovers. Within easy driving distance of Swaffham, Norwich and Kings Lynn. Close to Banham Zoo. Own sanitation required. Non members welcome. Booking essential.
Facilities ∮ ⑤ ⑫ ⓘⓔ ⓐ ⚏ ⬜ ⬤ ⬤
Nearest Town Thetford
Directions From Thetford take the A134, at the roundabout in Mundford turn right onto the A1065 signposted Swaffham. Site entrance is on the left within 2 miles by the WWII tank.
⇌ Thetford

WYMONDHAM
Rose Cottage Caravan Site Rose Cottage, Wicklewood, Wymondham, Norfolk, NR18 9PX
Tel: 01953 602158
Email: info@thegreenselfstoragecompany.com
Pitches For ⊕ ⊜ **Total** 5
Acreage 2 **Open** All year
Access Good **Site** Level
Nearest Bus Stop (Miles) ¾
A quite secluded site
Facilities ∮ ⑫ ⌐ ⬤⚏⚏
Nearest Town Wymondham
⇌ Wymondham

97

NORTHAMPTONSHIRE

CORBY

Stamford Caravan Club Site, Fineshade, Corby, Northamptonshire, NN17 3BB
Tel: 01780 444617
www.caravanclub.co.uk
Pitches For ⊕ ⊟ **Total** 85
Acreage 5½ **Open** Mar to Nov
Access Good **Site** Level
Tranquil, meadowland site surrounded by woodland. Ideal for walking, cycling and bird watching. Within easy reach of the Fens and Rutland Water. Own sanitation required. Non members welcome. Booking essential.
Facilities ⨍ ⌂ ♨ ⬚ ⇌ ⬚ ⬚ ⬚ 🛜
Nearest Town Corby
Directions From north on the A43, 2¼ miles past the roundabout at the A47 junction turn left signposted Fineshade. After crossing the railway bridge turn left in front of Forestry Commission Station into site.
⇌ Corby

KETTERING

Kestrel Caravans, Windy Ridge, Warkton Lane, Kettering, Northamptonshire, NN16 9XG
Tel: 01536 514301
Pitches For ⛺ ⊕ ⊟ **Total** 20
Acreage 2 **Open** All Year
Access Good **Site** Level
Nearest Bus Stop (Miles) ½
Very quiet park.
Facilities ⨍ ⌂ ⬚ ⇌ ⌒ ♨ ⬚ ⬚ ⬚
Nearest Town Kettering
Directions Leave the A14 at junction 10 and go into Kettering, go past the petrol station and turn next right into Warkton Lane, Park is ½ a mile on the right.
⇌ Kettering

NORTHAMPTON

Billing Aquadrome, Crow Lane, Great Billing, Northampton, Northamptonshire, NN3 9DA
Tel: 01524 781453
Email: enquiries@pureleisure-holidays.co.uk
www.billingaquadrome.com
Pitches For ⛺ ⊕ ⊟ **Total** 1000
Acreage 234 **Open** Feb to Jan
Access Good **Site** Level
Nearest Bus Stop (Miles) Outside
Set in 235 acres of parkland with 7 fishing lakes and rivers. Full Leisure Club and events programme. Ideal for families.
Facilities ⬚ ⨍ ⌂ ⬚ ⇌ ⌒ ☉ ⬚ ⬚ ⬚
🛈 🍴 ⬚ ⬚ ✕ ♀ ⬚ ♠ ⬚ ⬚ ⬚ ⇌ ⬚ ⬚ ⬚ ☀
🛜
Nearest Town Northampton
Directions Leave the M1 at junction 15 and take the A45 for 6 miles following signs for Billing Aquadrome.
⇌ Northampton

NORTHUMBERLAND

ALNWICK

Railway Inn Caravan Park, Acklington, Morpeth, Northumberland, NE65 9BP
Tel: 01670 760320
Email: info@railway-inn.co.uk
www.railway-inn.co.uk
Pitches For ⊕ ⊟ **Total** 22
Acreage 1½ **Open** All Year
Access Good **Site** Level
Nearest Bus Stop (Miles) ½
Only 3 miles from the beach and near to castles.

Facilities ⬚ ⨍ ⌂ ⬚ ⇌ ⌒ ⬚
✕ ⬚ ⇌ ⬚ ⬚ ⬚
Nearest Town Amble
Directions From the A1 take the B6345 sp Felton and Amble, after approx 3 miles the Railway Inn is over the bridge on the right.
⇌ Acklington

BAMBURGH

Waren Caravan & Camping Park, Waren Mill, Bamburgh, Northumberland, NE70 7EE
Tel: 01668 214366
Email: waren@meadowhead.co.uk
www.meadowhead.co.uk
Pitches For ⛺ ⊕ ⊟ **Total** 180
Open 08-Mar to 31-Oct
Access Good **Site** Lev/Slope
Nearest Bus Stop (Miles) ½
Close to Bamburgh Castle, Holy Island and Alnwick Castle & Gardens.
Facilities ⬚ ⨍ ⌂ ⬚ ⇌ ⌒ ☉ ⬚ ⬚ ⬚ ⬚
🛈 ⬚ ⬚ ✕ ⬚ ⬚ ⬚ ♠ ⬚ ⇌ ⬚ ⬚ 🛜
Nearest Town Bamburgh
Directions From the A1 take the B1342 towards Bamburgh to Waren Mill. By Budle Bay turn right and follow signs for Waren Caravan Park.
⇌ Berwick-upon-Tweed

BEADNELL BAY

Beadnell Bay Camping & Caravanning Club Site, Beadnell, Chathill, Northumberland, NE67 5BX
Tel: 01665 720586
Email: beadnell.site@thefriedlyclub.co.uk
www.campingandcaravanningclub.co.uk/beadnell bay
Pitches For ⛺ ⊟ **Total** 150
Acreage 14 **Open** 21-Mar to 04-Nov
Site Lev/Slope
Nearest Bus Stop (Miles) Outside
2 miles of sandy beach just over the road. 6 miles from Bamburgh Castle. Laundry drying room. BTB 2 Star Graded and AA 2 Pennants. Non members welcome. You can also call us on 0845 130 7633.
Facilities ⬚ ⌒ ☉ ⬚ ⬚ ⬚
🛈 ⬚ ⬚ ⇌ ⬚ ⬚ 🛜
Directions From south leave the A1 and follow the B1430 signposted Seahouses. At Beadnell ignore signs for Beadnell Village, site is on the left after the village, just beyond the left hand bend. From north leave the A1 and follow the B1342 via Bamburgh and Seahouses, site is on the right just before Beadnell Village.

BELLINGHAM

Bellingham Camping & Caravanning Club Site, Tweed House, Brown Rigg, Bellingham, Hexham, Northumberland, NE48 2JY
Tel: 01434 220175
Email: bellingham.site@thefriedlyclub.co.uk
www.campingandcaravanningclub.co.uk
Pitches For ⛺ ⊕ ⊟ **Total** 64
Acreage 5 **Open** 15-Mar to 03-Nov
Access Good **Site** Level
Nearest Bus Stop (Miles) ½
Set in Northumberland National Park. Pennine Way passes the site. Near to Kielder Water, Kielder Castle and Hadrians Wall. Ideal for Newcastle and Gateshead shopping. Non members welcome. You can also call us on 0845 130 7633.
Facilities ⨍ ⌂ ⬚ ⇌ ⌒ ☉ ⬚ ⬚ ⬚ ⬚
🛈 ⬚ ⬚ ♠ ⬚ ⇌ ⬚ ⬚ 🛜
Nearest Town Kielder

Directions Take the A69, after Hexham in ½ mile turn right signposted Acomb, Chollerford and Bellingham. At Chollerford turn left onto the B6318, go over the river and turn second left onto the B6320 signposted Wark and Bellingham.
⇌ Hexham

BELLINGHAM

Stonehaugh Campsite, Stonehaugh Shields, Hexham, Northumberland, NE48 3BU
Tel: 01434 230798
Email:
enquiries@stonehaughcampsite.com
www.stonehaughcampsite.com
Pitches For ⛺ ⊕ ⊟ **Total** 50
Acreage 3½ **Open** April to Sept
Access Good **Site** Level
Rural site set within Northumberland National Park. Situated between Kielder Water and Hadrians Wall, and close to the Penine Way and cycle routes.
Facilities ⬚ ⌒ ☉ ⬚ ⬚ ⇌ ☀
Nearest Town Hexham
Directions From Hexham take the A6079 to Chollerford, go over the bridge and staright over at the roundabout. Then follow the B6320 for Wark and Bellingham, after 5 miles turn left to Stonehaugh.
⇌ Hexham

BERWICK-UPON-TWEED

Berwick Seaview Caravan Club Site, Billendean Road, Spittal, Berwick-upon-Tweed, Northumberland, TD15 1QU
Tel: 01289 305198
www.caravanclub.co.uk
Pitches For ⛺ ⊕ ⊟ **Total** 98
Acreage 6 **Open** Mar to Jan
Access Good **Site** Lev/Slope
Nearest Bus Stop (Miles) Outside
Overlooking a river estuary with views of Holy Island. Just a short walk into Berwick. Near a safe sandy beach. Close to Swan Leisure Pool, Lindisfarne Priory and Paxton House. Non members welcome. Booking essential.
Facilities ⬚ ⨍ ⌂ ⬚ ⇌ ⌒ ⬚ ⬚
🛈 ⬚ ⬚ ⇌ ⬚ ⬚ 🛜
Nearest Town Berwick-on-Tweed
Directions From the A1 take the A1167 signposted Spittal, at the roundabout turn right into Billendean Terrace, site is ½ mile on the right.
⇌ Berwick-upon-Tweed

BERWICK-UPON-TWEED

Haggerston Castle, Beal, Nr Berwick-upon-Tweed, Northumberland, TD15 2PA
Tel: 01289 381333
Email: haggerstoncastle@haven.com
www.haventouring.com/
tohaggerstoncastle
Pitches For ⊕ ⊟ **Total** 132
Open Mid March to End Oct
Access Good **Site** Level
Nearest Bus Stop (Miles) Outside
Situated in an area of great heritage interest. Lots to do on the Park including kids clubs, family entertainment, horse riding, golf, tennis and so much more.
Facilities ⬚ ⬚ ⨍ ⌂ ⬚ ⇌ ⌒ ☉ ⬚ ⬚ ⬚
🛈 🍴 ⬚ ⬚ ✕ ♀ ⬚ ♠ ⬚ ⬚ ☀ ⬚ ⇌ ⬚ ⬚ ⬚ ☀
🛜
Nearest Town Berwick-upon-Tweed
Directions On the A1, 7 miles south of Berwick-upon-Tweed.
⇌ Berwick

NORTHUMBERLAND,

BERWICK-UPON-TWEED

Ord House Country Park, East Ord,
Berwick-upon-Tweed, Northumberland,
TD15 2NS
Tel: 01289 305288
Email: enquiries@ordhouse.co.uk
www.ordhouse.co.uk
Pitches For Å ⚑ ⚑ ☵ Total 75
Acreage 42 **Open** All Year
Access Good **Site** Lev/Slope
Nearest Bus Stop (Miles) Outside
Ideal for exploring north Northumberladn and
the Scottish Borders.
Facilities ♿ ✦ ⌁ 🎦 ⌂ ⌁ ⊙ ↵ ⚐ 🖵 🖀
♨ ⌕ ⊙ ✗ ▽ Ѧ ✿ ↦ ⊟ 🖵 ⚊ 🎧 📶
Nearest Town Berwick-upon-Tweed
Directions Take the A1 Berwick bypass and
turn off at roundabout for East Ord.
🚶 Berwick-upon-Tweed

DUNSTAN HILL

**Dunstan Hill Camping & Caravanning
Club Site,** Dunstan Hill, Dunstan, Alnwick,
Northumberland, NE66 3TQ
Tel: 01665 576310
Email:
dunstan.hillsite@thefriendlyclub.co.uk
www.campingandcaravanningclub.co.uk/
dunstanhill
Pitches For Å ⚑ ⚑ Total 150
Acreage 14 **Open** 21-Mar to 04-Nov
Access Good **Site** Level
Nearest Bus Stop (Miles) Outside
In north east England just 1 mile from the
coast. One of the Parks major attractions is
Kielder Water, Europes largest man made
lake. Access to Dunstanburgh Castle from
the site. BTB 4 Star Graded and AA 3
Pennants. Non members welcome. You can
also call us on 0845 130 7633.
Facilities ♿ ✦ ⌁ 🎦 ⌂ ⌁ ⊙ ↵ ⚐ 🖵 🖀
🖵 ⊙ ⚊ Ѧ ↦ ⊟ 🖵 ⚊ 🎧 📶
Nearest Town Alnwick
Directions Travelling north on the A1 take
the B1340 sp Seahouses, follow to the T-
Junction at Christon Bank and turn right, take
the next right sp Embleton, turn right at the
crossroads then first left sp Craster.
Travelling south on the A1 take the B6347
through Christon Bank, take a right turn to
Embleton, turn right at the crossroads, then
first left sp Craster, site is 1 mile on the left.
🚶 Alnmouth

HALTWHISTLE

**Haltwhistle Camping & Caravanning
Club Site,** Burnfoot Park Village,
Haltwhistle, Northumberland, NE49 0JP
Tel: 01434 320106
Email:
haltwhistle.site@thefriendlyclub.co.uk
www.campingandcaravanningclub.co.uk/
haltwhistle
Pitches For Å ⚑ ⚑ Total 50
Acreage 3½ **Open** 21-Mar to 04-Nov
Site Level
Nearest Bus Stop (Miles) ¾
On the banks of the River South Tyne for
fishing. Close to the Pennine Way. BTB 4
Star Graded and AA 3 Pennants. Non
members welcome. You can also call us on
0845 130 7633.
Facilities ✦ 🎦 ⌂ ⌁ ⊙ ↵ ⚐ 🖵 🖀
🖵 ⊙ ⚊ ↦ ⊟ 🖵 ⚊ 📶
Directions Follow signs from the A69 by-
pass, DO NOT go into Haltwhistle.
🚶 Haltwhistle

HALTWHISTLE

Seldom Seen Caravan Park, Haltwhistle,
Northumberland, NE49 0NE
Tel: 01434 320571
www.seldomseencaravanpark.co.uk
Pitches For Å ⚑ ⚑ Total 20
Open March **to** January
Access Good **Site** Level
Nearest Bus Stop (Miles) ¼
Central touring area, ideal for the Roman
wall. David Bellamy Gold Award for
Conservation.
Facilities ✦ 🎦 ⌂ ⌁ ⊙ ↵ 🖀
🖵 ⊙ ▽ Ѧ ↦ ⊟ ✗ ⚊
Nearest Town Haltwhistle
Directions Off the A69 east of Haltwhistle,
signposted.
🚶 Haltwhistle

HAYDON BRIDGE

Poplars Riverside Caravan Park,
Eastland Ends, Haydon Bridge, Hexham,
Northumberland, NE47 6BY
Tel: 01434 684427
Pitches For Å ⚑ ⚑ Total 14
Acreage 2½ **Open** March **to** October
Access Good **Site** Level
Nearest Bus Stop (Miles) ¼
Small, peaceful site close to the village.
Fishing on site. Near to Hadrians Wall.
Facilities ✦ 🎦 ⌂ ⌁ ⊙ ↵ ⚐ 🖵 🖀
🖵 ⊙ ⚊ Ѧ ↦ ⊟ ✗ ⚊
Nearest Town Hexham
Directions Take the A69 Newcastle to
Carlisle road, follow signs from the bridge in
the village.
🚶 Haydon Bridge

HEXHAM

Ashcroft Farm Caravan Site, Ashcroft
Farm, Bardon Mill, Nr Hexham,
Northumberland, NE47 7JA
Tel: 01434 344409
Pitches For ⚑ ⚑ Total 5
Acreage 2 **Open** Easter **to** Sept
Access Good **Site** Level
Nearest Bus Stop (Miles) Entrance
Alongside the River Tyne. Close to the village
and its amenities. 2 miles from Hadrians
Wall, Vindolanda.
Facilities 🖀 🖵 ↦ ⚊
Nearest Town Hexham
Directions Follow the A69 west from
Hexham for 11 miles. Turn left into Bardon
Mill Village and after 300 metres turn left then
next right to the farm.
🚶 Bardon Mill

HEXHAM

Fallowfield Dene Caravan Park, Acomb,
Hexham, Northumberland, NE46 4RP
Tel: 01434 603553
Email: info@fallowfielddene.co.uk
www.fallowfielddene.co.uk
Pitches For Å ⚑ ⚑ Total 32
Nearest Bus Stop (Miles) ¼
One Camping Pod on site for hire and 1 hire
caravan.
Facilities ♿ ✦ 🎦 ⌂ ⌁ ⊙ ↵ ⚐ 🖵 🖀
♨ ⊙ ↦ ⊟ 🖵 ⚊ ⚊
Nearest Town Hexham
Directions From the A69 follow signs for
Acomb, Bellingham and Rothbury (A6079).
🚶 Hexham

HEXHAM

Hexham Racecourse Caravan Site, High
Yarridge, Hexham, Northumberland, NE46
2JP
Tel: 01434 606847

Email: hexrace.caravan@btconnect.com
Pitches For Å ⚑ ⚑ Total 50
Open May **to** Sept
Access Good **Site** Sloping
Nearest Bus Stop (Miles) 2
Set in beautiful open countryside.
Facilities ✦ 🎦 ⌂ ⌁ ⊙ ↵ ⚐ 🖵 🖀
⊙ ⚊ ✿ ↦ ⊟ ⚊
Nearest Town Hexham
Directions From the A69 follow signs for
Hexham. Follow the main street to the traffic
lights and bear left onto the B6305
signposted Allendale. After 3 miles turn left
at the T-Junction, site is 1½ miles.
🚶 Hexham

MORPETH

Forget-Me-Not Holiday Park, Croftside,
Longhorsley, Morpeth, Northumberland,
NE65 8QY
Tel: 01670 788364
Email: info@forgetmenotholidaypark.co.uk
www.forgetmenotholidaypark.co.uk
Pitches For ⚑ ⚑ Total 23
Open Mar **to** Oct
Access Good **Site** Level
Nearest Bus Stop (Miles) 1
Ideal Touring, Beautiful Northumbrian
countryside.
Facilities ✦ 🖵 ⌂ ⌁ ⊙ ↵ ⚐ 🖵 🖀
⊙ ⚊ ✗ ▽ 🖵 ✿ Ѧ ↦ ⊟ ⚊ ⚊ 📶
Nearest Town Morpeth
Directions From Morpeth North A697 7
miles.
🚶 Morpeth

OVINGHAM

High Hermitage Caravan Park, The
Hermitage, Ovingham, Prudhoe,
Northumberland, NE42 6HH
Tel: 01661 832250
Email: hermitagegardens@yahoo.co.uk
www.highhermitagecaravanpark.co.uk
Pitches For Å ⚑ ⚑ Total 34
Acreage 8¼ **Open** 01-Mar **to** 07-Jan
Access Good **Site** Gently Sloping
Nearest Bus Stop (Miles) Outside
Quiet, rural, riverside site with extensive
wildlife. Grassy slope sheltered by trees on
north, east and west sides. Fishing on the
Tyne. Giant chess and draughts. Ideal for
touring the Roman Wall and associated sites
plus gorgeous Northumberland countryside
and beaches.
Facilities ✦ 🖵 ⌂ ⌁ ⊙ ↵ ⚐ 🖵 🖀
🖵 ⊙ ⚊ ⊟ ⚊ ⚊
Nearest Town Prudhoe
Directions Take the A69 to Hexham and take
exit to Wylam. Go straight ahead at first
crossroads to Wylam, follow road and turn
right at the bottom to Ovingham, site
entrance is 1½ miles down this river road
opposite water intake area. Look out for white
painted stones at the bottom of our entrance.
🚶 Prudhoe

SEAHOUSES

Seafield Caravan Park, Seafield Road,
Seahouses, Northumberland, NE68 7SP
Tel: 01665 720628
Email: info@seafieldpark.co.uk
www.seafieldpark.co.uk
Pitches For ⚑ ⚑ Total 18
Open 09-Feb **to** 09-Jan
Access Good **Site** Level
Nearest Bus Stop (Miles) ¼
In the centre of Seahouses, near the harbour
and just a short walk to the beach.
Facilities ♿ ✦ 🖵 🎦 ⌂ ⌁ ⊙ ↵ ⚐ 🖵 🖀
🖵 ✗ Ѧ ⚊ ↦ ⊟ 🖵 📶
Nearest Town Alnwick

Directions Travelling south leave the A1 at Alnwick and take the B1340 to Seahouses. Travelling north leave the A1 at Belford and take the B1342 through Bamburgh to Seahouses.
🚉 Alnmouth

WOOLER
Highburn House Caravan & Camping Park, Wooler, Northumberland, NE71 6EE
Tel: 01668 281344
Email: relax@highburn-house.co.uk
www.highburn-house.co.uk
Pitches For Å ⊞ ⊞ **Total** 100
Acreage 12 **Open** April **to** December
Access Good **Site** Level
Nearest Bus Stop (Miles) ¼
Stream runs through middle of site, beautiful view over hills and valley.
Facilities ⬥ ⚿ ⒡ ▯ ⬚ ⬚ ⌐ ⊙ ⌐ ⛱
▯ ⬚ ⓘ ⬚ ⬚ ⬚ ✿✙⊟
Nearest Town Wooler
Directions Off A1 take A697 to Wooler town centre, at the top of Main Street take left turn, 400 metres on left is our site.
🚉 Berwick

NOTTINGHAMSHIRE
CARLTON-ON-TRENT
Carlton Manor Touring Park, Ossington Road (off A1), Carlton-on-Trent, Nr Newark, Nottinghamshire, NG23 6NU
Tel: 01530 835662
Pitches For Å ⊞ ⊞ **Total** 22
Acreage 2 **Open** Apr **to** Nov
Access Good **Site** Level
Nearest Bus Stop (Miles) ¼
Clean sites with spotless toilets. Warden on site at all times. The Great Northern Pub is opposite the Park gates for good food and beer. Train spotting on site. We allow individual motorcyclists, but no groups. Shops, fishing and doctor in village. 10 miles from Robin Hood country, 12 miles from Lincoln and 50 miles from Skegness. You can also contact Mrs Goodman on 07772 037909.
Facilities ⚿ ⬚⌐⊙⛱ ⒧✙⊟ ⚞ ⚘
Nearest Town Newark
Directions From Newark take the A1 north towards Doncaster, site is 6 miles, signposted.
🚉 Carlton Village

HOLME PIERREPONT
National Water Sports Caravan & Camping Park, Adbolton Lane, Holme Pierrepont, Nottingham, Notts, NG12 2LU
Tel: 0115 982 4721
Email: nwsccampsite@nottscc.gov.uk
www.nwscnotts.com
Pitches For Å ⊞ ⊞ ⒡ **Total** 300
Acreage 28 **Open** All Year
Access Good **Site** Level
Nearest Bus Stop (Miles) ¼
Set in 270 acres of county park at the National Water Sports Centre. Close to Nottingham Castle and Galliers of Justice.
Facilities ⬥ ⚿ ▯ ⬚ ⬚ ⌐ ⛱
⚞ ⬚ ⬚✙⊟⬚ ⬚

Nearest Town Nottingham
Directions Off the A52, signposted National Water Sports Centre, 3 miles from Nottingham city centre.
🚉 Nottingham

MANSFIELD
Tall Trees Park, Old Mill Lane, Forest Town, Mansfield, Nottinghamshire, NG19 0JP
Tel: 01623 626503
Email: info@talltreestouringpark.co.uk
www.talltreestouringpark.co.uk
Pitches For Å ⊞ ⊞ ⒡ **Total** 24
Acreage 3 **Open** All Year
Access Good **Site** Sloping
Nearest Bus Stop (Miles) Outside
Peaceful rural Park surrounded by open farmland. Within walking distance of amenities. Close to Clumber Park.
Facilities ⬥ ⚿ ▯ ⬚⌐⛱⊙⌐⛱ ⬚ ⬚
✿✙⊟⬚⚿
Nearest Town Mansfield
Directions From the A60 at Worksop turn at Fourways onto Old Mill Lane, the Park is on the left hand side.
🚉 Mansfield

NEWARK
Milestone Caravan Park, Great North Road, Cromwell, Newark, Nottinghamshire, NG23 6JE
Tel: 01636 821244
Email: enquiries@milestonepark.co.uk
www.milestonepark.co.uk
Pitches For ⊞ ⊞ ⒡ **Total** 100
Acreage 22 **Open** All Year
Access Good **Site** Level
Nearest Bus Stop (Miles) Outside
River Trent walks, level cycling, lock walk.
Facilities ⬥ ⚿ ▯ ⬚⌐⊙⌐⛱ ⬚
⚞ ⬚ ⬚✙⊟⬚ ⚿ ⚘ ⚘
Nearest Town Newark
Directions From Newark 5 miles on A1 north, HGV garage, come off A1 ai signs to Cromwell behind garage we are on the left.
🚉 Newark

NOTTINGHAM
Manor Farm Caravan Site, Manor Farm, Church Lane, Thrumpton, Nottinghamshire, NG11 0AX
Tel: 0115 983 0341
Pitches For ⊞ ⊞ **Total** 12
Acreage 3 **Open** All Year
Access Good **Site** Level
Nearest Bus Stop (Miles) Outside
Facilities ⚿ ⬚ ⌐⊙⚘✙⊟⚿
Nearest Town Nottingham
Directions From the M1 junction 24, take the A453 Nottingham South, after 3 miles turn left to Thrumpton Village.
🚉 Nottingham

NOTTINGHAM
Riverdale Park, Gunthorpe Bridge, Gunthorpe, Nottinghamshire, NG14 7EY
Tel: 01159 665173
Email: jane@rongrundy.co.uk
Pitches For ⊞ ⊞ **Total** 5
Open Mar **to** 06-Jan

Access Good **Site** Level
Nearest Bus Stop (Miles) ¼
Near the River Trent.
Facilities ⚿ ⬚⌐⌐ ⚘
Nearest Town Nottingham
Directions Take the A612 east from Nottingham, go through Burton Joyce to Lowdham, then take the A6097 to the village of Gunthorpe.
🚉 Radcliffe-on-Trent/Nottingham

NOTTINGHAM
Thorntons Holt Camping Park, Stragglethorpe, Radcliffe-on-Trent, Nottinghamshire, NG12 2JZ
Tel: 0115 933 2125
Email: camping@thorntons-holt.co.uk
www.thorntons-holt.co.uk
Pitches For Å ⊞ ⊞ **Total** 155
Acreage 15 **Open** All Year
Access Good **Site** Level
Nearest Bus Stop (Miles) Outside
Only 3 miles from Nottingham. Ideal base for touring Sherwood Forest and the Vale of Belvoir. Pub and restaurant nearby.
Facilities ⬥ ⚿ ▯ ⬚⌐⊙⌐⛱⬚⬚ ⚞
⚞ ⬚ ⬚ ⬚ ⬚✙⊟⬚ ⚘ ⚘
Nearest Town Nottingham
Directions 3 miles east of Nottingham turn south off A52 towards Cropwell Bishop. Park is ¼ mile on left.
🚉 Radcliffe-on-Trent

RATCLIFFE ON SOAR
Red Hill Marina, Ratcliffe-on-Soar, Nottinghamshire, NG11 0EB
Tel: 01509 672770
www.redhill-marine.co.uk
Pitches For Å ⊞ ⊞ **Total** 15
Open All Year **Access** Good **Site** Level
By a river. Train station adjoins site.
Facilities ⚿ ⬚⬚✕⊟⬚
Nearest Town Nottingham
Directions Leave the M1 at junction 24 and take the A453, 1½ miles on the left hand side.
🚉 East Midlands Parkway

SUTTON-IN-ASHFIELD
Teversal Camping & Caravanning Club Site, -, Silverhill Lane, Teversal, Nottinghamshire, NG17 3JJ
Tel: 01623 551838
www.campingandcaravanningclub.co.uk/teversal
Pitches For Å ⊞ ⊞ **Total** 126
Acreage 6 **Open** All Year
Access Good **Site** Level
Nearest Bus Stop (Miles) ¼
Within easy reach of the market towns Chesterfield, Sutton-in-Ashfield and Mansfield. Six berth caravan available for hire. Heart of England AA campsite of the year 2010 and named Caravan Holiday Park of the Year. Non members welcome. You can also call us on 0845 130 7633.
Facilities ⬥ ⚿ ▯ ⬚⌐⊙⌐⛱⬚⬚ ⚞
⚞ ⬚ ⬚ ⬚✙⊟⬚ ⚞
Nearest Town Sutton-in-Ashfield
Directions Leave the M1 at junction 28 take the A38 towards Mansfield. Turn It at the lights, go straight over next

lights and turn lt at the Tesco express. Turn rt onto the B6014, turn left at Caravan Arms and site is on the left.
⚑ Sutton-in-Ashfield

TUXFORD
Greenacres Caravan & Touring Park, Lincoln Road, Tuxford, Newark, Nottinghamshire, NG22 0JN
Tel: 01777 870264
Email: stay@greenacres-tuxford.co.uk
www.greenacres-tuxford.co.uk
Pitches For Å 🚐 🚍 **Total** 67
Acreage 4½ **Open** Mid Mar **to** End Oct
Access Good **Site** Level
Nearest Bus Stop (Miles) Park Entrance
Ideal for night halt or for touring Robin Hood country. Static caravans for sale and hire. Secure Storage during Winter.
Facilities ♿ ⨍ 🕮 ⌴ 🕈 ⊙ ⚲ 🖃 🞉
🏋 🛈 🛁 ⚓ ⌦ 🖭 🛆 ✄ 🎝 ☂
Nearest Town Retford
Directions From A1 (north or south) follow signs. Park is on the left 250yds after Fountain Public House.
⚑ Retford

TUXFORD
Marnham Meadows Holiday Park, Hollowgate Lane, High Marnham, Newark, Nottinghamshire, NG23 6SG
Tel: 01636 822775
Pitches For Å 🚐 🚍 **Total** 35
Open Apr **to** Oct
Access Good **Site** Level
Near the River Trent, the National Cycle Path to Lincoln and Sundown Adventure Park. Brownlow Arms Pub just a few minutes walk. Ralley Field.
Facilities ⨍ 🖃 🞉 ⌦ 🖭 ✎ 🎝
Nearest Town Newark/Lincoln
Directions From Newark take the A1 north to Tuxford, or from Lincoln take the A57 to Dunham.
⚑ Newark/Lincoln

TUXFORD
Orchard Park Touring Caravan & Camping, Orchard Park, Marnham Road, Tuxford, Newark, Nottinghamshire, NG22 0PY
Tel: 01777 870228
Email: info@orchardcaravanpark.co.uk
www.orchardcaravanpark.co.uk
Pitches For Å 🚐 🚍 **Total** 60
Acreage 7 **Open** Mar **to** Nov
Access Good **Site** Level
Nearest Bus Stop (Miles) ½
A quiet, sheltered park, spaciously set in an old fruit orchard. Central for Sherwood Forest, Clumber Park, Lincoln and Nottingham.
Facilities ♿ ⨍ 🕮 🕈 ⌴ 🕈 ⊙ ⚲ 🖃 🞉
🏋 🏋 🛈 🛁 🖭 ⚓ ⌦ 🖭 🖭 🎝 ⚒ ☂
Nearest Town Newark
Directions Turn off the A1 dual carriageway at Tuxford, when you reach the T-Junction in the village turn right signposted Darlton. In ¼ mile turn right signposted Marnham, site is ½ a mile on the right.
⚑ Retford

WORKSOP
Clumber Park Caravan Club Site, Lime Tree Avenue, Clumber Park, Worksop, Nottinghamshire, S80 3AE
Tel: 01909 484758
www.caravanclub.co.uk
Pitches For 🚐 🚍 **Total** 183
Acreage 20 **Open** All Year
Access Good **Site** Level

Situated in 4000 acres of parkland (once part of Sherwood Forest), ideal for walking and cycling. Visitor Centre 10 minutes away. Close to Creswell Crags Cave Tours. Non members welcome. Booking essential.
Facilities ⨍ 🕮 🕈 ⌴ 🕈 ⊙ ⚲ 🛁 ⚓ 🖭 🖃 🞉
Nearest Town Worksop
Directions From the A1, at the roundabout junction of the A57 and the A614 turn onto the A614 signposted Nottingham. After ½ a mile turn right into Clumber Park through a stone arch, after 1 mile turn right, site is 50 yards on the left.
⚑ Worksop

WORKSOP
Riverside Caravan Park, Central Avenue, Worksop, Nottinghamshire, S80 1ER
Tel: 01909 474118
www.riversideworksop.co.uk
Pitches For Å 🚐 🚍 **Total** 60
Acreage 6 **Open** All Year
Site Level
Nearest Bus Stop (Miles) ¼
Just a 5 minute walk from the town centre, where Market days are wednesday, friday and saturday. Ideal for canal walks and cycling. Showers take £1 coins.
Facilities ⨍ 🕮 🕈 ⌴ 🕈 ⊙ ⚲ 🞉 ⌦ 🖭 🖃 🎝
Nearest Town Worksop
Directions From the A57 roundabout turn into Newcastle Avenue, turn first left into Stubbing Lane. Turn next right into Central Avenue, go past the cricket ground and into the Park.
⚑ Worksop

OXFORDSHIRE
BANBURY
Barnstones Caravan & Camping Site, Barnstones, Main Street, Great Bourton, Nr Banbury, Oxfordshire, OX17 1QU
Tel: 01295 750289
Pitches For Å 🚐 🚍 🚍 **Total** 49
Acreage 3 **Open** All Year
Access Good **Site** Level
Nearest Bus Stop (Miles) Outside
Very beautiful countryside. Ideal for the Cotswolds, Oxford, Stratford-upon-Avon and Warwick.
Facilities ♿ ⨍ 🕮 🕮 🕈 ⌴ 🕈 ⊙ ⚲ 🛁 🖃 🞉
🏋 🛈 🛁 🖭 ⚓ ⌦ 🖭 🖭 🎝
Nearest Town Banbury
Directions Leave the M40 at junction 11 and follow signs to Southam and Banbury over two roundabouts, at the third roundabout turn onto the A423. After 2 miles turn right signposted Great Bourton, the Site entrance is 120yds on the right.
⚑ Banbury

BLETCHINGDON
Greenhill Leisure Park, Greenhill Farm, Station Road, Bletchingdon, Oxfordshire, OX5 3BQ
Tel: 01869 351600
Email: info@greenhill-leisure-park.co.uk
www.greenhill-leisure-park.co.uk
Pitches For Å 🚐 🚍 🚍 **Total** 92
Acreage 7 **Open** All Year
Access Good **Site** Lev/Slope
Quiet and spacious farm site. Pets Corner, farm animals and riverside walks. Two new fishing lakes have been created. Rally field available. 3 miles from Blenheim Palace. Ideal for touring the Cotswolds.
Facilities ♿ ⨍ 🕮 🕮 🕈 ⌴ 🕈 ⊙ ⚲ 🛁 🖃 🞉
🏋 🛈 🛁 ⚓ 🖭 ⌦ 🖭 🖭 🎝 ⚒ ☂
Nearest Town Woodstock

Directions 3 miles east of Woodstock and 8 miles north of Oxford on the B4027. 2½ miles from the A34 and 7 miles south of the M40 junction 9.
⚑ Islip

BURFORD
Burford Caravan Club Site, Bradwell Grove, Burford, Oxfordshire, OX18 4JJ
Tel: 01993 823080
www.caravanclub.co.uk
Pitches For 🚐 🚍 **Total** 119
Acreage 10 **Open** Mar **to** Nov
Access Good **Site** Level
Attractive and spacious site. Area for volleyball, netball and football (goal posts). Opposite Cotswold Wildlife Park. Non members welcome. Booking essential.
Facilities ♿ ⨍ 🕮 🕮 🕈 ⌴ 🕈 ⊙ ⚲ 🛁 🖃 🞉
🏋 🛈 🛁 🖭 ⚓ ⌦ 🖭 🖭 🎝 ☂
Directions Leave Oxford on A40, after approx. 23 miles at large roundabout in Burford turn left onto A361 and follow signs for Cotswold Wildlife Park. After 2 miles at crossroads turn right, DO NOT turn right into New Bradwell Village, site is 70 yards on the right opposite entrance to Wildlife Park.

BURFORD
Wysdom Touring Park, The Bungalow, Burford School, Burford, Oxfordshire, OX18 4JG
Tel: 01993 823207
Pitches For 🚐 🚍 **Total** 25
Open Mar **to** Jan
Access Good **Site** Level
Nearest Bus Stop (Miles) ¼
Ideally situated to visit the Cotswolds.
Facilities ⨍ 🕮 🕮 🕈 ⌴ 🕈 ⊙ ⚲ 🞉 ⌦ 🖭 🛁 🛆
Nearest Town Burford
Directions From the A40 towards Cheltenham Burford take the A361 towards Lechlade we are 2nd turning on right.
⚑ Kingham

CHIPPING NORTON
Chipping Norton Camping & Caravanning Club Site, Chipping Norton Road, Chadlington, Chipping Norton, Oxfordshire, OX7 3PE
Tel: 01608 641993
Email: chipping.site@thefriendlyclub.co.uk
www.campingandcaravanningclub.co.uk/chippingnorton
Pitches For Å 🚐 🚍 **Total** 105
Open 21-Mar **to** 04-Nov
Site Lev/Slope
Nearest Bus Stop (Miles) Outside
Perfect for exploring the Cotswolds. 11 miles from Blenheim Palace. BTB 4 Star Graded and AA 3 Pennants. Non members welcome. You can also call us on 0845 130 7633.
Facilities ♿ ⨍ 🕮 🕈 ⌴ 🕈 ⊙ ⚲ 🞉 🛁 🖃 🞉
🏋 🛈 🛁 🖭 ⌦ 🖭 🖭 🞉
Directions Take the A44 or the A361 to Chipping Norton. Pick up the A361 Burford road, turn left at the crossroads and the site is 150 yards. From Burford stay on the A361 and turn right at the sign for Chadlington.

OXFORD
Camping & Caravanning Club Site, 426 Abingdon Road, Oxford, Oxfordshire, OX1 4XG
Tel: 01865 244088
Email: oxford.site@thefriendlyclub.co.uk
www.campingandcaravanningclub.co.uk/oxford
Pitches For Å 🚐 🚍 **Total** 85
Acreage 5 **Open** All Year

Access Good **Site** Level
Nearest Bus Stop (Miles) Outside
In one of Britains most popular tourist destinations, this university city has a lot more to offer with more than 650 listed buildings. AA 3 Pennants. Non members welcome. You can also call us on 0845 130 7633.
Facilities ∮ ⓌⒶℙ☉◁◢◿▣☎
▯ℚ☻⚓➡️🄳🛜
Nearest Town Oxford
Directions From the M40 take the A34 at the A423, turn left immediately after junction into Abingdon Road, site is on the left behind Touchwood Sports.
⇌ Oxford

WITNEY
Hardwick Parks, Downs Road, Standlake, Nr Witney, Oxfordshire, OX29 7PZ
Tel: 01865 300501
Email: info@hardwickparks.co.uk
www.hardwickparks.co.uk
Pitches For ⚠ ⚑ ⛟ ⚑≋ **Total** 214
Acreage 40 **Open** April **to** October
Access Good **Site** Level
Nearest Bus Stop (Miles) Outside
On the edge of the Cotswolds. Two lakes on the park. Holiday homes for hire.
Facilities ᗌ ∮ ▯Ⓦℙ☉◢▣☎
ℚ▯ℚ☻✕⛟▣⚓➡️🄳◿➳🛜
Nearest Town Witney
Directions A415 Witney to Abingdon road, signposted 4 miles out of Witney on the main road.
⇌ Oxford

WITNEY
Lincoln Farm Park, High Street, Standlake, Nr Witney, Oxfordshire, OX29 7RH
Tel: 01865 300239
Email: info@lincolnfarmpark.co.uk
www.lincolnfarmpark.co.uk
Pitches For ⚠ ⚑ ⛟ **Total** 90
Acreage 8 **Open** Feb **to** Mid Nov
Access Good **Site** Level
Nearest Bus Stop (Miles) Outside
Leisure centre with two indoor swimming pools, saunas, spa and fitness centre. Two village pubs each serving food nearby.
Facilities ᗌ ∮ ▯ⓌⓌℙ☉◁◢▣☎
ℚℙℚⒶ⛟▣⚓➡️🄳🛜
Nearest Town Witney
Directions On the A415 5 miles from Witney and 9 miles from Abingdon.
⇌ Oxford

SHROPSHIRE
BISHOPS CASTLE
Cwnd House Farm, Wentnor, Bishops Castle, Shropshire,
Tel: 01588 650237
Pitches For ⚠ ⚑ ⛟ **Total** 10
Acreage 2 **Open** May **to** Oct
Access Good **Site** Level
Farm site with scenic views. Ideal touring centre.
Facilities Ⓦ ▯⚓➡️🄳
Nearest Town Church Stretton
Directions Cwnd House Farm is on Longden Pulverbatch road from Shrewsbury (13 miles) Bishops Castle is southwest. From Craven Arms take the A489 to Lydham Heath, turn right, site is about 1 mile past the Inn on the Green, take second turn right by the black and white boards
⇌ Church Stretton

BISHOPS CASTLE
Daisy Bank Caravan Park, Snead, Montgomery, Powys, SY15 6EB
Tel: 01588 620471
Email: enquiries@daisy-bank.co.uk
www.daisy-bank.co.uk
Pitches For ⚠ ⚑ ⛟ **Total** 55
Acreage 8 **Open** All Year
Access Good **Site** Lev/Slope
Nearest Bus Stop (Miles) ½
Facilities ᗌ ∮ ▯ⓌⒶℙ☉◁◢▣☎
ℚ▯ℚ☻⛟▣◁Ⓐ➳ ⚓🛜
Nearest Town Bishops Castle
Directions A489 between Lydham and Churchstoke.
⇌ Craven Arms

BISHOPS CASTLE
The Green Caravan Park, Wentnor, Bishops Castle, Shropshire, SY9 5EF
Tel: 01588 650605
Email: karen@greencaravanpark.co.uk
www.greencaravanpark.co.uk
Pitches For ⚠ ⚑ ⛟ **Total** 140
Open Easter **to** Oct
Access Good **Site** Level
Picturesque, riverside site in an area of outstanding natural beauty. Superb walking in the countryside. Excellent birdlife. Central for touring. David Bellamy Gold Award for Conservation. Pub 2 mins walk from site entrance.
Facilities ∮ ▯Ⓦ▯ℙ☉◁◢▣☎
ℚ▯ℚ☻✕⛟▣◿➳ ⚓🛜
Nearest Town Bishops Castle
Directions Follow brown tourism signs from the A488 and the A489.
⇌ Craven Arms

BRIDGNORTH
The Riverside Caravan Park, Kidderminster Road, Bridgnorth, Shropshire, WV15 6BY
Tel: 01746 762393
www.theriversidecaravanpark.co.uk
Pitches For ⚑ ⛟ **Total** 8
Open March **to** January
Access Good **Site** Level
Nearest Bus Stop (Miles) Outside
On the banks of the River Severn. Just a 10 minute walk to Bridgnorth. Watch the Severn Valley Railway steam by.
Facilities ∮ ☎ℚℚ ☉ ➳◢
Nearest Town Bridgnorth
Directions From Bridgnorth on the A442 road to Kidderminster, take the first turning on the right (150 metres).
⇌ Telford

BRIDGNORTH
Woodend Farm, Woodend Lane, Highley, Shropshire, WV16 6HY
Tel: 01746 861571
Email: charlesdavies07@btinternet.com
Pitches For ⚠ ⚑ ⛟
Open All Year
Access Good **Site** Lev/Slope
Nearest Bus Stop (Miles) ½
Access to the River Severn and Severn Valley Railway. Village has a new Leisure Centre, large outdoor pool, gardens and an 18 hole golf course. Ideal base for Ludlow, Much Wenlock, Shrewsbury, Ironbridge, Bewdley and safari park. You can also contact us on Mobile: 07976 247473.
Facilities ∮ Ⓦℙ☎ ☎ ▯ℚ◿ ➳
Nearest Town Bridgnorth
Directions From Bridgnorth take the B4555 to Highley. In Highley turn left opposite the leisure centre, follow the lane down hill bearing to the left until in the farm yard.
⇌ Highley

CHURCH STRETTON
Small Batch, Little Stretton, Church Stretton, Shropshire, SY6 6PW
Tel: 01694 723358
Pitches For ⚠ ⚑ ⛟ **Total** 40
Acreage 1½ **Open** Easter **to** Oct
Access Good **Site** Level
Scenic views and ideal touring.
Facilities ∮ Ⓦℙ☉☉ ▯⚓➡️🄳
Directions A49 south, 2 miles south of Church Stretton turn right onto the B5477. Take the second left, at T-Junction turn right up to site through stream.
⇌ Church Stretton

CRAVEN ARMS

Kevindale, Broome, Craven Arms, Shropshire, SY7 0NT
Tel: 01588 660199
Email: keith@kevindale.co.uk
www.kevindale.co.uk
Pitches For ⚹ ⛺ ⛟ **Total** 12
Acreage 2 **Open** Apr **to** Oct
Access Good **Site** Level
Nearest Bus Stop (Miles) Outside
Scenic views, near village inn with good food. Close to Mid Wales Border, ideal walking. Two acre field, rallys welcome.
Facilities ♿ ✦ 🛁 📷 ⊙ ⛽ 🏧📞
Nearest Town Craven Arms
Directions From Craven Arms which is situated on the A49 Hereford to Shewsbury road, take the B4368 Clun/Bishops Castle road, in 2 miles take the B4367 Knighton road and after 1¼ miles turn right into Broome Village.
⇌ Broome

ELLESMERE

Fernwood Caravan Park, Lyneal, Nr Ellesmere, Shropshire, SY12 0QF
Tel: 01948 710221
Email: enquiries@fernwoodpark.co.uk
www.fernwoodpark.co.uk
Pitches For ⛺ ⛟ **Total** 60
Acreage 7 **Open** Mar **to** Nov
Access Good **Site** Lev/Slope
Nearest Bus Stop (Miles) 1
40 acres of woodland open to caravanners. Lake with wildfowl and coarse fishing.
Facilities ♿ ✦ 🛁 🚻📷⊙⛽ ▪ 🔲 📞
🏧 ⊙ 🛒 🏕🏧📞⛽ ✒ ※
Directions A495 from Ellesmere signposted Whitchurch. In Welshampton, right turn on B5063 signed Wem. Over canal bridge right sign Lyneal.
⇌ Wem

LUDLOW

Orleton Rise Holiday Park, Green Lane, Orleton, Ludlow, Shropshire, SY8 4JE
Tel: 01584 831617
Email: karen@lucksallpark.co.uk
www.orletonrise@.co.uk
Pitches For ⚹ ⛺ ⛟ **Total** 18
Open Mar **to** Jan
Access Good **Site** Level
Nearest Bus Stop (Miles) ¼
Ludlow castle
Facilities ♿ ✦ 🛁 🚻📷⊙⛽ ▪ 🔲 📞
🏧 ⊙ 🏧📞 ※ 🌐
Nearest Town Ludlow
Directions Ludlow South A49 turn right at Woolferton B4362 to left on B4361 turn right into Green Lane, Orleton.
⇌ Ludlow

MINSTERLEY

The Old School Caravan Park, Shelve, Minsterley, Shrewsbury, Shropshire, SY5 0JQ
Tel: 01588 650410
www.oldschoolcaravanpark.co.uk
Pitches For ⚹ ⛺ ⛟ **Total** 22
Acreage 1½ **Open** Mar **to** Jan
Site Slight Slope
Nearest Bus Stop (Miles) Outside
In an area of outstanding natural beauty, good walks and fishing. Close to Stiperstones and Long Mynd. Reduced rates available from 4th continous nights stay. Excluding Bank Holidays. Interested please ring.
Facilities ✦ 🛁 📷📞⊙⛽ 📞
🏧 🛒🏧📞 ※ ✒
Nearest Town Shrewsbury

Directions On the A5 in Shrewsbury turn onto the A488 to Bishops Castle. After 16 miles go through the village of Hope and the site is on the left 50 metres after the bus stop and phone box.
⇌ Shrewsbury

MUCH WENLOCK

Much Wenlock Caravan Club Site, Stretton Road, Much Wenlock, Shropshire, TF13 6DQ
Tel: 01746 785234
www.caravanclub.co.uk
Pitches For ⛺ ⛟ **Total** 73
Acreage 10 **Open** Apr **to** Oct
Access Good **Site** Level
Interesting site with abundant wildlife, set on the slopes of Wenlock Edge. A walkers paradise. Close to Ironbridge Gorge, museum and bridge. Near Severn Valley Railway and Blists Hill Open Air Museum. Own sanitation required. Non members welcome. Booking essential.
Facilities ✦ 🔲 🛁 🚻📷 🛒🏧📞 🔲 📞
Nearest Town Much Wenlock
Directions M54 at junc 6 take A5223 sp l/bridge, watch for change of signs from l/bridge to Much Wenlock. At Jiggers r/about t rt on A4169, after 1¾ miles t lt sp Much Wenlock. At T-junc opposite Gaskell Arms t rt on A458, after ¼ mile t lt on B4371, site 3 miles on the lt.
⇌ Much Wenlock

OSWESTRY

Oswestry Camping & Caravanning Club Site, Cranberry Moss, Kinnerley, Oswestry, Shropshire, SY10 8DY
Tel: 01743 741118
Email: oswestry.site@thefriendlclub.co.uk
www.campingandcaravanclub.co.uk/oswestry
Pitches For ⚹ ⛺ ⛟ **Total** 65
Open All Year
Access Good **Site** Level
Nearest Bus Stop (Miles) Outside
Close to the old Oswestry Hill Fort, Park Hall, Whittington Castle, Shrewsbury Abbey, Attingham Park, Wroxeter Roman City, Offas Dyke and Pistyll Falls. Local produce sold in the site shop. Non members welcome. You can also call us on 0845 130 7633.
Facilities ♿ ✦ 🔲 🛁📷⊙⛽ ▪ 🔲 📞
🏧 ⊙ 🛒🏧📞 🌐
Nearest Town Oswestry
Directions Turn off the A5 at the roundabout at the north end of the dual carriageway signed B4396 Knockin.
⇌ Shrewsbury

SHREWSBURY

Beaconsfield Farm Holiday Park, Battlefield, Shrewsbury, Shropshire, SY4 4AA
Tel: 01939 210370
Email: mail@beaconsfield-farm.co.uk
www.beaconsfield-farm.co.uk
Pitches For ⛺ ⛟ **Total** 60
Acreage 15 **Open** All Year
Access Good **Site** Level
Exclusively for ADULTS over 21 years. 5 Star, well landscaped, level park with coarse fishing. A La Carte restaurant on the park. 1½ miles to Park & Ride. Ideal base for Shrewsbury and the Welsh border. Holiday homes for sale and hire.
Facilities ♿ ✦ 🛁 🔲 🛁📷⊙⛽ ▪ 🔲 📞
🏧 ⊙ 🛒 ✕ ✈🏧📞 ✒ ⚓ ※ ✒
Nearest Town Shrewsbury
Directions 1½ miles north of Shrewsbury on the A49.
⇌ Shrewsbury

SHREWSBURY

Cartref Caravan & Camping Site, Cartref, Fords Heath, Nr Shrewsbury, Shropshire, SY5 9GD
Tel: 01743 821688
Email: alanpat@edwardscartref.wanadoo.co.uk
www.cartrefcaravansite.co.uk
Pitches For ⛺ ⛟ **Total** 47
Acreage 1½ **Open** Easter **to** Oct
Access Good **Site** Level
Peaceful countryside. Ideal for touring or an overnight stop. Adult Only section of 11 pitches.
Facilities ♿ ✦ 🛁 📷📞⊙⛽ 📞
🏧 🛒🏧📞 ※
Directions From Shrewsbury bypass A5 trunk road take the A458 Welshpool West. 2 miles to Ford Village, turn south at Ford, follow camp signs. Signposted from the A5 bypass on the Montgomery junction B4386.
⇌ Shrewsbury

SHREWSBURY

Ebury Hill Camping & Caravanning Club Site, Ebury Hill, Ring Bank, Haughton, Shrewsbury, Shropshire, SY4 4GB
Tel: 01743 709334
Email: ebury.hillsite@thefriendlyclub.co.uk
www.campingandcaravanningclub.co.uk/eburyhill
Pitches For ⚹ ⛺ ⛟ **Total** 100
Acreage 18 **Open** 15-Mar **to** 04-Nov
Access Good **Site** Lev/Slope
Set on an ancient Iron Age hill fort, with panoramic views. Close to Shrewsbury and Ironbridge Gorge. Fishing on site. BTB 4 Star Graded, David Bellamy Gold Award and AA 1 Pennant. Non members welcome. You can also call us on 0845 130 7633.
Facilities ✦ 🔲 🛁
🏧 ⊙ 🛒🏧📞📷 ✒ ⚓ 🌐
Nearest Town Shrewsbury
Directions From the A5/A49 take the B5062 signposted Newport, pass Haughmond Abbey and turn left signposted Hadnall. Site is on the left in approx. 1 mile.
⇌ Shrewsbury

SHREWSBURY

Middle Darnford Farm, Ratlinghope, Pontesbury, Shrewsbury, Shropshire, SY5 0SR
Tel: 01694 751320
Pitches For ⚹ ⛺ ⛟
Acreage 2 **Open** 15-Mar **to** Dec
Access Good **Site** Level
Excellent views.
Facilities 🛁 🏧 📞 🏧
Nearest Town Church Stretton
Directions From the A49 turn at Leebotwood and follow the road through Woolstaston over Long Myn Hill and the Farm is on the left hand side.
⇌ Church Stretton

SHREWSBURY

Severn House, Montford Bridge, Shrewsbury, Shropshire, SY4 1ED
Tel: 01743 850229
Email: booking@severnhousecampsite.co.uk
www.severnhousecampsite.co.uk
Pitches For ⚹ ⛺ ⛟ **Total** 25
Acreage 2½ **Open** Apr **to** Oct
Access Good **Site** Level
Nearest Bus Stop (Miles) ¼
Riverside site with 300 metres of river for fishing. Dog walk, local shop, buses, pub and meals nearby. Regular bus service.

Facilities ♿ ⓕ ♨ ⚿ ☏ ⌖ ☉ ⌂ 🏕
⚷ ⚑ ☺ ♨ ⊞ ▣ ✔ ☀

Nearest Town Shrewsbury

Directions 4 miles north west of Shrewsbury on the A5 towards Oswestry and North Wales. At signposts for the site turn onto the B4380 and Montford Bridge is ½ mile.
⇌ Shrewsbury

TELFORD

Severn Gorge Park, Bridgnorth Road, Telford, Shropshire, TF7 4JB
Tel: 01952 684789
Email: info@severngorgepark.co.uk
Pitches For ⚲ ⚲ ⚲⌇ **Total** 12
Open All Year
Access Good **Site** Level
Nearest Bus Stop (Miles) Outside
ADULTS ONLY PARK ideal for Ironbridge, Severn Gorge Cosford Air Museum Bridgenorth.
Facilities ♿ ⚷ ⓕ ⚑ ♨ ⚿ ⌖ ☉ ⌂ ⚐
▣ ☺ ☺♨⊞▣ A
Nearest Town telford
⇌ Telford

WEM

Lower Lacon Caravan Park, Wem, Shropshire, SY4 5RP
Tel: 01939 232376
Email: info@llcp.co.uk
www.llcp.co.uk
Pitches For ⚑ ⚲ ⚲ **Total** 270
Acreage 48 **Open** All Year
Access Good **Site** Level
Nearest Bus Stop (Miles) Outside
Facilities ♿ ⓕ ♨ ⚿ ⌖ ☉ ⌂ ⚐ ▣ 🏕
⚷ ☺ ☺✗ ⚑ ▣ ♨ ⌇☷⊞▣ ☀ ⚘
Nearest Town Wem
Directions 1 mile from Wem on the B5065. From the A49 then the B5065, 3 miles.
⇌ Wem

WHITCHURCH

Green Lane Farm Caravan & Camp Site, Green Lane Farm, Prees, Whitchurch, Shropshire, SY13 2AH
Tel: 01948 840460
Email: greenlanefarm@tiscali.co.uk
www.greenlanecaravanpark.co.uk
Pitches For ⚑ ⚲ ⚲ **Total** 36
Acreage 2½ **Open** Mar **to** Oct
Access Good **Site** Level
Nearest Bus Stop (Miles) ¼
Central for all local attractions, Hawkstone, Shrewsbury, Chester, Llangollen, Nantwich, etc.
Facilities ♿ ⓕ ♨⚿⌖ 🏕 ⚑ ▣ ♨☀H☷⚐ ☀
⚘
Nearest Town Whitchurch
Directions 350 yards off the the main A41 between Whitchurch and Newport.
⇌ Whitchurch

WHITCHURCH

Roden View Caravan & Camping, Roden View, Dobsons Bridge, Whixall, Whitchurch, Shropshire, SY13 2QL
Tel: 01948 710320
Email: jean@roden-view.co.uk
www.roden-view.co.uk
Pitches For ⚑ ⚲ ⚲ **Total** 14
Acreage 4½ **Open** All Year
Access Good **Site** Level
Near to the Shropshire Union Canal and Whixall Moss. 5 miles from Ellesmere, Shropshires Lake District. Large fishing pool.
Facilities ⓕ ♨ ⚿⌖ ☉ ⌂ 🏕 ☺ ☺▣ ✔
Nearest Town Wem
Directions From Shrewsbury Wem Church turn left after second garage, then turn right for Whixall, at the next T-Junction turn left then immediately right, 2½ miles to the next T-Junction turn right. ½ mile the house is on the right before Dobsons Bridge.
⇌ Wem

SOMERSET
BATH

Bath Chew Valley Caravan Park, Ham Lane, Bishop Sutton, Somerset, BS39 5TZ
Tel: 01275 332127
Email: enquiries@bathchewvalley.co.uk
www.bathchewvalley.co.uk
Pitches For ⚲ ⚲ **Total** 45
Acreage 4 **Open** All Year
Access Good **Site** Level
ADULTS ONLY PARK. A site for peace and tranquility, set in an area of outstanding natural beauty. Luxury bathroom and toilets. ETB 5 Star Graded, the only 5 Star Park in North East Somerset. Practical Caravan Top 100 Overall Winner 2009 & 2012
Facilities ♿ ⓕ ♨ ⚿ ⌖ ☉ ⌂ ⚐ ▣ 🏕
⚑ ☺ ☺H☷ ▣ A☀ ⚘ ⚷
Nearest Town Bath
Directions Approaching Bath on A37 or A38 Bristol to Wells or Bristol to Taunton roads, take A368 which links both to Bishop Sutton, turn opposite the Red Lion Pub.
⇌ Bath

BATH

Bury View Farm, Corston Fields, Nr. Bath, Somerset, BA2 9HD
Tel: 01225 873672
Email: salbowd@btinternet.com
www.buryviewfarm.co.uk
Pitches For ⚑ ⚲ ⚲ **Total** 18
Acreage 2 **Open** All Year
Access Good **Site** Level
Nearest Bus Stop (Miles) ¼
Quiet site, close to the city of Bath and Bristol. Within easy reach of Cheddar, Wells and Longleat. Open all year subject to weather.
Facilities ♿ ⓕ ⚿⌖ ☉ 🏕 ☺H▣

SOMERSET

Nearest Town Keynsham/Bath
Directions From Bath take the A4 Bristol road, at Newton-St-Loe roundabout take second left onto the A39 for Wells and Weston-super-Mare, Park is 1 mile.
⇆ Keynsham/Bath

BREAN SANDS

Channel View Touring Park, Warren Road, Brean, Burnham-on-Sea, Somerset, TA8 2RR
Tel: 01278 751055
www.breanfarm.co.uk
Pitches For ▲ ⬛ 🚐 **Total** 50
Acreage 3 **Open** Apr to Oct
Access Good **Site** Gentle Slope
Nearest Bus Stop (Miles) ½
Quiet and friendly site, on the beach side overlooking farmland.
Facilities ⬧ ⅃ 🌐 🍴 🛁 ⊙ ⊸ ⬛ 🏪 ⬛ ⅃ 🌐
⚲

Nearest Town Brean Sands
Directions Leave the M5 at junction 22 and follow signs to Burnham-on-Sea, Berrow and Brean. Site is ¼ mile past the Brean Down Inn on the left hand side.
⇆ Highbridge

BREAN SANDS

Northam Farm Holiday Park, Brean, Nr Burnham-on-Sea, Somerset, TA8 2SE
Tel: 01278 751244
Email: stay@northamfarm.co.uk
www.northamfarm.co.uk
Pitches For ▲ ⬛ 🚐 ⬛≋ **Total** 350
Acreage 30 **Open** 1st Mar to 3rd Nov
Access Good **Site** Level
Nearest Bus Stop (Miles) Outside
Footpath to beach 200 Metres.
Facilities ⬧ ⅃ 🌐 🍴 🛁 ⊙ ⊸ ⬛ 🏪
🏪 ⊙ ⬛ ✗ 🅰 🌊 🏪 ⬛ ⬛ ✦ 🌫 ⚲
Nearest Town Burnham-on-Sea
Directions M5 Junction 22. Follow signs to Brean, ¼ mile past Leisure Park on righthand side.
⇆ Weston-super-Mare

BREAN SANDS

Warren Farm Holiday Centre, Brean Sands, Burnham-on-Sea, Somerset, TA8 2RP
Tel: 01278 751227
Email: enquiries@warren-farm.co.uk
www.warren-farm.co.uk
Pitches For ▲ ⬛ 🚐 **Total** 500
Acreage 100 **Open** April to End Oct
Access Good **Site** Level
Nearest Bus Stop (Miles) ¼
Flat, grassy, family park with excellent facilities, indoor play area and family entertainment at the Beachcomber Inn. 100 metres from 5 miles of sandy beach. Dogs are welcome free in designated areas. AA Holiday Centre.
Facilities ⬧ ✗ ⅃ 🌐 🍴 🛁 ⊙ ⊸ ⬛ 🏪
🏪 ⊙ ⬛ ✗ ▾ 🅰 🌊 🏪 ⬛ ⬛ ✦ 🌫
⚲ 🌫
Nearest Town Burnham-on-Sea
Directions Leave M5 at junction 22, follow signs to Burnham-on-Sea, Berrow and Brean on the B3140. Site is 1¼ miles past the leisure centre.
⇆ Weston-super-Mare

BRIDGWATER

Currypool Mill, Cannington, Bridgwater, Somerset, TA5 2NH
Tel: 01278 671135
Email: info@currypoolmill.co.uk
www.currypoolmill.co.uk
Pitches For ▲ ⬛ 🚐 **Total** 42

Open Easter **to** Mid Nov
Access Good **Site** Level
Quiet location near the Quantock Hills and Somerset coast. Set amongst streams and waterfalls. Dog walking fields, putting and croquet. Disabled toilet and shower.
Facilities ⬧ ⅃ 🌐 🍴 🛁 ⊙ ⊸ ⬛ 🏪
🏪 ⊙ 🅰 🏪 ⬛ ⬛ 🌫 ⚲
Nearest Town Bridgwater
Directions From Bridgwater take the A39 Minehead road, after approx. 5 miles take a left hand turning signposted Spaxton and Aisholt. Currypool is approx. ½ mile on the left.
⇆ Bridgwater

BRIDGWATER

Mill Farm Caravan & Camping Park, Fiddington, Bridgwater, Somerset, TA5 1JQ
Tel: 01278 732286
www.millfarm.biz
Pitches For ▲ ⬛ 🚐
Open All Year
Access Good **Site** Level
Lovely family park situated between the Quantock hills and the north Somerset coastline.
Facilities ⬧ ⅃ 🌐 🍴 🛁 ⊙ ⊸ ⬛ 🏪 ⬛ 🏪
🏪 ⊙ ⬛ ▾ 🅰 🌊 ✦ 🏪 ⬛ ⬛ 🌫 ⚲ 🌫
Nearest Town Bridgwater
Directions Follow the A39 towards Minehead for 6 miles. At Keenthorne turn right for Fiddington, Mill Farm is 1 milefrom main road.
⇆ Bridgwater

BRUTON

Batcombe Vale Caravan & Camping Park, Batcombe, Shepton Mallet, Somerset, BA4 6BW
Tel: 01749 831207
Email: gary.butler1@virgin.net
www.batcombevale.co.uk
Pitches For ▲ ⬛ 🚐 **Total** 32
Acreage 7 **Open** April **to** Sept
Access Good **Site** Level
Own secluded valley of lakes and wild gardens. Fishing and boating on site. Near Longleat, Stourhead and Glastonbury. All shops are 2 miles away.
Facilities ⅃ 🌐 🍴 🛁 ⊙ ⊸ ⬛ 🏪
🏪 ⊙ 🏪 ⬛ ✦
Nearest Town Bruton
Directions Access must be via Bruton or Evercreech fro
m where it is well signed.
⇆ Bruton

BURNHAM-ON-SEA

Diamond Farm Caravan & Touring Park, Diamond Farm, Weston Road, Brean, Nr Burnham-on-Sea, Somerset, TA8 2RL
Tel: 01278 751263
Email:
trevor@diamondfarm42.freeserve.co.uk
www.diamondfarm.co.uk
Pitches For ▲ ⬛ 🚐 **Total** 100
Acreage 6 **Open** April **to** 15-Oct
Access Good **Site** Level
Nearest Bus Stop (Miles) Outside
A quiet, family site alongside River Axe and only 800yds from the beach. All modern facilities.
Facilities ⬧ ⬧ ⅃ 🌐 🍴 🛁 ⊙ ⊸ ⬛ 🏪
🏪 ⊙ ⬛ ✗ 🅰 🏪 ⬛ ⬛ ✦ 🌫 ⚲
Nearest Town Burnham-on-Sea
Directions M5 junction 22, follow signs to Brean, ½ mile past leisure park turn right to Lympsham/Weston-super-Mare. Diamond Farm is 800yds on the left hand side.
⇆ Weston-super-Mare

BURNHAM-ON-SEA

Westbrook Farm, Harp Road, Brent Knoll, Somerset, TA9 4HQ
Tel: 01278 760386
www.westbrook-farm.co.uk
Pitches For ▲ ⬛ 🚐 **Total** 45
Acreage 2 **Open** Mar to Oct
Access Good **Site** Level
Nearest Bus Stop (Miles) ½
3 miles from Burnham-on-Sea and central for sightseeing in Somerset. Ideal stop-over off the M5.
Facilities ⬧ ⅃ 🌐 🍴 🛁 ⊙ ⊸ ⬛ 🏪
🏪 🏪 ⬛ ⬛ 🌫 ⚲
Nearest Town Burnham-on-Sea
Directions Leave the M5 at junction 22 and take the A38 towards Bristol. After ½ a mile turn right just past the motorhome dealership sp Mark, site is ½ a mile on the left.
⇆ Highbridge

CHARD

Alpine Grove Woodland Park, Forton, Chard, Somerset, TA20 4HD
Tel: 01460 63479
Email: stay@alpinegrovetouringpark.com
www.alpinegrovetouringpark.com
Pitches For ▲ ⬛ 🚐 **Total** 40
Acreage 8 **Open** 01-Apr **to** 30-Sep
Access Good **Site** Level
Nearest Bus Stop (Miles) ¼
Ideal for woodland walks and fossil hunting. 20 minutes from the World Heritage coastline. New self catering log cabins available for hire all year round. ETC 4 Star Graded, AA 3 Pennants and Gold David Bellamy Award.
Facilities ⬧ ⅃ 🌐 🍴 🛁 ⊙ ⊸ ⬛ 🏪 ⬛ 🏪
🏪 ⊙ ⬛ 🏪 ⬛ ⬛ 🌫 ⚲ 🌫
Nearest Town Chard
Directions From Chard take the A30 signposted Cricket St Thomas, turn right onto the B3167 and follow brown tourism signs.
⇆ Crewkerne

CHARD

Barleymows Farm Shop & Restaurant, Snowdon Hill Farm, Chard, Somerset, TA20 3PS
Tel: 01460 62130
Email: barleymows@btconnect.com
www.barleymowsfarmshop.co.uk
Pitches For ▲ ⬛ 🚐 ⬛≋ **Total** 5
Acreage 5 **Open** All Year
Access Good **Site** Level
Nearest Bus Stop (Miles) 1
Maize maze & activity field open July to Sept Fully comprehensive farm shop and resturant.
Facilities ⅃ 🌐 🍴 🛁 🏪 ✗ 🅰 🏪 ⬛ ⬛
Nearest Town Chard/Lyme Regis
Directions Take the A30 west from Chard, Park is ¾ miles on the right hand side.
⇆ Axminster

CHARD

Ilminster Caravan Club Site, Beetham, Chard, Somerset, TA20 3QA
Tel: 01460 234519
www.caravanclub.co.uk
Pitches For ⬛ 🚐 **Total** 73
Acreage 5 **Open** Mar to Oct
Access Good **Site** Level
Peaceful and pleasant park set in South Somerset countryside. Near Chard Reservoir & Nature Reserve which hosts 150 species of bird including Osprey. Close to Montacute House and Cricket St. Thomas Wildlife Park. Non members welcome. Booking essential.
Facilities ⅃ 🌐 🍴 🛁 ⊙ ⊸ ⬛ 🏪
🏪 ⊙ 🏪 ⬛ ⬛ 🌫 ⚲
Nearest Town Chard

Directions From east on the A303, at the crossroads at the end of Ilminster bypass turn left by the thatched cottage into a narrow lane signposted Crickleaze. Site is second entrance on the left (250 yards). NB: DO NOT use first entrance as its difficult to back out.

✈ Chard

CHARD

South Somerset Holiday Park, A30 Exeter Road, Howley, Nr Chard, Somerset, TA20 3EA
Tel: 01460 66036
Email: sshpltd@btconnect.com
www.southsomersetholidaypark.co.uk
Pitches For 🚐 🚍 **Total** 110
Acreage 7 **Open** All Year
Access Good **Site** Gentle Slope
30 minutes drive from the south coast, many other attractions within 40 minutes ie Fleet air Arm Museum.
Facilities 🚿 ⚡ 🖿 🚾 🖊 ⌐ ☉ 🍴 🔲 ◨ 🖬 ⛱
Nearest Town Chard
Directions 3 miles west of Chard on the A30. Towards Honiton.

CHEDDAR

Bucklegrove Holiday Park, Wells Road, Rodney Stoke, Cheddar, Somerset, BS27 3UZ
Tel: 01749 870261
Email: info@bucklegrove.co.uk
www.bucklegrove.co.uk
Pitches For ⛺ 🚐 🚍 **Total** 140
Acreage 7½ **Open** 04-Mar **to** 04-Jan
Access Good **Site** Level/Gently Sloping
Nearest Bus Stop (Miles) Outside
Family friendly Park in the heart of Somerset with stunning views. Near to Cheddar Gorge. Free indoor heated pool. Ideal for walking and touring.

Facilities 🚿 ⚡ 🖿 🚾 🖊 ⌐ ☉ 🍴 🔲 ◨ 🖬 ⛱
🏋 ◉ 🖂 ✕ 🍽 🏇 ⬢ 🍴 🖽 ◨ ◨ ⛱ 📶
Nearest Town Cheddar
Directions Midway between Wells and Cheddar on the A371.
✈ Weston-super-Mare

CHEDDAR

Cheddar Bridge Touring Park, Draycott Road, Cheddar, Somerset, BS27 3RJ
Tel: 01934 743048
Email: enquiries@cheddarbridge.co.uk
www.cheddarbridge.co.uk
Pitches For ⛺ 🚐 🚍 **Total** 40
Acreage 4 **Open** Mar **to** 10-Nov
Access Good **Site** Level
Nearest Bus Stop (Miles) ¼
Alongside River Yeo.
Facilities 🚿 ⚡ 🖿 🚾 🖊 ⌐ ☉ 🍴 🔲 ◨ 🖬 ⛱
🏋 🏋 ◉ 🖽 🖂 ◨ 🖬 ⛱ 📶
Directions On the A371, 100 yards south of Cheddar Village orange signs.
✈ Weston-Super-Mare

CHEDDAR

Netherdale Caravan & Camping Site, Bridgwater Road, Sidcot, Winscombe, Somerset, BS25 1NH
Tel: 01934 843007/843481
Email: camping@netherdale.net
www.netherdale.net
Pitches For ⛺ 🚐 🚍 **Total** 25
Acreage 3½ **Open** Mar **to** Oct
Access Good **Site** Lev/Slope
Excellent walking area, footpath from site to valley and Mendip Hills. Good views. Cafe/restaurant adjoining site. Many historical places and beaches within easy reach. Pets welcome on a lead. Only individual motorcycles accepted, not groups. 3 miles from a dry ski slope and a well equipped sports centre.

Facilities ⚡ 🚾 🖊 ⌐ 🍴 🔲 ◨ 🖬 ⛱
🏋 ◉ 🖂 🖽 🖂 ⛱
Directions Midway between Bristol and Bridgwater on A38. From Weston-super-Mare follow A371 to join A38 at Sidcot Corner, site is ¼ mile south. From Wells and Cheddar follow A371 westwards to join A38, a mile south of site.
✈ Weston-super-Mare

CHEDDAR

Rodney Stoke Inn, Rodney Stoke, Nr Cheddar, Somerset, BS27 3XB
Tel: 01749 870209
Email: annetteneil@aol.com
www.rodneystokeinn.co.uk
Pitches For ⛺ 🚐 🚍 **Total** 31
Acreage 2 **Open** March **to** October
Access Good **Site** Level
Nearest Bus Stop (Miles) ¼
ADULTS ONLY SITE in a central location for the Cheddar Gorge and Caves, the City of Wells and Wookey Hole Caves.
Facilities ⚡ 🚾 🖊 ⌐ 🍴 ✕ 🖽 ◨ 🖬 A
Directions Take the A371 from Cheddar towards Wells for 3 miles.
✈ Weston-Super-Mare

CHEDDAR

Splott Farm, Blackford, Nr Wedmore, Somerset, BS28 4PD
Tel: 01278 641522
Pitches For ⛺ 🚐 **Total** 37
Acreage 4 **Open** Mar **to** Oct
Access Good **Site** Sloping
Nearest Bus Stop (Miles) 1
Very peaceful site with views of the Mendip Hills (and Quantocks), very rural area. Ideal touring, Weston-super-Mare, Wells, Cheddar, Burnham-on-Sea, Wookey.
Facilities ⚡ 🚾 🖊 ⌐ ☉ 🍴 🔲 ◨ 🖬 ⛱
🏋 🏋 ◍ 🖽 🖂 ⛱

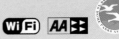

Nearest Town Burnham-on-Sea/Cheddar
Directions Leave M5 at junction 22, take 1st left and follow signs for Mark approx 4 miles.
⇌ Highbridge

CONGRESBURY
Oak Farm Touring Park, Weston Road, Congresbury, Somerset, BS49 5EB
Tel: 01934 833246
Pitches For ⬜ 🚐 **Total** 40
Acreage 2 **Open** Apr to 01-Oct
Access Good **Site** Level
Nearest Bus Stop (Miles) Outside
Near river on bus route, cycling close by on closed railway line.
Facilities ⨍ ⬜⬛♿⊙⌁☂ ⚓⬜ ❄ ⚲
Nearest Town Weston-super-Mare
Directions 4 miles from junc. 21 on M5, on the A370 midway between Bristol and Weston Super Mare.
⇌ Yatton

CROWCOMBE
Quantock Orchard Caravan Park, Flaxpool, Crowcombe, Taunton, Somerset, TA4 4AW
Tel: 01984 618618
Email: member@flaxpool.freeserve.co.uk
www.quantock-orchard.co.uk
Pitches For ⋀ ⬜ 🚐 **Total** 77
Acreage 7½ **Open** All Year
Access Good **Site** Level
Nearest Bus Stop (Miles) ¼
Nearest Town Taunton/Minehead
⇌ Taunton

DULVERTON
Exbridge Lakeside Caravan Club Site, Higher Grants, Exebridge, Dulverton, Somerset, TA22 9BE
Tel: 01398 324068

www.caravanclub.co.uk
Pitches For ⬜ 🚐 **Total** 80
Acreage 11 **Open** Mar to Nov
Access Good **Site** Level
Nearest Bus Stop (Miles) ½
Situated in a quiet village with lovely views towards Exmoor. Ideal for keen anglers. Within easy reach of Exmoor National Park and Lorna Doone country. Near Rosemoor Gardens, Dunkery Beacon and Dunster Castle. Non members welcome. Booking essential.
Facilities ⬡⨍⬜⬛♿⊙⌁☂⬜ ⚲☂
🏪⊙⬛♨⬛⬜✉⬜⚲☂
Nearest Town Dulverton
Directions Leave M5 at junc 27 take A361 towards Barnstaple. After 6 miles at the r/about t rt on A396, at the r/about by Exeter Inn t lt sp Dulverton. At Black Cat junc on sharp lt hand bend keep rt, at xroads by Petrol Station continue on A396. Site is 2½ miles on lt.

DULVERTON
Exe Valley Caravan Site, Bridgetown, Somerset, TA22 9JR
Tel: 01643 851432
Email: info@exevalleycamping.co.uk
www.exevalleycamping.co.uk
Pitches For ⋀ 🚐 **Total** 50
Acreage 4 **Open** Mid March to Mid Oct
Access Good **Site** Level
Nearest Bus Stop (Miles) Outside
ADULTS ONLY. Most improved site in Exmoor. Within Exmoor National Park. Free fly fishing on site. Just a few minutes walk from the local pub serving good food. Motorhome service point.
Facilities ⬡⨍⬛♿☂⊙⌁⬛⬜☂
🏪⊙⬛♨⬛⚲⬛⚲☂
Nearest Town Dulverton
Directions Leave the M5 at junction 27 and take the A361 towards Tiverton. From the

roundabout on the Tiverton by-pass take the A396 signposted Minehead. Take care after 7 miles to stay on the A396 at the Black Cat junction, and DO NOT go through Dulverton. Turn left 100 yards beyond Badgers Holt Pub in the centre of Bridgetown.

DULVERTON
Exmoor House Caravan Club Site, Dulverton, Somerset, TA22 9HL
Tel: 01398 323268
www.caravanclub.co.uk
Pitches For ⬜ 🚐 **Total** 67
Acreage 4 **Open** Mar to Jan
Access Good **Site** Level
Nearest Bus Stop (Miles) ¼
Quiet and pretty site with valley views. 200 yards from the village. Ideal base to explore Exmoor National Park. Near the Lorna Doone Trail, Dunster Castle and Knightshayes Court. Non members welcome. Booking essential.
Facilities ⬡⨍⬜⬛♿☂⊙⌁⬜ ⚲☂
🏪⊙⬛♨⬛⚲☂
Nearest Town Dulverton
Directions M5 junc 27 take A361 sp Barnstaple, after 6 mls at r/about t rt on A396. At r/about by Exeter Inn t lt sp Dulverton, at Black Cat junc on sharp lt hand bend bear rt to xroads and continue straight on A396. After 2¾ mls by Petrol Station fork lt on B3222, after 3 mls t lt by the Bridge Inn, site is 200 yds.

EXFORD
Westermill Farm, Exford, Exmoor, Somerset, TA24 7NJ
Tel: 01643 831238
Email: cad@westermill.com
www.westermill.com
Pitches For ⋀ 🚐 **Total** 60
Acreage 6 **Open** All Year

Access Poor **Site** Level
Nearest Bus Stop (Miles) 2½
Beautiful, secluded site in a hidden valley beside a river for fishing, bathing and paddling. Fascinating 500 acre farm with Waymarked walks. Centre of Exmoor National Park. Free hot showers. Camp fire areas. Charming cottages nestling by trees for hire. David Bellamy Gold Award for Conservation.
Facilities ⌂⊞🚿🅿⏱⊙🔌🆑 ♿ 🅿 🕻🛒⊞🖵 ♪
Nearest Town Minehead
Directions Leave Exford on the Porlock road. After ½ a mile fork left, continue for 2 miles along the valley until Westermill is seen on a tree and fork left.
🚉 Taunton

FROME

Seven Acres Touring Caravan & Camping Park, West Woodlands, Frome, Somerset, BA11 5EQ
Tel: 01373 464222
Pitches For ▲ 🚐 🚙 **Total** 32
Acreage 7 **Open** Mar to Oct
Access Good **Site** Level
As seen on national television. Acres of level, landscaped grounds with a stream meandering through. On the outskirts of the Longleat Estate and within easy reach of Stourhead, Cheddar Caves and Stonehenge.
Facilities 🚿 🕻 🛁 🚽 🅿 ⊙🔌 🍴 🍽 🛒⊞🖵
Nearest Town Frome
Directions From the Frome by-pass take the B3092 towards Maiden Bradley and Mere. Seven Acres is situated approx. 1 mile from the by-pass.
🚉 Frome

GLASTONBURY

Greenacres Camping, Barrow Lane, North Wootton, Glastonbury, Somerset, BA4 4HL
Tel: 01749 890497
Email: stay@greenacres-camping.co.uk
www.greenacres-camping.co.uk
Pitches For ▲ 🚙 **Total** 40
Acreage 4½ **Open** Apr to Sept **Site** Level
Nearest Bus Stop (Miles) 2
Quiet site in stunning Somerset countryside, with views of Glastonbury Tor and the Mendip Hills. Ideal for families. Huge pitches! Cycle hire on site. Facebook page www.facebook.com/camping in Somerset.
Facilities 🚿 🕻⊞🅿 ⊙🔌 🛒⊞🖵🅿 ♪
Nearest Town Glastonbury
Directions Leave the M5 at junction 23 and take the A39 to Glastonbury. Follow signs from Brownes Garden Centre. Or follow signs from the A361 at Steanbow for 2 miles.
🚉 Castle Cary

GLASTONBURY

The Old Oaks Touring Park, Wick Farm, Wick, Glastonbury, Somerset, BA6 8JS
Tel: 01458 831437
Email: info@theoldoaks.co.uk
www.theoldoaks.co.uk
Pitches For ▲ 🚐 🚙 🚐≡ **Total** 100
Acreage 10 **Open** 08-Feb to 17-Nov
Access Good **Site** Level/Sloping
Nearest Bus Stop (Miles) 1½
ADULT ONLY Park in a stunning location with beautiful views. Blissfully tranquil. Ideal for walking, cycling or just relaxing. ¾ miles from Glastonbury Tor. Camping Cabins/Pods for Glamping.
Facilities ♿ 🚿 🕻⊞🅿🛁 ⊙🔌 🍴 🛒⊞🖵
🕻 🏧🛒⊞🖵🅿 🕻 ♪
Directions From Glastonbury take the A361 towards Shepton Mallet. In 2 miles turn left at signpost for Wick, Park is on the left in 1 mile.
🚉 Castle Cary

HIGHBRIDGE

Greenacre Place Touring Caravan Park, Bristol Road, Edithmead, Highbridge, Somerset, TA9 4HA
Tel: 01278 785227
Email: info@greenacreplace.com
www.greenacreplace.com
Pitches For 🚐 🚙 **Total** 10
Acreage 1 **Open** March to November
Access Good **Site** Level
Nearest Bus Stop (Miles) ½
ADULTS ONLY. Small, peaceful caravan park with easy access. Short drive to sandy beaches. Ideally placed for touring Somerset.
Facilities 🚿 ⌂🕻🅿 ⊙ 🔌🛒⊞🖵 ⊞🖵 ♪
Nearest Town Burnham-on-Sea
Directions Just off the M5 junction 22.
🚉 Highbridge

ILMINSTER

Thornleigh Caravan Park, Hanning Road, Horton, Ilminster, Somerset, TA19 9QH
Tel: 01460 53450
Email: thornleighsite@btinternet.com
www.thornleighcaravansite.co.uk
Pitches For ▲ 🚐 🚙 **Total** 20
Acreage 1¼ **Open** Mar to Oct
Access Good **Site** Level
Nearest Bus Stop (Miles) ¼
Flat site in a village location, ideal for touring Somerset and Devon. Heated shower block. ½ hour drive to the south coast. 6 miles to Cricket St Thomas Gardens. National Trust properties nearby. Village Inn with restaurant, Post Office, stores and public telephone nearby. Rural rally site with village hall close by.Booking essential.
Facilities ♿ 🚿 🕻⊞🅿🛁 ⊙🔌 🍴 🛒⊞🖵 ♪
Nearest Town Ilminster
Directions A303 West Ilminster, take the A358 signposted Chard. ¼ mile turn right signposted Horton and Broadway. Site on the left opposite the church, ¾ mile.
🚉 Taunton/Crewkerne

LANGPORT

Bowdens Crest Caravan & Camping Park, Bowdens, Langport, Somerset, TA10 0DD
Tel: 01458 250553
Email: bowcrest@btconnect.com
www.bowdenscrest.co.uk
Pitches For ▲ 🚐 🚙 **Total** 30
Acreage 16 **Open** All Year
Access Good **Site** Level
Nearest Bus Stop (Miles) 2
Countryside
Facilities ♿ 🚿 🕻⊞🅿🛁 ⊙🔌 🍴 🛒⊞🖵
🕻 ⊙🍴🛒⊞🅿 🍴 🛒⊞🖵🅿 ☀ ♪
Nearest Town Langport
Directions Off the A372 Langport to Bridgwater road.
🚉 Bridgwater

LANGPORT

Thorney Lakes Caravan Site, Thorney Lakes, Muchelney, Langport, Somerset, TA10 0DW
Tel: 01458 250811
Email: enquiries@thorneylakes.co.uk
www.thorneylakes.co.uk
Pitches For ▲ 🚐 🚙 🚐≡ **Total** 36
Acreage 7 **Open** Mar to Nov
Access Good **Site** Level
Site is an orchard on Somerset Moors. Ideal for walking and cycling.
Facilities 🚿 🕻⊞🅿 ⊙🔌 🛒⊞🖵 ✏ ♪
Nearest Town Langport
Directions Turn off the A303 dual carriageway signposted Martock, Ash and Kingsbury Episcopi. Follow signs to

Kingsbury Episcopi, at the T-Junction in the village turn right, site is 1 mile on the right.
🚉 Yeovil/Taunton

MARTOCK

Southfork Caravan Park, Parrett Works, Martock, Somerset, TA12 6AE
Tel: 01935 825661
Email: southforkcaravans@btconnect.com
www.southforkcaravans.co.uk
Pitches For ▲ 🚐 🚙 **Total** 27
Acreage 2 **Open** All Year
Access Good **Site** Level
Nearest Bus Stop (Miles) 2
Set in open countryside near River Parrett. Numerous places of interest nearby for all age groups. Ideal base for touring. 3 holiday homes for hire. Caravan storage available.
Facilities 🚿 🕻⊞🅿 ⊙🔌 🛒 🖵 🅿
🕻 ⊙🍴🛁🛒⊞🖵🅿
Nearest Town Martock/Yeovil
Directions Situated 2 miles north west of A303 (between Ilchester and Ilminster). From A303 east of Ilminster, at roundabout take first exit sp South Petherton and follow camping signs. From A303 west of Ilchester, after Cartgate roundabout (junction with A3088 to Yeovil) take exit sp Martock and follow camping signs.
🚉 Yeovil

MINEHEAD

Butlins Minehead, Warren Road, Minehead, Somerset, TA24 5SH
Tel: 01643 700515
Email: touringcaravans.minehead@bourne-leisure.co.uk
www.butlins.com
Pitches For 🚐 🚙 **Total** 44
Open April to Nov
Access Good **Site** Level
Nearest Bus Stop (Miles) Outside
Our fabulous Minehead Resort has a Touring Site for caravan holiday makers. Beautifully set in Exmoor National Park there's plenty to do in the local countryside, at the lakes and on the soft sand beaches. Make Minehead your caravan destination for your next trip.
Facilities ♿ 🚿 🕻⊞🅿 ⊙🔌 🛒 🖵 🅿
🕻 ⊙🍴🛁🚿🐕🍴≡☀🛒⊞🖵🅿🖵 ♪
Nearest Town Minehead
Directions Heading north take the M5 to Taunton (Junction 25), then the A358 and A39 to Minehead. Heading south on the M5, you can follow the signposts for the A39 from junction 24. You can•™t miss us, we•™e just half a mile along the seafront road from Minehead town centre.

Sat nav post code: TA24 5SH

If you•™e coming by train

There are train links from London, Bristol and Birmingham to Minehead. Taunton is the nearest mainline station. Buses X28 and 28 transfer between Taunton station and Butlins Minehead - there's one every half hour and the final stop is inside the Resort itself. Be warned, it's a 1 1/2 - hour journey.

If you're coming by coach

National Express Coaches arrive at the Resort•™ Main Entrance, where we•™l meet you.
🚉 Taunton

MINEHEAD

Minehead & Exmoor Caravan & Camping Park, Porlock Road, Minehead, Somerset, TA24 8SW
Tel: 01643 703074
www.mineheadandexmoorcamping.co.uk
Pitches For ▲ 🚐 🚙 **Total** 50
Acreage 3½

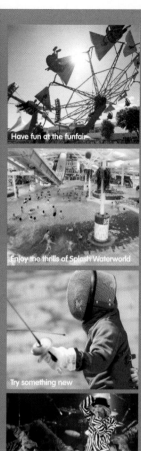

Access Good **Site** Level
Nearest Bus Stop (Miles) Outside
Situated on the edge of Exmoor National Park.
Facilities 🚿 ♿ 🚻 🛒 🛁 👤 ⊙ 🍴 🔌 🏪
🎮 🔥 🏊 ⛱ ✂ 🔧
Nearest Town Minehead
Directions 1 mile west of Minehead town centre on the A39, Park is on the right hand side.
�+= Taunton

MINEHEAD

Hoburne Blue Anchor, Blue Anchor Bay, Nr Minehead, Somerset, TA24 6JT
Tel: 01643 821360
Email: blueanchor@hoburne.com
www.hoburne.com
Pitches For ⛺ 🚐 🚚 **Total** 103
Acreage 29 **Open** 26-Feb **to** 30-Oct
Access Good **Site** Level
Nearest Bus Stop (Miles) Outside
Nearest Town Minehead
�+= Minehead

MINEHEAD

Minehead Camping & Caravanning Club Site, Hill Road, North Hill, Minehead, Somerset, TA24 5LB
Tel: 01643 704138
Email:
minehead.site@thefriendlyclub.co.uk
www.campingandcaravanningclub.co.uk/minehead
Pitches For ⛺ 🚐 🚚 **Total** 60
Acreage 3¾ **Open** 30-Apr **to** Sept
Access Poor **Site** Sloping
In Exmoor National Park with fine views of the town of Minehead. Sloping site, chocks required. BTB 4 Star Graded and AA 3 Pennants. Non members welcome. You can also call us on 0845 130 7633.

Facilities 🚿 ♿ 🚻 🛒 🛁 👤 ⊙ 🍴 🔌 🏪
🎮 🔥 🏊 ⛱ 🔧 🏪 🛜
Nearest Town Minehead
Directions From the A39 head towards the town centre, in the main street turn opposite W.H.Smith into Blenheim Road, after 50 yards turn left again. Go up the hill and left around a hairpin bend, turn right at the cottages. Go past the church on the right and continue round two bends, site is on the right.
�+= Minehead

MINEHEAD

St. Audries Bay Holiday Club, West Quantoxhead, Minehead, Somerset, TA4 4DY
Tel: 01984 632515
Email: info@staudriesbay.co.uk
www.staudriesbay.co.uk
Pitches For ⛺ 🚐 🚚 **Total** 20
Acreage 12 **Open** Easter **to** Oct
Access Good **Site** Level
Nearest Bus Stop (Miles) ½
Nearest Town Minehead
�+= Taunton

PORLOCK

Burrowhayes Farm Caravan & Camping Site & Riding Stables, West Luccombe, Porlock, Nr Minehead, Somerset, TA24 8HT
Tel: 01643 862463
Email: info@burrowhayes.co.uk
www.burrowhayes.co.uk
Pitches For ⛺ 🚐 🚚 **Total** 120
Acreage 8 **Open** 15-Mar **to** 31-Oct
Access Good **Site** Lev/Slope
Nearest Bus Stop (Miles) 0.5
A walkers paradise. direct access in woodland and open moorland. Beside Horner Water.
Facilities 🚿 ♿ 🚻 🛒 🛁 👤 ⊙ 🍴 🔌 🏪
🎮 🔥 🏪 🔧 🏪

Nearest Town Minehead
Directions A39 from Minehead towards Porlock. Take 1st left turning after "Allerford". Site is ¼ mile on right.
�+= Taunton

PORLOCK

Porlock Caravan Park, Highbank, Porlock, Nr Minehead, Somerset, TA24 8ND
Tel: 01643 862269
Email: info@porlockcaravanpark.co.uk
www.porlockcaravanpark.co.uk
Pitches For ⛺ 🚐 🚚 **Total** 40
Acreage 3½ **Open** Mid March **to** Oct
Access Good **Site** Level
Nearest Bus Stop (Miles) ¼
Scenic views, Ideal touring and walking.
Facilities 🚿 ♿ 🚻 🛒 🛁 👤 ⊙ 🔌 🏪
🎮 🔥 🏪 🔧 ⛱ 🛜
Nearest Town Minehead
Directions A39 from Minehead to Lynton, take the B3225 in Porlock to Porlock Weir. Site signposted.
�+= Taunton

SPARKFORD

Long Hazel Park, High Street, Sparkford, Nr Yeovil, Somerset, BA22 7JH
Tel: 01963 440002
Email: longhazelpark@hotmail.com
www.longhazelpark.co.uk
Pitches For ⛺ 🚐 🚚 ⛱ **Total** 50
Acreage 3½ **Open** All Year
Access Good **Site** Level
Nearest Bus Stop (Miles) Outside
ADULTS ONLY. Full disabled shower unit. Near to an inn and restaurant. Ideal for touring or an overnight halt. Haynes International Motor Museum and Fleet Air Arm Museum nearby. Two pine lodges for hire with wheelchair access and 12 pine lodges for sale. Please note, dogs are not

permitted in the pine lodges.
Facilities 🛁 ⏚ 🏠 🖵 🔥 🎋 ⊙ 🍴 🔲 ☎
🍴 🔵 🏧 🚿 🝙 🄰 ⚡ 📶
Directions From Wincanton take the A303
to the end of Sparkford by-pass. At the
services turn left into Sparkford Village, site
is approx. 400 yards on the left.
🚆 Yeovil/Sherborne/Castle Cary

STREET

Bramble Hill Caravan & Camping Park,
Bramble Hill, Walton, Nr Street, Somerset,
BA16 9RQ
Tel: 01458 442548
Pitches For Å ⚓ ♨ **Total** 30
Acreage 2 **Open** Easter to October
Access Good **Site** Level
Nearest Bus Stop (Miles) ¼
ADULTS ONLY. Peaceful and quiet Park.
Dogs are welcome if kept on leads. 1½ miles
from Sainsburys. Well secured caravan
storage available.
Facilities 🍴 🏠 🔥 ⊙ 🍴 🝙 ☎ 🍴 🏧 🄰 ⚡
Nearest Town Street
Directions Take the A39 from Street to
Walton for 2 miles, pass the church and the
Pike & Musket Pub and turn left, signposted.
Park is 500 metres.
🚆 Castle Cary

TAUNTON

Ashe Farm Caravan & Camp Site, Ashe
Farm, Thornfalcon, Taunton, Somerset,
TA3 5NW
Tel: 01823 443764
Email: info@ashefarm.co.uk
www.ashefarm.co.uk
Pitches For Å ⚓ ♨ **Total** 30
Acreage 7 **Open** Apr to Oct
Access Good **Site** Level
Nearest Bus Stop (Miles) ¼

Ideal touring centre, easy reach of Quantock
and Blackdown Hills.
Facilities 🛁 🍴 ⏚ 🏠 🔥 🎋 ⊙ 🍴 🝙 🔲 ☎
🍴 🝙 🔵 🚿
Nearest Town Taunton
Directions 4 miles southeast Taunton on
A358, turn right at the Nags Head towards
West Hatch, site is ¼ mile on the right.
🚆 Taunton

TAUNTON

Cornish Farm Touring Park, Cornish
Farm, Shoreditch, Taunton, Somerset, TA3
7BS
Tel: 01823 327746
Email: info@cornishfarm.com
www.cornishfarm.com
Pitches For Å ⚓ ♨ **Total** 50
Acreage 3½ **Open** All Year
Access Good **Site** Level
Nearest Bus Stop (Miles) ½
Excellent facilities. Ideal touring park. Good
for the racecourse and Somerset County
Cricket Ground. AA 4 Pennants.
Facilities 🛁 🍴 ⏚ 🏠 🔥 🎋 ⊙ 🍴 🔲 ☎
🍴 🔵 🏧 🔵 🝙 🚿
Nearest Town Taunton
Directions Leave the M5 at junction 25, at
first traffic lights turn left, turn third left into
Ilminster Road. At the roundabout turn right,
next roundabout turn left, at the T-Junction
follow brown tourism signs to the site. Total
of 3 miles from the M5.
🚆 Taunton

TAUNTON

Waterrow Touring Park, Waterrow,
Wiveliscombe, Taunton, Somerset, TA4 2AZ
Tel: 01984 623464
Email: info@waterrowpark.co.uk
www.waterrowpark.co.uk

Pitches For Å ⚓ ♨ **Total** 45
Acreage 8 **Open** All Year
Access Good **Site** Landscaped
Nearest Bus Stop (Miles) Outside
EXCLUSIVELY FOR ADULTS. In a peaceful,
attractive location in the Tone Valley with a
woodland river walk. Excellent heated
facilities. Elizabethan cottage (sleeps 3) for
hire. Good pub nearby. Watercolour painting
holidays. Ideal touring base.
Facilities 🛁 🍴 ⏚ 🏠 🔥 🎋 ⊙ 🍴 🔲 ☎
🔵 🝙 🔵 🔵 ✂ 🄰 🝙 📶
Nearest Town Taunton
Directions Leave the M5 at junc 25 and take
the A358 sp Minehead. Then take the B3227
sp Wiveliscombe, 3 miles after Wiveliscombe
you will pass the Rock Pub, the park is on
the left within 300 yards. Do not follow Sat
Nav
🚆 Taunton/Tiverton

WATCHET

Warren Bay Caravan Park, Watchet,
Somerset, TA23 0JR
Tel: 01984 631460
Pitches For Å ⚓ ♨ **Total** 150
Acreage 26 **Open** Easter/1 Apr to Oct
Access Good **Site** Sloping
Nearest Bus Stop (Miles) Outside
We have our own private beach. West
Somerset Railway nearby.
Facilities 🛁 🍴 ⏚ 🏠 🔥 🎋 ⊙ 🍴 🔲 ☎
🍴 🔵 🏧 🝙 🔵 🝙 🔵 🚿
Nearest Town Watchet
Directions On the B3191 between Watchet
and Blue Anchor. 1 mile from Watcheton
right.
🚆 Taunton

WELLINGTON

Cadeside Caravan Club Site, Nynehead Road, Wellington, Somerset, TA21 9HN
Tel: 01823 663103
www.caravanclub.co.uk
Pitches For ⊞ ⊟ **Total** 16
Acreage 4¾ **Open** All Year
Access Good **Site** Level
Nearest Bus Stop (Miles) Outside
Rural site with countryside views. Surrounded by Quantock Hills, Brendon Hills and Blackdown Hills. Non members welcome. Booking essential. Own sanitation required
Facilities ∫ ℓ ⊡ ⊛⊬⊟⊠⚲
Nearest Town Wellington
Directions Leave the M5 at junction 26 and take the A38 signposted Wellington, at roundabout turn onto the B3187 signposted Wellington. After ½ mile turn right signposted Nynehead, site is 80 yards on the right.

WELLINGTON

Gamlins Farm Caravan Park, Gamlins Farmhouse, Greenham, Wellington, Somerset, TA21 0LZ
Tel: 01823 672859
Email: nataliehowe@hotmail.com
www.gamlinsfarmcaravanpark.co.uk
Pitches For ▲ ⊞ ⊟ **Total** 30
Acreage 4 **Open** March **to** End Oct
Access Good **Site** Level
Nearest Bus Stop (Miles) Outside
Scenic valley setting with a Free coarse fishing lake. 45 minutes from the coast. Ideal for touring, Exmoor, Quantocks and The Blackdowns. Static caravans available for hire. You can also telephone us on mobile: 07967 683738.
Facilities ∫ ⊡ ⊞⊡⊟ ⚲⊙⊒ ⊠ 🍽
 ℓ⊛⊡✔ ⚶ ⚶ ❄ 🗢
Directions Take the M5 to junction 26 Wellington, then take the A38 signposted Tiverton and Exeter. On the dual carriageway turn right to Greenham, go over two sets of crossroads, round a bend and the site is on the right. Follow brown tourism signs from J26 for 6 miles to the site.
⊭ Taunton/Tiverton

WELLINGTON

Greenacres Touring Park, Haywards Lane, Chelston, Wellington, Somerset, TA21 9PH
Tel: 01823 652844
Email: enquiries@greenacres-wellington.co.uk
www.greenacres-wellington.co.uk
Pitches For ⊞ ⊟ **Total** 30
Acreage 2½ **Open** Apr **to** Sept
Access Good **Site** Level
Nearest Bus Stop (Miles) ¼
Nr Pub, bus stop, Camping & caravan Leisure shop, fishing, Garden Nurseries.
Facilities ⊙⚡∫ ⊡⊞⊟⚲⊙ 🍽⊬⊟🄰
Nearest Town Wellington
Directions Approx 1 mile to Wellington.
⊭ Taunton

WELLS

Cheddar & Mendip Heights Camping & Caravanning Club Site, Mendip Heights, Townsend, Priddy, Wells, Somerset, BA5 3BP
Tel: 01749 870241
Email: cheddar.site@thefriendlyclub.co.uk
www.campingandcaravanningclub.co.uk/cheddar
Pitches For ▲ ⊞ ⊟ **Total** 90
Acreage 4½ **Open** 15-Mar **to** 05-Nov
Access Good **Site** Lev/Slope
Situated in a designated area of outstanding natural beauty, in the heart of the Mendip Hills. Holiday caravan available for hire. Non members welcome. You can also call us on 0845 130 7633.
Facilities ⊙ ∫ ⊡ ⊞⊡⚲ ⊙⊙⊒ ⊠ 🍽
 ⚶ ⊡ ⊛ ⊠⊟ ⚶ ⚶ ❄
Nearest Town Wells
Directions From Wells take the A39 north east for 3½ miles, then take the B3135 towards Cheddar for 4½ miles. Signposted ¼ mile north west of Priddy.

WELLS

Homestead Park, Wookey Hole, Wells, Somerset, BA5 1BW
Tel: 01749 673022
Email: homesteadpark@onetel.com
www.homesteadpark.co.uk
Pitches For ▲ **Total** 30
Acreage 2 **Open** Easter **to** October
Access Good **Site** Level
Nearest Bus Stop (Miles) Outside
ADULTS ONLY - Sorry no children. TENTS ONLY. Sheltered site on the banks of the River Axe. Ideal for Wookey Hole Caves, National Trust sites, Mendip Hills, walking and climbing. Leisure centre nearby.
Facilities ⊞⊡⚲⊙ 🍽 ⊙ ⊛⊬⊟ 🄰
Directions Leave Wells by A371 towards Cheddar, turn right for Wookey Hole. Site 1¼ miles on the left in the village.
⊭ Bristol/Bath

WESTON-SUPER-MARE

Country View Holiday Park, 29 Sand Road, Sand Bay, Weston-super-Mare, Somerset, BS22 9UJ
Tel: 01934 627595
Email: info@cvhp.co.uk
www.cvhp.co.uk
Pitches For ▲ ⊞ ⊟ **Total** 185
Acreage 10 **Open** March **to** Jan
Access Good **Site** Level
Nearest Bus Stop (Miles) ¼
200 yards from Sand Bay beach. Heated swimming pool and bar on site. Excellent toilet/shower facilities.
Facilities ⊙ ∫ ⊡ ⊞⊡⚲ ⊙⊙⊒ ⊠ 🍽
 ⚶ ⊠ ⚶ ⚵ ⊠ ⚶ ⊛⊟⊟ ⚶ ⚶ ❄ 🗢
Nearest Town Weston-super-Mare
Directions Leave the M5 at junction 21, follow signs to Sand Bay along The Queensway into Lower Norton Lane, turn right into Sand Road.
⊭ Weston-super-Mare

WESTON-SUPER-MARE

Dulhorn Farm Holiday Park, Weston Road, Lympsham, Weston-super-Mare, Somerset, BS24 0JQ
Tel: 01934 750298
Email: dfhp@btconnect.com
www.dulhornfarmholidaypark.co.uk
Pitches For ▲ ⊞ ⊟ **Total** 87
Acreage 3 **Open** March **to** Oct
Access Good **Site** Level
Nearest Bus Stop (Miles) ¼
Quiet family site situated on a working farm in the countryside. Some facilities for the disabled. Ideal touring. Only 5 miles from Weston-super-Mare.
Facilities ⊙ ∫ ⊡ ⊞⊡⚲ ⊙⊙⊒ ⊠ 🍽
 ⚶ ⊡ ⊛ ⊠⊬⊟⊟ ⚶ ⚶ ⚲ ❄
Nearest Town Weston-super-Mare
Directions On the A370, 5 miles from Weston-super-Mare and 4 miles from Burnham-on-Sea.
⊭ Weston-super-Mare

WESTON-SUPER-MARE

Sand Farm, Sand Farm Lane, Sand Bay, Weston-super-Mare, Somerset, BS22 9UF
Tel: 01934 620995
Email: christine.bates@tiscali.co.uk
www.kewstoke.org/stay.htm
Pitches For ▲ ⊞ ⊟ **Total** 11
Acreage 1¼ **Open** Easter **to** Oct
Access Good **Site** Level
Quiet, farm site, 100 yards from the beach. Ideal for touring and walking. Regular (open top) bus service to W-S-M, 2½ miles from the town centre. Static caravans available for hire. Ralleys welcome. Bring Your Horse On Holiday, stables available. You can also contact us on Mobile: 07949 969722.We are motorbike & pet freindly.
Facilities ⊙ ∫ ⊡ ⊞⚲ ⊙ ⊛ ⊬⊟ ⚶
Nearest Town Weston-super-Mare
Directions Leave M5 at junc 21 and head towards W-S-M, then take the slip road for Sand Bay. Follow all signs to Sand Bay until the beach is in front of you, turn right into Beach Road then next right into Sand Farm Lane.
⊭ Weston-super-Mare

WESTON-SUPER-MARE

West End Farm Caravan Park, Laneys Drove, Locking, Weston-super-Mare, Somerset, BS24 8RH
Tel: 01934 822529
Email: robin@westendfarm.org
www.westendcaravan.com
Pitches For ▲ ⊞ ⊟ **Total** 75
Acreage 10 **Open** All Year
Access Good **Site** Level
Nearest Bus Stop (Miles) ½
Just 2½ miles from the beach. Ideal for touring and the Mendips.
Facilities ⊙ ∫ ⊟ ⊡⊞⚲ ⊙ ⊙⊒ ⊠ 🍽
 ⚶ ⊛⊬⊟⊟ ⚶ ❄ 🗢
Nearest Town Weston-super-Mare
Directions Leave the M5 at junction 21 and follow signs for the Helicopter Museum. Turn right after the Helicopter Museum into Laney's Drove.
⊭ Weston-super-Mare

WILLITON

Home Farm Holiday Centre, St Audries Bay, Williton, Somerset, TA4 4DP
Tel: 01984 632487
www.homefarmholidaycentre.co.uk
Pitches For 🅰 ⬛ 🚐 **Total** 40
Open All Year
Access Good **Site** Lev/slope
Nearest Bus Stop (Miles) Outside
Private beach, Secluded Park.
Facilities ⬛ ⬛ ⬛ ⬛ ⬛ ⬛ ⬛ ⬛ ⬛ ⬛
⬛ ⬛ ⬛ ⬛ ⬛ ⬛ ⬛ ⬛ ⬛
Nearest Town Watchet
Directions 17 miles from Bridgewater on A39 to West Quantoxhead B3191 for ½ mile to drive entrance.
🚂 Taunton

WINCANTON

Wincanton Racecourse Caravan Club Site, Wincanton, Somerset, BA9 8BJ
Tel: 01963 34276
www.caravanclub.co.uk
Pitches For 🅰 ⬛ 🚐 **Total** 57
Acreage 5 **Open** Mar **to** Oct
Access Good **Site** Level
Nearest Bus Stop (Miles) ½
Attractive site with beautiful views of Bruton Forest and the Downs. Close to Stourhead House, Hadspen Garden and Haynes Motor Museum. 9 hole Pay & Play golf adjacent, discounts available. Non members welcome. Booking essential.
Facilities
⬛ ⬛ ⬛ ⬛ ⬛ ⬛ ⬛ ⬛ ⬛ ⬛ ⬛ ⬛
Directions From east on the A303 take the B3081 signposted Wincanton Racecourse, follow signs for the racecourse through Charlton Musgrove. At junction turn left signposted racecourse, site is 1½ miles on the right.
🚂 Wincanton

WINSFORD

Halse Farm Caravan & Tent Park, Halse Farm, Winsford, Exmoor, Somerset, TA24 7JL
Tel: 01643 851259
Email: cad@halsefarm.co.uk
www.halsefarm.co.uk
Pitches For 🅰 ⬛ 🚐 **Total** 44

Acreage 3 **Open** Mid Mar **to** Oct
Access Good **Site** Lev/Slope
Nearest Bus Stop (Miles) 1
In Exmoor National Park, on a working farm with beautiful views. Ideal for those who enjoy peaceful countryside. Quality heated toilet block and FREE showers. David Bellamy Gold Award for Conservation and ETC 4 Star Graded.
Facilities ⬛ ⬛ ⬛ ⬛ ⬛ ⬛ ⬛ ⬛ ⬛ ⬛
⬛ ⬛ ⬛ ⬛ ⬛ ⬛ ⬛ ⬛ ⬛
Nearest Town Dulverton
Directions Signposted from the A396 Tiverton to Minehead road. In Winsford take small road in front of Royal Oak Inn. 1 mile up hill and over cattle grid, our entrance is immediately on the left.
🚂 Taunton

STAFFORDSHIRE

ALTON

Alton, The Star Camping & Caravanning Club Site, Star Road, Cotton, Stoke-on-Trent, Staffordshire, ST10 3DW
Tel: 01538 702219
Email: altonstar.site@thefriendlyclub.co.uk
www.campingandcaravanningclub.co.uk
Pitches For 🅰 ⬛ 🚐 **Total** 195
Open 02-Mar **to** 11-Nov
Access Good **Site** Sloping
Nearest Bus Stop (Miles) ¼
Situated in the centre of beautiful countryside within 9 miles of Leek, Uttoxeter and Ashbourne. Close to Alton Towers. Within easy reach of the Peak District and Dovedale. Non members welcome. You can also call us on 0845 130 7633.
Facilities ⬛ ⬛ ⬛ ⬛ ⬛ ⬛ ⬛ ⬛ ⬛ ⬛ ⬛
⬛ ⬛ ⬛ ⬛ ⬛ ⬛ ⬛
Nearest Town Cheadle
Directions From the A52 take the B5417, 1¼ miles from Alton Towers.
🚂 Blyth Bridge

BURTON-ON-TRENT

Willowbrook Farm, Burton Road, Alrewas, Burton-on-Trent, Staffordshire, DE13 7BA
Tel: 01283 790217
Pitches For 🅰 ⬛ 🚐 **Total** 11
Acreage 3 **Open** All Year
Access Good **Site** Level
Nearest Bus Stop (Miles) ½
Close to Twycross Zoo, Drayton Manor Park, Lichfield Cathedral, National Memorial Arboretum and Tamworths Snowdome.
Facilities ⬛ ⬛ ⬛ ⬛ ⬛ ⬛ ⬛ ⬛
Nearest Town Lichfield/B-on-T
Directions On the south bound side of the main A38 Burton-on-Trent and Lichfield road, ½ a mile north of Alrewas.
🚂 Lichfield

CANNOCK

Cannock.chase Camping & Caravanning Club Site, Old Youth Hostel, Wandon, Rugeley, Staffordshire, WS15 1QW
Tel: 01889 582166
Email:
cannock.chase@thefriendlyclub.co.uk
www.campingandcaravanningclub.co.uk/
cannockchase
Pitches For 🅰 ⬛ 🚐 **Total** 60
Acreage 5 **Open** 15-Mar **to** 04-Nov
Site Sloping
On the edge of Cannock Chase. 12 miles from Drayton Manor Park. BTB 4 Star Graded and AA 3 Pennants. Non members welcome. You can also call us on 0845 130 7633.
Facilities ⬛ ⬛ ⬛ ⬛ ⬛ ⬛ ⬛ ⬛ ⬛ ⬛ ⬛
⬛ ⬛ ⬛ ⬛ ⬛ ⬛ ⬛
Directions Take the A460 to Hednesford, turn right at signpost Rawnsley/Hazelslade, then turn first left, site is ½ mile past the golf club.
🚂 Rugeley Town

CHEADLE

Hales Hall Caravan & Camping Park, Oakamoor Road, Cheadle, Staffordshire, ST10 4QR
Tel: 01538 753305
Email:
enquiries@haleshallcaravanandcampingpark.com
www.haleshallcaravanandcampingpark.com

Pitches For 🏕 🚐 🚚 🚙≮ **Total** 50
Acreage 6 **Open** March to October
Access Good **Site** Sloping
Nearest Bus Stop (Miles) Outside
Only 5 miles from Alton Towers.
Facilities 🚰 🚿 ⊞ 🍴 ⌂ ⚊ 🔲 🛒
🛒 🏧 🏪 ♀ 🔦 🏧 🚼 🖼 🛒 🔧 🌿 🐾
Nearest Town Cheadle
Directions 1 mile from Cheadle on the
B5417 en-route to Alton Towers.
🚉 Stoke-on-Trent

LEEK

Blackshaw Moor Caravan Club Site,
Leek, Staffordshire, ST13 8TW
Tel: 01538 300203
www.caravanclub.co.uk
Pitches For 🚐 🚚 **Total** 89
Acreage 8½ **Open** Mar to Jan
Access Good **Site** Level
Nearest Bus Stop (Miles) ¼
Situated on the edge of the Peak District with
lovely views and walks. Just a short walk from
Tittesworth Reservoir & Nature Reserve.
Only 9 miles from Alton Towers. Non
members welcome. Booking essential.
Facilities ♿ 🚰 ⊞ 🍴 ⌂ ⚊ 🔲 🛒
🛒 🏧 🏪 🏧 🚼 🖼 🌿 🌐
Directions From Leek take the A53, site is
on the right ¼ mile past the Three
Horseshoes Inn.
🚉 Leek

LEEK

Glencote Caravan Park, Station Road, Nr
Leek, Staffordshire, ST13 7EE
Tel: 01538 360745
Email: canistay@glencote.co.uk
www.glencote.co.uk
Pitches For 🏕 🚐 🚚 **Total** 70
Acreage 6 **Open** Feb to Dec
Access Good **Site** Level
Nearest Bus Stop (Miles) Outside
Nearest Town Leek
🚉 Stoke-on-Trent

LEEK

Leek Camping & Caravanning Club Site,
Blackshaw Grange, Blackshaw Moor, Leek,
Staffordshire, ST13 8TL
Tel: 01538 300285
Email: leek.site@thefriendlyclub.co.uk
www.campingandcaravanningclub.co.uk/
leek
Pitches For 🏕 🚐 🚚 **Total** 70
Acreage 6 **Open** All Year
Site Lev/Slope
Nearest Bus Stop (Miles) ¼
On the edge of the Peak District. Ideal for
visiting Alton Towers. BTB 4 Star Graded and
AA 3 Pennants. Non members welcome. You
can also call us on 0845 130 7633.
Facilities ♿ 🚰 ⊞ 🍴 ⌂ ⚊ 🔲 🛒
🛒 🏧 🏪 🏧 🚼 🖼 🛒 🌐
Directions Just 2 miles from Leek on the
A53 Leek to Buxton road. The site is located
200 yards past the sign for Blackshaw Moor
on the left hand side.
🚉 Buxton

LICHFIELD

**Cathedral Grange Touring Caravan
Park,** Grange Lane, Lichfield,
Staffordshire, WS13 8HX
Tel: 07980 685093
Pitches For 🏕 🚐 🚚 🚙≮ **Open** All Year
Access Good **Site** Level
Nearest Bus Stop (Miles) ¼
Near to Lichfield Cathedral. Just a short drive
to Drayton Manor Park, Darwin House, a
snowdome and an Odeon. You can also call
us on Mobile: 07966 403938.

Facilities 🚰 ⊞ 🚿 🍴 ⌂ ⚊ 🔲 🛒
Nearest Town Lichfield
Directions From Lichfield take the A51
towards Rugeley, at the traffic lights turn right
onto Eastern Avenue, then turn first left into
Grange Lane.
🚉 Lichfield

LONGNOR

Longnor Wood Holiday Park, Newtown,
Longnor, Near Buxton, Derbys., SK17 0NG
Tel: 01298 83648
Email: info@longnorwood.co.uk
www.longnorwood.co.uk
Pitches For 🏕 🚐 🚚 🚙≮ **Total** 47
Acreage 10½ **Open** Mar to 10-Jan
Access Good **Site** Level
Nearest Bus Stop (Miles) 1¼
ADULTS ONLY PARK surrounded by woods
and set in rolling countryside.
Facilities 🚰 ⊞ 🚿 🍴 ⌂ ⚊ 🔲 🛒
🛒 🏧 🏪 🏧 🚼 🖼 🛒 🅰 🌿 🌐
Nearest Town Buxton
Directions From the village of Longnor,
follow brown tourism caravan signs along the
Leek road.
🚉 Buxton

TAMWORTH

**Drayton Manor Camping and
Caravanning Club Site** Nr Tamworth,
Staffordshire, B78 3TW
Tel: 0845130 7633
Email: enquiries@thefriendlyclub.co.uk
www.campingandcaravanningclub.co.uk/
draytonmanor
Pitches For 🏕 🚐 🚚 **Total** 90
Open 15-Mar to 04-Nov
Access Good **Site** Lev/Slope
Calte Abbey, market town of Tamworth and
its historic castle and Belfry golf course.
Facilities ♿ 🚰 ⊞ 🚿 🍴 ⌂ ⚊ 🔲 🛒
🛒 🏧 🏪 🏧 🚼 🖼 🛒
Nearest Town Tamworth
Directions Turn left towards Drayton Manor
and follow on. Take 5th exit on roundabout.
Stay on A51 until you see city centre signs.
🚉 Wilnecott

UTTOXETER

**Uttoxeter Racecourse Caravan Club
Site,** Wood Lane, Uttoxeter, Staffordshire,
ST14 8BD
Tel: 01889 564172
www.caravanclub.co.uk
Pitches For 🏕 🚐 🚚 **Total** 76
Acreage 3 **Open** Mar to Nov
Access Good **Site** Level
Surrounded by the Weaver Hills. Free
admission to racecourse, bar, betting area,
picnic area and play area. Golf course
adjacent. Close to Alton Towers, Lichfield
Cathedral and Sudbury Hall. Non members
welcome. Booking essential.
Facilities 🚰 ⊞ 🚿 🍴 ⌂ ⚊ 🔲 🛒
🛒 🏧 🏪 🏧 🚼 🖼 🛒 🌿
Directions From the A50 take the A518 sp
Racecourse, site is 1½ miles on the left. Turn
into third gate at Caravan Club sign.
🚉 Uttoxeter

SUFFOLK

BURY ST EDMUNDS

The Dell Touring Park, Beyton Road,
Thurston, Bury St Edmunds, Suffolk, IP31
3RB
Tel: 01359 270121
Email: thedellcaravanpark@btinternet.com
www.thedellcaravanpark.co.uk
Pitches For 🏕 🚐 🚚 **Total** 60
Open All Year

Access Good **Site** Level
Nearest Bus Stop (Miles) Outside
Ideal for touring East Anglia. 1 hour from
Cambridge, Norwich and coast. Free Wi-Fi.
New hard standing pitches. Excellent toilet
blocks.
Facilities ♿ 🚰 ⊞ 🚿 🍴 ⌂ ⚊ 🔲 🛒
🛒 🏧 🏪 🖼 🛒 🔲
Nearest Town Bury St Edmunds
Directions Take A14 eastbound 6 miles from
Bury follow Thurston signs.
🚉 Thurston

DUNWICH

Cliff House Holiday Park, Minsmere
Road, Dunwich, Suffolk, IP17 3DQ
Tel: 01728 648282
Email: info@cliffhouseholidays.co.uk
www.cliffhouseholidays.co.uk
Pitches For 🏕 🚐 🚚 🚙≮ **Total** 120
Acreage 30 **Open** Mar to Oct
Access Good **Site** Level
Cliff top woodland setting with sea views and
direct access to the beach. In an area of
outstanding natural beauty near to Minsmere
Bird Reserve, Southwold and Aldeburgh, and
only 30 miles from Norwich and Ipswich.
Facilities ♿ 🚰 ⊞ 🍴 ⌂ ⚊ 🔲 🛒
🛒 🏧 🏪 ♀ 🔦 🏧 🚼 🖼 🛒 🌿 🌐 🌐
Directions From the A12 north at Yoxford,
turn right to Westleton, at the end turn left,
then turn right to Dunwich. Follow brown
tourism signs to Cliff House.
🚉 Darsham

EYE

Honeypot Caravan & Camping Park,
Wortham, Eye, Suffolk, IP22 1PW
Tel: 01379 783312
Email: honeypotcamping@talk21.com
www.honeypotcamping.co.uk
Pitches For 🏕 🚐 🚚 **Total** 35
Acreage 7 **Open** Mid April to Mid Sept
Access Good **Site** Level
Nearest Bus Stop (Miles) Outside
Highly recommended site with plenty of
peace and quiet. Fishing on site. Discounts
available, please enquire (excludes Bank
Holidays).Celebrating 40 years of the same
family ownership.
Facilities 🚰 ⊞ 🍴 ⌂ ⚊ 🔲 🛒
🛒 🏧 🏪 🗙 🏧 🚼 🖼 🛒 🔧
Directions Four miles south west of Diss,
on the south side of the A143.
🚉 Diss

FELIXSTOWE

Peewit Caravan Park, Walton Avenue,
Felixstowe, Suffolk, IP11 2HB
Tel: 01394 284511
Email: peewitpark@aol.com
www.peewitcaravanpark.co.uk
Pitches For 🏕 🚐 🚚 **Total** 40
Acreage 3 **Open** Easter/1 April to 31-Oct
Access Good **Site** Level
Nearest Bus Stop (Miles) ½
Quiet and secluded setting, 900 metres from
the seafront. Central for North Essex and
coastal Suffolk.
Facilities ♿ 🚰 ⊞ 🍴 ⌂ ⚊ 🔲 🛒
🛒 🏧 🏪 🖼 🛒 🔲
Directions Take the A14 to Felixstowe
Docks, at Gate No.1 turn towards the town
centre, site is 100 metres on the left.

HADLEIGH

**Polstead Camping & Caravanning Club
Site,** Holt Road, Bower House Tye,
Polstead, Suffolk, CO6 5BZ
Tel: 01787 211969
Email: polstead.site@thefriendlyclub.co.uk

www.campingandcaravanningclub.co.uk/
polstead
Pitches For ▲ ⬚ ⬚ **Total** 60
Acreage 4½ **Open** 14-Feb **to** 14-Jan
Access Good **Site** Level
Nearest Bus Stop (Miles) ½
On the edge of a beautiful conservation area.
Near to Long Melford, Sudbury and the Stour
Valley where Constable's Flatford Mill can be
found. Non members welcome. You can also
call us on 0845 130 7633.
Facilities ∤ 🖻 🕾 🖻 🖙 🖍 ⊙ 😄 🖮 🖪
😂 🖰 🕾 🖃 🕾 ☎ 🖤
Nearest Town Hadleigh
Directions From the A134, A14 or A12 join
the A1071 (Hadleigh road). Site is in Polstead
Heath off Holt Road.
🚶 Sudbury

IPSWICH

Low House Touring Caravan Centre,
Low House, Bucklesham Road, Foxhall,
Ipswich, Suffolk, IP10 0AU
Tel: 01473 659437
Email: low.house@btinternet.com
www.tourbritain.com
Pitches For ⬚ ⬚ **Total** 30
Acreage 3½ **Open** All Year
Access Good **Site** Level
Camp in a beautiful garden packed with
ornamental trees and plants, arches and
bower doves, rabbits, bantams and guinea
fowl. Wildlife all around. Ornamental Tree
Walk and Pets Corner. New friendly wardens.
Heated toilet and shower block.
Facilities ∤ 🖷 🖍 ⊙ 🖪
🖎 🖰 🕾 🖪 🖮 🖃 🖪 🖃 🕾
Nearest Town Ipswich
Directions Turn off A14 Ipswich Ring Road
(South) via slip road onto A1156 (sp East
Ipswich). In 1 mile turn right (signposted), in
½ mile turn right sp Low House, site is on
the left in ¼ mile.
🚶 Ipswich

KESSINGLAND

**Kessingland Camping & Caravanning
Club Site,** Whites Lane, Kessingland, Nr
Lowestoft, Suffolk, NR33 7TF
Tel: 01502 742040
Email:
kessingland.site@thefriendlyclub.co.uk
www.campingandcaravanningclub.co.uk/
kessingland
Pitches For ▲ ⬚ ⬚ **Total** 90
Acreage 5 **Open** 21-Mar **to** 04-Nov
Access Good **Site** Level
Nearest Bus Stop (Miles) ½
Next to Suffolk Wildlife Park. Set in a quiet
seaside resort, close to Great Yarmouth. 5
miles from Pleasurewood Hills. BTB 4 Star
Graded, AA 4 Pennants and Loo of the Year
Award. Non members welcome. You can also
call us on 0845 130 7633.
Facilities ⛫ ∤ 🖷 🖍 ⊙ 😄 🖮 🖪 🖤
🖎 🖰 🖪 🕾 🖮 🖃 🖪
Nearest Town Lowestoft
Directions From Lowestoft on the A12, leave
at roundabout in Kessingland following
Wildlife Park signs. Turn right through park
entrance.
🚶 Lowestoft

LEISTON

Beach View holiday Park, Sizewell
Common, Leiston, Suffolk, IP16 4TU
Tel: 01728 830724
Email:
enquiries@beachviewholidaypark.co.uk
www.beachviewholidaypark.co.uk
Pitches For ▲ ⬚ ⬚ **Total** 60
Acreage 17 **Open** 15-Mar **to** 30-Nov

Access Good **Site** Level
On the beach. Sea fishing from a private
beach. Ideal for bird watching, shore fishing,
walking and cycling.
Facilities ∤ 🖷 🖍 ⊙ 😄 🖮 🖪 🖤
😂 🖰 🕾 🖋 🖓 🖪 🖮 🖃 🖪 🕾 🖤
Nearest Town Leiston
Directions From Leiston take the turning to
Sizewell Beach (2 miles), turn right sp
Sizewell Hall, before the entrance gates to
the Hall turn left to Cliff House.
🚶 Saxmundham

LOWESTOFT

**Beach Farm Residential & Holiday Park
Ltd.,** Arbor Lane, Pakefield, Lowestoft,
Suffolk, NR33 7BD
Tel: 01502 572794
Email: beachfarmpark@aol.com
www.beachfarmpark.com
Pitches For ⬚ ⬚ **Total** 2
Acreage ¼ **Open** Mar **to** 02-Jan
Access Good **Site** Level
Nearest Bus Stop (Miles) ¼
Beach 500 yards, Africa alive 2 miles.
Facilities ∤ 🖷 🖍 ⊙ 😄 🖮 🖪 🖤
🖎 🖰 🖋 🖓 🖻 ⏣ 🖮 🖃 🖪 🕾 🖤
Nearest Town Lowestoft
Directions Follow A12 Ipswich to main
roundabout (water Tower) 2 miles Pakefield.
🚶 Lowestoft

LOWESTOFT

Chestnut Farm, Gisleham, Lowestoft,
Suffolk, NR33 8EE
Tel: 01502 740227
Pitches For ▲ ⬚ ⬚ **Total** 40
Acreage 3 **Open** April **to** Oct
Access Good **Site** Level
Sheltered country meadow site. 2 miles from
Kessingland Beach.
Facilities ∤ 🖷 🖍 ⊙ 🖤
Nearest Town Lowestoft
Directions Turn off the A12 at Kessingland
bypass southern roundabout sp Rushmere,
Mutford and Gisleham. The farm drive is
second on the left after ¾ miles.
🚶 Oulton Broad

LOWESTOFT

Heathland Beach Caravan Park Ltd.,
London Road, Kessingland, Lowestoft,
Suffolk, NR33 7PJ
Tel: 01502 740337
Email: heathlandbeach@btinternet.com
www.heathlandbeach.co.uk
Pitches For ▲ ⬚ ⬚ **Total** 63
Acreage 5 **Open** Apr **to** Oct
Access Good **Site** Level
Nearest Bus Stop (Miles) Outside
Privately owned park surrounded by
countryside. Beach access.
Facilities ⛫ ∤ 🖷 🖍 ⊙ 😄 🖮 🖪 🖤
😂 🖰 🕾 🖋 🖓 ⏣ 🖪 🖮 🖃 🖪 🖋 🕾
Nearest Town Lowestoft
Directions 3 miles south of Lowestoft off the
old A12, take the B1437.
🚶 Lowestoft

SAXMUNDHAM

Whitearch Touring Park, Main Road,
Benhall, Saxmundham, Suffolk, IP17 1NA
Tel: 01728 604646
www.caravancampingsites.co.uk
Pitches For ▲ ⬚ ⬚ **Total** 50
Acreage 14½ **Open** Apr **to** Oct
Access Good **Site** Level
Nearest Bus Stop (Miles) ¼
Fishing and tennis on site. No cycling on site.
Near the Suffolk coast, Snape Maltings
Concert Hall, Minsmere Bird Reserve,

American Theme Park and castles.
Facilities ⛫ ∤ 🖷 🖍 ⊙ 😄 🖮 🖪 🖤
😂 🖰 🖋 🖻 🖃 🕾
Nearest Town Saxmundham
Directions Just off the main A12 junction
with the B1121 at the Ipswich end of
Saxmundham by-pass.
🚶 Saxmundham

SHOTLEY

Shotley Caravan Park, Gate Farm Road,
Shotley, Suffolk, IP9 1QH
Tel: 01473 787421
www.shotleycaravanpark.com
Pitches For ⬚ ⬚
Acreage 7 **Open** Mar **to** Oct
Access Good **Site** Lev/Slope
Nearest Bus Stop (Miles) Outside
ADULTS ONLY SITE. Enjoy peace and
tranquillity in this area of outstanding natural
beauty, with panoramic views over the River
Orwell. Large pond with ducks. Free eggs
from our chickens for all caravanners. Ideal
site for the over 50s. Tourers/rallies welcome.
Close to a marina, restaurants, pubs, fish &
chips, church, doctors and garage. Easy
access from the A12/A14.
Facilities ∤ 🖷 🖍 🖪 🖮 🖃 🖪 🕾 🔧
Nearest Town Ipswich/Felixstowe
Directions From Orwell Bridge take exit
A137 and follow the B1456 once in Shotley
(10 miles from Ipswich). Go past the Rose
Pub on the right and after 1 mile turn left into
Gate Farm Road and go through the green
gates.
🚶 Ipswich

STOWMARKET

Stonham Barns Holiday Park, Pettaugh
Road, Stonham Aspal, Stowmarket,
Suffolk, IP14 6AT
Tel: 01449 711901
Email:
enquiries@stonhambarnsleisure.co.uk
www.starglade leisure.co.uk
Pitches For ⬚ ⬚ ⬚ ⏚ **Total** 60
Acreage 3 **Open** All Year
Access Good **Site** Level
Nearest Bus Stop (Miles) ¼
Excellent facilities for all the family. Ideal for
exploring the beautiful Suffolk countryside.
Golf course, shops, restaurant, showground
and owl sanctuary all on site. Quiet areas
available. Large groups welcome.Fishing
lakes on site.
Facilities ⛫ ∤ 🖷 🖍 ⊙ 😄 🖮 🖪 🖤
😂 🖰 🖋 🖓 🖃 🖮 🖃 🕾
Nearest Town Bury St Edmunds
Directions From the A14 between Ipswich
and Stowmarket, leave at Junction 51, at the
roundabout take the third exit onto the A140,
then turn right onto the A1120 to Stonham
Aspal.
🚶 Stowmarket

SUDBURY

Willowmere Caravan Park, Bures Road,
Little Cornard, Sudbury, Suffolk, CO10
0NN
Tel: 01787 375559/310422
Email: awillowmere@aol.com
Pitches For ▲ ⬚ ⬚ **Total** 40
Acreage 2 **Open** Easter **to** 01-Oct
Access Good **Site** Level
Nearest Bus Stop (Miles) Outside
Quiet country park near a river.
Facilities ∤ 🖷 🖍 ⊙ 😄 🖤 🖰 🕾 🖮 🖋
Nearest Town Sudbury
Directions Leave Sudbury on the B1508 to
Bures and Colchester, 1 mile from Sudbury.
🚶 Sudbury

THEBERTON

Cakes & Ale, Abbey Lane, Theberton, Suffolk, IP16 4TE
Tel: 01728 831655
Email: cakesandalepark@gmail.com
www.cakesandale.co.uk
Pitches For ▲ 🚐 🚙 ≣≋ **Total** 170
Open Apr **to** Oct
Access Good **Site** Level
Nearest Bus Stop (Miles) 1
Central to Suffolk Heritage coast.
Facilities ...
Nearest Town Aldeburgh
⇌ Saxmundham

WOODBRIDGE

Moon and Sixpence, Newbourne Road, Waldringfield, Woodbridge, Suffolk, IP12 4PP
Tel: 01473 736650
Email: info@moonandsixpence.eu
www.moonandsixpence.eu
Pitches For ▲ 🚐 🚙 **Total** 75
Acreage 5 **Open** Apr **to** Oct
Access Good **Site** Level
Nearest Bus Stop (Miles) Outside
Picturesque location. Sheltered, terraced site. Own private lake and sandy beach. Compact 9 hole golf course, 3 hard tennis courts and volley ball/basket ball courts.
Facilities ...
Nearest Town Woodbridge
Directions Turn off A12, Ipswich Eastern By-Pass, onto unclassified road signposted Waldringfield, Newbourn. Follow caravan direction signs.
⇌ Woodbridge

SURREY

CHERTSEY

Chertsey Camping & Caravanning Club Site, Bridge Road, Chertsey, Surrey, KT16 8JX
Tel: 01932 562405
Email: chertsey.site@thefriendlyclub.co.uk
www.campingandcaravanningclub.co.uk/chertsey
Pitches For ▲ 🚐 🚙 **Total** 200
Acreage 12 **Open** All Year
Site Level
Nearest Bus Stop (Miles) 1
On the banks of the River Thames, fishing on site. Table tennis on site. 4 miles from Thorpe Park. Close to London. BTB 4 Star Graded and AA 4 Pennants. Non members welcome. You can also call us on 0845 130 7633.
Facilities ...
Directions Leave the M25 at junction 11 and follow the A317 to Chertsey. At the roundabout take the first exit to the traffic lights and go straight across to the next set of traffic lights, turn right and after 400 yards turn left into the site.
⇌ Chertsey

HORSLEY

Horsley Camping & Caravanning Club Site, Ockham Road North, East Horsley, Surrey, KT24 6PE
Tel: 01483 283273
Email: horsley.site@thefriendlyclub.co.uk
www.campingandcaravanningclub.co.uk/horsley
Pitches For ▲ 🚐 🚙 **Total** 130

Acreage 10½ **Open** 21-Mar **to** 04-Nov
Access Good **Site** Level
Nearest Bus Stop (Miles) 1
Peaceful site, only 40 minutes from London by train. Fishing lake on site. Non members welcome. You can also call us on 0845 130 7633.
Facilities ...
Nearest Town Guildford
Directions Leave the M25 at junction 10 and travel south on the A3. Turn left onto the B2039, the site is the fourth turning on the right.
⇌ East Horsley

LALEHAM

Laleham Camping Club, Laleham Park, Thameside, Laleham, Middlesex, TW18 1SS
Tel: 01932 564149
Email: lalehamcampingclub@gmail.com
www.lalehamcampingclub.co.uk
Pitches For ▲ 🚐 🚙 **Total**
Open Apr **to** 01-Oct
Access Good **Site** Level
Nearest Bus Stop (Miles) ½
Alongside the River Thames.
Facilities ...
Nearest Town Staines
⇌ Staines

LINGFIELD

Long Acres Caravan & Camping Park, Newchapel Road, Lingfield, Surrey, RH7 6LE
Tel: 01342 833205
Email: longacrescamping@yahoo.co.uk
www.longacrescamping.co.uk
Pitches For ▲ 🚐 🚙 **Total** 60
Acreage 7 **Open** All Year
Access Good **Site** Level
Nearest Bus Stop (Miles) ½
Ideal for visiting London, Surrey, Kent, Sussex, Hever Chartwell, Ardingly Showground, Wakehurst Place and many other attractions.
Facilities ...
Nearest Town East Grinstead
Directions From the M25 junc 6 take the A22 south towards East Grinstead. At Newchapel roundabout turn left onto the B2028 to Lingfield, site is 700 yards on the right.
⇌ Lingfield

REDHILL

Alderstead Heath Caravan Club Site, Dean Lane, Redhill, Merstham, Surrey, RH1 3AH
Tel: 01737 644629
www.caravanclub.co.uk
Pitches For ▲ 🚐 🚙 **Total** 150
Acreage 30 **Open** All Year
Access Good **Site** Level
Nearest Bus Stop (Miles) ½
Quiet, level pitched site which drops into rolling wooded countryside, and has wonderful views of the North Downs. Close to Wisley Gardens, NT Chartwell, Thorpe Park and Chessington World of Adventure. Non members welcome. Booking essential.
Facilities ...
Nearest Town Redhill
Directions Leave M25 at junc 8 take A217 signposted Reigate, after 300yds fork left signposted Merstham. At T-junc turn left onto A23, after ½ mile turn right into Shepherds Hill signposted Caterham, after 1 mile turn left into Dean Lane site in ½ mile
⇌ Redhill

SUSSEX (EAST)

BATTLE

Battle Normanhurst Court Caravan Club Site, Stevens Crouch, Battle, East Sussex, TN33 9LR
Tel: 01424 773808
www.caravanclub.co.uk
Pitches For 🚐 🚙 **Total** 149
Acreage 18 **Open** Mar **to** Oct
Access Good **Site** Lev/Slope
Set in a former garden with splendid trees and shrubs, and lovely views of the Downs. Close to Battle Abbey, Hastings, Rye and Sussex vineyards. Non members welcome. Booking essential.
Facilities ...
Nearest Town Battle
Directions From the A269 in Ninfield take the B2204 signposted Battle. Just past Catsfield keep left, after 1¼ miles turn left onto the A271 signposted Eastbourne, site is ½ mile on the left.
⇌ Battle

BATTLE

Brakes Coppice Park, Forewood Lane, Crowhurst, East Sussex, TN33 9AB
Tel: 01424 830322
Email: brakesco@btinternet.com
www.brakescoppicepark.co.uk
Pitches For ▲ 🚐 🚙 **Total** 30
Acreage 3¼ **Open** March **to** October
Access Good **Site** Sloping
Nearest Bus Stop (Miles) 1
Secluded, 11 acre woodland park with level pitches. TV aerial point to serviced pitches.
Facilities ...
Directions Turn right off the A2100 (Battle to Hastings road) 2 miles from Battle. Follow signs to Crowhurst, 1¼ miles turn left into site.
⇌ Crowhurst

BATTLE

Crazy Lane Tourist Park, Whydown Farm, Crazy Lane, Sedlescombe, East Sussex, TN33 0QT
Tel: 01424 870147
www.crazylane.co.uk
Pitches For ▲ 🚐 🚙 **Total** 36
Acreage 3 **Open** March **to** Oct
Access Good **Site** Level
Nearest Bus Stop (Miles) Outside
15 minutes to the beach. Ideal for the countryside and Hastings. NEW shower and toilet block.
Facilities ...
Nearest Town Battle/Hastings
Directions Travelling south on A21, turn left into Crazy Lane, 100 yds past junction A21/B2244, opposite Black Brooks Garden Centre.
⇌ Battle

BATTLE

Senlac Wood, Catsfield Road, Catsfield, Nr Battle, East Sussex, TN33 9LN
Tel: 01424 773969
Email: senlacwood@xlninternet.co.uk
www.senlacwood.co.uk
Pitches For ▲ 🚐 🚙 **Total** 50
Acreage 10 **Open** March **to** Oct
Access Good **Site** Level
Nearest Bus Stop (Miles) Outside
In a woodland setting with walks and fishing nearby. Ideal for touring this historic 1066 country. Approx. 7 miles from the beach.

Facilities ⌁ 🏠 ⚅ 📶 📵 ☺ 🍴
🏪 🔥 ⊙ 🚿 🚻 🛁 ➡📵 ⧖ ⚡ 📶
Nearest Town Battle
Directions From Battle take the A271 North Trade Road, after about 2½ miles turn left onto the B2204. Site is on the left in ½ a mile.
⚓ Battle

BEXHILL-ON-SEA

Cobbs Hill Farm Caravan & Camping Park, Watermill Lane, Bexhill-on-sea, East Sussex, TN39 5JA
Tel: 01424 213460
Email: cobbshillfarmuk@hotmail.com
www.cobbshillfarm.co.uk
Pitches For ⚑ 🚚 🚐 ➡ ⊏ Total 55
Acreage 17½ **Open** Apr **to** Oct
Access Good **Site** Level
Situated on a small farm in quiet countryside with a network of footpaths leading from the Park. Spacious play area and an animal viewing area. Two static caravans available for hire.
Facilities ⚓ ⌁ 🏠 ⚅ 📵 ☺ 🍴 ⊙ ⧖ ⚡ 📵 📶
🏪 🔥 ⊙ 📵 ⊛ ➡📵 ⧖ ⚡ 📶
Nearest Town Bexhill-on-Sea
Directions Signposted off the A269. Turn into Watermill Lane and the Site is 1 mile on the left.
⚓ Bexhill-on-Sea

BEXHILL-ON-SEA

Kloofs Caravan Park, Sandhurst Lane, Bexhill-on-sea, East Sussex, TN39 4RG
Tel: 01424 842839
Email: camping@kloofs.com
www.kloofs.com
Pitches For ⚑ 🚚 🚐 Total 62
Acreage 22 **Open** All Year
Access Good **Site** Level
Quiet, tranquil, rural park only 2 miles from the beach. USRV's upto 40'.
Facilities ⚓ ⌁ 🏠 ⚅ 📶 📵 ☺ 🍴 ⊙ ⧖ ⚡ 📵 📶
🏪 🔥 ⊙ 📵 ➡📵 📵 ⧖ 📶
Nearest Town Bexhill-on-Sea
Directions From the A259 at the Bexhill/Little Common roundabout turn into Peartree Lane, go up the hill to the crossroads and turn left into Whydown Road, Sandhurst Lane is 300 metres on the left.
⚓ Cooden Beach

BRIGHTON

Brighton Valley Caravan Club Site, East Brighton Park, Brighton, BN2 5TS
Tel: 01273 626546
www.caravanclub.co.uk
Pitches For ⚑ 🚚 🚐 Total 169
Acreage 17 **Open** All Year
Access Good **Site** Level
Nearest Bus Stop (Miles) ½
Situated in the South Downs, adjacent to recreation grounds. Only 2 miles from Brighton with its beach, pier, Royal Pavilion, sea life centre, boutiques and seafront attractions. Non members welcome. Booking essential.
Facilities ⚓ ⌁ 🏠 ⚅ 📶 📵 ☺ 🍴
🔥 🏪 📵 ➡📵 📵 📶
Nearest Town Brighton
Directions From A27 take B2123 signed Falmer, at lights by Downs Hotel t rt into Warren Rd. At next lights t lt into Wilson Avenue, cross the racecourse at 1¼ miles t lt at foot of hill (last turn before the lights) into East Brighton Park, site is ½ mile on lt.
⚓ Brighton

CROWBOROUGH

Crowborough Camping & Caravanning Club Site, Goldsmith Recreation Ground, Crowborough, East Sussex, TN6 2TN
Tel: 01892 664827
Email:
crowborough.site@thefriendlyclub.co.uk
www.campingandcaravanningclub.co.uk/crowborough
Pitches For ⚑ 🚚 🚐 Total 90
Acreage 13 **Open** 21-Mar **to** 04-Nov
Site Lev/Slope
Nearest Bus Stop (Miles) Outside
On the edge of Ashdown Forest. Adjacent to a sports centre. Kitchen available at extra charge. BTB 4 Star Graded and AA 3 Pennants. Non members welcome. You can also call us on 0845 130 7633.
Facilities ⚓ ⌁ 🏠 ⚅ 📵 ☺ 🍴 ⊙ ⧖ ⚡ 📵 📶
🏪 🔥 ⊙ 📵 ➡📵 📵 ⧖ 📶
Directions Take the A26 turn off into the entrance to Goldsmiths Ground signposted leisure centre, at the top of the road turn right into site lane.
⚓ Jarvis Brook

EASTBOURNE

Fairfields Farm Caravan & Camping Park, Eastbourne Road, Westham, Pevensey, East Sussex, BN24 5NG
Tel: 01323 763165
Email: enquiries@fairfieldsfarm.com
www.fairfieldsfarm.com
Pitches For ⚑ 🚚 🚐 Total 60
Acreage 3 **Open** Apr **to** Oct
Access Good **Site** Level
Nearest Bus Stop (Miles) ¼
2 miles from the beach and 3 miles from Eastbourne town centre.
Facilities ⚓ ⌁ 🏠 ⚅ 📵 ☺ 🍴 ⊙ ⧖ ⚡ 📵 📶
🏪 🔥 ⊙ ➡📵 📵 📵 ➡ 🔥
Nearest Town Eastbourne
Directions On the B2191 in the village of Westham. 3 miles east of Eastbourne.
⚓ Pevensey & Westham

HORAM

Horam Manor Touring Park, Horam, Nr Heathfield, East Sussex, TN21 0YD
Tel: 01435 813662
Email: camping@horam-manor.co.uk
www.horam-manor.co.uk
Pitches For ⚑ 🚚 🚐 Total 90
Acreage 7 **Open** Mar **to** Oct
Access Good **Site** Lev/Slope
Nearest Bus Stop (Miles) ¼
A tranquil rural setting, but with plenty to do on the estate, and many places to visit.
Facilities ⚓ ⌁ 🏠 ⚅ 📵 ☺ 🍴 ⊙ ⧖ ⚡ 📵 📶
🏪 🔥 ⊙ 📵 ➡📵 📵 📶
Nearest Town Heathfield/Eastbourne
Directions On A267, 3 miles south of Heathfield, 10 miles north of Eastbourne.
⚓ Eastbourne/Polegate

HORAM

Woodland View Touring Park, Horebeech Lane, Horam, Heathfield, East Sussex, TN21 0HR
Tel: 01435 813597
Pitches For ⚑ 🚚 🚐 Total 25
Acreage 2 **Open** March **to** Nov
Access Good **Site** Sloping
Nearest Bus Stop (Miles) ¼
Next to the Cuckoo Trail.
Facilities ⌁ ⚅ 📵 ☺ 🍴 ⊙ ⧖ 📵 📶 ⧖ 📵🔥
Nearest Town Eastbourne/Polegate
Directions ¼ of a mile off the A267.
⚓ Eastbourne/Polegate

PEVENSEY

Normans Bay Camping & Caravanning Club Site, Normans Bay, Pevensey, East Sussex, BN24 6PR
Tel: 01323 761190
Email:
normans.baysite@thefriendlyclub.co.uk
www.campingandcaravanningclub.co.uk/normansbay
Pitches For ⚑ 🚚 🚐 Total 200
Acreage 13 **Open** 21-Mar **to** 04-Nov
Access Good **Site** Level
Nearest Bus Stop (Miles) ½
Site has its own beach and is close to where the Normans landed. BTB 4 Star Graded and AA 3 Pennants. Non members welcome. You can also call us on 0845 130 7633.
Facilities ⚓ ⌁ 🏠 ⚅ 📵 ☺ 🍴 ⊙ ⧖ ⚡ 📵 📶
🏪 🔥 ⊙ 📵 ➡📵 📵 ⧖ 📶
Nearest Town Pevensey
Directions From the A259 in Pevensey Bay Village take the first turn left (coast road) signed Beachlands only. After 1¼ miles site is on the left hand side.
⚓ Normans Bay

ROBERTSBRIDGE

Park Farm Camp Site, Bodiam, Robertsbridge, East Sussex, TN32 5XA
Tel: 01580 831982
Email: info@parkfarmcamping.co.uk
www.parkfarmcamping.co.uk
Pitches For ⚑ 🚚 🚐 Total 180
Acreage 18 **Open** Apr **to** Oct
Access Good **Site** Level
Nearest Bus Stop (Miles) 1
Alongside the River Rother in a beautiful area. Within walking distance of the pub and Bodiam Castle. Camp fires allowed. 10 miles to beach
Facilities ⌁ 🏠 ⚅ 📵 ☺ 🍴 ⊙ ⧖ 🍴
🔥 📵 ➡📵 📵 ⧖ 📶
Nearest Town Hawkhurst
Directions 3 miles south of Hawkhurst on the B2244. 3 miles north of Sedlescombe.
⚓ Robertsbridge

UCKFIELD

Heaven Farm, Furners Green, Uckfield, East Sussex, TN22 3RG
Tel: 01825 790226
Email: heavenfarmleisure@btinternet.com
www.heavenfarm.co.uk
Pitches For ⚑ 🚚 🚐 ⊏ Total 30
Acreage 4 **Open** All Year
Access Good **Site** Lev/Slope
Nearest Bus Stop (Miles) 1
Farm museum, The Stable Reataurant & Tea Rooms, nature trail. Ideal for National Trust gardens, Bluebell Railway and Brighton. Booking is essential. Granery Flowers and gift shop.
Facilities ⚓ ⌁ 🏠 ⚅ 📵 ☺ 🍴 🔥 🏪 ✕ 🔧
Nearest Town Uckfield
Directions On the A275 between East Grinstead (A22) and Haywards Heath (A272).
⚓ Haywards Heath

UCKFIELD

Honeys Green Caravan Park, Easons Green, Halland, Uckfield, East Sussex, TN22 5GJ
Tel: 01732 860205
Email: honeysgreenpark@tiscali.co.uk
Pitches For Å ⊕ ⊕ **Total** 22
Acreage 17 **Open** All year
Access Good **Site** Level
Nearest Bus Stop (Miles) ¼
Small, peaceful, rural park in a pretty wooded location with our own coarse fishing lake. Lovely walks nearby.
Facilities f 🖰 🖼 🖀 ⌐ ☺ ↵ ♨
🎕 🖀 🖫 ✔ 🖪 ✔ ☀
Nearest Town Uckfield
Directions On the A22, 3 miles south of Uckfield at the Halland roundabout take the B2192 signposted Blackboys/Heathfield, Park is a few hundred yards on the left.
⇌ Uckfield

WINCHELSEA

Rye Bay Caravan Park, Pett Level Road, Winchelsea Beach, East Sussex, TN36 4NE
Tel: 01797 226340
Pitches For Å ⊕ ⊕ **Total** 40
Open Whitsun **to** Mid Sept
Access Good **Site** Fairly Level
Nearest Bus Stop (Miles) Outside
Near the beach.
Facilities f 🖰 🖼 ⊙ ☺ ♨
🎕 🖀 ♀ 🖫 ⊠ 🅰 ✔ 🖪
Nearest Town Hastings
Directions 3 miles west of Rye and 7 miles east of Hastings.
⇌ Rye

SUSSEX (WEST)
ARUNDEL

Maynards Caravan & Camping Park, Crossbush, Arundel, West Sussex, BN18 9PQ
Tel: 01903 882075
Pitches For Å ⊕ ⊕ **Total** 70
Acreage 3 **Open** All Year
Access Good **Site** Level
Nearest Bus Stop (Miles) Outside
3 miles from a sandy beach. Near Arundel Castle and Wild Fowl Reserve.
Facilities ⅙ f 🖰 🖼 ⌐ ⊙ ☺ ♨ 🎕 🖀 🅰 ✔ 🖪
Nearest Town Arundel
Directions Just off the main A27, turn into the Beefeater Restaurant car park.
⇌ Arundel

ARUNDEL

Ship & Anchor Marina, Heywood & Bryett Ltd, Ford, Arundel, West Sussex, BN18 0BJ
Tel: 01243 551262
Email:
enquiries@shipandanchormarina.co.uk
Pitches For Å ⊕ ⊕ **Total** 160
Acreage 12 **Open** Mar **to** Oct
Access Good **Site** Level
Beside the River Arun with a public house on site. 3 miles to beaches. Advance booking is advisable for hook-ups and groups.
Facilities f 🖰 🖼 ⌐ ⊙ ☺ ♨
🎕 🖀 🖀 ⊠ ✕ ♀ 🅰 ✔ 🖪 ☀
Nearest Town Arundel/Littlehampton
Directions From the A27 at Arundel, follow road signposted to Ford for 2 miles. Site is on the left after level-crossing at Ford.
⇌ Ford

BILLINGHURST

Limeburners (Camping) Ltd., Lordings Road, Newbridge, Billinghurst, West Sussex, RH14 9JA
Tel: 01403 782311
Email: chippy.sawyer@virgin.net
Pitches For Å ⊕ ⊕ ⊕⁴ **Total** 40
Open Apr **to** Oct
Access Good **Site** Level
Nearest Bus Stop (Miles) 1½
Attached to a public house.
Facilities f 🖼 🖀 ⌐ ⊙ ☺ ♨
🖀 ✕ ♀ 🅰 ✔ 🖪 🖪
Nearest Town Billinghurst
Directions 1½ miles west of Billinghurst on the A272, turn left onto the B2133, Park is 500 yards on the right.
⇌ Billinghurst

BOGNOR REGIS

Rowan Park Caravan Club Site, Rowan Way, Bognor Regis, West Sussex, PO22 9RP
Tel: 01243 828515
www.caravanclub.co.uk
Pitches For Å ⊕ ⊕ **Total** 94
Acreage 8 **Open** Mar **to** Nov
Access Good **Site** Level
Nearest Bus Stop (Miles) ½
2 miles from the beach, South Coast World and a leisure centre. Close to Weald & Downland Open Air Museum, D-Day Museum & Battle of Britain Aviation and Amberley Chalk Pits Museum. Non members welcome. Booking essential.
Facilities f 🖰 🖼 🖀 ⌐ ☺ ♨
🎕 🖀 🖀 🅰 ✔ 🖪 🖪 ☀ ☂
Nearest Town Bognor Regis
Directions From north on the A29, ½ mile past Shripney Village at the roundabout turn right into Rowan Way, site is 100 yards on the right, opposite Halfords.
⇌ Bognor Regis

CHICHESTER

Bell Caravan Park, Bell Lane, Birdham, Nr Chichester, West Sussex, PO20 7HY
Tel: 01243 512264
Pitches For ⊕ ⊕ **Total** 15
Acreage ¼ **Open** March **to** October
Access Good **Site** Level
Nearest Bus Stop (Miles) ¼
Facilities f 🖼 🖀 ⌐ ♨ 🎕 🖀 🅰 ✔ 🖪
Nearest Town Chichester
Directions From Chichester take the A286 towards Wittering for approx. 4 miles. At Birdham turn left into Bell Lane, site is 500yds on the left.
⇌ Chichester

CHICHESTER

Chichester Camping & Caravanning Club Site, Main Road, Southbourne, Hampshire, PO10 8JH
Tel: 01243 373202
Email:
chichester.site@thefriendlyclub.co.uk
www.campingandcaravanningclub.co.uk/chichester
Pitches For Å ⊕ ⊕ **Total** 58
Acreage 3 **Open** 07-Feb **to** 18-Nov
Access Good **Site** Level
Nearest Bus Stop (Miles) outside
500 yards through a footpath to the beach. Ideal touring, well placed for visiting the Sussex Downs and south coast resorts. Close to the City of Portsmouth. BTB 3 Star Graded and AA 3 Pennants. Non members welcome. You can also call us on 0845 130 7633.

Facilities ⅙ f 🖰 🖼 🖀 ⌐ ⊙ ☺ ♨ 🖪
🎕 🖀 🖀 ✔ 🖪 🖪 ☂
Nearest Town Chichester
Directions On the A259 from Chichester, site is on the right past Inlands Road.
⇌ Southbourne

CHICHESTER

Ellscott Park, Sidlesham Lane, Birdham, Chichester, West Sussex, PO20 7QL
Tel: 01243 512003
Email: camping@ellscottpark.co.uk
www.ellscottpark.co.uk
Pitches For Å ⊕ ⊕ **Total** 50
Acreage 3 **Open** 01-Apr **to** Mid Oct
Access Good **Site** Level
Nearest Bus Stop (Miles) ¼
The famous West Wittering beach. 1½ miles from Chichester Harbour for yachting and boating. Ideal site for walking, cycling and sight-seeing.
Facilities ⅙ f 🖼 🖀 ⌐ ⊙ ☺ ♨
🎕 🅰 ✔ 🖪 🖪 ☀ ☀
Nearest Town Chichester
Directions From the A27 Chichester by-pass turn south onto the A286 towards Witterings. Travel for approx. 4 miles then turn left towards Butterfly Farm, site is 500 metres on the right.
⇌ Chichester

CHICHESTER

Red House Farm, Earnley, Chichester, West Sussex, PO20 7JG
Tel: 01243 512959
Email: bookings@rhfcamping.co.uk
www.rhfcamping.co.uk
Pitches For Å ⊕ ⊕ **Total** 50
Acreage 4½ **Open** Easter **to** Oct
Access Good **Site** Level
Nearest Bus Stop (Miles) ¼
Flat and open site on a working farm in a country area. 1 mile from the village and beach. No all male or female groups permitted.
Facilities ⅙ f 🖼 🖀 ⌐ ⊙ ☺ ♨ 🎕 🖀 ✔ 🖪
Nearest Town Bracklesham Bay
Directions From Chichester take the A286 south to Witterings, after 5 miles turn left onto the B2198 opposite the garage to Bracklesham Bay. After 1 mile on sharp right hand bend turn left to Earnley, site is 200 yards on the left.
⇌ Chichester

CHICHESTER

Stubcroft Farm Campsite, Stubcroft Lane, East Wittering, Chichester, West Sussex, PO20 8PJ
Tel: 01243 671469
Email: mail@stubcroft.com
www.stubcroft.com
Pitches For Å ⊕ ⊕ ⊕⁴ **Total** 50
Acreage 5 **Open** All Year
Access Good **Site** Level
Nearest Bus Stop (Miles) ¼
Secluded site on a working sheep farm. Within walking distance of the South Coasts best beaches and Chichester Harbour. Many attractions within a 15-20 minute drive.
Facilities f 🖼 🖀 ⌐ ☺ ♨
🖫 🎕 🖀 ✔ 🖪 🖪 ☀
Nearest Town Chichester/The Witterings
Directions From the A27 Chichester by-pass, take the A286 south for The Witterings. After 3-4 miles at the mini roundabout by the Total Garage fork left onto the B2198. ½ a mile past the Bell Pub turn right into Tile Barn Lane, after the S bend go 200 yards over 2 speed humps and turn first left, site is ½ a mile on the right hand side.
⇌ Chichester

GRAFFHAM

Graffham Camping & Caravanning Club Site, Great Bury, Graffham, Petworth, West Sussex, GU28 0QJ
Tel: 01798 867476
Email:
graffham.site@thefriendlyclub.co.uk
www.campingandcaravanningclub.co.uk/
graffham
Pitches For ▲ ♦ ♦ **Total** 90
Open 21-Mar **to** 04-Nov
Site Sloping
Set in 20 acres of woodland with many walks. Gas BBQs only. BTB 4 Star Graded and AA 3 Pennants. Non members welcome. You can also call us on 0845 130 7633.
Facilities ♿ ✆ ⚏ ♠ ⏚ ⊙ ⌁ ⛟ ▣ ☎
♿ ♿ ⊙ ♠ ❤ ⏚ ▣ ❃ ⬆
Directions From Petworth take the A285, pass Badgers Pub on the left and the BP Garage on the right, take the next right turn signposted Selham Graffham (with brown camping sign), follow signs to site. From Chichester take the A285 through Duncton and turn left signposted Selham Graffham (with brown camping sign).
⭆ Chichester

HENFIELD

Farmhouse Caravan & Camping Site, Tottington Drive, Small Dole, Henfield, West Sussex, BN5 9XZ
Tel: 01273 493157
Pitches For ▲ ♦ ♦ **Total** 70
Acreage 4 **Open** Mar **to** Nov
Access Good **Site** Level
Nearest Bus Stop (Miles) ¼
Small farm site within the South Downs National Park. Beach 5 miles, Brighton and Worthing 10 miles. Sorry no vans or pickups.
Facilities ✆ ⚏ ⏚ ☎ ♿ ♠ ⏚ ⛟ ❤
Nearest Town Brighton
Directions Turn first left off A2037 (Henfield/ Upperbeeding). After Small Dole sign into Tottington Drive, farm at end.
⭆ Shoreham

HORSHAM

Honeybridge Park, Honeybridge Lane, Dial Post, Nr Horsham, West Sussex, RH13 8NX
Tel: 01403 710923
Email: enquiries@honeybridgepark.co.uk
www.honeybridgepark.co.uk
Pitches For ▲ ♦ ♦ **Total** 200
Acreage 15 **Open** All Year
Access Good **Site** Level
Nearest Bus Stop (Miles) ¼
Delightfully situated within an Area of Outstanding Natural Beauty. A rural retreat with a relaxed atmosphere providing

spacious touring and camping pitches, heated amenity blocks, licensed shop and play area. Ideal touring base, convenient for the coast, London and theme parks. Luxury lodges and static caravans for sale.
Facilities ♿ ✆ ⚏ ⊞ ⚌ ⏚ ⊙ ⌁ ⛟ ▣ ☎
♿ ⊙ ⊞ ♠ ⏚ ❃ ❤ ▣ ⊟ ❃ ⚘
Nearest Town Worthing
Directions 10 miles south of Horsham on the A24, turn at Old Barn Nurseries.
⭆ Horsham

HORSHAM

Sumners Ponds Fishery & Campsite, Chapel Road, Barns Green, Horsham, West Sussex, RH13 0PR
Tel: 01403 732539
Email: bookings@sumnersponds.co.uk
www.sumnersponds.co.uk
Pitches For ▲ ♦ ♦ **Total** 86
Acreage 40 **Open** All Year
Access Good **Site** Level
Nearest Bus Stop (Miles) ¼
Extensive fishing on four lakes. Woodland paths and pasture. Lakeside cafe, village pub and shop within a 5 minute walk.
Facilities ♿ ✆ ⚏ ⚌ ⏚ ⊙ ⌁ ⛟ ☎
♿ ♿ ✗ ⏚ ❤ ▣ ⊡ ✎ ⚘
Nearest Town Horsham
Directions Take the A264 from Horsham towards Billingshurst and Bognor. Pass the Toyota garage on the right and turn left on the humpback bridge. Follow road to Barns Green and pass the pub and shop then look for signs on the right.
⭆ Horsham

LITTLEHAMPTON

Daisyfields Touring Park, Cornfield Close, Worthing Road, Littlehampton, West Sussex, BN17 6LD
Tel: 01903 724240
Email: daisyfields@bt.connect.com
www.camping-caravaning.co.uk
Pitches For ▲ ♦ ♦ **Total** 80
Acreage 6½ **Open** All Year
Access Good **Site** Level
Nearest Bus Stop (Miles) ¼
1½ miles to a sandy beach. 1 mile to the River Arun. Open all year dependant on the weather. Pets welcome with camper vans and caravans only. No commercial vehicles.
Facilities ✆ ⚌ ⏚ ⊙ ☎
⊙ ⊞ ⏚ ❃ ❤ ▣ ⊡
Nearest Town Littlehampton
Directions The site is situated on the A259 Worthing to Bognor Regis, between two Body Shop roundabouts. 3 miles from Arundel.
⭆ Littlehampton

SELSEY

Warner Farm Touring Park, Warner Lane, Selsey, West Sussex, PO20 9EL
Tel: 01243 604499
Email: touring@bunnleisure.co.uk
www.warnerfarm.co.uk
Pitches For ▲ ♦ ♦ **Total** 250
Acreage 12½ **Open** Mar **to** Oct
Access Good **Site** Level
Nearest Bus Stop (Miles) ¼
Full use of 3 clubhouses located on our caravan parks.
Facilities ♿ ✆ ⚏ ⊞ ⚌ ⏚ ⊙ ⌁ ⛟ ▣ ☎
♿ ♿ ⊙ ⊞ ✗ ♈ ⏚ ♠ ⏚ ⟲ ❃ ❤ ▣ ⊡ ⚘
🛜
Nearest Town Selsey
Directions A27 west join B2145 signs Selsey. At Selsey go 2 miniroundabouts turn left into School Lane, right into Paddock Lane finally left into Warner Lane.
⭆ Chichester

SLINDON

Slindon Camping & Caravanning Club Site, Slindon Park, Nr Arundel, West Sussex, BN18 0RG
Tel: 01243 814387
Email: slindon.site@thefriendlyclub.co.uk
www.campingandcaravanningclub.co.uk/
slindon
Pitches For ▲ ♦ ♦ **Total** 40
Acreage 2 **Open** 21-Mar **to** Sept
Access Good **Site** Lev/Slope
Nearest Bus Stop (Miles) ½
Within the National Trust property of Slindon Park. 6 miles from Goodwood Racecourse. BTB 2 Star Graded and AA 1 Pennant. Non members welcome. You can also call us on 0845 130 7633.
Facilities ✆ ☎ ♿ ⊙ ⊞ ♠ ❤ ▣ ⊡ 🛜
Nearest Town Chichester
Directions From the A27 Chichester to Fontwell road, turn left into Brittons Lane (second turn left after the B2233 on the right), then take the second turn right to Slindon. Site is on this road.
⭆ Barnham

WEST WITTERING

Nunnington Farm Camping Site, Nunnington Farm, West Wittering, West Sussex, PO20 8LZ
Tel: 01243 514013 **No Booking**
Email: enquiries@nunningtonfarm.com
www.camping-in-sussex.com
Pitches For ▲ ♦ ♦ **Total** 125
Acreage 4½ **Open** Easter **to** Mid Oct
Access Good **Site** Level
Nearest Bus Stop (Miles) Outside
Near the beach.

Facilities ⚓ ⌁ 📶🚻📶⌁⊙⌁ 🚿🔲🚽
🚉 ⚑ ⊙ 🛆 ✤↦🔲
Nearest Town Chichester
Directions 7 miles south of Chichester on the A286 B2179. 200yds before village on left, look for signs.
≠ Chichester

WEST WITTERING

Wicks Farm Camping Park, Redlands Lane, West Wittering, Chichester, West Sussex, PO20 8QE
Tel: 01243 513116
www.wicksfarm.co.uk
Pitches For 🅰 🚐 🚎≷ **Total** 40
Acreage 2¼ **Open** Apr **to** Nov
Access Good **Site** Level
Nearest Bus Stop (Miles) ¼
Facilities 🚻📶⌁⌁⊙⌁ 🚿 🔲🚽
🚉 ⚑ ⊙ 🛆 🛆 ✤↦🔲 🔲
Nearest Town West Wittering/Chichester
Directions From Chichester take the A286 for Birdham, then take the B2179 for West Wittering.
≠ Chichester

WORTHING

Northbrook Farm Caravan Club Site, Titnore Way, Worthing, West Sussex, BN13 3RT
Tel: 01903 502962
www.caravanclub.co.uk
Pitches For 🚐 🚎 **Total** 70
Acreage 12½ **Open** Mar **to** Nov
Nearest Bus Stop (Miles) ½
Set in open countryside yet only 2 miles from the coast. West Worthing Tennis Club adjacent for tennis, squash, restaurant and bar. Near to Arundel Castle. NB: Own sanitation required. Non members welcome. Booking essential.
Facilities ⌁ 🚻📶🚿 🚉 🔲 ⊙ 🛆 🛆↦🔲🚽✦
Nearest Town Worthing
Directions From north on A24, in Findon at r/about junc with A280 t rt sp Chichester. After 4 miles at r/about take 2nd exit to r/about on far side of bridge over A27 t lt (first exit sp Ferring). After ¾ mile at brown sign t lt into Titnore Way, site is 120 yds on lt.
≠ Worthing

WARWICKSHIRE

BIDFORD-ON-AVON

Cottage of Content, Barton, Bidford-on-Avon, Warwickshire, B50 4NP
Tel: 01789 772279
Email: cofc@btinternet.com
Pitches For 🅰 🚐 🚎 **Total** 25
Acreage 2 **Open** May **to** Oct
Access Good **Site** Sloping
Nearest Bus Stop (Miles) ½
By River Avon
Facilities ⌁ 📶⌁⊙⌁ 🚿 🚽 🚿
🚉✕↦🔲🚽🚽⌁✦
Nearest Town Bidford on Avon
Directions 1 mile from Bidford follow Honeybourne road for mile. Turn left at crossroads signposted Barton, situated on bend in mile.
≠ Honeybourne

LEAMINGTON SPA

Lairhillock Touring Park Sandy Lane, Marton, Rugby, Warwicks, CV23 9TP
Tel: 01926 632119
Email: lairhillockpark@aol.com
www.lairhillocktouringpark.co.uk
Pitches For 🅰 🚐 🚎 🚎≷ **Total** 38

Acreage 2½ **Open** All year
Access Good **Site** Level
Nearest Bus Stop (Miles) ½
Close to Warwick Castle, Stratford on Avon snd Coventry Cathedral
Facilities ⚓ ⌁ 🚻📶⌁⊙⌁ 🚿↦🔲🚿🛆
Nearest Town Leamington Spa
Directions B4453 to Princethorpe turn right onto A423 through Marton follow brown tourist signs to site.
≠ Leamington Spa

LONG COMPTON

Long Compton Camping, Mill Farm, Barton Road, Long Compton, Shipston-on-Stour, Warwickshire, CV36 5NZ
Tel: 01608 684663
Pitches For 🅰 🚐 🚎 **Total** 11
Acreage 3 **Open** Apr **to** Oct
Access Good **Site** Level
Nearest Bus Stop (Miles) ½
On the fringe of the Cotswolds.
Facilities 📶⌁⊙⌁ 🚉↦
Nearest Town Moreton-in-Marsh
Directions Turn off A3400 in Long Compton for Barton-on-the-Heath. Site on right in ½ a mile.
≠ Moreton-in-Marsh

STRATFORD-UPON-AVON

Dodwell Park, Evesham Road, Stratford-upon-Avon, Warwickshire, CV37 9SR
Tel: 01789 204957
Email: enquiries@dodwellpark.co.uk
www.dodwellpark.co.uk
Pitches For 🅰 🚐 🚎 **Total** 50
Acreage 2 **Open** All Year
Access Good **Site** Lev/Slope
Nearest Bus Stop (Miles) Outside
Over 50 years as a family business. Ideal for the Shakespeare Theatre, the Cotswolds and Warwick Castle.
Facilities ⌁ 🚻📶⌁⊙⌁ 🚿 🚽
🚉 ⊙ 🛆 ✤↦🔲 🚽 🚽
Nearest Town Stratford-upon-Avon
Directions 2 miles southwest of Stratford on B439 (formerly the A439)- Not the racecourse site.
≠ Stratford-upon-Avon

STRATFORD-UPON-AVON

Island Meadow Caravan Park, Aston Cantlow, Warwickshire, B95 6JP
Tel: 01789 488273
Email:
holiday@islandmeadowcaravanpark.co.uk
www.islandmeadowcaravanpark.co.uk
Pitches For 🅰 🚐 🚎 **Total** 34
Acreage 3 **Open** Mar **to** Oct
Access Good **Site** Level
Nearest Bus Stop (Miles) ¼
Small, quiet island, adjacent to a picturesque village. Cafe/Restaurant and childrens play area nearby. Ideal centre for Shakespeare Country.
Facilities ⚓ ⌁ 🚻📶⌁⊙⌁ 🚿🔲🚽
🚉 ⊙ 🛆 ✤↦🔲🚽✦
Nearest Town Stratford-upon-Avon
Directions From the A46 or the A3400 follow signs for Aston Cantlow Village. Park is ½ mile west of the village in Mill Lane.
≠ Wilmcote

STUDLEY

Outhill Caravan Park, Outhill, Studley, Warwickshire, B80 7DY
Tel: 01527 852160
Pitches For 🚐 🚎 **Total** 15
Acreage 11 **Open** Apr **to** Oct
Access Good **Site** Level

Peace and quiet. No electricity and no hot water. Advance booking is essential. No tents.
Facilities 📶↦⌁≋
Nearest Town Henley-in-Arden
Directions From A435 (Birmingham to Evesham road) turn towards Henley-in-Arden on A4189. Take third turning to the right (approx 1¼ miles), check in at Outhill Farm (first on left).

WARWICK

Warwick Racecourse Caravan Club Site, Hampton Street, Warwick, Warwickshire, CV34 6HN
Tel: 01926 495448
www.caravanclub.co.uk
Pitches For 🚐 🚎 **Total** 55
Acreage 3¼ **Open** Mar **to** Jan
Access Good **Site** Level
Nearest Bus Stop (Miles) ¼
Grass and tarmac site in the racecourse enclosure. Very short walk to the centre of Warwick and its castle. Only 8 miles from Stratford-upon-Avon. Non members welcome. Booking essential.
Facilities ⚓ ⌁ 🚻📶⌁⊙⌁ 🚿 🚽
🚉 ⊙ 🛆↦🔲🚽
Nearest Town Warwick
Directions Leave the M40 at junction 15 and take the A429 sp Warwick. After 1 mile at brown camping sign turn left into Shakespeares Avenue, at T-junction turn right onto the B4095, site is ½ mile on the left.
≠ Warwick

WOLVEY

Wolvey Caravan & Camping Park, Villa Farm, Wolvey, Nr Hinckley, Leicestershire, LE10 3HF
Tel: 01455 220493/220630
www.wolveycaravanpark.itgo.com
Pitches For 🅰 🚐 🚎 **Total** 110
Acreage 7 **Open** All Year
Access Good **Site** Level
Nearest Bus Stop (Miles) Outside
A quiet site, ideally situated to explore the many places of interest in the Midlands.
Facilities ⚓ ⌁ 🚻📶⌁⊙⌁ 🚿🔲🚽
🚉 ⊙ 🛆 🛆↦🔲⌁✦
Nearest Town Hinckley
Directions Leave the M6 at junction 2 and take the B4065, follow signs for Wolvey and camping signs. Or leave the M69 at junction 1 and take the B4065, follow signs for Wolvey and camping signs.
≠ Hinckley

WEST MIDLANDS

HALESOWEN

Clent Hills Camping & Caravanning Club Site, Fieldhouse Lane, Romsley, Halesowen, West Midlands, B62 0NH
Tel: 01562 710015
Email: clent.site@thefriendlyclub.co.uk
www.campingandcaravanningclub.co.uk/clenthills
Pitches For 🅰 🚐 🚎 **Total** 95
Acreage 7½ **Open** 21-Mar **to** 04-Nov
Access Good **Site** Sloping
Nearest Bus Stop (Miles) ½
In the heart of the West Midlands. Ideal for walkers and cyclists. BTB 4 Star Graded and AA 3 Pennants. Non members welcome. You can also call us on 0845 130 7633.
Facilities ⚓ ⌁ 🚻📶⌁⊙⌁ 🚿 🔲🚽
🚉 ⊙ 🛆↦🔲🚽✦≋
Nearest Town Halesowen

Directions Travelling northwest on the M5, leave at junction 3 onto the A456. Then take the B4551 to Romsley, turn right at Sun Hotel, take the 5th left turn then the next left and the site is 330 yards on the left hand side.
≠ Old Hill

MERIDEN
Somers Wood Caravan Park, Somers Road, Meriden, North Warwickshire, CV7 7PL
Tel: 01676 522978
Email: enquiries@somerswood.co.uk
www.somerswood.co.uk
Pitches For 🚐 🚙 � **Total** 48
Acreage 4 **Open** All Year
Access Good **Site** Level
Nearest Bus Stop (Miles) ½
ADULTS ONLY SITE. Adjacent to a golf course with clubhouse. Approx. 3 miles from the N.E.C. Birmingham. Fishing adjacent.
Facilities ♿ ✚ 🖾 🛁 🚻 ♪ ⊙ ⌐ 🍴 🔲 ☎
🛉 🖪 🏪 ✕ 🗦 🖃 🏠 🍴 ☎
Nearest Town Solihull
Directions Leave the M42 at junction 6, take the A45 to Coventry. Immediately on the left pick up signs for the A452 Leamington. Down to roundabout and turn right onto the A452 signed Leamington/Warwick, at the next roundabout turn left into Hampton Lane. Site is ½ mile on the left hand side.
≠ Hampton-in-Arden

SUTTON COLDFIELD
Kingsbury Water Park Camping & Caravanning Club Site, Kingsbury Water Park, Bodymoor Heath Lane, Sutton Coldfield, West Midlands, B76 0DY
Tel: 01827 874101
Email:
kingsbury.site@thefriendlyclub.co.uk
www.campingandcaravanningclub.co.uk/kingsburywaterpark
Pitches For 🛆 🚐 🚙 **Total** 150
Open All Year
Site Level
Nearest Bus Stop (Miles) 1
Surrounding the site are the 600 acres of Kingsbury Water Park. BTB 5 Star Graded, AA 4 Pennants and Loo of the Year Award. Non members welcome. You can also call us on 0845 130 7633.
Facilities ♿ ✚ 🖾 🛁 🚻 ♪ ⊙ ⌐ 🍴 🔲 ☎
🛉 🖪 🏪 🗦 🖃 🍴 ☎
Directions Leave the M42 at junction 9 and take the B4097 towards Kingsbury. At the roundabout turn left and continue past the main entrance to the water park, go over the motorway and turn next right, follow lane for ½ mile to the site.
≠ Tamworth

SUTTON COLDFIELD
Marston Caravan & Camping Park, Kingsbury Road, Marston, Near Sutton Coldfield, West Midlands, B76 0DP
Tel: 01675 470902
www.marstoncaravanandcamping.co.uk
Pitches For 🛆 🚐 🚙 **Total** 125
Acreage 10 **Open** All Year
Access Good **Site** Level

Nearest Bus Stop (Miles) Outside
Facilities ✚ 🖾 🛁 🚻 ♪ ⊙ ⌐ 🍴 🔲 ☎
🛉 🖪 🖃 🍴 ☎
Nearest Town Sutton Coldfield
Directions 2 miles approx
≠ Sutton Coldfield

WILTSHIRE
BRADFORD-ON-AVON
Church Farm Touring Caravan & Camping Site, Church Farm, Winsley, Bradford-on-Avon, Wiltshire, BA15 2JH
Tel: 01225 722246
Email: stay@churchfarmcottages.com
www.churchfarmcamping.co.uk
Pitches For 🛆 🚐 🚙 **Total** 20
Open Easter **to** Oct
Access Good **Site** Level
Nearest Bus Stop (Miles) ¼
Countryside site on a working farm in an area of outstanding natural beauty. Ideal for Bath, Bradford-on-Avon, the Kennet & Avon Canal, Stonehenge, Salisbury and Longleat Safari Park, also close to three National Trust properties and gardens. Village pub just 500 metres.
Facilities ✚ 🖾 ♪ ⊙ ⌐ 🔲 ☎
🛉 🖪 ✕ 🗦 🖃 🖃
Nearest Town Bradford-on-Avon
Directions From Bradford-on-Avon follow B3108 for 2 miles to Winsley, at roundabout take 2nd exit signed Bath/Limpney Stoke. (Ignore 1st exit to Winsley church) Farm is ¾ mile on right.
≠ Bradford-on-Avon

CALNE
Blackland Lakes, Blackland Leisure Ltd, Stockley Lane, Calne, Wiltshire, SN11 0NQ
Tel: 01249 810943
Email: enquiries@blacklandlakes.co.uk
www.blacklandlakes.co.uk
Pitches For 🛆 🚐 🚙 **Total** 180
Acreage 15 **Open** All Year
Access Good **Site** Level
Nearest Bus Stop (Miles) Outside
A natural, interesting, scenic and secure site with three lakes for super coarse fishing. 1 mile perimeter trail for dogs, walking and cycling. Winter bookings must be prepaid.
Facilities ♿ ✚ 🖾 🛁 🚻 ♪ ⊙ ⌐ 🍴 🔲 ☎
🛉 🖪 🗦 🖃 🖃 ✍ ⚓
Nearest Town Calne
Directions Signposted from the A4 east of Calne.
≠ Chippenham

CHIPPENHAM
Piccadilly Caravan Park, Folly Lane West, Lacock, Chippenham, Wiltshire, SN15 2LP
Tel: 01249 730260
Email: piccadillylacock@aol.com
Pitches For 🛆 🚐 🚙 **Total** 43
Acreage 2½ **Open** Apr **to** Oct
Access Good **Site** Level
Nearest Bus Stop (Miles) ¼
Close to the National Trust village of Lacock, Piccadilly is a small, family run, beautifully maintained Park.

Facilities ✚ 🖾 🛁 🚻 ♪ ⊙ ⌐ 🔲 ☎
🛉 🖪 🗦 🖃 🖃 ✍
Nearest Town Chippenham
Directions Turn right off the A350 Chippenham to Melksham road, 5 miles south of Chippenham, close to Lacock. Signposted to Gastard (with caravan symbol).
≠ Chippenham

CHIPPENHAM
Plough Lane Caravan Site, Kington Langley, Chippenham, Wiltshire, SN15 5PS
Tel: 01249 750146
Email: enquiries@ploughlane.co.uk
www.ploughlane.co.uk
Pitches For 🚐 🚙 **Total** 50
Acreage 4 **Open** Easter **to** Oct
Access Good **Site** Level
ADULTS ONLY SITE.
Facilities ♿ ✚ 🖾 🛁 🚻 ♪ ⊙ ⌐ 🍴 🔲 ☎
🛉 🖪 🗦 🖃 🏠 ☎
Nearest Town Chippenham
Directions Well signposted from the A350 north of Chippenham.
≠ Chippenham

DEVIZES
Devizes Camping & Caravanning Club Site, Spout Lane, Nr Seend, Melksham, Wiltshire, SN12 6RN
Tel: 01380 828839
Email: devizes.site@thefriendlyclub.co.uk
www.campingandcaravanningclub.co.uk/devizes
Pitches For 🛆 🚐 🚙 **Total** 90
Open All Year
Site Level
Nearest Bus Stop (Miles) ¼
Bordering the Kennett & Avon Canal. BTB 4 Star Graded, AA 4 Pennants and David Bellamy Silver Award. Non members welcome. You can also call us on 0845 130 7633.
Facilities ♿ ✚ 🖾 🛁 🚻 ♪ ⊙ ⌐ 🍴 🔲 ☎
🖪 🗦 🖪 🖃 🍴 ☎
Directions Take the A365 from Melksham, turn right down the lane beside Three Magpies Public House, site is on the right.
≠ Melksham

DEVIZES
Lower Foxhangers Campsite, Lower Foxhangers Farm, Rowde, Devizes, Wiltshire, SN10 1SS
Tel: 01380 828254
Email: sales@foxhangers.co.uk
www.foxhangers.co.uk
Pitches For 🛆 🚐 🚙 **Total** 18
Acreage 2 **Open** Easter **to** Oct
Access Good **Site** Lev/Slope
Nearest Bus Stop (Miles) ½
Located beside Kennet Avon Canal for walking, fishing, boating and cycling.
Facilities ♿ 🖾 🛁 🚻 ♪ ⊙ ⌐ 🔲 ☎
🛉 🖪 🖃 🖃 ✍
Nearest Town Devizes
Directions 2 miles west of Devizes on the A361. ½ mile east of the A361 and the A365.
≠ Chippenham

WILTSHIRE

DEVIZES

The Bell Camping, Touring & Motorcaravan Site, Andover Road, Lydeway, Devizes, Wiltshire, SN10 3PS
Tel: 01380 840230
Pitches For 🏕 ⛺ 🚐 🚗 Total 26
Acreage 5 **Open** April **to** October
Access Good **Site** Level
Nearest Bus Stop (Miles) Outside
Ideal for Stonehenge, Avebury, Bath, Longleat Safari Park, ational Trusts Lacock and Bowood.
Facilities 🏕 📶 🎣 🍴 ☉ ⌗ 🚿 ⬛ 🔲 ♿
🏧 🔁 🔲 🔲
Nearest Town Devizes
Directions 5 miles east of Devizes on the A342 Andover road.
🚆 Pewsey

MARLBOROUGH

Hillview Park, Hillview Park House, Sunnyhill Lane, Oare, Marlborough, Wiltshire, SN8 4JG
Tel: 01672 563151
Pitches For 🏕 ⛺ Total 10
Open Apr **to** Sept
Access Good **Site** Level
Nearest Bus Stop (Miles) Outside
½ a mile from Kennet & Avon Canal. Cycleway nearby. No hard standings, caravans and motor vans over 20 feet cannot be accommodated. Sorry, no children over the age of 5.
Facilities 🏕 📶 🎣 🍴 ☉ ⌗ 🚿 ⬛ 🔲 🔲
Nearest Town Marlborough
Directions 5 miles south of Marlborough on the A345 junction.
🚆 Pewsey

MARLBOROUGH

Postern Hill Caravan & Camping Site, Postern Hill, Marlborough, Wiltshire, SN8 4ND
Tel: 01672 515195
www.campingintheforest.co.uk
Pitches For 🏕 ⛺ 🚐 🚗 Total 170
Open All Year
Access Good **Site** Level
Nearest Bus Stop (Miles) Outside
Facilities 🏕 📶 🎣 ☉ ⌗ 🚿 ⬛ 🚿 🔲 🔲 ⚴
🔌
Nearest Town Marlborough
Directions On A345
🚆 Bedwyn

NETHERHAMPTON

Coombe Caravan Park, Coombe Nurseries, Race Plain, Netherhampton, Salisbury, Wiltshire, SP2 8PN
Tel: 01722 328451
Email: enquiries@coombecaravanpark.co.uk
www.coombecaravanpark.co.uk
Pitches For 🏕 ⛺ 🚐 Total 60
Acreage 3 **Open** Mar **to** Oct
Access Good **Site** Level
Adjacent to racecourse (flat racing), ideal touring, lovely views.
Facilities 🏕 🍴 📶 🎣 ☉ ⌗ 🚿 ⬛ 🔲 🚿
🏧 🔲 🔲
Nearest Town Salisbury
Directions Take A36-A30 Salisbury - Wilton road, turn off at traffic lights onto A3094 Netherhampton - Stratford Tony road, cross on bend following Stratford Tony road, 2nd left behind racecourse, site on right, signposted.
🚆 Salisbury

ORCHESTON

Stonehenge Touring Park, Orcheston, Nr Shrewton, Wiltshire, SP3 4SH
Tel: 01980 620304
Email: stay@stonehengetouringpark.com
www.stonehengetouringpark.com
Pitches For 🏕 ⛺ 🚐 Total 30
Acreage 2 **Open** All Year
Access Good **Site** Level
Nearest Bus Stop (Miles) ¼
5 miles from Stonehenge and Salisbury Plain. Within easy reach Bath and the New Forest. ETB 3 Star Graded and AA 3 Pennants.
Facilities 🏕 🍴 📶 🎣 🍴 ☉ ⌗ 🚿 ⬛ 🔲 🚿
🏧 🔲 🚿 🍴 🔲 🔲 🔲 ☎
Nearest Town Salisbury
Directions On the A360, 11 miles from both Salisbury and Devizes.
🚆 Salisbury

SALISBURY

Alderbury Caravan & Camping Park, Southampton Road, Whaddon, Salisbury, Wiltshire, SP5 3HB
Tel: 01722 710125
Email: alderbury@aol.com
www.alderburycaravanpark.co.uk
Pitches For 🏕 ⛺ 🚐 🚗 Total 39
Acreage 2 **Open** All Year
Site Level
Nearest Bus Stop (Miles) Outside
Ideal touring for Salisbury, Stone Henge, south coast ferry ports, Paultons Park.
Facilities 🏕 🍴 📶 🎣 ☉ ⌗ 🚿 ⬛ 🔲 🔲
Nearest Town Salisbury
Directions A36 from Salisbury approx. 3 miles.
🚆 Salisbury

SALISBURY

Green Hill Farm Caravan & Camping Park, Greenhill Farm, New Road, Landford, Salisbury, Wiltshire, SP5 2AZ
Tel: 01794 324117
Email: info@greenhillholidays.co.uk
www.greenhillholidays.co.uk
Pitches For 🏕 ⛺ 🚐 🚗 Total 160
Acreage 15 **Open** All Year
Access Good **Site** Level
Nearest Bus Stop (Miles) Outside
On the edge of the New Forest, you can walk into the forest directly from the Park. Brand new toilet facilities opened in 2012
Facilities 🏕 🍴 📶 🎣 🍴 ☉ ⌗ 🚿 ⬛ 🔲
🏧 🔲 🚿 🍴 🔲 🚿 🔲 🔲 ⚴ 🔌
Nearest Town Romsey/Salisbury
Directions Leave the M27 at junction 2 and take the A36 towards Salisbury. In Plaitford look out for the BP garage, turn next left into New Road.
🚆 Romsey

SALISBURY

Salisbury Camping & Caravanning Club Site, Hudsons Field, Castle Road, Salisbury, Wiltshire, SP1 3RR
Tel: 01722 320713
Email: Salisbury.site@thefriendlyclub.co.uk
www.campingandcaravanningclub.co.uk/salisbury
Pitches For 🏕 ⛺ 🚐 Total 150
Acreage 4½ **Open** 21-Mar **to** 04-Nov
Access Good **Site** Lev/Slope
Nearest Bus Stop (Miles) ¼
1½ miles from Salisbury, plenty to do in the area. BTB 4 Star Graded and AA 4 Pennants. Non members welcome. You can also call us on 0845 130 7633.
Facilities 🏕 🍴 📶 🎣 🍴 ☉ ⌗ 🚿 ⬛ 🔲 🔲
🏧 🔲 🚿 🍴 🔲 🔲 🔲 ☎
Nearest Town Salisbury

Directions 1½ miles from Salisbury and 7 miles from Amesbury on the A345. Hudsons Field is a large open field next to Old Sarum.
🚆 Salisbury

SALISBURY

Summerlands Caravan Park, Rockbourne Road, Coombe Bissett, Salisbury, Wiltshire, SP5 4LP
Tel: 01722 718259
Email: enquiries@summerlandscaravanpark.co.uk
www.summerlandscaravanpark.co.uk
Pitches For 🏕 ⛺ 🚐 🚗 Total 26
Open Apr **to** Oct
Access Good **Site** Level
Nearest Bus Stop (Miles) 1
Off the beaten track in an area of outstanding natural beauty.
Facilities 🏕 🍴 📶 🎣 🍴 ☉ ⌗ 🚿 ⬛ ☎ 🏧 🔁 🔲
Nearest Town Salisbury
Directions A354 from Salisbury to Blandford (6 miles) fork left to Rockbourne,300m left onto Byway ¾ to site. (Byway a little bumpy)
🚆 Salisbury

TILSHEAD

Brades Acre, Tilshead, Salisbury, Wiltshire, SP3 4RX
Tel: 01980 620402
Email: bradesacre@hotmail.co.uk
www.bradesacre.co.uk
Pitches For 🏕 ⛺ 🚐 🚗 Total 35
Acreage 1½ **Open** All Year
Access Good **Site** Level
Nearest Bus Stop (Miles) ¼
Touring for Stonehenge, Salisbury Cathedral, Wilton and Longleat Houses. Avebury, Orcheston riding.
Facilities 🏕 🍴 📶 🎣 🍴 ☉ ⌗ 🚿 ⬛ ☎
🏧 🔲 🚿 ✕ 🔲 🔲 ⚴
Nearest Town Salisbury/Devizes
Directions A360, 10 miles to Devizes, 13 miles to Salisbury.
🚆 Salisbury

TROWBRIDGE

Stowford Manor Farm, Stowford, Wingfield, Trowbridge, Wiltshire, BA14 9LH
Tel: 01225 752253
Email: stowford1@supanet.com
www.stowfordmanorfarm.co.uk
Pitches For 🏕 ⛺ 🚐 Total 20
Acreage 1½ **Open** Easter **to** Oct
Access Good **Site** Level
Alongside a river for fishing and swimming. Next to a Medieval farm.
Facilities 🏕 📶 🎣 ☉ ⌗ 🚿 ☎ 🔲 🔌
Nearest Town Trowbridge
Directions From Trowbridge take the A366 west towards Radstock for 3 miles, farm is on the left hand side.
🚆 Trowbridge

WARMINSTER

Longleat Caravan Club Site, Warminster, Wiltshire, BA12 7NL
Tel: 01985 844663
www.caravanclub.co.uk
Pitches For ⛺ 🚐 Total 165
Acreage 14 **Open** Mar **to** Nov
Access Good **Site** Level
The Caravan Clubs most beautiful parkland site, set in the heart of the Longleat Estate. Miles of woodland walks. Just a short walk from Longleat House & Safari Park with its maze and childrens adventure castle. Non members welcome. Booking essential.
Facilities 🏕 🍴 📶 🎣 🍴 🔲 ☎
🏧 🚿 🍴 🔲 🔲 🔲 🔲
Nearest Town Warminster

Directions From the A36 Warminster bypass take the A362 sp Frome. At roundabout turn left into Longleat Estate entrance and follow Longleat House route through the toll booths for 2 miles, then Caravan Club pennant signs for 1 mile.

WESTBURY

Brokerswood Country Park,
Brokerswood, Nr Westbury, Wiltshire, BA13 4EH
Tel: 01373 822238
Email:
info@brokerswoodcountrypark.co.uk
www.brokerswoodcountrypark.co.uk
Pitches For ▲ ♦ ♦ ♦ **Total** 65
Acreage 5 **Open** All Year
Access Good **Site** Level
Site adjoins an 80 acre area of forest open to the public. Woodland walks, narrow gauge railway, adventure playground and fishing lake.
Facilities
Nearest Town Westbury/Trowbridge
Directions At Yarnbrook on the A350, turn onto the A363 and follow road. At The Rising Sun Pub turn left, then turn left off the right hand bend before Southwick and continue for 2½ miles.
⚍ Westbury

WORCESTERSHIRE

BEWDLEY

Bank Farm Holiday Parks Ltd., Bank Farm, Arley, Bewdley, Worcestershire, DY12 3ND
Tel: 01299 401277
Email: bankfarm@tinyworld.co.uk
www.bankfarmholidaypark.co.uk
Pitches For ♦ ♦ **Total** 5
Open All Year
Access Good **Site** Level
Alongside a river in the Wyre Forest with river and valley views. 9 hole pitch n putt on site. Near the River Severn and the Severn Valley Railway Station at Arley. Holiday homes for hire and sale.
Facilities
Nearest Town Bewdley
Directions Just off the B4194 3½ miles outside Bewdley, near Kidderminster.
⚍ Kidderminster

EVESHAM

Evesham Vale Caravan Park, Yessell Farm, Boston Lane, Charlton, Nr Evesham, Worcestershire, WR11 2RD
Tel: 01386 860377
Pitches For ▲ ♦ ♦ **Total** 40
Acreage 20 **Open** Apr **to** Oct
Access Good **Site** Level
Nearest Bus Stop (Miles) Outside
On the Blossom Trail route, near a river for fishing. Central for the Cotswolds, Stratford and Worcester.
Facilities
Nearest Town Evesham
Directions From Evesham take the A44, after approx 1½ miles turn right for Charlton. Park is on the left hand side after approx. ¾ miles.
⚍ Evesham

EVESHAM

Ranch Caravan Park, Station Road, Honeybourne, Nr Evesham, Worcestershire, WR11 7PR
Tel: 01386 830744
Email: enquiries@ranch.co.uk
www.ranch.co.uk
Pitches For ♦ ♦ **Total** 120
Acreage 48 **Open** Mar **to** Nov
Access Good **Site** Level
Nearest Bus Stop (Miles) ¼
Situated in meadow land in Vale of Evesham on north edge of Cotswolds. Meals available in licensed club.
Facilities
Nearest Town Evesham
Directions From Evesham take B4035 to Badsey and Bretforton. Turn left to Honeybourne. At village crossroads take Bidford direction, site on left in 400 yards.
⚍ Honeybourne

GREAT MALVERN

Blackmore Camping & Caravanning Club Site, Blackmore Camp Site No.2, Hanley Swan, Worcestershire, WR8 0EE
Tel: 01684 310280
Email:
blackmore.site@thefriendlyclub.co.uk
www.campingandcaravanningclub.co.uk/blackmore
Pitches For ▲ ♦ ♦ **Total** 180
Acreage 17 **Open** All Year
Access Good **Site** Level
Close to the River Severn. Situated in the Malvern Hills, ideal walking country. Close to the market towns of Ledbury, Tewkesbury and Evesham. BTB 5 Star Graded and AA 4 Pennants. Non members welcome. You can also call us on 0845 130 7633.
Facilities
Nearest Town Great Malvern
Directions Take the A38 to Upton-on-Severn, turn north over the river bridge, turn second left then first left signposted Hanley Swan. Site is on the right after 1 mile.
⚍ Malvern

KIDDERMINSTER

Wolverley Camping & Caravanning Club Site, Brown Westhead Park, Wolverley, Nr Kidderminster, Worcestershire, DY10 3PX
Tel: 01562 850909
Email:
wolverley.site@thefriendlyclub.co.uk
www.campingandcaravanningclub.co.uk/wolverley
Pitches For ▲ ♦ ♦ **Total** 120
Acreage 12 **Open** 15-Mar **to** 04-Nov
Access Good **Site** Lev/Slope
Nearest Bus Stop (Miles) ¼
A quiet and secluded site with pretty walks along the canal, and some excellent pubs. BTB 3 Star Graded and AA 3 Pennants. Non members welcome. You can also call us on 0845 130 7633.
Facilities
Nearest Town Kidderminster
Directions From Kidderminster take the A449 to Wolverhampton, turn left at the traffic lights onto the B4189 signposted Wolverley. Look for brown camping sign and turn right, the site entrance is on the left.
⚍ Kidderminster

MALVERN

Kingsgreen Caravan Park, Berrow, Nr Malvern, Worcestershire, WR13 6AQ
Tel: 01531 650272
Pitches For ▲ ♦ ♦ **Total** 45
Acreage 3 **Open** Mar **to** Oct
Access Good **Site** Level
Beautiful area on the Malvern Hills and Malvern with its famous Elgar Route. Historic Black and White timber towns, Tewkesbury and Upton-on-Severn. BH & HPA Member.
Facilities
Nearest Town Ledbury/Malvern
Directions From Ledbury take the A417 towards Gloucester. Over the M50 then take the first turning left to Malvern, we are 1 mile on the right. OR M50 Southbound junction 2, turn left onto the A417, in 1 mile turn left to the Malverns.
⚍ Ledbury/Malvern

SHRAWLEY

Brant Farm Caravan Park, Shrawley, Worcestershire, WR6 6TD
Tel: 01905 621008
Pitches For ▲ ♦ ♦ **Total** 12
Acreage 1 **Open** Apr **to** 30-Oct
Access Good **Site** Level
Nearest Bus Stop (Miles) ¼
Quiet location in scenic woodland. Two pubs within a 5 minute walk.
Facilities
Nearest Town Stourport-on-Severn
Directions Take the A449 from Worcester to Holt Heath, then take the B4196 signposted Shrawley. Continue to the Rose & Crown Pub and the Park is 100 yards further on on the left hand side.
⚍ Kidderminster/Worcester

STOURPORT-ON-SEVERN

Lickhill Manor Caravan Park, Lickhill Manor, Stourport-on-Severn, Worcestershire, DY13 8RL
Tel: 01299 871041/877820
Email: excellent@lickhillmanor.co.uk
www.lickhillmanor.co.uk
Pitches For ▲ ♦ ♦ ♦ **Total** 120
Acreage 9 **Open** All Year
Access Good **Site** Level
Nearest Bus Stop (Miles) ¼
Alongside river (fishing rights held). Walks through the unspoilt Wyre Forest. West Midlands Safari Park and Severn Valley Railway nearby.
Facilities
Nearest Town Stourport-on-Severn
Directions From Stourport take the B4195 to Bewdley, at traffic lights on the crossroads follow caravan signs, after ½ mile turn right at the sign.
⚍ Kidderminster

STOURPORT-ON-SEVERN

Lincomb Lock Caravan Park, Lincomb Lock, Titton, Stourport-on-Severn, Worcestershire, DY13 9QR
Tel: 01299 823836
Email: lincomb@hillandale.co.uk
www.hillandale.co.uk
Pitches For ▲ ♦ ♦ ♦ **Total** 14
Acreage 1 **Open** Mar **to** 06-Jan
Access Good **Site** Level
Nearest Bus Stop (Miles) ½
ADULTS ONLY. Alongside River Severn. Many local attractions including West Midlands Safari Park, Severn Valley Railway, Riverside Amusements, the ancient Wyre Forest and local museums.

Facilities ⚡ 🚿 ♿ 🅿 ☏ ☉ 🍴 ☕
🍴📶🔌🔲 💷 ⁄ A
Nearest Town Stourport-on-Severn
Directions 1 mile from Stourport on the
A4025 turn right at park signs. Or from the
A449 join the A4025 at Crossway Green,
after 1 mile turn left at park signs.
⚇ Kidderminster

WORCESTER

Ketch Caravan Park, Bath Road,
Worcester, Worcestershire, WR5 3HW
Tel: 01905 820430
Pitches For ⛺ 🚐 🚍 **Total** 32
Acreage 6½ **Open** Apr **to** Oct
Access Good **Site** Level
Nearest Bus Stop (Miles) ¼
On the River Severn.
Facilities ⚡ 🚿 ☏ 🅿 ☉ 🍴 🍴🛒✕🐕✓
Nearest Town Worcester
Directions Leave the M5 at junction 7 and
follow signs for Malvern until you come to
the A38. Turn for Worcester and park
entrance is approx. 100 yards on the left.
⚇ Worcester

WORCESTER

Mill House Caravan & Camping Site, Mill
House, Hawford, Worcester,
Worcestershire, WR3 7SE
Tel: 01905 451283
Email: millhousecaravansite@yahoo.co.uk
www.facebook.com/millhousecaravansite
Pitches For ⛺ 🚐 🚍 **Total** 100
Open Apr **to** Oct
Site Level
Nearest Bus Stop (Miles) ¼
Small river around the site.
Facilities 🍴 ⚡ ♿ 🅿 ☉ 🍴
🍴 ☉ ✕🔌💷 ✓
Nearest Town Worcester
Directions On the A449 3 miles north of the
centre of Worcester
. 3 miles from junc 6 M5.
⚇ Worcester

WORCESTER

Seaborne Leisure, Court Meadow,
Kempsey, Worcester, Worcestershire,
WR5 3JL
Tel: 01905 820295
Email: enquiries@seaborneleisure.co.uk
www.seaborneleisure.co.uk
Pitches For ⛺ 🚐 🚍 **Total** 105
Acreage 40 **Open** Mar **to** Oct
Access Good **Site** Level
Nearest Bus Stop (Miles) ¼
Adjacent to the River Severn with views
towards the Malvern Hills. Ideally situated for
places of interest.
Facilities 🍴 ⚡ ♿ 🅿 ☉ 🍴 💷 ☕
🍴 ☉ ✕ ☏ 🔌💷 🛒
Nearest Town Worcester
Directions 2 miles south of Worcester. From
Worcester take the A38 towards Tewkesbury,
when in the village of Kempsey turn right by
the village shop (Church Street), site is
signposted, approx 50 yards down Court
Meadow.
⚇ Worcester

WYTHALL

Chapel Lane Caravan Club Site, Chapel
Lane, Wythall, Birmingham, B47 6JX
Tel: 01564 826483
www.caravanclub.co.uk
Pitches For 🚐 🚍 **Total** 108
Acreage 14 **Open** All Year
Access Good **Site** Level
Nearest Bus Stop (Miles) Outside
Rural and open site set in the shadow of an
old chapel. The Transport Museum is
adjacent, and a short walk leads you to
Becketts Farm Shop which has a restaurant.
Only 9 miles from the NEC and close to many
museums. Non members welcome. Booking
essential.
Facilities ♿ ⚡ 🚿 ♿ 🅿 ☉ 💷 ☕
🍴 🔌 ☉ 🛒🔌🔲🔌 📶
Nearest Town Birmingham
Directions M1 leave at junc 23A and take
A42/M42, exit at junc 3 and take A435. At r/
about turn left into Middle Lane, after 150
yards turn left into Chapel Lane, after 300
yards turn right by the church then
immediately turn right again into site.
⚇ Birmingham NEC

YORK (COUNTY OF)
SHERIFF HUTTON

York Meadows Caravan Park York Road,
Sheriff Hutton, York, YO60 6QP
Tel: 01347 878508
Email:
reception@yorkmeadowscaravanpark.com
www.yorkmeadowscaravanpark.com
Pitches For ⛺ 🚐 🚍 **Total** 70
Acreage 15 **Open** March **to** October
Access Good **Site** Level
Ideal for visiting York, coastal areas, North
York Moors, Castle Howard. Centre of three
major walking routes.
Facilities ⚡ 🚿 ♿ 🅿 ☉ 🍴 💷 ☕
🍴 🔌 ☉ 🛒🔌🔲🔌 🌿 📶
Nearest Town York
Directions 8 miles from York. Take A64 to
Scarborough. Turn left to Flaxton & Sheriff
Hutton. Turn left to Strensall. Park is on the
right
⚇ York

YORK

Chowdene Camping & Caravan Site,
Chowdene, Malton Road, York, YO32 9TD
Tel: 01904 289359
Email: touraco@talktalk.net
www.caravanstv.com
Pitches For ⛺ 🚐 🚍 **Total** 20
Acreage 1½ **Open** Mar **to** Nov
Access Good **Site** Level
Nearest Bus Stop (Miles) Outside
Small, quiet, family run site. VW Camper
friendly and we welcome the smaller camper
vehicles. Excellent for York and its many
attractions. Adjacent to a Park & Ride. Some
hardstandings available.
Facilities ⚡ 🚿 🅿 ☕🔌🔲
Nearest Town York
Directions From the A1 take the A64 for
approx 17 miles. Ignoring the first turning,
take the A1036 at the roundabout for York.

After 1 mile (at the third roudabout with a
large tile shop), continue and drive slowly for
200 yards and see our site sign on the right,
after the bungalow turn into our drive and go
100 yards to the site.
⚇ York

YORK

Moor End Farm, Acaster Malbis, York,
YO23 2UQ
Tel: 01904 706727
Email: roger@acaster99.fsnet.co.uk
www.moor-end-farm.co.uk
Pitches For ⛺ 🚐 🚍 **Total** 20
Acreage 1 **Open** Easter **to** Oct
Access Good **Site** Level
Nearest Bus Stop (Miles) Outside
Ideal for York and the York/Selby cycle track.
Facilities ♿ ⚡ 🚿 🅿 ☉ 🍴🔌🔲 💷 🛒🔌🔲
Nearest Town York
Directions Follow signs from A64/1237
intersection at Copmanthorpe.
⚇ York

YORK

Moorside Caravan Park, Lords Moor
Lane, Strensall, York, YO32 5XJ
Tel: 01904 491865/491208
www.moorsidecaravanpark.co.uk
Pitches For ⛺ 🚐 🚍 **Total** 50
Open Mar **to** Oct
Access Good **Site** Level
NO CHILDREN. Fishing lake on site. Near
York Golf Course.
Facilities ♿ ⚡ 🚿 ♿ 🅿 ☉ 🍴 💷 ☕
🍴 🍴 🛒✕🔌💷 🌿 📶
Nearest Town York
Directions Take the A1237, then take the
Strensall turn and head towards Flaxton.
⚇ York

YORK

Naburn Lock Caravan Park, Naburn,
York, YO19 4RU
Tel: 01904 728697
Email: petercatherine@naburnlock.co.uk
www.naburnlock.co.uk
Pitches For 🚐 🚍 **Total** 100
Open Mar **to** Oct
Access Good **Site** Level
Nearest Bus Stop (Miles) Outside
Close to the historic City of York. One hours
drive from the Yorkshire Dalesand seaside
resorts. Adults only area.
Facilities ♿ ⚡ 🚿 ♿ 🅿 ☉ 🍴 💷 🛒🔌🔲
🍴 ☉🔌🔲🔲 ✓ A
Nearest Town York
Directions From the A19/A64 interchange
at the McArthur Glen Designer Outlet, take
the A19 for York, after 200 yards turn first
left onto the B1222.
⚇ York

YORK

**York Beechwood Grange Caravan Club
Site,** Malton Road, York, YO32 9TH
Tel: 01904 424637
www.caravanclub.co.uk
Pitches For 🚐 🚍 **Total** 115
Acreage 11 **Open** Mar **to** Jan
Access Good **Site** Level

Set in open countryside, yet only 3 miles from York. Boules pitch on site. Plenty to do and see in York from river cruises to the Jorvik Viking Centre and the National Railway Museum. Non members welcome. Booking essential.
Facilities
Nearest Town York
Directions Turn off the A64 onto the A1237 signposted Thirsk. At roundabout turn right into road signposted local traffic only, site is at the end of the drive.
⇌ York

YORK
York Rowntree Park Caravan Club Site, Terry Avenue, York, YO23 1JQ
Tel: 01904 658997
www.caravanclub.co.uk
Pitches For Å 🚐 🚐 **Total** 102
Acreage 4 **Open** All Year
Access Good **Site** Level
Nearest Bus Stop (Miles) ½
On the banks of the River Ouse. Within walking distance of York. Close to York Minster, Jorvik Viking Centre, Castle Howard, York Castle Museum and The Shambles. Non members welcome. Booking essential.
Facilities
Nearest Town York
Directions From A64 south of York take A19 sp York Centre, DO NOT turn onto A1237. After 2 mls join the one-way system sp City Centre, at Mecca Bingo keep lt continue over bridge. T lt immediately before Swan Pub after 250 yds t rt into Terry Ave, site on right.
⇌ York

YORK
York Touring Caravan Site, Towthorpe Moor Lane, Towthorpe, York, YO32 9ST
Tel: 01904 499275
Email: info@yorkcaravansite.co.uk
www.yorkcaravansite.co.uk
Pitches For Å 🚐 🚐 **Total** 28
Open All Year
Access Good **Site** Level
Golf range and 9 hole golf course on site. ETB 4 Star Graded and AA 4 Pennants.
Facilities
Nearest Town York
Directions From the A64 take turnoff signposted Strensall and Haxby, site is 1½ miles on the left.
⇌ York

YORKSHIRE (EAST)
BRANDES BURTON
Fosse Hill Caravan Park, Catwick Lane, Brandes Burton, Driffield, East Yorkshire, YO25 8SB
Tel: 01964 542608
Email: janet@fossehill.co.uk
www.fossehill.co.uk
Pitches For Å 🚐 🚐 **Total** 110
Open Mar to Oct
Access Good **Site** Level
Nearest Bus Stop (Miles) 1
Family run site set in countryside. Just 1 mile from the village of Brandesburton, and only 3 miles from the seaside town of Hornsea. Excellent base for visiting the North Yorks Moors, York, Beverley, Hull and the famous Deep.
Facilities
Nearest Town Hornsea

Directions ½ a mile east of the A165 Hull to Bridlington road.
⇌ Beverley

BRIDLINGTON
Fir Tree Caravan Park, Jewison Lane, Bridlington, East Yorkshire, YO16 6YG
Tel: 01262 676442
Email: info@flowerofmay.com
www.flowerofmay.com
Pitches For 🚐 **Total** 46
Acreage 25 **Open** Mar to Oct
Access Good **Site** Level
Nearest Bus Stop (Miles) ½
Pets are welcome by arrangement only.
Facilities
Nearest Town Bridlington
Directions From roundabout on A165 take B1255 to Flamborough for 2 miles. Jewison Lane is on the left and site is on the left after the level crossing.
⇌ Bridlington

BRIDLINGTON
Old Mill Caravan Park, Bempton, Bridlington, Yorkshire (East), YO16 6XE
Tel: 01262 673565
Pitches For 🚐 **Total** 55
Acreage 2 **Open** Apr to Oct
Access Good **Site** Level
Nearest Bus Stop (Miles) ½
Bempton Bird Sanctuary, Flamborough Head cliffs, Danes Dyke.
Facilities
Nearest Town Bridlington
Directions From Bridlington take the B1255 to Flamborough turn for Bempton 1 mile on the right.
⇌ Bempton

BRIDLINGTON
Poplars Touring Park, 45 Jewison Lane, Sewerby, Bridlington, East Yorkshire, YO15 1DX
Tel: 01262 677251
www.the-poplars.co.uk
Pitches For Å 🚐 🚐 **Total** 30
Acreage 1½ **Open** 05-Mar to Oct
Access Good **Site** Level
Nearest Bus Stop (Miles) ½
Small quiet site in a good touring location. ¾ miles to the beach. Pub with food adjacent.
Facilities
Nearest Town Bridlington
Directions From Bridlington take the B1255 towards Flamborough for 1½ miles. Jewison Lane is a left turn off the Z bend after Marton Hall.
⇌ Bridlington

BRIDLINGTON
South Cliff Caravan Park, Wilsthorpe, Bridlington, East Yorkshire, YO15 3QN
Tel: 01262 671051
Email: southcliff@eastriding.gov.uk
www.southcliff.co.uk
Pitches For Å 🚐 🚐 **Total** 172
Open Mar to Nov
Access Good **Site** Level
Nearest Bus Stop (Miles) Outside
Direct access to the beach. Golf course adjacent to the park.
Facilities
Nearest Town Bridlington
Directions Situated on the A1038 Hull to Bridlington road 1 mile south of Bridlington.
⇌ Bridlington

BRIDLINGTON
Thornwick & Sea Farm Holiday Centre, North Marine Road, Flamborough, Bridlington, Yorkshire (East), YO15 1AU
Tel: 01262 850369
Email: enquiries@thornwickbay.co.uk
www.thornwickbay.co.uk
Pitches For Å 🚐 🚐 **Total** 180
Acreage 15 **Open** Mar to Oct
Access Good **Site** Level
Nearest Bus Stop (Miles) Outside
Set on Flamborough Headland Heritage Coast. Ideal for families with varied entertainment. All pitches individualy paddocked.
Facilities
Nearest Town Bridlington
Directions From Bridlington follow B1255 east to Flamborough village and onward yo North Landing.
⇌ Bridlington

DRIFFIELD
Seaside Caravan Park, Ulrome, Driffield, East Yorkshire, YO25 8TT
Tel: 01262 468228
www.seaside-caravan-park.co.uk
Pitches For Å 🚐 🚐 **Total** 130
Acreage 12 **Open** Mid Mar to Oct
Access Good **Site** Level
Nearest Bus Stop (Miles) Outside
Adjacent to the beach with views from Brid Bay to Flamborough Head.
Facilities
Nearest Town Bridlington
Directions From Bridlington take the A165 south, after 5 miles turn left onto the B1242 signposted Hornsea. After 1½ miles go through Ulrome Village to the Park.
⇌ Bridlington

GOOLE
Dobella Lane Farm, Rawcliffe, Goole, East Yorkshire, DN14 8SQ
Tel: 01405 839261
Pitches For Å 🚐 🚐 🚐 **Total** 5
Acreage ½ **Open** All Year
Access Good **Site** Level
Nearest Bus Stop (Miles) ¼
Very private garden site on a working farm. English country garden, ideal for bird watching. Pub and restaurant in the village, and a new area for skateboarding. Near to Goole Docks Waterways Museum, Howden Minster, Selby Abbey and Blacktuft Sands.
Facilities
Nearest Town Goole
Directions Leave the M62 at junction 36 and head towards Selby into Rawcliffe. In the village turn left and follow road for ½ a mile, at the brick bus shelter turn left, go over the motorway and we are the first farm on the right.
⇌ Rawcliffe

HORNSEA
Four Acres Caravan Park, Hornsea Road, Atwick, Driffield, East Yorkshire, YO25 8DG
Tel: 01964 536940
Email: caravanfouracres@aol.com
www.fouracrescaravanpark.co.uk
Pitches For 🚐 🚐 **Total** 61
Acreage 4 **Open** Mar to Oct
Access Good **Site** Level
Nearest Bus Stop (Miles) Outside

Near to the beach, local pub, indoor bowls, swimming baths and a Sunday market.
Facilities ⬚
Nearest Town Hornsea
Directions As you approach Hornsea turn left at the roundabout on the B1242 for approx. 2 miles, site is on the right hand side.
⚏ Bridlington

HULL

Sand-le-Mere Holiday Village Main Street, Tunstall, East Yorkshire, HU12 0JF
Tel: 01964 670403
Email: info@sand-le-mere.co.uk
www.sand-le-mere.co.uk
Pitches For ⬚ **Total** 100
Acreage 140 **Open** Mar **to** Nov
Access Good **Site** Level
Nearest Bus Stop (Miles) Outside
Near the beach and all facilities.
Facilities ⬚
Nearest Town Withernsea
Directions From Hull take the A1033 to Hedon, turn left at the roundabout to Preston and follow signs for Burton Pidsea and Roos.
⚏ Hull

SKIPSEA

Mill Farm Country Park, Mill Lane, Skipsea, East Yorkshire, YO25 8SS
Tel: 01262 468211
Pitches For ⬚ **Total** 56
Acreage 6 **Open** 15-Mar **to** 29-Sep
Access Good **Site** Level
Nearest Bus Stop (Miles) Outside
Farm walk, beach nearby. RSPB site at Bempton. Good centre for many places of local interest. Nearby there is a village shop and Post Office, a pub and a heated swimming pool.
Facilities ⬚
Nearest Town Hornsea
Directions The A165 Hull to Bridlington Road, at Beeford take B1249 to Skipsea. At crossroads turn right, then first left up Cross Street which leads on to Mill Lane, site is on the right.
⚏ Bridlington

SKIPSEA

Skirlington Leisure Park, Low Skirlington, Skipsea, Driffield, Yorkshire (East), YO25 8SY
Tel: 01262 468213
Pitches For ⬚ **Total** 275
Acreage 20 **Open** Mar **to** Oct
Access Good **Site** Level
Nearest Bus Stop (Miles) Outside

Facilities ⬚
Nearest Town Hornsea
Directions On the B1242 between Hornsea and Bridlington.
⚏ Bridlington

STAMFORD BRIDGE

Weir Caravan Park, Stamford Bridge, East Yorkshire, YO41 1AN
Tel: 01759 371377
Email: enquiries@yorkshireholidayparks.co.uk
www.yorkshireholidayparks.co.uk
Pitches For ⬚ **Total** 20
Acreage 7 **Open** Mar **to** Oct
Access Good **Site** Level
Nearest Bus Stop (Miles) ¼
On the edge of a river. 5 minute walk from the village and shops, pubs, etc..
Facilities ⬚
Nearest Town York
Directions From the A166 Bridlington road, turn left before the bridge.
⚏ York

YORKSHIRE (NORTH)

BARDEN

Howgill Lodge, Barden, Skipton, North Yorkshire, BD23 6DJ
Tel: 01756 720655
Email: fiona@howgill-lodge.co.uk
www.howgill-lodge.co.uk
Pitches For ⬚ **Total** 50
Acreage 7 **Open** Apr **to** Oct
Access Good (Narrow) **Site** sloping
Nearest Bus Stop (Miles) ¼
Facilities ⬚
Nearest Town Skipton
Directions A59 to Bolton Abbey. B6160 signed Burnsall. Turn off for Appletreewick.
⚏ Ilkley

BENTHAM

Riverside Caravan Park, High Bentham, Lancaster, Lancashire, LA2 7FJ
Tel: 015242 61272
Email: info@riversidecaravanpark.co.uk
www.riversidecaravanpark.co.uk
Pitches For ⬚ **Total** 61
Acreage 6 **Open** Mar **to** 02-Jan
Access Good **Site** Level
Nearest Bus Stop (Miles) ½
Riverside site, great for families. Flat footpaths for easy walking. We sell milk, eggs, tea and coffee. Local shops and pub just a 5 minute walk.

Facilities ⬚
Nearest Town High Bentham
Directions Follow caravan signs off the B6480 at The Black Bull Hotel in High Bentham.
⚏ High Bentham

BOLTON ABBEY

Bolton Abbey Estate Caravan Club Site, Bolton Abbey, Skipton, North Yorkshire, BD23 6AN
Tel: 01756 710433
www.caravanclub.co.uk
Pitches For ⬚ **Total** 57
Acreage 4 **Open** Mar **to** Jan
Access Good **Site** Level
Nearest Bus Stop (Miles) Outside
Situated in the Bolton Abbey estate, this pretty site is surrounded by woodland and the Yorkshire Dales. Many miles of walks around the site. Close to Bolton Priory and Skipton castle. Non members welcome. Booking essential.
Facilities ⬚
Nearest Town Skipton
Directions From the A59 Gisburn to Harrogate road, at Bolton Bridge roundabout take the B6160 sp Bolton Abbey. After 2¾ miles turn right into Strid car park, go through the double gates ahead into the site.
⚏ Skipton

BOROUGHBRIDGE

Blue Bell Caravan Park, Kirby Hill, Boroughbridge, North Yorkshire, YO51 9DS
Tel: 07946 549529
Email: townend450@btinternet.com
Pitches For ⬚ **Total** 24
Acreage 2 **Open** Mar **to** Dec
Nearest Bus Stop (Miles) Outside
Well drained and dry site.
Facilities ⬚
Nearest Town Ripon
Directions On the B6265 in Kirby Hill, at the rear of the Blue Bell Pub.
⚏ Harrogate

BOROUGHBRIDGE

Boroughbridge Camping & Caravanning Club Site, Bar Lane, Roecliffe, Boroughbridge, North Yorkshire, YO51 9LS
Tel: 01423 322683
Email: boroughbridge.site@thefriendlyclub.co.uk
www.campingandcaravanningclub.co.uk/boroughbridge
Pitches For ⬚ **Total** 85
Acreage 5 **Open** All Year
Site Level

Nearest Bus Stop (Miles) Outside
On the banks of the River Ure for fishing, boat launching facility. Table tennis and pool table on site. Close to the Yorkshire Dales. Lodges available for hire. BTB 5 Star Graded and AA 4 Pennants. Non members welcome. You can also call us on 0845 130 7633.
Facilities
Directions From junction 48 of the A1M north and southbound slip roads, follow signs for Bar Lane Industrial Estate and Roecliffe Village. Site entrance is ¼ mile from the roundabout.
Harrogate

FILEY
Centenary Way Camping & Caravan Park, Muston Grange, Filey, North Yorkshire, YO14 0HU
Tel: 01723 516415
Pitches For ▲ ⬜ ⬜ **Total** 75
Acreage 3½ **Open** Mar to Oct
Access Good **Site** Level
Nearest Bus Stop (Miles) ¼
Just a ten minute walk to the beach and Filey town. Handy for Scarborough and Bridlington. 45 minutes to the North Yorkshire Moors, York and Whitby.
Facilities
Directions Take the A165 from Bridlington, at the roundabout turn right onto the A1039, after 200 yards turn right into Centenary Way, follow lane to the very end.
Filey

FILEY
Filey Brigg Caravan Park, Country Park, Church View Drive, Filey, North Yorkshire, YO14 9ET
Tel: 01723 513852
Email: fileybrigg@scarborough.gov.uk
Pitches For **Total** 154
Acreage 9 **Open** Easter **to** New Year
Access Good **Site** Level
Nearest Bus Stop (Miles) ¼
Sea views from the Park. Just a short walk to the town and beach.
Facilities
Nearest Town Filey
Directions Follow signs for Country Park.
Filey

FILEY
Muston Grange Caravan Park, Muston Road, Filey, North Yorkshire, YO14 0HU
Tel: 01723 512167
Email: admin@mustongrange.com
www.mustongrange.com

Pitches For ▲ ⬜ ⬜ **Total** 248
Open Mar to Oct
Access Good **Site** Level
Nearest Bus Stop (Miles) ¼
Beach, fishing resort.
Facilities
Nearest Town Filey
Directions Turn towards Bridlington site is 100yds from roundabouton Scarborough - Bridlington road.
Filey

FILEY
Orchard Farm Holiday Village,
Stonegate, Hunmanby, Filey, North Yorkshire, YO14 0PU
Tel: 01723 891582
Email: info@orchardfarmholidayvillage.co.uk
www.orchardfarmholidayvillage.co.uk
Pitches For ▲ ⬜ ⬜ **Total** 85
Acreage 14 **Open** Mar to Oct
Access Good **Site** Level
Nearest Bus Stop (Miles) ¼
1 mile from the beach. Ideal base for all North Yorkshire attractions.
Facilities
Nearest Town Filey
Directions From Filey take the A165 towards Bridlington, Hunmanby is 2 miles on the right.
Hunmanby

FILEY
Reighton Sands Holiday Park, Reighto Gap, Filey, North Yorkshire, YO14 9SH
Tel: 01723 890476
Email: reightonsands@haven.com
www.haventouring.com/toreightonsands
Pitches For ▲ ⬜ ⬜ **Total** 317
Open Mid Mar **to** Oct
Access Good **Site** Lev/Slope
Nearest Bus Stop (Miles) Outside
A quiet and easy going Holiday Park with direct access to miles of glorious sand. Enjoy kids clubs, family entertainment, a golf course and water fun.
Facilities
Nearest Town Filey/Scarborough
Directions Signposted on the A165 Filey to Bridlington road, 2 miles south of Filey.
Filey

GRASSINGTON
Hawkswick Cote Park, Arncliffe, Skipton, North Yorkshire, BD23 5PX
Tel: 01756 770226
Email: hawkswickcote@northdales.co.uk
www.northdales.co.uk

Pitches For ▲ ⬜ ⬜ **Total** 30
Open Mar to Nov
Access Good **Site** Level
Nearest Bus Stop (Miles) 2.5
We are in the heart of Yorkshire Dales, with quintesential villages all around with pubs and eating houses.
Facilities
Nearest Town Grassington
Directions Take the B6160 towards Kettlewell. After Kilnsey Cray take a left toward Amcliffe. Park 1¼ mileson left.
Skipton

GRASSINGTON
Threaplands Camping & Caravan Park, Threaplands House, Cracoe, Nr Skipton, North Yorkshire, BD23 6LD
Tel: 01756 730248
Pitches For ▲ ⬜ ⬜ **Total** 30
Acreage 8 **Open** Mar to Oct
Access Good **Site** Level
Nearest Bus Stop (Miles) ¼
Scenic views. Bakery on site selling fresh bread, cakes and milk etc.. Ideal for touring and walking.
Facilities
Nearest Town Skipton
Directions 6 miles from Skipton on the B6265 to Cracoe. ¼ mile past Cracoe keep going straight on, site is ¼ mile on the left.
Skipton

HARROGATE
Bilton Park, Village Farm, Bilton Lane, Harrogate, North Yorkshire, HG1 4DH
Tel: 01423 863121
Email: welcome@biltonpark.co.uk
www.biltonpark.co.uk
Pitches For ▲ ⬜ ⬜ ⬜ **Total** 25
Acreage 8½ **Open** Apr **to** Oct
Access Good **Site** Level
Nearest Bus Stop (Miles) ½
Conversation area, cycle ways
Facilities
Nearest Town Harrogate
Directions From the A59 in Harrogate, turn at Skipton Pub into Bilton Lane, Park is 1½ miles down the road.
Harrogate

HARROGATE
High Moor Farm Caravan Park, Skipton Road, Harrogate, North Yorkshire, HG3 2LT
Tel: 01423 563637
Email: highmoorfarmpark@btconnect.com
www.highmoorfarmpark.co.uk

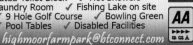

Pitches For ⛺ 🚐 **Total** 300
Open Apr/Easter **to** Oct
Access Good **Site** Level
Nearest Bus Stop (Miles) Outside
Facilities ⛐ ⨍ 🖳 🕸 🅿 🍴 ☉ 🍽 💧 🔟 💩
🕼 🛢 🟠 🗙 🍸 🐾 🖭 🌡 ✖🖭 🖵 🥤 🌿
Nearest Town Harrogate
Directions On the A59 4 miles from Harrogate on the left hand side.
🚉 Harrogate

HARROGATE
Ripley Caravan Park, Ripley, Harrogate, North Yorkshire, HG3 3AU
Tel: 01423 770050
Email: ripleycaravanpark@talk21.com
www.ripleycaravanpark.com
Pitches For ⛺ 🚐 🚐 🚐 **Total** 100
Acreage 25 **Open** Easter **to** Oct
Access Good **Site** Level
Nearest Bus Stop (Miles) ¼
Quiet family site, ideal for touring the Dales, Harrogate and York. David Bellamy Gold Award, AA 5 Pennants and ETB 5 Star Graded.
Facilities ⛐ ⨍ 🖵 🖳 🕸 🅿 🍴 🥤 🔟 💩
🕼 🕼 🛢 🔟 🐾 🌡 ✖🖭 🖵 🌿
Nearest Town Harrogate
Directions From Harrogate take A61 towards Ripon, after 3 miles at Ripley roundabout take the B6165 Knaresborough road, site is 300 yards on the left.
🚉 Harrogate

HARROGATE
Rudding Holiday Park, Follifoot, Harrogate, North Yorkshire, HG3 1JH
Tel: 01423 870439
Email: stay@ruddingpark.com
www.ruddingpark.co.uk
Pitches For ⛺ 🚐 🚐
Open Mar **to** Jan
Access Good **Site** Level
Nearest Bus Stop (Miles) Outside
Ideal location for exploring the Moors, Dales and cities. Only 3 miles from the Spa town of Harrogate. Golf on site.
Facilities ⛐ ⨍ 🖵 🖳 🕸 🅿 🍴 🥤 🔟 💩
🕼 🕼 🛢 🗙 🔟 🐾 🌡 🥢 ✖🖭 🖵 🌿 📶
Nearest Town Harrogate
Directions From the A1 take the A59 to the A658 and turn south signposted Bradford. Continue for 4½ miles then turn right and follow signs.
🚉 Harrogate

HARROGATE
Shaws Trailer Park, Knaresborough Road, Harrogate, North Yorkshire, HG2 7NE
Tel: 01423 884432
www.residentialsite.uk
Pitches For 🚐 🚐 **Total** 77
Acreage 11 **Open** All Year
Access Good **Site** Level
Nearest Bus Stop (Miles) Outside
A quiet and peaceful ADULTS ONLY park. Ideal for touring Yorkshire Dales, spa town of Harrogate (1½ miles) and gardens, Knaresborough (4 miles) and historic York.

Health centre next door. Caravan and Motorhomes max. 25 ft.
Facilities ⛐ ⨍ 🖵 🖳 🕸 🅿 🍴 ☉ 🥤 🔟 💩
🕼 🛢 🔟 ✖🖭 🅿 🌿
Nearest Town Harrogate
Directions On the A59 between Harrogate and Starbeck Railway Station. Entrance is adjacent to Johnsons Cleaners, 100 yards south of the Ford garage.
🚉 Starbeck

HARROGATE
The Yorkshire Hussar Inn Holiday Caravan Park, Markington, Harrogate, North Yorkshire, HG3 3NR
Tel: 01765 677327
Email: enquiry@yorkshire-hussar-inn.co.uk
www.yorkshire-hussar-inn.co.uk
Pitches For ⛺ 🚐 🚐 **Total** 20
Acreage 5 **Open** Apr **to** Oct
Access Good **Site** Level
Ideal touring centre for the Dales. LUXURY HOLIDAY CARAVANS FOR HIRE. Situated at the rear of an Inn in a garden setting in the village. Fountains Abbey 1¼ miles.
Facilities ⨍ 🖵 🖳 🕸 🅿 🍴 🥤 🔟 💩
🕼 🛢 🛢 🍸 🌡 ✖🖭 🅿 🌿
Nearest Town Harrogate/Ripon
Directions 1 mile west of A61 (Harrogate/Ripon road). Ripon 5 miles. Harrogate 7 miles.
🚉 Harrogate

HAWES
Bainbridge Ings Caravan & Camping Site, Hawes, North Yorkshire, DL8 3NU
Tel: 01969 667354
Email: janet@bainbridge-ings.co.uk
www.bainbridge-ings.co.uk
Pitches For ⛺ 🚐 🚐 **Total** 80
Acreage 5 **Open** Apr **to** Oct
Access Good **Site** Level
Nearest Bus Stop (Miles) ½
A quiet, clean, family run site with beautiful views and only ½ mile from Hawes. Motorcycles are accepted but not in groups of more than two.
Facilities ⨍ 🖵 🖳 🕸 🅿 🍴 🥤 🔟 💩
🛢 🔟 ✖🖭 🌿
Directions Approaching Hawes from Bainbridge on the A684 turn left at the signpost marked Gayle and we are 300yds on at the top of the hill.
🚉 Garsdale

HAWES
Honeycott Caravan Park, Ingleton Road, Hawes, North Yorkshire, DL8 3LH
Tel: 01969 667310
Email: info@honeycott.co.uk
www.honeycott.co.uk
Pitches For 🚐 🚐 **Total** 13
Acreage 1½ **Open** Mar **to** Octo
Access Good **Site** Sloping
Nearest Bus Stop (Miles) ¼
Peaceful Park with great views, just a 10 minute walk from Hawes. Ideal base from which to explore the Yorkshire Dales.
Facilities ⨍ 🖵 🖳 🕸 🅿 🍴 ☉ 🔟 💩
🕼 🕼 🛢 ✖🖭 🌿 📶

Nearest Town Hawes
Directions ½ a mile west of Hawes on the B6255 Ingleton road. 17 miles west of Leyburn and 20 miles east of the M6 junction 37.
🚉 Garsdale

HAWES
Shaw Ghyll, Simonstone, Hawes, North Yorkshire, DL8 3LY
Tel: 01969 667359
Email: rogerstott@aol.com
www.yorkshirenet.co.uk/accgde/ydcotts.htm
Pitches For ⛺ 🚐 **Total** 30
Acreage 2½ **Open** Apr **to** Oct
Access Good **Site** Level
Quiet sheltered site, ideal for walks and families, pleasant aspect, river and lovely scenic walks.
Facilities ⨍ 🖳 🕸 🅿 🍴 ☉ 🥤 🍽 ✖🖭 🖵 🌿
Nearest Town Hawes
Directions 2 miles north of Hawes following the Muker road.

HELMSLEY
Foxholme Touring Caravan & Camping Park, Harome, Helmsley, North Yorkshire, YO62 5JG
Tel: 01439 771904
Pitches For ⛺ 🚐 🚐 **Total** 60
Acreage 6 **Open** Easter **to** Oct
Access Good **Site** Level
Nearest Bus Stop (Miles) 1
ADULTS ONLY PARK in an ideal touring area. Near National Park, Abbeys and Herriot country.
Facilities ⛐ ⨍ ⨍ 🖳 🕸 🅿 🍴 🥤 🔟 💩
🕼 🛢 🔟 🥤 🅿 🌿 🔍
Nearest Town Helmsley
Directions A170 towards Scarborough, after ½ mile turn right to Harome, turn left at church, through village, follow caravan signs.
🚉 Malton

HELMSLEY
Golden Square Caravan Park, Oswaldkirk, Helmsley, York, North Yorkshire, YO62 5YQ
Tel: 01439 788269
Email: reception@goldensquarecaravanpark.com
www.goldensquarecaravanpark.com
Pitches For ⛺ 🚐 🚐 **Total** 110
Acreage 10 **Open** 01-Mar **to** 31-Oct
Access Good **Site** Level
Nearest Bus Stop (Miles) Outside
Nearest Town Helmsley

🚉 Thirsk/Malton

HELMSLEY
Wombleton Caravan Park, Moorfield Lane, Wombleton, Kirkbymoorside, North Yorkshire, YO62 7RY
Tel: 01751 431684
Email: info@wombletoncaravanpark.co.uk
www.wombletoncaravanpark.co.uk
Pitches For ⛺ 🚐 🚐 **Total** 118
Acreage 5 **Open** Mar **to** Oct
Access Good **Site** Level
Nearest Bus Stop (Miles) 1

Ideal for North Yorkshire Steam Railway, Duncombe Park, Nunnington Hall, Rievaulx Abbey, Helmsley Castle and Flamingo Land.
Facilities
Nearest Town Helmsley
Directions Leave Helmsley by A170 for 4 miles, turn right for Wombleton. Go through Wombleton and the Park is ½ a mile on the left.

HELMSLEY

Wrens of Ryedale, Gale Lane, Nawton, North Yorkshire, YO62 7SD
Tel: 01439 771260
Email: maria@wrensofryedale.co.uk
www.wrensofryedale.co.uk
Pitches For ▲ ⌂ ⌂ **Total** 45
Acreage 3½ **Open** Apr **to** Oct
Access Good **Site** Level
Nearest Bus Stop (Miles) ¼
Attractive, quiet, family run site. Situated on edge of Yorkshire Moors National Park. Very good centre for touring.
Facilities
Nearest Town Scarborough/York
Directions Leave Helmsley by the A170. 2½ miles to Beadlam, pass the church on left, in 20 yards turn right. Site is 500 yards down the lane.
≠ Malton

INGLETON

The Trees Caravan Park, Westhouse, Ingleton, North Yorkshire, LA6 3NZ
Tel: 015242 41511
Email: stocks@greenwoodleghe.co.uk
www.caravancampingsites.co.uk/ northyorkshire/thetrees
Pitches For ⌂ ⌂ **Total** 29
Acreage 3 **Open** Apr **to** Oct
Access Good **Site** Level
Set in beautiful country scenery. Ideal for walking and touring. Mountains, caves and waterfalls nearby.
Facilities
Nearest Town Ingleton
Directions From Ingleton, travel 1¼ miles along the A65 towards Kirkby Lonsdale (about ¼ mile past the A687 junction - Country Harvest). Turn left at signpost for Lower Westhouse, site is on the left in 50yds.
≠ Bentham

KNARESBOROUGH

Allerton Park Caravan Park, Allerton Mauleverer, Nr Knaresborough, North Yorkshire, HG5 0SE
Tel: 01423 330569
Email: enquiries@yorkshireholidayparks.co.uk
www.yorkshireholidayparks.co.uk
Pitches For ▲ ⌂ ⌂ **Total** 20
Acreage 17 **Open** Feb **to** 03-Jan
Access Good **Site** Level
Nearest Bus Stop (Miles) ½
Woodland park with plenty of wildlife and walks. David Bellamy Silver Award for Conservation.

Facilities
Nearest Town Knaresborough
Directions On the A59 York to Harrogate road, ½ mile east of Aim.
≠ Harrogate

KNARESBOROUGH

Kingfisher Caravan & Camping Park, Low Moor Lane, Farnham, Knaresborough, North Yorkshire, HG5 9JB
Tel: 01423 869411
Pitches For ▲ ⌂ ⌂ **Total** 50
Acreage 10 **Open** Mar **to** Oct
Access Good **Site** Level
Ideal touring base for the Dales, convenient for Harrogate and York. Adjacent to a golf range.
Facilities
Nearest Town Knaresborough
Directions From Knaresborough take the A6055. In 1¼ miles turn left to Farnham Village, in Farnham turn left, park is approx. 1 mile on the left.
≠ Knaresborough

KNARESBOROUGH

Spen House Caravan Site, Spen House, Minskip, York, North Yorkshire, YO51 9JF
Tel: 01423 322542
Email: sam@spenhouse.freeserve.co.uk
www.spenhouse.co.uk
Pitches For ▲ ⌂ ⌂
Acreage 3½ **Open** All Year
Access Good **Site** Level
Nearest Bus Stop (Miles) Outside
Family and dog friendly site with pitches for 5 Vans and unlimited tents. Ideal base for walking, biking, sightseeing or simply relaxing!
Facilities
Nearest Town Boroughbridge
Directions Leave the A1 Motorway at junction 48 and follow signs for Minskip on the A6055 for ½ a mile. Site is on the right hand side of the village 200 meters.
≠ Knaresborough

LEYBURN

Akebar Park, Leyburn, North Yorkshire, DL8 5LY
Tel: 01677 450201
Email: info@akebarpark.com
www.akebarpark.com
Pitches For ▲ ⌂ ⌂ **Total** 200
Acreage 40 **Open** Mar **to** Dec
Access Good **Site** Level
Nearest Bus Stop (Miles) Outside
Situated on a family farm in a sheltered valley in Lower Wensleydale, alongside streams and ponds at the entrance to the Yorkshire Dales National Park. Private 18 hole golf course.
Facilities
Nearest Town Leyburn
Directions From the A1 at Leeming Bar take the A684 to Bedale and Leyburn. Park entrance is 7 miles.
≠ Northallerton

MALTON

Ashfield Caravan Park, Kirby Misperton, Malton, Yorkshire (North), YO17 6UU
Tel: 01653 668555
Email: mail@ashfieldcaravanpark.co.uk
www.ashfieldcaravanpark.co.uk
Pitches For ⌂ ⌂ ⌂ **Total** 30
Acreage 2 **Open** Mar **to** Oct
Site Level
Nearest Bus Stop (Miles) ¼
Ideal for Flamingo Land, Castle Howard, Whitby, York, Scarborough.
Facilities
Nearest Town Pickering
Directions A169 to Kirbymisperton next left passed Flamingo land.

MASHAM

Old Station Caravan & Camping Park, Old Station, Low Burton, Masham, North Yorkshire, HG4 4DF
Tel: 01765 689569
Email: oldstation@tiscali.co.uk
www.oldstation-masham.co.uk
Pitches For ▲ ⌂ ⌂ **Total** 50
Acreage 3 **Open** Mar **to** Nov
Access Good **Site** Level
Nearest Bus Stop (Miles) Outside
Picturesque and peaceful countryside site just outside the town, with Dales scenery. Bus route to the Dales. Convenient for local events and attractions.
Facilities
Nearest Town Masham
Directions From Ripon take the A6108 north west for 8 miles. Or from Bedale take the B6268 south west for 4 miles. Or from Leyburn take the A6108 south for 8 miles.
≠ Northallerton

MUKER

Usha Gap Caravan & Camp Site, Usha Gap, Muker, Richmond, North Yorkshire, DL11 6DW
Tel: 01748 886214
Email: ushagap@btinternet.com
www.ushagap.btinternet.co.uk
Pitches For ▲ ⌂ ⌂ **Total** 24
Acreage 1 **Open** All Year
Access Good **Site** Level
Nearest Bus Stop (Miles) Outside
Alongside a small river. Shops and a pub ¼ mile. Ideal touring and good walking.
Facilities
Nearest Town Hawes
≠ Darlington

PATELEY BRIDGE

Heathfield Caravan Park, Ramsgill Road, Pateley Bridge, Harrogate, Yorkshire (North), HG3 5PY
Tel: 01423 711652
Email: heathfieldcp1@gmail.com
www.heathfieldhp.co.uk
Pitches For ▲ ⌂ ⌂
Open Mar **to** Oct
Access Good **Site** Sloping
Nearest Bus Stop (Miles) 1

131

Alongside river superb scenic walks set in Nidderdale.
Facilities ⚒ ⨍ ⊞ ⊓ ⊘ ⊙ ⊔ ▦ ▢ ☂
℠ ⊙ ⊛ ⬠ ⚓ ✳ ⊬ ⊟ ⬗ ☈
Nearest Town Pateley Bridge
Directions Follow Low Wath Road for 1 mile, turn left after Bridge Inn and follow signs.
⚑ Harrogate

PATELEY BRIDGE
Manor House Farm Caravan Site, Manor House Farm, Summerbridge, Harrogate, North Yorkshire, HG3 4JS
Tel: 01423 780322 mobile0772324
Pitches For ⛺ ⛟ ⛞ **Total** 40
Open Mar **to** Oct
Access Good **Site** Terraced
Close to the River Nidd and the Nidderdale Way. Ideal for walking. Sorry, No Dogs.
Facilities ⨍ ⊡ ⬠ ⊓ ⊙ ⊔ ▦ ▢ ☂
⚏ ⧄ ⊟ ⊬ ☈
Nearest Town Harrogate/Pateley Bridge
Directions Situated on the B6165 between Harrogate and Pateley Bridge.
⚑ Harrogate

PATELEY BRIDGE
Riverside Caravan Park, Low Wath Road, Pateley Bridge, Harrogate, North Yorkshire, HG3 5HL
Tel: 01423 711383
Email: riversidecp@btinternet.com
Pitches For ⛺ ⛟ ⛞ **Total** 50
Open Apr **to** Oct
Access Good **Site** Level
Nearest Bus Stop (Miles) ¼
Situated amidst beautiful scenery by the River Nidd, yet only a 5 minute walk from Pateley Bridge. Fishing permits are available from reception. 5 minute walk from an indoor swimming pool.
Facilities ⨍ ⊡ ⬠ ⊓ ⊙ ⊔ ▦ ▢ ☂
⊙ ⊬ ⊟ ✎
Nearest Town Pateley Bridge
Directions From Harrogate take the B6165 into Pateley Bridge. Go down the main street and over the bridge (River Nidd), turn right at the petrol station into Low Wath Road and the entrance is on the right just past the first bungalow.
⚑ Harrogate

PICKERING
Black Bull Caravan Park, Malton Road, Pickering, North Yorkshire, YO18 8EA
Tel: 01751 472528
Email:
enquiries@blackbullcaravanpark.com
www.blackbullcaravanpark.com
Pitches For ⛺ ⛟ ⛞ **Total** 72
Acreage 4 **Open** Mar **to** Oct
Access Good **Site** Level
Nearest Bus Stop (Miles) Outside
Central location for many attractions and the gateway to the North Yorks Moors and steam railway, Eden Camp, Flamingoland and much more. Holiday Caravans also available for hire.
Facilities ⨍ ⊡ ⬠ ⊓ ⊙ ⊔ ▦ ▢ ☂
℠ ⊙ ⊛ ⬠ ⛁ ⚓ ✳ ⊟ ⊟ ⊟ ⊬
Nearest Town Pickering
Directions 1 mile south of Pickering on the A169 Malton road.
⚑ Malton

PICKERING
Overbrook Caravan Park, Maltongate, Thornton-le-Dale, Nr Pickering, North Yorkshire, YO18 7SE
Tel: 01751 474417

Email:
enquiry@overbrookcaravanpark.co.uk
www.overbrookcaravanpark.co.uk
Pitches For ⛟ ⛞ **Total** 50
Acreage 3½ **Open** Mar **to** 07-Jan
Access Good **Site** Sloping
Nearest Bus Stop (Miles) ½
ADULTS ONLY park in one of North Yorkshires prettiest villages. Peaceful, picturesque location.
Facilities ⨍ ⊡ ⬠ ⊓ ⊙ ⊔ ▦ ▢ ☂
⊙ ⊬ ⊟ ⬗ ⊿ ☈
Nearest Town Pickering
Directions From the A1 follow the A64 onto the A169, then the A170 from Pickering.
⚑ Malton

PICKERING
Rosedale Caravan Park, Rosedale Abbey, Pickering, North Yorkshire, YO18 8SA
Tel: 01751 417272
Email: info@flowerofmay.com
www.flowerofmay.com
Pitches For ⛺ ⛟ ⛞
Open Easter **to** Oct
Access Good **Site** Level
Nearest Bus Stop (Miles) ¼
Idyllic retreat. Ideal for walking and hiking through the beautiful North Yorkshire Moors. Pets wellcome by arrangement
Facilities ⨍ ⊡ ⬠ ⊓ ⊙ ⊔ ▦ ▢ ☂
℠ ⚏ ⊙ ⊛ ⬠ ⚓ ⊟ ⊟ ⊬
Nearest Town Pickering
Directions Turn off the A170 towards Rosedale.
⚑ Malton

PICKERING
Vale of Pickering Caravan Park, Carr House Farm, Allerston, Pickering, North Yorkshire, YO18 7PQ
Tel: 01723 859280
Email: tony@valeofpickering.co.uk
www.valeofpickering.co.uk
Pitches For ⛺ ⛟ ⛞ **Total** 120
Acreage 8 **Open** 01-Mar **to** 02-Jan
Access Good **Site** Level
Nearest Bus Stop (Miles) 1
High standard of service and superb facilities. Peaceful play area and games area. ETB 5 Star Graded.
Facilities ⚒ ⨍ ⊡ ⬠ ⊓ ⊙ ⊔ ▦ ▢ ☂
℠ ⊙ ⊛ ⧄ ✳ ⊟ ⊟ ⬗ ⊬ ☈
Nearest Town Scarborough
Directions From Pickering take the A170 to Allerston, turn right opposite Cayley Arms Hotel, due south 1¼ miles.
⚑ Malton

PICKERING
Wayside Caravan & Camping Park, Wrelton, Pickering, North Yorkshire, YO18 8PG
Tel: 01751 472608
Email: wrelton@waysideholidaypark.co.uk
www.waysideparks.co.uk
Pitches For ⛟ ⛞ **Total** 45
Acreage 5 **Open** Easter **to** Early Oct
Access Good
Nearest Bus Stop (Miles) ¼
Ideal for touring the North York Moors. Walks nearby and historic steam railway.
Facilities ⨍ ⊡ ⬠ ⊓ ⊙ ⊔ ▦ ▢ ☂
⊙ ⊛ ✳ ⊟ ⊟ ⊬
Nearest Town Pickering
Directions 2½ miles west of Pickering off the A170 at Wrelton, turn right off the by-pass.
⚑ Malton

RICHMOND
Brompton Caravan Park, Brompton-on-Swale, Easby, Richmond, Yorkshire (North), DL10 7EZ
Tel: 01748 824629
Email:
brompton.caravanpark@btinternet.com
www.bromptoncaravanpark.co.uk
Pitches For ⛺ ⛟ ⛞ ⛞ **Total** 177
Acreage 14 **Open** Mid March **to** Oct
Access Good **Site** Level
Nearest Bus Stop (Miles) Outside
Along river, ideal touring and camping new for 2012 camping pods.
Facilities ⚒ ⨍ ⊡ ⬠ ⊓ ⊙ ⊔ ▦ ▢ ☂
℠ ⊙ ⊛ ⧄ ✳ ⬠ ⊟ ⊟ ⊿ ⊬
Nearest Town Richmond
Directions Richmond follow signs from centre for A1 south, Brompton on Swale.
⚑ Darlington

RICHMOND
Orchard Caravan Park, Reeth, Richmond, North Yorkshire, DL11 6TT
Tel: 01748 884475
Email: peter.daly7@btinternet.com
Pitches For ⛺ ⛟ ⛞ **Total** 56
Acreage 3½ **Open** Apr **to** Oct
Access Good **Site** Level
Nearest Bus Stop (Miles) ½
All grassed area in an apple orchard, beside the River Swale. Sports area adjacent. Ideal for walkers.
Facilities ⨍ ⬠ ⊓ ⊙ ⊔ ⚏ ⊙ ⊟ ⊬
Nearest Town Richmond
Directions Approx. 11½ miles from Richmond.
⚑ Darlington

RICHMOND
Richmond Hargill House Caravan Club Site, Gilling West, Richmond, North Yorkshire, DL10 5LJ
Tel: 01748 822734
www.caravanclub.co.uk
Pitches For ⛟ ⛞ **Total** 66
Acreage 4½ **Open** Mar **to** Nov
Access Good **Site** Lev/Slope
Nearest Bus Stop (Miles) Outside
Situated in Herriot country with wonderful views of the Yorkshire Dales National Park. Non members welcome. Booking essential.
Facilities ⨍ ⊡ ⬠ ⊓ ▢
⚏ ⊙ ⊛ ⊟ ☂
Nearest Town Richmond
Directions Leave the A1 at Scotch Corner and take the A66 signposted Penrith. At the crossroads turn left signposted Gilling West, site is 100 yards on the left.
⚑ Richmond

RICHMOND
Scotch Corner Caravan Park, Scotch Corner, Richmond, North Yorkshire, DL10 6NS
Tel: 01748 822530
Email: marshallleisure@aol.com
www.scotchcornercaravanpark.co.uk
Pitches For ⛺ ⛟ ⛞ **Total** 96
Acreage 10 **Open** Easter **to** Oct
Access Good **Site** Level
Nearest Bus Stop (Miles) Outside
Cafe/Restaurant adjacent. Ideal for touring. All year storage.
Facilities ⚒ ⨍ ⊡ ⬠ ⊓ ⊙ ⊔ ▦ ▢ ☂
℠ ⊙ ⊟ ⊟ ⊬ ☈
Nearest Town Richmond
Directions Leave the A1 at Scotch Corner and take the A6108 signposted Richmond. Continue for approx. 250 yards then cross the central reservation and return for 200 yards, Park entrance is on the left.
⚑ Darlington

RICHMOND

Swale View Caravan Park, Reeth Road, Richmond, Yorkshire (North), DL10 4SF
Tel: 01748 823106
Email: swaleview@teesdaleonlin.co.uk
www.swaleviewpark.co.uk
Pitches For ▲ ⚏ ⚌ ⚌≤ **Total** 55
Acreage 5 **Open** All year
Access Good **Site** Level
Nearest Bus Stop (Miles) Outside
Facilities ⚭ ⚬ ⚮ ⚯ ⚰ ⚱ ⚲ ⚳ ⚴ ⚵
⚶ ⚷ ⚸ ⚹ ⚺ ⚻ ⚼ ⚽ ⚾ ⚿ ⛀ ⛁
Directions A6108, 2½ miles towards Reeth.
⚏ Darlington

RICHMOND

Tavern House Caravan Park, Newsham, Nr Richmond, North Yorkshire, DL11 7RA
Tel: 01833 621223
Email:
kathy@tavernhouse.orangehome.co.uk
Pitches For ▲ ⚏ ⚌ **Total** 6
Acreage 1½ **Open** Mar **to** Oct
Access Good **Site** Lev/Slope
Nearest Bus Stop (Miles) Outside
ADULTS ONLY PARK, ideal for walking, fishing and visiting historic towns.
Facilities ⚮ ⚯ ⚰ ⚱ ⚲ ⚳ ⚴ ⚵ ⚶ ⚷
Nearest Town Barnard Castle/Richmond
Directions 7 miles west from Scotch Corner on the A66 turn left, 1 mile into the middle of the village, on the right.
⚏ Darlington

RIPON

River Laver Holiday Park, Studley Road, Ripon, North Yorkshire, HG4 2QR
Tel: 01765 690508
Email: riverlaver@lineone.net
www.riverlaver.co.uk
Pitches For ⚏ ⚌ **Total** 8
Acreage 5 **Open** 01-Mar **to** End Nov
Access Good **Site** Level
Ideal base for the Yorkshire Moors and Dales. Easy access to Fountains Abbey and road network.
Facilities ⚭ ⚮ ⚯ ⚰ ⚱ ⚲ ⚳ ⚴ ⚵ ⚶
⚷ ⚸ ⚹ ⚺ ⚻ ⚼
Nearest Town Ripon
Directions ½ mile from Ripon on the B6265 towards Fountains Abbey.
⚏ Harrogate

RIPON

Riverside Meadows Country Caravan Park, Ure Bank Top (Dept No.1), Ripon, North Yorkshire, HG4 1JD
Tel: 01765 602964
Email: info@flowerofmay.com
www.flowerofmay.com

Pitches For ▲ ⚏ ⚌ **Total** 200
Acreage 28 **Open** Mar **to** Oct
Access Good **Site** Lev/Slope
Nearest Bus Stop (Miles) ½
Countryside park alongside a river. Ideal for touring the Yorkshire Dales. Bar complex for all the family. Pets are welcome by arrangement.
Facilities ⚮ ⚯ ⚰ ⚱ ⚲ ⚳ ⚴ ⚵ ⚶ ⚷
⚸ ⚹ ⚺ ⚻ ⚼ ⚽ ⚾ ⚿ ⛀ ⛁ ⛂ ⛃
Nearest Town Ripon
Directions Leave the A1 onto the A61 north of Ripon town centre, ½ mile.
⚏ Harrogate

RIPON

Sleningford Watermill, North Stainley, Ripon, North Yorkshire, HG4 3HQ
Tel: 01765 635201
www.sleningfordwatermill.co.uk
Pitches For ▲ ⚏ ⚌ **Total** 90
Acreage 14 **Open** Apr **to** Oct
Access Good **Site** Level
Nearest Bus Stop (Miles) Outside
Alongside a river for fly fishing. Ideally situated for the Yorkshire Dales and Moors. 2 miles from Lightwater Valley Theme Park.
Facilities ⚭ ⚮ ⚯ ⚰ ⚱ ⚲ ⚳ ⚴ ⚵ ⚶
⚷ ⚸ ⚹ ⚺ ⚻ ⚼
Nearest Town Ripon
Directions From Ripon take the A6108 north for 5 miles, go through North Stainley and the Park is on the right.
⚏ Thirsk

RIPON

Woodhouse Farm Caravan Park,
Woodhouse Farm, Winksley, Ripon, Yorkshire (North), HG4 3PG
Tel: 01765 658309
Email: info@woodhousewinksley.com
www.woodhousewinksley.com
Pitches For ▲ ⚏ ⚌ **Total** 160
Acreage 20 **Open** Mid March **to** Oct
Access Good **Site** Level
Nearest Bus Stop (Miles) ¼
Secluded country setting.
Facilities ⚭ ⚮ ⚯ ⚰ ⚱ ⚲ ⚳ ⚴ ⚵ ⚶
⚷ ⚸ ⚹ ⚺ ⚻ ⚼ ⚽ ⚾ ⚿ ⛀ ⛁ ⛂
Nearest Town Ripon
Directions Located 6 miles to the west of Ripon off the B6265
⚏ Harrogate

SCARBOROUGH

Blue Dolphin Holiday Centre, Gristhorpe Bay, Filey, North Yorkshire, YO14 9PU
Tel: 01723 515155
Email: bluedolphin@haven.com
www.haventouring.com/tobluedolphin
Pitches For ▲ ⚏ ⚌ **Total** 343

Acreage 5 **Open** 23-Mar **to** 25-Oct
Access Good **Site** Lev/Slope
Nearest Bus Stop (Miles) Outside
⚏ Filey

SCARBOROUGH

Cayton Village Caravan Park, Mill Lane, Cayton Bay, Scarborough, North Yorkshire, YO11 3NN
Tel: 01723 583171
Email: info@caytontouring.co.uk
www.caytontouring.co.uk
Pitches For ▲ ⚏ ⚌≤ **Total** 310
Acreage 21 **Open** Mar **to** Oct
Access Good **Site** Level
Nearest Bus Stop (Miles) Outside
Luxurious facilities, playground, shop, dog walk and bus service from park entrance. Seasonal pitches, winter storage and caravan sales. Grass, hard standing and super sites. Low season supersaver & OAP discounts. Scarborough 3 miles, Filey 4 miles, Beach ½ mile. Adjoining village with pubs, chip shop and PO.
Facilities ⚭ ⚮ ⚯ ⚰ ⚱ ⚲ ⚳ ⚴ ⚵ ⚶
⚷ ⚸ ⚹ ⚺ ⚻ ⚼ ⚽ ⚾ ⚿
Nearest Town Scarborough
Directions On the A165, 3 miles south of Scarborough turn inland at Cayton Bay roundabout. The park is ½ a mile on the right hand side. On the A64 take the B1261 sp Filey. At Cayton take the second left at the Blacksmiths Arms on to Mill Lane, the park is on the left.
⚏ Seamer

SCARBOROUGH

Crows Nest Caravan Park, Gristhorpe, Filey, Yorkshire (North), YO14 9PS
Tel: 01723 582206
Email:
enquiries@crowsnestcaravanpark.com
www.crowsnestcaravanpark.com
Pitches For ▲ ⚏ ⚌ **Total** 50
Acreage 20 **Open** Mar **to** Oct
Access Good **Site** Lev/Slope
Nearest Bus Stop (Miles) Outside
New super pitches and toilet block.
Facilities ⚭ ⚮ ⚯ ⚰ ⚱ ⚲ ⚳ ⚴ ⚵ ⚶
⚷ ⚸ ⚹ ⚺ ⚻ ⚼ ⚽ ⚾ ⚿
Nearest Town Scarborough
Directions Just off the A165 Scarborough to Filey coast road.
⚏ Scarborough

SCARBOROUGH

Flower of May Holiday Park, Lebberston Cliff, Scarborough, North Yorks., YO11 3NU
Tel: 01723 584311
Email: info@flowerofmay.com
www.flowerofmay.com

ST. HELENS TOURING CARAVAN & CAMPING PARK
St Helens in the Park
WYKEHAM • SCARBOROUGH • YO13 9QD
TEL/FAX: (01723) 862771

St. Helens nestles on the edge of the beautiful North Yorkshire Moors National Park, just 6 miles from Scarborough. This 36 acre site is divided into terraces with tree screening to create more intimate areas - a feature which enables different areas to vary in character and outlook. With first class facilities, St. Helens is ideal for young families. For dog owners there is a 3 acre dog run exclusively for pets. For those without children, St. Helens offers an 'Adult Zone' which provides peace and quiet. Fishing and watersports at nearby Wykeham Lakes, Cycle Route through Wykeham Estate and a short pathway leads you to a country pub and restaurant. Seasonal Pitches. Storage Welcomed.

www.sthelens caravanpark.co.uk

OPEN 11 MONTHS OF THE YEAR.

AA ★★★★

Pitches For ▲ ⬤ ⬤ **Total** 300
Acreage 13 **Open** Easter **to** Oct
Access Good **Site** Level
Nearest Bus Stop (Miles) Outside
Family run park with superb facilities. Exciting playground, luxury leisure centre with indoor pool and golf. Family bars. Supermarket. Serviced pitches now available with metered electric. Pets are welcome by arrangement.
Facilities ⬤ ⬤ ⬤ ⬤ ⬤ ⬤ ⬤ ⬤ ⬤ ⬤ ⬤ ⬤ ⬤ ⬤ ⬤ ⬤ ⬤ ⬤ ⬤

Nearest Town Scarborough
Directions 3 miles south of Scarborough off A165 signposted at roundabout.
⇥ Scarborough

SCARBOROUGH

Killerby Old Hall Caravan Park, Killerby Old Hall, Killerby, Cayton, Scarborough, Yorkshire (North), YO11 3TW
Tel: 01723 583799
Email: killerbyhall@btconnect.com
www.killerbyoldhall.com
Pitches For ⬤ ⬤ **Total** 20
Open Mar **to** 03-Jan **Access** Good **Site** Level
1 mile to beach
Facilities ⬤ ⬤ ⬤ ⬤ ⬤ ⬤ ⬤ ⬤ ⬤ ⬤
Nearest Town Filey
Directions Follow A165 to Scarborough or Filey sign to Cayton
⇥ Seamer

SCARBOROUGH

Lebberston Touring Park, Filey Road, Lebberston, Scarborough, North Yorkshire, YO11 3PE
Tel: 01723 585723
Email: info@lebberstontouring.co.uk
www.lebberstontouring.co.uk

Pitches For ⬤ ⬤ **Total** 125
Acreage 7½ **Open** March **to** October
Access Good **Site** Lev/Slope
Quiet, country park. Well spaced pitches with extensive views over Vale of Pickering and the Yorkshire Wolds. All pets on a lead. Dog area. Trailer tents accepted. Visit Britain 5 Stars and AA 4 Pennants.
Facilities ⬤ ⬤ ⬤ ⬤ ⬤ ⬤ ⬤ ⬤ ⬤ ⬤
⬤ ⬤ ⬤ ⬤ ⬤ ⬤ ⬤ ⬤ ⬤
Nearest Town Scarborough/Filey
Directions From A64 or A165 take B1261 to Lebberston and follow signs.
⇥ Scarborough/Filey

SCARBOROUGH

Scalby Close Park, Burniston Road, Scarborough, North Yorkshire, YO13 0DA
Tel: 01723 365908
Email: info@scalbyclosepark.co.uk
www.scalbyclosepark.co.uk
Pitches For ▲ ⬤ ⬤ **Total** 42
Acreage 3 **Open** Mar **to** Oct
Access Good **Site** Level
Nearest Bus Stop (Miles) ½
Sheltered, tree lined, level pitches. Ideal for touring North Yorkshire Moors and the coast. Near to Scarborough.
Facilities ⬤ ⬤ ⬤ ⬤ ⬤ ⬤ ⬤ ⬤ ⬤ ⬤
⬤ ⬤ ⬤ ⬤ ⬤
Directions 2 miles north of Scarboroughs North Bay, signed 400 yards.

SCARBOROUGH

Scarborough Camping & Caravanning Club Site, Field Lane, Burniston Road, Scarborough, North Yorkshire, YO13 0DA
Tel: 01723 366212
Email:
scarborough.site@thefriendlyclub.co.uk
www.campingandcaravanningclub.co.uk/
scarborough

Pitches For ▲ ⬤ ⬤ **Total** 300
Acreage 20 **Open** 21-Mar **to** 04-Nov
Nearest Bus Stop (Miles) Outside
Near the beach and the North Yorks Moors National Park. Non members welcome. You can also call us on 0845 130 7633.
Facilities ⬤ ⬤ ⬤ ⬤ ⬤ ⬤ ⬤ ⬤ ⬤ ⬤
⬤ ⬤ ⬤ ⬤ ⬤ ⬤ ⬤ ⬤ ⬤
Directions Located 1 mile north of Scarborough on the west side of the A165.
⇥ Scarborough

SCARBOROUGH

Spring Willows Leisure Park, c/o Blue Sky Resorts, Main Road, Staxton, Scarborough, Yorkshire (North), YO12 4SB
Tel: 01723 891505
Email: swreception@springwillows.co.uk
www.springwillows.co.uk
Pitches For ⬤ ⬤ **Total** 40
Open 10-Feb **to** 02-Jan
Access Good **Site** Level
Nearest Bus Stop (Miles) ¼
Easy reach of Bridlington, Filey, Scarborough and Whitby.
Facilities ⬤ ⬤ ⬤ ⬤ ⬤ ⬤ ⬤ ⬤ ⬤ ⬤
⬤ ⬤ ⬤ ⬤ ⬤ ⬤ ⬤ ⬤ ⬤
Nearest Town Scarborough
Directions From Scarborough take the A64 then A1039
⇥ Seamer

SCARBOROUGH

St Helens Caravan & Camping, Wykeham, Scarborough, North Yorkshire, YO13 9QD
Tel: 01723 862771
Email: caravans@wykeham.co.uk
www.sthelenscaravanpark.co.uk
Pitches For ▲ ⬤ ⬤ **Total** 250
Acreage 36 **Open** 15-Feb **to** 15-Jan
Access Good **Site** Level

Nearest Bus Stop (Miles) Outside
Nearest Town Scarborough
⇥ Scarborough

SELBY

Oakmere Caravan Park, Hill Farm, Skipwith, Selby, North Yorkshire, YO8 5SN
Tel: 01757 288910
Email: oakmerecaravan@aol.com
www.oakmerecaravan.webeden.co.uk
Pitches For ⚏ ⚏ **Total** 30
Acreage 5 **Open** Mar **to** Nov
Access Good **Site** Level
Nearest Bus Stop (Miles) Outside
On site coarse fishery. Close to historic York, the market town of Selby and a designer outlet. 45 minutes form the East coast.
Facilities ⚒ ⚊ ▦ ⚏ ☔ ☺ ⚊ ▣ ☎
⚏ ☺ ⚼ ▣ ⚑ ✕ ⚏
Nearest Town York
Directions From York take the A19 signposted Selby. At Escrick turn left signposted Skipwith, Oakmere is 3 miles on the left.
⇥ York

SETTLE

Langcliffe Park, Settle, North Yorkshire, BD24 9LX
Tel: 01729 822387
Email: info@langcliffe.com
www.langcliffe.com
Pitches For ⚏ ⚏ ⚏ ⚏≤ **Total** 75
Acreage 13 **Open** Mar **to** 15-Jan
Access Good **Site** Level
Nearest Bus Stop (Miles) ¼
Peaceful site in a beautiful area, surrounded by the Yorkshire Dales. Located 1 mile from Settle to Carlisle railway.
Facilities ⚒ ⚊ ▦ ⚏ ☔ ☺ ☺ ⚊ ▣ ☎
⚏ ☺ ⚼ ▦ ▣ ⚑ ✕ ⚏
Directions From the A65 south, take the B6479 into Settle. Go through Market Square, under the viaduct, then turn first right to Horton in Ribblesdale, Park is on the left.
⇥ Settle

SKIPTON

Eshton Road Caravan Site, Eshton Road, Gargrave, Nr Skipton, North Yorkshire, BD23 3PN
Tel: 01756 749229
Pitches For ⚏ ⚏ ⚏
Acreage 2 **Open** All Year
Access Good **Site** Level
Nearest Bus Stop (Miles) Outside
Alongside the Leeds Liverpool Canal, on the edge of the Yorkshire Dales National Park.
Facilities ⚒ ▦ ⚏ ☔ ☺ ⚊ ☎ ☺⚼⚊
Directions 4 miles from Skipton on the A65.
⇥ Gargrave

SLINGSBY

Robin Hood Caravan Park, Slingsby, York, North Yorkshire, YO62 4AP
Tel: 01653 628391
Email: info@robinhoodcaravanpark.co.uk
www.robinhoodcaravanpark.co.uk
Pitches For ⚏ ⚏ ⚏ **Total** 48
Acreage 4 **Open** Mar **to** Oct
Access Good **Site** Level
Nearest Bus Stop (Miles) ¼
In the heart of picturesque Ryedale, this privately owned park offers peace and tranquillity. An ideal centre for York, the Moors, Heartbeat country and the seaside resorts of Scarborough, Whitby and Filey.
Facilities ⚒ ⚒ ⚒ ▦ ▦ ☔ ☺ ⚊ ·
⚏ ☺ ⚼ ⚏ ☺ ⚊ ▦ ▣ ▣ ⚑ ✕ ⚏
Nearest Town Malton
Directions Direct access from the B1257 Malton to Helmsley road.
⇥ Malton

SLINGSBY

Slingsby Camping & Caravanning Club Site, Railway Street, Slingsby, North Yorkshire, YO62 4AN
Tel: 01653 628335
Email: slingsby.site@thefriendlyclub.co.uk
www.campingandcaravanningclub.co.uk/slingsby
Pitches For ⚏ ⚏ ⚏ ⚏ **Total** 60
Acreage 2 **Open** 21-Mar **to** 04-Nov
Access Good **Site** Level
Nearest Bus Stop (Miles) ½
An ideal base to discover the North Yorkshire Moors. York with all its attractions is just a short drive away. BTB 5 Star Graded and AA 3 Pennants. Non members welcome. You can also call us on 0845 130 7633.
Facilities ⚒ ⚒ ⚒ ▦ ▦ ☔ ☺ ⚊ ⚊ ▣ ☎
⚏ ☺ ⚊ ⚼ ▦ ▣ ⚑ ✕ ⚏
Directions From the A64 turn left signposted Castle Howard, drive through Castle Howard Estate until you reach the Malton to Helmsly road. Go straight into Slingsby Village, go round the bend onto Railway Street and continue through the village ¼ mile to the site entrance.
⇥ Malton

SNEATON

North Yorkshire Moors Caravan Club Site, Sneaton, Whitby, North Yorkshire, YO22 5JE
Tel: 01947 810505
www.caravanclub.co.uk
Pitches For ⚏ ⚏ **Total** 92
Acreage 12 **Open** Mar **to** Nov
Access Good **Site** Level
Tranquil site in the North Yorks Moors National Park (Heartbeat country). 5 miles from a sandy beach. Ideal for walkers. Boules pitch

and mini golf on site. Own sanitation required. Non members welcome. Booking essential.
Facilities ⚒ ⚏ ⚒ ▣ ☺ ⚊ ⚼ ▣ ⚏
Directions From the A171 take the B1416 signposted Ruswarp, after 3¾ miles on a sharp left hand bend continue through red gates signposted Maybeck (care required), site is ½ mile on the right.
⇥ Whitby

TADCASTER

Whitecote Caravan Park, Ryther Road, Ulleskelf, Nr Tadcaster, North Yorkshire, LS24 9DY
Tel: 01937 835231
www.whitecotecaravanpark.co.uk
Pitches For ⚏ ⚏ ⚏
Open Mar **to** Jan **Access** Good **Site** Level
Nearest Bus Stop (Miles) ¼
Holiday caravan for hire.
Facilities ⚒ ▦ ⚏ ☔ ☺ ☎
⚏ ☺ ⚼ ⚊ ▦ ▣ ⚏ ✕
Nearest Town York
⇥ Ulleskelf

THIRSK

Hillside Caravan Park, Canvas Farm, Knayton, Thirsk, North Yorkshire, YO7 4BR
Tel: 01845 537349
Email: info@hillsidecaravanpark.co.uk
www.hillsidecaravanpark.co.uk
Pitches For ⚏ ⚏ **Total** 35
Acreage 5 **Open** 04-Feb **to** 04-Jan
Access Good **Site** Level
⇥ Northallerton

THIRSK

Sowerby Caravan Park, Sowerby, Thirsk, North Yorkshire, YO7 3AG
Tel: 01845 522753
Email: sowerbycaravans@btconnect.com
www.ukparks.co.uk/sowerby
Pitches For ⚏ ⚏ **Total** 25
Acreage 1½ **Open** Mar **to** Oct
Access Good **Site** Level
Nearest Bus Stop (Miles) ½
Alongside a river. Ideal location for touring.
Facilities ⚒ ⚒ ⚒ ▦ ⚏ ☔ ☺ ⚊ ⚊ ▣ ☎
⚏ ☺ ⚊ ⚊ ▦ ▣ ▣ ✕
Directions From Thirsk go through Sowerby towards Dalton, the park is ½ mile south of Sowerby on the right.
⇥ Thirsk

THORNABY-ON-TEES

White Water Park Caravan Club Site, Tees Barrage, Stockton-on-Tees, North Yorkshire, TS18 2QW
Tel: 01642 634880
www.caravanclub.co.uk

Pitches For 🏕 🚐 🚍 **Total** 115
Acreage 15 **Open** All Year
Access Good **Site** Level
Nearest Bus Stop (Miles) ½
Part of the largest white water canoeing and rafting course in Britain. Teeside Park nearby provides shopping, cinema and bowling alley. Just a short drive to the coast. Non members welcome. Booking essential.
Facilities 🔧 ✆ 🖪 🖫 🖵 🖭 🛆 🖾 ☎
🖲 ⊘ 🏕 ❌ 🖻 🖸 🖳 ⚲
Nearest Town Stockton-on-Tees
Directions From A19 take A66 sp Darlington. Follow sp for Teeside Retail Park, continue in n/side lane after 200yds take 1st exit sp Teeside Retail Park. At lights t rt over A66, cross r/way br straight over mini r/about cross Tees Barrage Bridge, site is on rt past Talpore Pub.
🚆 Stockton-on-Tees

WHITBY
Abbot's House Farm Camping & Caravan Site, Abbot's House Farm, Goathland, Whitby, North Yorkshire, YO22 5NH
Tel: 01947 896270
www.abbotshouse.org.uk
Pitches For 🏕 🚐 🚍 **Total** 90
Acreage 2½ **Open** Mar to Oct
Access Good **Site** Level
Nearest Bus Stop (Miles) ½
The North Yorkshire Moors Steam Railway runs through the farm. Yorkshire Televisions Heartbeat country. 9 miles from Whitby, 25 miles from Scarborough and 40 miles from York.
Facilities 🔧 ✆ 🖫 🖭 🖵 🖭 🛆 ☎
🖲 🖲 🏕 🖻 🖸 ⚲
Nearest Town Whitby
Directions From Whitby take the A171 west for approx. 3 miles, turn south onto the A169, after approx. 6 miles turn right signposted Goathland. Turn left opposite Goathland Garage.
🚆 Goathland

WHITBY
Grouse Hill Caravan & Camping Park, Nr Robin Hoods Bay, Fylingdales, Whitby, North Yorkshire, YO22 4QH
Tel: 01947 880543/880560
Email: stay@grousehill.co.uk
www.grousehill.co.uk
Pitches For 🏕 🚐 🚍 **Total** 198
Acreage 14 **Open** Mar to Oct
Access Good **Site** Level
Nearest Bus Stop (Miles) ¼
Friendly family run site, set in a tranquil moorland valley. Excellent base to explore the coast and country. 3 miles to the nearest beach (Boggle Hole), and a 5 minute walk to the local country inn.

Facilities ✆ 🖪 🖫 🖵 🖭 🖾 🖲 🖭 🛆 🖾 ☎
🖲 🖲 ⊘ 🖪 ❌ 🖻 🖸 🖳 ⚲ 🗲
Nearest Town Whitby
Directions Signed just off the A171 Scarborough to Whitby road, behind the Flask Inn.
🚆 Whitby

WHITBY
Middlewood Farm Holiday Park, Middlewood Lane, Fylingthorpe, Robin Hoods Bay, Whitby, North Yorkshire, YO22 4UF
Tel: 01947 880414
Email: info@middlewoodfarm.com
www.middlewoodfarm.com
Pitches For 🏕 🚐 🚍 **Total** 120
Acreage 7 **Open** Mar to 04-Jan
Access Good **Site** Level
Nearest Bus Stop (Miles) ¼
Peaceful family park, 10 minutes walk to the beach, pubs, shops and Robin Hoods Bay. Disabled facilities, bath and parent and baby room. Only 5 miles from Whitby. Magnificent views and walks.
Facilities 🔧 ✆ 🖫 🖵 🖭 🖭 🛆 🖾 ☎
🖲 🖲 🏕 🖻 🖸 ⚲
Nearest Town Whitby
Directions Signposted. Take the A171 Scarborough to Whitby road, 3 miles south of Whitby take the Fylingthorpe and Robin Hoods Bay road. follow the browncaravan and camping signs to guide you onto Middlewood Lane. park is 500 yds on left.
🚆 Whitby

WHITBY
Northcliffe and Seaview Holiday Parks, High Hawsker, Whitby, North Yorkshire, YO22 4LL
Tel: 01947 880477
Email: enquiries@northcliffe-seaview.com
www.northcliffe-seaview.com
Pitches For 🚐 **Total** 62
Open Mid Mar to Early Nov
Access Good
Nearest Bus Stop (Miles) ¼
Exclusive SEASONAL ONLY Touring Park. Luxury Award Winning park with panoramic sea views. All weather, all mains, individual plots. New childrens play park. Coast cafe/bar, farmstead shop & deli, licensed bar. Holiday Homes for sale or hire. David Bellamy Gold award park.
Facilities 🔧 ✆ 🖪 🖫 🖵 🖭 🖾 🖲 🖭 🛆 🖾 ☎
🖲 🖲 ⊘ 🖪 ❌ 🖻 🖸 🖳 ⚲ 🗲
Nearest Town Whitby
Directions South from Whitby 3 miles, turn left B1447 to Robin Hoods Bay.
🚆 Whitby

WHITBY
Runswick Bay Caravan & Camping Park, Hinderwell Lane, Runswick Bay, North Yorkshire, TS13 5HU
Tel: 01947 840997
Pitches For 🏕 🚐 🚍 **Total** 60
Acreage 6 **Open** Easter to Oct
Access Good **Site** Level
Nearest Bus Stop (Miles) Outside
Clifftop location with a 5 minute walk to the beach.
Facilities 🔧 ✆ 🖫 🖵 🖭 🛆 🖾 ☎
🖲 🏕 🖸
Nearest Town Whitby
Directions From Whitby take the A174, after 9 miles turn right signposted Runswick. At the T-Junction turn left and the site is 400 yards on the right.
🚆 Whitby

WHITBY
Serenity Caravan & Camping Park, High Street, Hinderwell, Whitby, North Yorkshire, TS13 5JH
Tel: 01947 841122
Email: patandni@aol.com
www.serenitycaravanpark.co.uk
Pitches For 🏕 🚐 🚍 **Total** 40
Acreage 5½ **Open** Mar to Oct
Access Good **Site** Sloping
Nearest Bus Stop (Miles) ¼
A very quiet, sheltered and secure, predominately adult site with lovely country views. Spectacular coastal, country and moorland walks. Close proximity to Cleveland Way, Runswick Bay and Staithes. Village shops and pubs all nearby.
Facilities ✆ 🖪 🖫 🖵 🖭 🖭 🛆 🖾 ☎
🖲 🖲 🏕 🖸 ⚲
Nearest Town Whitby
Directions From Whitby take the A174 signposted Sandsend. Go through Sandsend and Lythe and continue to Hinderwell.
🚆 Whitby

YORK (Near)
Alders Caravan Park, Home Farm, Alne, York, North Yorkshire, YO61 1RY
Tel: 01347 838722
Email: enquiries@homefarmalne.co.uk
www.alderscaravanpark.co.uk
Pitches For 🏕 🚐 🚍 **Total** 87
Acreage 12 **Open** Mar to Oct
Access Good **Site** Level
Nearest Bus Stop (Miles) ¼
Set in parkland on a working farm with woodland walks. On the bus route to York. Ideal touring base for the Dales, Moors, coast and York.
Facilities 🔧 ✆ 🖫 🖵 🖭 🖭 🛆 🖾 ☎
🖲 🖲 🏕 🖻 🖸 🖳 ⚲

Directions Exit the A19 north of York after Shipton by Beningbrough and follow brown tourism signs to Alne Village. Park is in the centre of the village.
⇌ York

YORK (Near)

Cawood Park, Ryther Road, Cawood, Vale of York, North Yorkshire, YO8 3TT
Tel: 01757 268450
Email: enquiries@cawoodpark.com
www.cawoodpark.com
Pitches For ⬤ ⬤ **Total** 42
Acreage 10 **Open** All Year
Access Good **Site** Level
Nearest Bus Stop (Miles) ½
Here at Cawood Holiday Park, which is a quiet rural park, we have worked hard to create an environment which keeps its natural simplicity to provide a trouble free holiday. Some pitches have views over our fishing lake. Ideal for York.
Facilities ⬤ ⬤ ⬤ ⬤ ⬤ ⬤
⬤ ⬤ ⬤ ⬤ ⬤ ⬤ ⬤ ⬤ ⬤
Directions From the A19 take the B1222 signposted Cawood, oppositethe entrance to Escrick Park Estate. Follow road and go over the bridge, at the traffic lights turn right and Cawood Park is ½ a mile on the left.
⇌ York/Selby

YORK (Near)

Goosewood Holiday Park, Sutton-on-the-Forest, York, North Yorkshire, YO61 1ET
Tel: 01347 810829
Email: enquiries@goosewood.co.uk
www.flowerofmay.com
Pitches For ⬤ ⬤ **Total** 100
Acreage 15 **Open** Mar to 02-Jan
Access Good **Site** Level
Nearest Bus Stop (Miles) ¼
Wooded walks and a fishing lake. Ideal for sightseeing in York and the Dales. Pets wellcome by arrangement.
Facilities ⬤ ⬤ ⬤ ⬤ ⬤ ⬤ ⬤
⬤ ⬤ ⬤ ⬤ ⬤ ⬤ ⬤ ⬤ ⬤ ⬤
Nearest Town York
Directions From the A1237 York ring road, take the B1363 to Helmsley, 4 miles to Goosewood.
⇌ York

YORK (Near)

Home Farm Camping & Caravan Park, Moreby, Stillingfleet, York, North Yorkshire, YO19 6HN
Tel: 01904 728263
Email: home_farm@hotmail.co.uk
Pitches For ⬤ ⬤ ⬤ **Total** 25
Acreage 3 **Open** Feb to Dec
Access Good **Site** Level
Nearest Bus Stop (Miles) Outside
Alongside the River Ouse. Ideal base to tour York and surrounding Dales and North Yorkshire Moors. 4 miles to the nearest shop or supermarket.
Facilities ⬤ ⬤ ⬤ ⬤ ⬤ ⬤ ⬤ ⬤ ⬤
Nearest Town York
Directions On the B1222 between the village of Naburn and Stlingfleet. 6 miles south of York City walls.
⇌ York

YORK (Near)

Sheriff Hutton Camping & Caravanning Club Site, Bracken Hill, Sheriff Hutton, North Yorkshire, YO60 6QG
Tel: 01347 878660
Email:
sheriff.hutton@thefriendlyclub.co.uk
www.campingandcaravanningclub.co.uk/
sheriffhutton
Pitches For ⬤ ⬤ ⬤ **Total** 90
Acreage 10 **Open** 21-Mar **to** 04-Nov
Access Good **Site** Level
Nearest Bus Stop (Miles) ¾
Close to the city of York. BTB 4 Star Graded, AA 3 Pennants and Loo of the Year Award. Non members welcome. You can also call us on 0845 130 7633.
Facilities ⬤ ⬤ ⬤ ⬤ ⬤ ⬤ ⬤ ⬤
⬤ ⬤ ⬤ ⬤ ⬤ ⬤ ⬤ ⬤ ⬤
Nearest Town York
Directions From York follow signposts for Earswick Strensall, keep left at the filling station and Ship Inn, site is second on the right.
⇌ York

YORK (Near)

The Ponderosa Caravan Park, East Moor, Sutton-on-the-Forest, Nr York, North Yorkshire, YO61 1ET
Tel: 01347 811233
Pitches For ⬤ ⬤ ⬤ **Total** 40
Acreage 3 **Open** All Year
Access Good **Site** Level
Nearest Bus Stop (Miles) Outside
Near to the historic city of York, North Yorkshire Moors and many local attractions.
Facilities ⬤ ⬤ ⬤ ⬤ ⬤ ⬤ ⬤ ⬤
⬤ ⬤ ⬤ ⬤ ⬤
Nearest Town York
Directions Signposted 800 yards off the B1363 Wigginton to Helmsley road, 6 miles from York.
⇌ York

YORK (Near)

Willow House Caravan Park, Wigginton Road, Wigginton, York, North Yorkshire, YO32 2RH
Tel: 01904 750060
Email: info@willowhouseyork.co.uk
www.willowhouseyork.co.uk
Pitches For ⬤ ⬤ ⬤ ⬤ **Total** 32
Acreage 4 **Open** All Year
Access Good **Site** Level
Nearest Bus Stop (Miles) Outside
ADULTS ONLY SITE. 3 miles from the centre of York. Handy for the Yorkshire Moors, Wolds, Dales and the coast. Shopping centres nearby.
Facilities ⬤ ⬤ ⬤ ⬤ ⬤ ⬤ ⬤ ⬤
⬤ ⬤ ⬤ ⬤ ⬤ ⬤ ⬤
Nearest Town York
Directions From York take the A1237 bypass to the B1363 Wigginton Road, site is ½ a mile on the right.
⇌ York

YORKSHIRE (SOUTH)

BARNSLEY

Greensprings Touring Park, Rockley Lane, Worsbrough, Barnsley, South Yorkshire, S75 3DS
Tel: 01226 288298
Pitches For ⬤ ⬤ ⬤ ⬤ **Total** 60
Acreage 4 **Open** Apr **to** Oct
Access Good **Site** Lev/Slope
Nearest Bus Stop (Miles) 1
Country site, well wooded with pleasant walks. Convenient for the M1. Ideal location for Sheffield venues.
Facilities ⬤ ⬤ ⬤ ⬤ ⬤ ⬤ ⬤
⬤ ⬤ ⬤ ⬤ ⬤ ⬤
Nearest Town Barnsley
Directions Junction 36 on M1. A61 to Barnsley, take left turn after ¼ mile signed to Pilley. Site is 1 mile along this road.
⇌ Barnsley

ROTHERHAM

Thrybergh Country Park, Doncaster Road, Thrybergh, Rotherham, South Yorkshire, S65 4NU
Tel: 01709 850353
www.rotherham.gov.uk
Pitches For ⬤ ⬤ **Total** 24
Acreage 1½ **Open** All Year
Access Good **Site** Level
Nearest Bus Stop (Miles) Outside
35 acre fly fishery with surfaced footpath on site. NEW toilet and show blocks for 2012.
Facilities ⬤ ⬤ ⬤ ⬤ ⬤ ⬤ ⬤
⬤ ⬤ ⬤ ⬤ ⬤ ⬤
Directions 4 miles north of Rotherham on the A630 between Thrybergh and Hooton Roberts.
⇌ Rotherham

SHEFFIELD

Fox Hagg Farm, Lodge Lane, Rivelin, Sheffield, South Yorkshire, S6 5SN
Tel: 0114 230 5589
Pitches For ⬤ ⬤ ⬤ **Total** 60
Acreage 2 **Open** Apr **to** Oct
Access Good **Site** Level
Nearest Bus Stop (Miles) ¼
On the outskirts of the Peak District, scenic views and nature walks. Ideal touring. All new showers.
Facilities ⬤ ⬤ ⬤ ⬤ ⬤ ⬤ ⬤ ⬤ ⬤ ⬤
Nearest Town Sheffield
Directions Off the A57, near Rivelin Post Office.
⇌ Sheffield

THORNE

Elder House Touring Park, Crow Tree Bank, Thorne levels, Nr Doncaster, South Yorkshire, DN8 5TD
Tel: 01405 813173
Pitches For ⬤ ⬤ **Total** 10
Acreage 2 **Open** All Year
Access Good **Site** Level
Peaceful, landscaped, rural and natural site. Near to Doncaster Racecourse, Transport Museum and Epworth Home of The Wesleys. Disabled toilet and shower. NB: We are CLOSED for Xmas & New Year. ETB 4 Stars.
Facilities ⬤ ⬤ ⬤ ⬤ ⬤ ⬤ ⬤ ⬤
Nearest Town Thorne
Directions Leave the M180 at junction 1 and take the A18 towards Scunthorpe. 2 miles after the roundabout, at the Black Bull Inn, turn right. After ½ mile turn left into farm drive and follow through to the park.
⇌ Thorne South

YORKSHIRE (WEST)

ELLAND

Elland Hall Farm Caravan Site, Exley Lane, Elland, West Yorkshire, HX5 0SL
Tel: 01422 372325
Email: enquiries@ellandhallfarm.co.uk
www.ellandhallfarm.co.uk
Pitches For ⬤ ⬤ ⬤ **Total** 10
Acreage 1 **Open** Apr **to** Oct
Access Good **Site** Level
Facilities ⬤ ⬤ ⬤ ⬤ ⬤ ⬤
Nearest Town Elland
Directions From Elland take the Brighouse road, at the railway bridge turn left into Exley Lane.
⇌ Halifax

HAWORTH

Upwood Holiday Park, Blackmoor Road, Oxenhope, Haworth, West Yorkshire, BD22 9SS
Tel: 01535 644242
Email: info@upwoodpark.co.uk
www.upwoodpark.co.uk

Pitches For ▲ ⬜ ➡ **Total** 100
Acreage 10 **Open** Mar to 04-Jan
Access Good **Site** Lev/Slope
Nearest Bus Stop (Miles) Outside
Pleasantly situated close to the Yorkshire Dales National Park. Beautiful, panoramic views over the surrounding countryside. One mile from the Bronte Village of Haworth and Worth Steam Railway. 12 Camping and Mega Pods available.
Facilities ♿ ⚡ 🚿 🛉 ♨ ⌂ 🍴 ⟳ 🔌 ⬛ 🛒 🛒
⛟ 🚲 🏪 ✗ ⛽ 🎱 📶 ∆ ➡🔲🔲 🔲 ∻ ⚲ 📶
Nearest Town Keighley
Directions Situated off the A629 Keighley to Halifax road. Turn by the Flappit Pub onto the B6144 towards Haworth, after 1 mile turn left onto Blackmoor Road, and the site entrance is by the bus stop.
⚞ Keighley

HEBDEN BRIDGE

Hebden Bridge Caravan Club Site, Cragg Vale, Hebden Bridge, West Yorks., HX7 5RU
Tel: 01422 882531
www.caravanclub.co.uk
Pitches For ⬜ ➡ **Total** 45
Acreage 2½ **Open** Mar to Nov
Access Good **Site** Level
Nearest Bus Stop (Miles) Outside
Screened site bordered by a stream. Three walks adjacent to the site. Visit Brontes Haworth Parsonage, walk the Moors and Pennine Way. Horse drawn canal boat rides available at Hebden Bridge (2½ miles). Own sanitation required. Non members welcome. Booking essential.
Facilities ⚡ 🚿 🛉 ⚡ ♨ 🛒 🛒 ➡🔲🔲 ∻
Directions Leave the A646 in Mythomroyd Village and take the B6138 signposted Rochdale (care required, narrow bridge). Site is 1 mile on the right.
⚞ Hebden Bridge

LEEDS

Glenfield Caravan Park, 120 Blackmoor Lane, Bardsey, Leeds, West Yorks., LS17 9DZ
Tel: 01937 574657
Email: glenfieldcp@aol.com
www.ukparks.co.uk/glenfieldcp
Pitches For ▲ ⬜ ➡ **Total** 30
Acreage 3½ **Open** All Year
Access Good **Site** Level
Nearest Bus Stop (Miles) Outside
Beautifully kept park. Lovely walks and places to eat nearby. Close to golf courses and a nature reserve for walking. Easy access and ideal touring base. New 5 Star heated shower block with toilets and laundry.
Facilities ♿ ⚡ 🚿 🛉 ♨ ⌂ 🛒 🛒 ➡ 🛒
🎱 🚲 🛒 ∻ ⚲
Directions From Leeds take the A58 towards Wetherby, after approx 8 miles turn left at Shadwell Harewood sign. After 1 mile take right hand fork, continue for 1 mile and site is on the left at the bottom of the hill.
⚞ Leeds

LEEDS

Moor Lodge Caravan Park, Blackmoor Lane, Bardsey, Leeds, West Yorks, LS17 9DZ
Tel: 01937 572424
Email: rodatmlcp@aol.com
www.moorlodgecaravanpark.co.uk
Pitches For ▲ ⬜ ➡ **Total** 12
Acreage 8 **Open** All Year
Access Good **Site** Level
Nearest Bus Stop (Miles) ½
ADULTS ONLY. Immaculate countryside park.
Facilities ⚡ ⚡ 🚿 🛉 ⚡ ♨ ⌂ 🔲 🎱 🚲 🛒 ➡A
Directions Turn off the A1 at Wetherby and

take the A58 towards Leeds for 4 miles, turn right after the New Inn Pub (Ling Lane). At the crossroads turn right and Moor Lodge is at the bottom of the hill on the right.
⚞ Leeds

OTLEY

Clarion Lodge Campsite, West Chevin Road, Menston, Nr Otley, West Yorkshire, LS29 6BL
Tel: 01943 876300
Email: clarionlodgecamp@aol.com
www.clarionlodgecampsite.co.uk
Pitches For ▲ ⬜ ➡ **Total** 20
Acreage 2 **Open** Mar to Nov
Access Good **Site** Level
Nearest Bus Stop (Miles) ½
Small, quiet, family run with spectacular countryside views.
Facilities ⚡ 🚿 🛉 ⚡ ♨ 🛒 ➡🔲
Directions From Otley take the A660 towards Guiseley. Turn left at the crossroads near the Hare & Hounds onto Buckle Lane, keep left at Chevin Inn and the Site is 200 yards on the right.
⚞ Guiseley

SILSDEN

Brown Bank Caravan Park, Brown Bank Lane, Silsden, West Yorkshire, BD20 0NN
Tel: 01535 653241
Email: timlaycock@btconnect.com
Pitches For ▲ ⬜ ➡ **Total** 15
Acreage 12 **Open** Apr to Oct
Access Good **Site** Level
Nearest Bus Stop (Miles) Outside
On the edge of Ilkley Moor with good views and excellent walks. Ideal base for touring. Many attractions within 15 miles.
Facilities ♿ ⚡ 🚿 🛉 ⚡ ♨ ⌂ 🛒 🛒
🎱 🚲 ∆ 🛒 ∻
Nearest Town Silsden
Directions From Silsden take the A6034, turn right on the bend into Brown Bank Lane, site is 1½ miles on the right. Also signposted from Addingham on the A6034.
⚞ Steeton

SILSDEN

Dales Bank Holiday Park, Low Lane, Silsden, Keighley, West Yorkshire, BD20 9JH
Tel: 01535 653321/656523
Pitches For ▲ ⬜ ➡ **Total** 52
Acreage 5 **Open** Apr to Oct
Access Good **Site** Level
Nearest Bus Stop (Miles) 1
Central for Ilkley, Craven Dales and Bronte Country. Bed & Breakfast available.
Facilities ♿ ⚡ 🚿 🛉 ⚡ ♨ ⌂ 🛒 🛒
🎱 🚲 🏪 ✗ ∆ ∆ 🛒 ➡🔲 ∻ ⚲
Directions In Silsden turn up one way street Briggate, after 100 yards turn into Bradley Road, after ¾ miles turn right, site entrance is third on the right.
⚞ Steeton

SILSDEN

Lower Heights Farm, Silsden, West Yorkshire, BD20 9HW
Tel: 01535 653035
Email: mmsrowling@aol.com
Pitches For ▲ ⬜ ➡ **Total** 5
Acreage 2 **Open** All year
Access Good **Site** Level
Nearest Bus Stop (Miles) ½
Quiet site with good views. Only 5 caravan pitches but any number of tents.
Facilities ⚡ 🚿 🛉 ⚡ ♨ ⌂ 🎱 🛒➡🔲
Nearest Town Skipton
Directions 1 mile from Silsden off A6034.
⚞ Steeton

WALES
ANGLESEY
AMLWCH
Point Lynas Caravan Park, Llaneilian, Amlwch, Anglesey, LL68 9LT
Tel: 01407 831130
Email: enquiries@pointlynas.co.uk
www.pointlynas.co.uk
Pitches For ▲ ➡ **Total** 12
Acreage 2 **Open** Apr to Oct
Site Lev/slope
Nearest Bus Stop (Miles) 1
Set in a quiet away from it all area. 250 metres from Porth Eilian Cove and Anglesey Coastal Path.
Facilities ⚡ 🚿 🛉 ⚡ ♨ ⌂ 🛒 🔲 🛒
🎱 🚲 🛒 ∻ ⚲ 📶
Nearest Town Amlwch
Directions From the A5025 at Cerrig Man follow signs for Llaneilian and then Porth Eilian. Park is on the left 400 metres past Llaneilian Church.
⚞ Holyhead

BEAUMARIS
Kingsbridge Caravan Park, Llanfaes, Beaumaris, Anglesey, LL58 8LR
Tel: 01248 490636
Email: info@kingsbridgecaravanpark.co.uk
www.kingsbridgecaravanpark.co.uk
Pitches For ▲ ⬜ ➡ **Total** 48
Acreage 14 **Open** Mar to Oct
Access Good **Site** Level
Nearest Bus Stop (Miles) ¼
4 Star Park with 2 underfloor heated shower blocks. 2 miles from historic Beaumaris. Telephone booking.
Facilities ⚡ 🚿 🛉 ⚡ ♨ ⌂ 🛒
⛟ 🎱 🚲 ∆ 🛒 ➡🔲
Nearest Town Beaumaris
Directions 1¼ miles past Beaumaris Castle. At crossroads turn left, 400yds to the site.
⚞ Bangor

BENLLECH
Ad Astra Caravan Park, Brynteg, Nr Benllech, Anglesey, LL78 7JH
Tel: 01248 853283
Email: brian@brynteg53.fsnet.co.uk
www.adastracaravanpark.co.uk
Pitches For ▲ ⬜ ➡ **Total** 40
Acreage 3 **Open** Mar to Oct
Access Good **Site** Level
Nearest Bus Stop (Miles) Outside
Scenic views, ideal base for touring.
Facilities ♿ ⚡ 🚿 🛉 ⚡ ♨ ⌂ 🛒 🔲 🛒
🎱 🚲 🛒 ➡🔲 ∻ ⚲
Nearest Town Benllech
Directions Turn left up the hill from Benllech Village square onto the B5108. Drive 1½ miles to California Inn, turn left onto the B5110. Park is 500 yards on right hand side.
⚞ Bangor

BENLLECH
Bodafon Caravan & Camping Park, Bodafon, Benllech, Anglesey, LL74 8RU
Tel: 01248 852417
Email: robert@bodafonpark.co.uk
www.bodafonpark.co.uk
Pitches For ▲ ⬜ ➡ **Total** 50
Acreage 5 **Open** Mar to Oct
Access Good **Site** Level
Nearest Bus Stop (Miles) ¼
Quiet family site with good views, ¾ miles from the beach. Ideal touring.

Facilities
Nearest Town Benllech Bay
Directions A5025 through Benllech, ¼ mile on left going through 30mph signs.
⚉ Bangor

BENLLECH

Cae Mawr Caravan Club Site, Llangefni Road, Marianglas, Anglesey, LL73 8NY
Tel: 01248 853737
www.caravanclub.co.uk
Pitches For 🚐 🚍 **Total** 76
Acreage 6½ **Open** Mar **to** Oct
Access Good **Site** Level
A sheltered site with cheerful hydrangers. 1 mile from the beach. Close to Beaumaris Castle, Butterfly Palace, Sea Zoo and NT Plas Newydd. Own sanitation required. Non members welcome. Booking essential.
Facilities
Nearest Town Benllech
Directions From A55 on approaching Bangor continue on A5 sp Holyhead. Cross Britannia Br. leave dual carriageway via second slip road t rt on A5025. Continue on A5025 (DO NOT turn left) then turn left on B5110. Site on the rt by Parciau Arms Pub.
⚉ Benllech

BENLLECH

Garnedd Touring Park, Lon Bryn Mair, Brynteg, Anglesey, LL78 8QA
Tel: 01248 853240
Email: mike@garnedd.com
www.garnedd.com
Pitches For 🏕 🚐 **Total** 20
Acreage 9 **Open** Mar **to** Oct
Access Good **Site** Level
Nearest Bus Stop (Miles) ¼
Five beaches within 5 minutes of the site. Wonderful views. Cottage and static caravan available for hire. You can also call us on Mobile: 07973 156371.
Facilities
Nearest Town Benllech
Directions From Menai Bridge take the A5025 signposted Amlwch and Benllech. After entering Benllech turn left at Londis Garage, turn into the fourth lane, site is 600 yards on the right.

BENLLECH

Golden Sunset Holidays, Benllech, Anglesey, LL74 8SW
Tel: 01248 852345
www.goldensunsetholidays.com
Pitches For 🏕 🚐 🚍 🚐
Acreage 30 **Open** Apr **to** Oct
Access Good **Site** Lev/Slope
Nearest Bus Stop (Miles) Outside
On coast, path to beach
Facilities
Nearest Town Llangefni
Directions located in the middle of Benllech
⚉ Bangor

BENLLECH

Home Farm Caravan Park, Marianglas, Anglesey, LL73 8PH
Tel: 01248 410614
Email: enq@homefarm-anglesey.co.uk
www.homefarm-anglesey.co.uk
Pitches For 🏕 🚐 🚍
Open Apr **to** Oct

Access Good **Site** Level
Nearest Bus Stop (Miles) ½
1 to 1½ miles from various beaches.
Facilities
Nearest Town Benllech
Directions Follow the A5025 from bridge for 11 miles, go through Benllech, keep left at the roundabout towards Amlwch. Park is ½ mile on the left, 300 yards after the church.
⚉ Bangor

BENLLECH

Penrhos Caravan Club Site, Brynteg, Benllech, Anglesey, LL78 7JH
Tel: 01248 852617
www.caravanclub.co.uk
Pitches For 🚐 🚍 **Total** 90
Acreage 9 **Open** Mar **to** Oct
Access Good **Site** Lev/Slope
Nearest Bus Stop (Miles) Outside
2 miles from a safe sandy beach. Near a farm trail, bird sanctuary, Beaumaris Castle and Sea Zoo. Take a trip on Snowdons rack and pinion mountain railway for breathtaking views. Non members welcome. Booking essential.
Facilities

Nearest Town Benllech
Directions Continue on A5025 sp Amlwch. Turn left onto B5510, continue straight on at crossroads with California Pub site is ½ mile on the right.
⚉ Benllech

BENLLECH

Plas Uchaf Caravan Park, Benllech Bay, Benllech, Anglesey, LL74 8NU
Tel: 01407 763012
Pitches For 🏕 🚐 🚍 **Total** 100
Acreage 18 **Open** Mar **to** Oct
Access Good **Site** Level
Nearest Bus Stop (Miles) ½
Family room, tarmac roads and perimeter parking, 30 plus picnic tables and 3 heated toilet blocks. Near the beach.
Facilities
Nearest Town Benllech
Directions ½ a mile from Benllech, signposted on the B5108 up the hill after the fire station.
⚉ Bangor

BRYNSIENCYN

Fron Caravan & Camping Site, Brynsiencyn, Anglesey, LL61 6TX
Tel: 01248 430310
Email: mail@froncaravanpark.co.uk
www.froncaravanpark.co.uk
Pitches For 🏕 🚐 🚍 **Total** 70
Acreage 5¼ **Open** Easter **to** Sept
Access Good **Site** Level
Nearest Bus Stop (Miles) Outside
Ideal for touring Angelsey and North Wales. Wales Tourist Board 5 Star Grading.
Facilities
Nearest Town Llanfairpwllgwyn
Directions At start of Llanfairpwllgwyn turn left onto A4080 to Brynsiencyn follow road through village site is on the right ¼ mile after village.
⚉ Bangor

LLANFWROG

Penrhyn Bay Caravan Park, Llanfwrog, Holyhead, Anglesey, LL65 4YG
Tel: 01407 730496/730411
Email: penrhyn.bay@btinternet.com
www.penrhynbay.com
Pitches For 🏕 🚐 🚍 **Total** 200
Acreage 15 **Open** 15-Mar **to** Oct
Access Good **Site** Level
Nearest Bus Stop (Miles) 2
On the coast overlooking the beach on one side and Holyhead Harbour on the other. Fishing, sailing, cycling and plenty of walks.
Facilities
Nearest Town Valley/Holyhead
Directions Take the A55 to Anglesey, take exit 3 to Valley, turn right at the traffic lights onto the A5025 and go through Llanfachraeth. Take the first turn left signposted Llanfwrog, Sandy Beach and Penrhyn, Site is on this road.
⚉ Valley/Holyhead

LLANGEFNI

Mornest Caravan Park, Pentre Berw, Gaerwen, Anglesey, LL60 6HU
Tel: 01248 421725
Email: heulwen@ygors.plus.com
www.mornestcaravanpark.co.uk
Pitches For 🏕 🚐 🚍 **Total** 45
Open Mar **to** Oct
Access Good **Site** Lev/Slope
Nearest Bus Stop (Miles) ¼
Facilities
Nearest Town Llangefni
Directions Go over Menai Bridge and take exit 7 off and follow signs through Gaerwen.
⚉ Bangor

MOELFRE

Melin Rhos Caravan Park, Lligwy, Moelfre, Anglesey, LL24 8RU
Tel: 01248 852417
Email: robert@bodafonpark.co.uk
www.bodafonpark.co.uk
Pitches For 🚐 🚍 **Total** 40
Acreage 4 **Open** Mar **to** Oct
Access Good **Site** Level
Quarter of an hours walk to the lovely beach at Lligwy.
Facilities
Nearest Town Benllech
Directions From Benllech continue along the A5025, at the roundabout turn left, after 2 miles go down a three lane hill and back up, at the top of the hill turn right and the site is approx. ½ a mile on the left.
⚉ Bangor

MOELFRE

Tyddyn Isaf Camping & Caravan Park, Lligwy Bay, Dulas, Anglesey, LL70 9PQ
Tel: 01248 410203
Email: mail@tyddynisaf.co.uk
www.tyddynisaf.co.uk
Pitches For 🏕 🚐 🚍 **Total** 80
Acreage 16 **Open** Mar **to** Oct
Access Good **Site** Sloping
Family run park with a private footpath to a fine, sandy beach. Loo of the Year Winner, AA 5 Pennant Premier Park, David Bellamy Gold Award, Welcome Host Award, WTB 5 Star Graded and Finalist of Practical Caravan Top 100 Parks in 2012.
Facilities
Nearest Town Benllech

Directions Take the A5025 from Britannia Bridge, go through Benllech approx. 8 miles, continue to Moelfre Island via left staying on the main road to Brynrefail Village. Turn right opposite the telephone box and International camping sign, we are ½ mile on the right down the lane.
≠ Bangor

MOELFRE

Tyn Rhos Caravan Park, Moelfre, Anglesey, LL72 8NL
Tel: 01248 852417
Email: robert@bodafonpark.co.uk
www.bodafonpark.co.uk
Pitches For Å ♔ ♔ **Total** 50
Acreage 10 **Open** Mar to Oct
Access Good **Site** Level
Near Lligwy Beach. Surrounded by numerous footpaths, including coastal path, fishing and ancient monuments.
Facilities ↕ ⅏ ♠ ⌂ ⟲ ◪ 🖚 ♥
⅏ ⬧ ♠ ⊞ 🖂 ⅏ ☀ ⚓
Nearest Town Benllech
Directions From Benllech proceed along the A5025 to the roundabout, turn right to Moelfre and at MDM Design turn left for 2 miles, site is on the right.
≠ Bangor

NEWBOROUGH

Awelfryn Caravan Park, Newborough, Llanfairpw, Anglesey, LL61 6SG
Tel: 01248 440230
Pitches For Å ♔ ♔
Acreage 1½ **Open** Mar to Oct
Access Good **Site** Level
Nearest Bus Stop (Miles) ¼
1½ miles to the beach.
Facilities ⅏ ⅏ ♠ ⌂ 🖚 ♥ ⅏ 🖂 ⊞
Nearest Town Newborough
Directions From Menai Bridge take the A4080 left to Newborough. In the village at the crossroads before the White Lion Inn, turn left into Church Road, site is on the left after the church.
≠ Llanfairpw

RHOSNEIGR

Shoreside Camp & Caravan Park, Station Road, Rhosneigr, Anglesey, LL64 5QX
Tel: 01407 810279
Email: shoresidecamping@gmail.com
www.shoresidecamping.co.uk
Pitches For Å ♔ ♔ **Total** 100
Acreage 6 **Open** Easter to Oct
Access Good **Site** Lev/Slope
Nearest Bus Stop (Miles) Outside
Bowling and tennis. Near the beach and opposite a golf club. 10 miles from Holyhead, day trips to Dublin.
Facilities ⅏ ⅏ ♠ ⌂ ⟲ 🖚 ♥
⅏ ⅏ 🖂 ⊞ 🖂 ☀ ⚓
Nearest Town Rhosneigr
Directions Take the A55 to junction 5, then take the A4080 to Rhosneigr, opposite the golf club.
≠ Rhosneigr

RHOSNEIGR

Ty Hen, Station Road, Rhosneigr, Anglesey, LL64 5QZ
Tel: 01407 810331
Email: info@tyhen.com
www.tyhen.com
Pitches For Å ♔ ♔ **Total** 80
Acreage 20 **Open** Apr to Oct
Access Good **Site** Level
Nearest Bus Stop (Miles) Outside
Near beaches, 2 fishing lakes, pool near RAF Valley.

Facilities ↕ ⅏ ♠ ⌂ ⟲ ⅏ ⟲ ⅏ ◪ 🖚 ♥
⅏ ⟲ ⌂ ♠ ⅏ 🖚 ⚓ ☀ ⅏ ♠ ⚓
Nearest Town Rhosneigr
Directions Big red gatepost next to Rhosneigr train station.
≠ Rhosneigr

RHOSNEIGR

Tyn Llidiart Camping Site, Tyn Llidiart, Tywyn Trewan, Bryngwran, Anglesey, LL65 3SW
Tel: 01407 810678
Email: ruthtynllidiart@aol.com
Pitches For Å ♔ ♔ **Total** 5
Acreage ¾ **Open** All Year
Access Fair **Site** Level
Pleasant, quiet site near the beach.
Facilities ⅏ ⅏ ⌂ 🖚 ♥ ⅏ 🖂 ⊞
Nearest Town Rhosneigr
Directions Take the A5 to Bryngwran, turn by the Post Office, after approx. 1 mile you will pass a garage on the left and three white cottages on the right, at the third cottage turn right, then fork right, go over the cattle grid and the site is on the left.
≠ Holyhead

TREARDDUR BAY

Tyn Rhos Camping Site, Ravenspoint Road, Trearddur Bay, Holyhead, Anglesey, LL65 2AX
Tel: 01407 860369
Pitches For Å ♔ ♔ **Total** 200
Acreage 20 **Open** Mar to Oct
Access Good **Site** Lev/Slope
Nearest Bus Stop (Miles) ½
Well established family run site, rural location with modern facilities. Views of Snowdonia, coastal walks, sandy beaches (Blue Flag Award) 10 minutes. Ideal touring base, Holyhead port town to Ireland - 3 miles. Separate rally field also available. Visit Wales 3 Star Graded.
Facilities ⅏ ⅏ ♠ ⌂ ⟲ 🖚 ♥
⅏ ♥ 🖚 ⊞ ⊞ ♥
Nearest Town Holyhead
Directions Follow the A55 across Anglesey, leaving at junction 2. First left off roundabout and follow signs for Trearddur Bay B4545. After approx. 1½ miles turn right onto Ravenspoint Road (after the Spar shop on the left), ¾ miles to the shared entrance, take left hand branch.
≠ Holyhead

TREARDDUR BAY

Valley of the Rocks, Porthdafarch Road, Trearddur Bay, Holyhead, Anglesey, LL65 2LL
Tel: 01407 765787
Pitches For Å ♔ ♔ **Total** 40
Open Mar to Oct
Access Good **Site** Lev/Slope
Nearest Bus Stop (Miles) 1
Near to the beach, boating, fishing, Southstack Lighthouse, Holyhead Mountain and many nice walks.
Facilities ⅏ ⅏ ♠ ⌂ ⟲ 🖚 ♥
⅏ ⅏ ⌂ ♠ ♥ 🖚 ☀
Nearest Town Holyhead
≠ Holyhead

VALLEY

Bodowyr Caravan & Camping Park, Bodowyr, Bodedern, Anglesey, LL65 3SS
Tel: 01407 741171
Email: bodowyr@yahoo.com
www.bodowyrcaravansite.co.uk
Pitches For Å ♔ ♔ **Total** 30
Acreage 2 **Open** Mar to Oct

Access Good **Site** Level
Nearest Bus Stop (Miles) ½
Peaceful farm 3 miles from beaches and close to a wide range of sporting facilities. Convenient for touring Anglesey and ferries to Ireland.
Facilities ↕ ⅏ ♠ ⌂ ⟲ 🖚 ⊞ ♥
⅏ ✕ ⅏ 🖚 ⊞
Nearest Town Holyhead
Directions From Holyhead take the A55, turn off at the Bodedern exit (junction 4) and turn left for Bodedern. Bodowyr is the first turning on the left. Site has international camping signs from the A5 junction.
≠ Valley

VALLEY

Pen-Y-Bont Farm Caravan & Camping Site, Four Mile Bridge, Valley, Anglesey, LL65 3EY
Tel: 01407 740481
Email: post@penybontfarm.co.uk
www.penybontfarm.co.uk
Pitches For Å ♔ ♔ **Total** 20
Acreage 4 **Open** Easter to Oct
Access Good **Site** Level
Nearest Bus Stop (Miles) ¼
Small, quiet, family site in an idyllic scenic location, near to beautiful beaches and the coastal path for walking. Ideal location for wind surfing, canoeing and cycling.
Facilities ⅏ ⅏ ♠ ⌂ 🖚 ♥ ⅏ 🖚 ☀
Nearest Town Holyhead/Trearddur Bay
Directions Leave the A55 at exit 3 following signs for Valley and Trearddur Bay (approx 2 miles). Site is on the right before approaching Four Mile Bridge.
≠ Valley/Holyhead

BRIDGEND
PORTHCAWL

Brodawel Camping Park, Brodawel House, Moor Lane, Nottage, Porthcawl, Bridgend, CF36 3EJ
Tel: 01656 783231
Pitches For Å ♔ ♔ **Total** 100
Acreage 5 **Open** Apr to Oct
Access Good **Site** Level
Nearest Bus Stop (Miles) ¼
Convenient to all beaches, very central for touring area. Off Licence. Designer Village Wales 3 miles.
Facilities ↕ ⅏ ♠ ⌂ ⟲ 🖚 ♥
⅏ ⅏ ♠ ⊞ ⅏ 🖚 ☀ ⚓
Nearest Town Porthcawl
Directions Leave the M4 at junction 37, turn onto the A4229 for Porthcawl for 2 miles, signposted Moor Lane.
≠ Pyle

CAERPHILLY
ABERCARN

Cwmcarn Forest Campsite, Cwmcarn Forest Visitor Centre, Nantcarn Road, Cwmcarn, Crosskeys, Caerphilly, NP11 7FA
Tel: 01495 272001
Email: cwmcarn-vc@caerphilly.gov.uk
www.cwmcarnforest.co.uk
Pitches For Å ♔ ♔ **Total** 20
Open 02-Jan to 23-Dec
Access Good
Nearest Bus Stop (Miles) ½
Beautiful valley setting. Good local walks and fishing. 17km mountain bike trail. Glamping pods 7 family plus 3 standard
Facilities ↕ ⅏ ♠ ⌂ ⟲ 🖚 ⊞ ⌂ ♥
✕ 🖚 ⊞ ⊞ ⅏

CAERPHILLY

Nearest Town Crosskeys
Directions Leave the M4 at junction 28 (signposted Risca Brynmawr) and take the A467 north for approx 7 miles. Forest Drive is well signposted with brown tourism signs.
⇌ Crosskeys

BARGOED

Parc Cwm Darran, Deri, Bargoed, Caerphilly, CF81 9NR
Tel: 01443 875557
Email: wyesidecc@powys.gov.uk
www.wyesidecamping.co.uk
Pitches For Å ⊕ ⊕ **Total** 30
Acreage 2 **Open** Apr **to** Sept
Access Good **Site** Sloping
Nearest Bus Stop (Miles) Outside
Close to Brecon Beacons.
Facilities
Nearest Town Bargoed
Directions Midway between Deri and Fochriw north of Bargoed on A469
⇌ Bargoed

CARMARTHENSHIRE

CARMARTHEN

Coedhirion Farm Park, Coedhirion, Llanddarog, Carmarthen, Carmarthenshire, SA32 8BQ
Tel: 01267 275666
Email: welshfarmhouse@hotmail.com
www.welshfarm.co.uk
Pitches For Å ⊕ ⊕ ⊕ **Total** 10
Acreage 1½ **Open** Mar **to** Oct
Access Good **Site** Level
Nearest Bus Stop (Miles) Outside
A small Park on a working farm amidst woodland and countryside. 5 minutes from the National Botanic Garden of Wales and 15 minutes from Ffos Las Racecourse. B&B and sewlf catering cottage also available.
Facilities
Nearest Town Carmarthen
Directions From Carmarthen take the A48 east for 6 miles, turn right then immediately right again into our driveway.
⇌ Carmarthen

CARMARTHEN

Pant Farm Caravan & Camping Park, Llangunnor Road, Carmarthen, Carmarthenshire, SA31 2HY
Tel: 01267 235665
Pitches For Å ⊕ ⊕
Open Mar **to** Nov
Access Good **Site** Level
Nearest Bus Stop (Miles) Outside
ADULTS ONLY SITE. Central and convenient location for touring South Wales.
Facilities
Nearest Town Carmarthen
Directions Carmarthen 1 mile east on B4300.
⇌ Carmarthen

CLYNDERWEN

Derwenlas, Clynderwen, Carmarthenshire, SA66 7SU
Tel: 01437 563504
Pitches For Å ⊕ ⊕ **Total** 4
Open Apr **to** Sept
Access Good **Site** Level
Facilities
Nearest Town Narberth
Directions 3 to 3½ miles north of Narberth on the A478.
⇌ Clynderwen

KIDWELLY

Tanylan Farm Holidays, Tanylan Farm, Kidwelly, Carmarthenshire, SA17 5HJ
Tel: 01267 267306
Email: tanylanfarm@gmail.com
www.tanylanfarmholidays.co.uk
Pitches For Å ⊕ ⊕ **Total** 100
Acreage 8 **Open** Mar **to** Sept
Access Good **Site** Level
Level ground on a former dairy farm. 400 yards from the beach. Membership to Park Resorts.
Facilities
Nearest Town Kidwelly
Directions In Kidwelly turn left at the Spar Supermarket, take the coastal road to Ferryside for approx. 1 mile and turn left at the duck pond.
⇌ Kidwelly

LAUGHARNE

Broadway Caravan Park, Broadway, Laugharne, Carmarthenshire, SA33 4NU
Tel: 01994 427272
Pitches For Å ⊕ ⊕ **Total** 6
Acreage 2
Access Good **Site** Level
Nearest Bus Stop (Miles) Outside
Disabled toilet & shower.
Facilities
Nearest Town Laugharne
Directions Take the A4066 from St. Clears to Laugharne, continue to Pendine and site is ½ mile on the left.
⇌ Carmarthen

LLANDDEUSANT

Black Mountain Caravan Park, Llanddeusant, Llangadog, Carmarthenshire, SA19 9YG
Tel: 01550 740217
Email: davidandsharon@blackmountainholidays.co.uk
www.blackmountainholidays.co.uk
Pitches For Å ⊕ ⊕ **Total** 25
Acreage 6 **Open** All Year
Access Good **Site** Lev/Slope
Small family run Park set in the Brecon Beacons. Ideal for walking, fishing and caving.
Facilities
Nearest Town Llangadog
Directions Take the A40 to Llangadog then the A4069 signposted Brynaman. Turn left at a disused pub (Three Horseshoes) and continue for 3 miles to Red Pig Pub.
⇌ Llangadog

LLANDDEUSANT

Blaenau Farm, Llanddeusant, Llangadog, Carmarthenshire, SA19 9UN
Tel: 01550 740277
Email: patrickofllynyfan@yahoo.co.uk
Pitches For Å ⊕ ⊕
Acreage 20 **Open** Easter **to** Oct
Access Poor **Site** Level
Nearest Bus Stop (Miles) 7
Isolated mountain farm, spectacular scenery, rich in wildlife.
Facilities
Nearest Town Llandovery
Directions A4069 to Llangadog and onto Three Horseshoes, turn left over river bridge. Follow signs to farm.
⇌ Llangadog

LLANDOVERY

Rhandirmwyn Camping & Caravanning Club Site, Rhandirmwyn, Llandovery, Carmarthenshire, SA20 0NT
Tel: 01550 760257
Email: rhandirmwyn.site@thefriendlyclub.co.uk
www.campingandcaravanningclub.co.uk/rhandirmwyn
Pitches For Å ⊕ ⊕ **Total** 90
Acreage 11 **Open** 15-Mar **to** 04-Nov
Access Good **Site** Level
Set in the beautiful Welsh countryside on the banks of the Afon Tywi. Ideal for fishing. Lodges available for hire. WTB 4 Star Graded, AA 3 Pennants, David Bellamy Gold Award and Loo of the Year Award. Non members welcome. You can also call us on 0845 130 7633.
Facilities
Nearest Town Llandovery
Directions From Llandovery take the A483, turn left signposted Rhandirmwyn. Turn left at the Post Office in Rhandirmwyn, site is on the left before the river.
⇌ Llandovery

LLANGADOG

Abermarlais Caravan Park, Llangadog, Carmarthenshire, SA19 9NG
Tel: 01550 777868
Email: aberma@tiscali.co.uk
www.abermarlaiscaravanpark.co.uk
Pitches For Å ⊕ ⊕ **Total** 88
Acreage 15½ **Open** 16-Mar **to** 16-Nov
Access Good **Site** Lev/slope
Nearest Bus Stop (Miles) Outside
Alongside small river, ideal touring and wildlife.
Facilities
Nearest Town Llangadog
Directions On the A40, 6 miles west of Llandovery and 6 miles east of Llandeilo.
⇌ Llangadog

LLANWRDA

Maesbach Caravan & Camping Park, Horseshoe Valley, Ffarmers, Llanwrda, Carmarthenshire, SA19 8EX
Tel: 01558 650650
Email: admin@maesbach.plus.com
Pitches For Å ⊕ ⊕ **Total** 20
Acreage 5 **Open** Mar **to** Oct
Access Good **Site** Lev/Slope
Nearest Bus Stop (Miles) 1
Tranquil family run peace lovers' retreat with magnificent countryside views, ideal for a relaxing holiday escape. Quiet lanes are perfect for walking, cycling and horse riding, or explore sandy beaches at the coast. Ideally placed for touring West Wales. Visit Llyn Brianne Reservoir, Roman Dolaucothi Gold Mines, Aberglasny or National Botanical Gardens, RSPB Reserve or Red Kite feeding station at Llanddeusant, Abergorlech mountain bike trail at Brechfa Forest or the village of Llandewi Brefi as featured in the TV series 'Little Britain', or why not just stay on the park and enjoy the silence!!
Facilities
Nearest Town Lampeter
Directions Turn right off A482 (Llanwrda to Lampeter road) 1½ miles past Pumpsaint sp Ffarmers, after approx. 1½ miles at Ffarmers turn right opposite the Drovers Arms Public House, Park is on the left in approx. ¾ miles.
⇌ Llanwrda

NEWCASTLE EMLYN
Afon Teifi Caravan & Camping Park,
Pentrecagal, Newcastle Emlyn,
Carmarthenshire, SA38 9HT
Tel: 01559 370532
Email: afonteifi@btinternet.com
www.afonteifi.co.uk
Pitches For ▲ ⚏ ⚌ **Total** 110
Acreage 6½ **Open** Mar **to** Oct
Access Good **Site** Level
Nearest Bus Stop (Miles) Outside
Situated by the River Teifi in the beautiful Teifi
Valley. Only 20 minutes from numerous
Cardigan Bay beaches. Swimming nearby.
Ideal touring centre.
Facilities ⛨ ⚿ ⑂ Ⅲ ⎙ ⌷ ⊙ ↯ ▣ ⚐ ⛾
ⓌⒾ ⊖ ⊗ Ⓐ Ⅱ ⚑ ✱ ⚡
Nearest Town Newcastle Emlyn
Directions On the A484 2 miles east of
Newcastle Emlyn.
⇥ Carmarthen

NEWCASTLE EMLYN
Moelfryn Caravan & Camp Park, Pant-Y-
Bwlch, Newcastle Emlyn, Carmarthenshire,
SA38 9JE
Tel: 01559 371231
Email:
moelfryn@moelfryncaravanpark.co.uk
www.moelfryncaravanpark.co.uk
Pitches For ▲ ⚏ ⚌ **Total** 25
Acreage 3 **Open** Mar **to** 10-Jan
Access Good **Site** Level
Situated in a tranquil, rural setting with
panoramic views for relaxation. Perfect base
for exploring the beauty of West Wales.
Facilities ⚿ Ⅲ ⎙ ⌷ ⊙ ▣ ⛾
ⓌⒾ ⊖ Ⓐ ⊟ ↯ ⊞ ▣ ✱ ⚡
Nearest Town Newcastle Emlyn
Directions From Carmarthen take the A484
to Cynwyl Elfed. Pass the Blue Bell Inn and
take the left fork after approx. 200 yards
B4333 towards Hermon and stay on this road
for 7 miles. There is a brown sign on your
left, take that turn and site is ¼ mile on the
right.
⇥ Carmarthen

PEMBREY
**Pembrey Country Park Caravan Club
Site,** Pembrey, Llanelli, Carmarthenshire,
SA16 0EJ
Tel: 01554 834369
www.caravanclub.co.uk
Pitches For ⚏ ⚌ **Total** 130
Acreage 12 **Open** Mar **to** Jan
Access Good **Site** Level
Set on the edge of a 520 acre country park.
Vast range of outdoor sporting activities
available including horse riding, dry slope
skiing and toboggan riding, pitch 'n' putt and
sea fishing. Ideal for walkers and bird/
butterfly watchers. Only 1 mile from a Blue
Flag sandy beach. Non members welcome.
Booking essential.
Facilities ⛨ ⚿ Ⅲ ⎙ ⌷ ⊙ ▣ ⛾
ⓌⒾ ⊖ ⊗ Ⓐ ⊟ ↯ ⊞ ▣ ⚡ ⚡
Nearest Town Llanelli
Directions Leave M4 at junc 48 and take
A4138 sp Llanelli, on the outskirts of Llanelli
turn right onto A484. In Pembrey Village turn
left at signpost Pembrey Country Park and
follow signs to Country Park, site is on the
right before park gates.
⇥ Llanelli

CEREDIGION (CARDIGANSHIRE)
ABERAERON
Aeron Coast Caravan Park, North Road,
Aberaeron, Ceredigion, SA46 0JF
Tel: 01545 570349
Email: enquiries@aeroncoast.co.uk
www.aeroncoast.co.uk
Pitches For ▲ ⚏ ⚌ **Total** 100
Acreage 8 **Open** Mar **to** Oct
Access Good **Site** Level
Good family facilities. Aberaeron is a
recognised beauty spot. Picturesque
harbour, coastal and river walks. Only 200yds
from shops. 5 Star Graded.
Facilities ⛨ ⚿ Ⅲ ⎙ ⌷ ⊙ ↯ ▣ ⚐ ⛾
ⓌⒾ ⊖ ⊗ ✕ ▽ Ⅱ ⚑ Ⓐ ⊟ ↯ ⊞ ▣ ⚡
Nearest Town Aberaeron
Directions Main coastal road A487 on
northern edge of Aberaeron, follow brown
tourism signs. Filling station at entrance.
⇥ Aberystwyth

ABERAERON
Cwmsaeson Caravan Park, Oakford,
Aberaeron, Ceredigion, SA47 0RY
Tel: 01545 581067
Email: elin@cwmsaeson.co.uk
www.cwmsaeson.co.uk
Pitches For ⚏ ⚌ **Total** 25
Acreage 3 **Open** Mar **to** Oct
Access Good **Site** Level
Quiet family site set in open countryside with
wonderful views. Ideal touring location for the
coast.
Facilities ⛨ ⚿ Ⅲ ⎙ ⌷ ⊙ ⚐ ⚡ ✱
Directions From the A487 at Llwyncelyn
(from the south) turn right towards Oakford.
After 1¼ miles at the T-Junction in Oakford
Village turn left, site is 800 yards on the left.
⇥ Aberaeron

ABERPORTH
Caerfelin Caravan Park, Aberporth, Nr
Cardigan, Ceredigion, SA43 2BZ
Tel: 01239 810540
Pitches For ⚏ ⚌ **Total** 5
Open Mid Mar **to** Oct
Access Good **Site** Level
Nearest Bus Stop (Miles) ¼
Well sheltered park nestled in a woodland
valley. Just a 5 minute walk to sandy beaches
and the village of Aberporth. Friendly
welcome assured.
Facilities ⛨ ⚿ Ⅲ ⎙ ⌷ ⊙ ↯ ⚐ ⛾
Ⅱ ⊗ ⊟ ▣
Directions Turn north off the A487 at
Blaenannerch onto the B433 to Aberporth.
Enter the village of Aberporth and turn right
at St. Cynwyls Church, park is 200 yards on
the left.
⇥ Carmarthen

ABERPORTH
Dolgelynen Holiday Park, Aberporth, Nr
Cardigan, Ceredigion, SA43 2HS
Tel: 01239 811095
Pitches For ▲ ⚏ ⚌ **Total** 24
Access Good **Site** Lev/Slope
Nearest Bus Stop (Miles) Outside
Quiet site overlooking the sea. 1 mile from
the beach. Many eating places close by.
Facilities ⚿ Ⅲ ⎙ ⌷ ⊙ ⚐ ⛾ Ⅱ ⊗ ⊟ ▣
Nearest Town Cardigan
Directions From Cardigan take the A487,
then take the B4333, second turning. From
Aberystwyth take the A487 towards
Cardigan, before Cardigan take the first

turning onto the B4333 sp Aberporth, site is
1 mile on the right.
⇥ Cardigan

ABERYSTWYTH
Morfa Bychan Holiday Park, Aberystwyth,
Ceredigion, SY23 4QQ
Tel: 01970 617254
Email: info@hillandale.co.uk
www.hillandale.co.uk
Pitches For ▲ ⚏ ⚌ ⚏ ⚟ **Total** 75
Acreage 6 **Open** Mar **to** Oct
Access Good **Site** Sloping
100 acre park overlooking Cardigan Bay with
our own private beach. Heated swimming
pool, water hook-ups.
Facilities ⛨ ⚿ Ⅲ ⎙ ⌷ ⊙ ↯ ▣ ⚐ ⛾
ⓌⒾ ⊖ ⊗ Ⓜ ⚑ Ⓐ Ⅱ ⚑ ✱ ⊟ ↯ ⊞ ▣ ▣ ⚡ ✱ ⚡
Nearest Town Aberystwyth
Directions Take the A487 south from
Aberystwyth, after ½ mile signposted to the
right, but this is NOT suitable for touring
caravans who should continue for 2½ miles
and turn right at the second sign. Follow signs
for 1½ miles.
⇥ Aberystwyth

ABERYSTWYTH
Ocean View, North Beach, Clarach Bay,
Aberystwyth, Ceredigion, SY23 3DT
Tel: 01970 828425
Email: enquiries@oceanviewholidays.com
www.oceanviewholidays.com
Pitches For ▲ ⚏ ⚌ **Total** 36
Acreage 3 **Open** Mar **to** Oct
Access Good **Site** Sloping
Nearest Bus Stop (Miles) Outside
Near beach and amenities of Clarach Bay.
Facilities ⚿ Ⅲ ⎙ ⌷ ⊙ ↯ ▣ ⚐ ⛾
Ⅱ ⊗ ⊟ ↯ ⊞ ▣ ▣ ✱ ⚡ ⚡
Nearest Town Aberystwyth
Directions Left off A487 (Aberystwyth to
Machynlleth) road. onto B4572 follow down
to Llangorwen Turn left at Crossroads 2nd
on right.
⇥ Aberystwyth

BORTH
Glanlerry Caravan Park, Borth,
Ceredigion, SY24 5LU
Tel: 01970 871413
Email:
enquiries@glanlerrycaravanpark.co.uk
www.glanlerrycaravanpark.co.uk
Pitches For ▲ ⚏ ⚌
Open Apr **to** Oct
Access Good **Site** Level
Nearest Bus Stop (Miles) Outside
Family only camping site. Sheltered touring
area, alongside a river bank with spectacular
scenery. ½ a mile from the beach.
Facilities ⛨ ⚿ Ⅲ ⎙ ⌷ ⊙ ↯ ⚐ ⛾
▣ ⊖ ⊗ Ⓐ ⊟ ↯ ⊞ ▣ ✱ ⚡
Nearest Town Borth
⇥ Borth

CARDIGAN
**Brongwyn Touring Caravan & Camping
Park,** Brongwyn Mawr, Penparc, Cardigan,
Ceredigion, SA43 1SA
Tel: 01239 613644
Email: enquiries@cardiganholidays.co.uk
www.tentsandtourers.co.uk
Pitches For ▲ ⚏ ⚌ **Total** 20
Acreage 3 **Open** May **to** Sept
Access Good **Site** Level
Nearest Bus Stop (Miles) ½
3 miles from Mwnt (seals and dolphins) ideal
base for exploring Cardigan Bay and North
Pembrokeshire.

CEREDIGION (CARDIGANSHIRE)

Facilities ♿ ⚡ 🏠 📶 🚿 ⛽ ⊙ 🔌 🚻 🛒
🍴 ⚓ 🛍 🔥 📮 🏦 🎣 ❄

Nearest Town Cardigan
Directions A487 from Cardigan towards Aberystwyth follow brown tourist signsin Penpar. Turn left towards Mwnt for ½ mile then tirn right opposite our sign.
⚐ Aberystwyth

CARDIGAN

Penralltllyn Caravan Park, Cilgerran, Cardigan, Pembrokeshire, SA43 2PP
Tel: 01239 682350
Pitches For ▲ 🚐 🚍 **Total** 20
Acreage 1 **Open** Easter **to** Oct
Site Level
Approx. 15 minutes from lots of beaches. Plenty of woodland walks and lakes in the valley.
Facilities ⚡ 📶 🔌 ⊣🔥
Nearest Town Cardigan
Directions 3 miles south east of Cardigan on the A484 (Cardigan to Carmarthen road). Turn over the bridge at Llechryd, go straight for 1½ miles, after crossroads Site is second entrance on the right. Wide farm lane which is kept in good condition.
⚐ Carmarthen

DEVILS BRIDGE

Woodlands Caravan Park, Devils Bridge, Aberystwyth, Ceredigion, SY23 3JW
Tel: 01970 890233
Email: enquiries@woodlandsdevilsbridge.co.uk
www.woodlandsdevilsbridge.co.uk
Pitches For ▲ 🚐 🚍 **Total** 50
Acreage 8 **Open** Easter **to** Oct
Access Good **Site** Level
Quiet country site adjoining a farm. Within walking distance of the famous Devils Bridge & Waterfalls and steam train. Excellent mountain bike trail nearby and bike shelter on site. Ideal for walking, bird watching, fishing and touring, or just relaxing!
Facilities ⚡ 🏠 📶 🔌 ⊙ ⊣ 🛒 🔌 🚻
🍴 ⚓ 🏦 🔥 ⚓ 🔥 📮 🏦 🛒 🏦
Nearest Town Aberystwyth
Directions 12 miles East of Aberystwyth on A4120 in Devils Bridge village and 300yds from bridge. Or 3 miles south west of Ponterwyd, turn off A44 at Ponterwyd.
⚐ Aberystwyth

LAMPETER

Hafod Brynog Caravan Park, Ystrad Aeron, Felinfach, Lampeter, Ceredigion, SA48 8AE
Tel: 01570 470084
Email: hafod@brynog.wanadoo.co.uk
Pitches For ▲ 🚐 🚍 **Total** 30
Acreage 8 **Open** Easter **to** Sept
Access Good **Site** Lev/Slope
Nearest Bus Stop (Miles) ¼
A quiet site with beautiful views. 6 miles from Cardigan Bay. Ideal for coastal and inland touring, or just relaxing.
Facilities ⚡ 📶 🔌 ⊙ ⊣ 🔌 🚻
🍴 🏦 ⊣ 📮 🏦 ❄
Nearest Town Aberaeron
Directions On the main A482 Lampeter to Aberaeron road, 6 miles from both. Site entrance is opposite the church and next to the pub in the village of Ystrad Aeron.
⚐ Aberystwyth

LLANARTH

Llanina Caravan Park, Llanarth, Nr New Quay, Ceredigion, SA47 0NP
Tel: 01545 580947
Email: llaninacaravanpark@tiscali.co.uk
www.llaninacaravanpark.co.uk

Pitches For ▲ 🚐 🚍 🚍 **Total** 45
Acreage 5 **Open** Apr **to** 30-Oct
Access Good **Site** Level
Nearest Bus Stop (Miles) Outside
Well placed to visit all beaches and coves along Cardigan Bay.
Facilities ⚡ 🏠 📶 🔌 ⊙ ⊣ 🚻
🍴 🏦 📮 ❄
Nearest Town New Quay
Directions Entrance is on the A487 at the B4342 junction to New Quay. 20 miles south of Aberystwyth.
⚐ Aberystwyth

LLANARTH

Shawsmead Caravan Club Site, Oakford, Llanarth, Ceredigion, SA47 0RN
Tel: 01545 580423
www.caravanclub.co.uk
Pitches For 🚐 🚍 **Total** 50
Acreage 4 **Open** Mar **to** Oct
Access Good **Site** Level
Peaceful meadowland site with pleasant views of the coast and Cardigan Bay. 4 miles from the coast. Ideal for bird watching including Red Kite. Close to two cheese factories and local craft centres. Non members welcome. Booking essential.
Facilities ⚡ 🏠 📶 🔌 ⊙ ⊣ 🔌 🚻
🍴 🏦 ⊣ 📮 🏦 ❄
Nearest Town Llanarth
Directions From the A487, in Llwyncelyn turn onto the B4342 signposted Ystrad Aeron. At the crossroads go straight on, site is 1¼ miles on the right.
⚐ Llanarth

LLANGRANNOG

Maes Glas Caravan Park, Penbryn, Sarnau, Llandysul, Ceredigion, SA44 6QE
Tel: 01239 654268
Email: enquiries@maesglascaravanpark.co.uk
www.maesglascaravanpark.co.uk
Pitches For ▲ 🚐 🚍 **Total** 10
Acreage 4 **Open** Mar **to** Oct
Access Good **Site** Level
Nearest Bus Stop (Miles) Outside
Near Penbryn beach. David Bellamy Gold Award for Conservation. Buses in summer only.
Facilities ⚡ 📶 🔌 ⊙ ⊣ 🔌 🚻
🍴 🏦 ⚓ 🔥 🏦 ⊣ 📮 🏦 ❄
Nearest Town Llangrannog
Directions Turn off the A487 between Cardigan and New Quay in the village of Sarnau by the old church, signposted Penbryn. Follow the road down for ¾ miles to the telephone box, at next junction bear left and the park entrance is on the right.
⚐ Aberystwyth

LLANON

Woodlands Holiday Park, Llanon, Ceredigion, SY23 5LX
Tel: 01974 202342
Email: info@woodlandsholidayparkllanon.co.uk
www.woodlandsholidayparkllanon.co.uk
Pitches For ▲ 🚐 🚍 **Total** 40
Acreage 4 **Open** Mar **to** Oct
Access Good **Site** Level
Nearest Bus Stop (Miles) ¼
Ideal for a quiet, relaxing break. 200 metres from the beach. 3 miles from the quaint harbourside town of Aberaeron.
Facilities ⚡ 🏠 📶 🔌 ⊙ ⊣ 🔌 🚻
🍴 🏦 ⊣ 📮 🏦 ❄ 🛜
Nearest Town Aberaeron

Directions 3 miles north of Aberaeron on the A487, in the village of Llanon, turn left at the International sign towards the sea.
⚐ Aberystwyth

LLANRHYSTUD

Morfa Caravan Park, Morfa, Llanrhystud, Ceredigion, SY23 5BU
Tel: 01974 202253
Email: morfa@morfa.net
www.morfa.net
Pitches For ▲ 🚐 🚍 **Total** 20
Open Apr **to** Oct
Access Good **Site** Level
Nearest Bus Stop (Miles) 1
Situated on seafront of sandy beach.
Facilities ♿ ⚡ 📶 🔌 ⊙ ⊣ 🛒 🔌 🚻
🍴 🏦 ⊙ 🏦 🔥 ⊣ 📮 ✂
Nearest Town Aberaeron
Directions From Aberystwyth take the A487 towards Aberaeron. In Llanrhystud turn right opposite the petrol station.
⚐ Aberystwyth

LLANRHYSTUD

Pengarreg Caravan Park, Llanrhystud, Ceredigion, SY23 5DJ
Tel: 01974 202247
Email: miller_i@btconnect.com
www.utowcaravans.co.uk
Pitches For ▲ 🚐 🚍
Open Mar **to** Jan
Access Good **Site** Level
Nearest Bus Stop (Miles) ¼
On the beach and by a river. Ideal for hillside walks. Two play areas.
Facilities ♿ ⚡ 📮 🏠 📶 🔌 ⊙ ⊣ 🛒 🔌 🚻
🍴 🏦 ⊙ 🏦 ✗ ⚓ 🏦 🔥 ⊣ 📮 ✂ ❄
Nearest Town Aberystwyth
Directions 9 miles south of Aberystwyth on the A487, opposite the Texaco Garage.
⚐ Aberystwyth

NEW QUAY

Cardigan Bay Camping & Caravanning Club Site, Llwynhelyg, Cross Inn, Ceredigion, SA44 6LW
Tel: 01545 560029
Email: cardigan.baysite@thefriendlyclub.co.uk
www.campingandcaravanningclub.co.uk/ cardiganbay
Pitches For ▲ 🚐 🚍 **Total** 90
Acreage 14 **Open** 21-Mar **to** 04-Nov
Access Difficult **Site** Lev/Slope
Nearest Bus Stop (Miles) 1
Near to golden beaches, forests and lakes. 3 miles from horse racing and close to many attractions. WTB 4 Star Graded and AA 3 Pennants. Non members welcome. You can also call us on 0845 130 7633.
Facilities ♿ ⚡ 🏠 📶 🔌 ⊙ ⊣ 🛒 🔌 🚻
🍴 🏦 🏦 🔥 ⊣ 📮 🏦 ❄
Directions From the A487 Cardigan to Aberystwyth road, at Synod Inn turn left onto the A486 signposted New Quay. After 2 miles in the village of Cross Inn turn left after the Penrhiwgated Arms Pub, site is on the right after approx. ¾ miles.
⚐ Aberystwyth

NEW QUAY

Cei Bach Country Club, Parc-Y-Brwcs, Cei Bach, New Quay, Ceredigion, SA45 9SL
Tel: 01545 580237
Email: paul.wynne4@virgin.net
www.cei-bach.co.uk
Pitches For ▲ 🚐 🚍 **Total** 60
Acreage 3 **Open** Mar **to** Oct
Access Poor **Site** Sloping

Nearest Bus Stop (Miles) 1
On the beach with great views of the coast line. Coastal walk to Aberaeron.
Facilities ⚡ 🚿 🏪 ♿ 🛒 ⊙ 🚠 🔥 ▢ ☎
🛟 🚮 🔌 🛟 🔲
Nearest Town New Quay
Directions From the A487 take the B4342 for New Quay. Follow the road to Quay-West and Cambrian Hotel crossroads, take the road signed for Cei Bach for 1 mile.
🚉 Aberystwyth

NEW QUAY

Frondeg Caravan Park, Gilfachreda, Nr New Quay, Ceredigion, SA45 9SP
Tel: 01545 580444
Email: steve@cbmwc.org
Pitches For ▲ ⚑ 🚐 **Total** 12
Acreage 1 **Open** Apr **to** Oct
Access Good **Site** Level
Nearest Bus Stop (Miles) ¼
Rural family site in quite valley, 10 minutes walk from beaches, home to Cardigan Bays Bottlenose Dolphins.
Facilities 🚿 🏪 ♿ 🛒 ⊙ 🚠 ▢ ☎
Nearest Town Newquay
Directions 1 mile from Newquay in village of Gilfachreda.
🚉 Aberystwyth

NEW QUAY

Pencnwc Holiday Park, Cross Inn, New Quay, Llandysul, Ceredigion, SA44 6NL
Tel: 01545 560479
Email: holidays@pencnwc.co.uk
www.pencnwc.co.uk
Pitches For ▲ ⚑ 🚐 **Total** 100
Acreage 10 **Open** Mar **to** Oct
Access Good **Site** Level
Nearest Bus Stop (Miles) Outside
Open spaces. 2 miles from the beach. Ideal touring.
Facilities ♿ ⚡ 🚿 🏪 ♿ 🛒 ⊙ 🚠 ▢ ☎
🍽 🛟 🐕 🛒 🍴 🍷 🍺 🎱 🎮 🐎 🛟 🚮 🔌 ▢ ☎ 🏊 ⚓
🏸
Nearest Town Aberystwyth
Directions Take the A487 south to Synod Inn, then take the A486 towards New Quay, Park is 2 miles on the left.
🚉 Aberystwyth

NEW QUAY

Tydu Vale Caravan Park, Pantrhyn, Cwmtodu, Llwyndafydd, Ceredigion, SA44 6LH
7852469335
Pitches For ▲ ⚑ 🚐 **Total** 6
Acreage 2 **Open** Mar **to** Oct
Access Good **Site** Sloping
Nearest Bus Stop (Miles) 1
Coastal path 100 yards away.
Facilities ⚡ ⚡ 🚿 🏪 ⊙ 🛒 🐕 🎱 ✕ 🐎 🛟
Nearest Town Cardigan
Directions A487 main road.
🚉 Aberystwyth

NEW QUAY

Wern Mill Camping Site, Gilfachreda, New Quay, Ceredigion, SA45 9SP
Tel: 01545 580699
Pitches For ▲ ⚑ 🚐 **Total** 50
Acreage 2½ **Open** Easter **to** Oct
Access Good **Site** Level
Very sheltered, family site. ½ mile from two sandy beaches. Idyllic walks. Ideal centre for touring Mid Wales.
Facilities ⚡ 🚿 🏪 ♿ 🛒 ⊙ 🚠 ☎
🍽 🛟 🚮 🛟 ☎
Nearest Town New Quay

Directions From Aberystwyth take the A487 via Aberaeron to Llanarth. Gilfachrheda is located 1½ miles from Llanarth on the B4342 to New Quay road.
🚉 Aberystwyth

NEWCASTLE EMLYN

Cenarth Falls Holiday Park, Cenarth, Newcastle Emlyn, Ceredigion, SA38 9JS
Tel: 01239 710345
Email: enquiries@cenarth-holipark.co.uk
www.cenarth-holipark.co.uk
Pitches For ▲ ⚑ 🚐 **Total** 30
Acreage 2 **Open** Mar **to** Mid Nov
Access Good **Site** Level
Nearest Bus Stop (Miles) ¼
Ideal touring location for the coast and countryside. Near Coastal National Park. Indoor swimming pool with sauna, steam rooms, jacuzzi and leisure suite. Holders of numerous awards including Wales in Bloom, Calor Gas Best Park in Britain Award and David Bellamy Gold Award.
Facilities ♿ ⚡ 🚿 🏪 ♿ 🛒 ⊙ 🚠 ▢ ☎
🛟 🐕 🛒 ✕ 🍷 🍴 🎱 🐎 🌲 🐎 🛟 🚮 🔌 ▢ ☎ ⚓
Nearest Town Newcastle Emlyn
Directions 3 miles west of Newcastle Emlyn on the A484. Cross Cenarth Bridge and travel for ¼ mile, turn right at directional signs for the park.
🚉 Carmarthen

SARNAU

Brynawelon Touring & Camping Park, Sarnau, Llandysul, Ceredigion, SA44 6RE
Tel: 01239 654584
Email: info@brynaweloncp.co.uk
www.brynaweloncp.co.uk
Pitches For ▲ ⚑ 🚐 **Total** 40
Acreage 4 **Open** Mar **to** Oct
Access Good **Site** Level
Nearest Bus Stop (Miles) ¼
Quiet family site with rural surroundings. 2 miles from Penbryn Beach.
Facilities ♿ ⚡ 🚿 🏪 ♿ 🛒 ⊙ 🚠 ▢ ☎
🛟 🐕 🎱 🚮 🔌 ▢ 🏸 📶
Nearest Town Cardigan
Directions Travelling north on A487 take a right turn at Sarnau crossroads, site is 600 yards on the left.
🚉 Carmarthen

SARNAU

Dyffryn Bern Caravan Park, Penbryn, Sarnau, Llandysul, Ceredigion, SA44 6RD
Tel: 01239 810900
Email: info@dyffryn.com
www.dyffryn.com
Pitches For ▲ ⚑ 🚐
Open Mar **to** Dec **Access** Poor
Site Lev/slope
Nearest Bus Stop (Miles) ¼
Near beaches.
Facilities ⚡ 🚿 🏪 ♿ 🛒 ⊙ 🚠 ▢ 🐕 🌲 ▢
Nearest Town Cardigan
Directions ¼ mile from the A487 between Penbyn and Tresaith beaches.
🚉 Carmarthen

SARNAU

Treddafydd Farm, Treddafydd, Sarnau, Llandysul, Ceredigion, SA44 6PZ
Tel: 01239 654551
Pitches For ▲ ⚑ 🚐 **Total** 10
Acreage 1 **Open** May **to** Sept
Access Good **Site** Sloping
Nearest Bus Stop (Miles) ½
1 mile from sandy Penbryn beach.
Facilities ⚡ 🏪 ♿ 🛒 ⊙ 🚠 ▢ ▢ 🔲

Nearest Town Cardigan
Directions 1 mile from the A487, in the village of Sarnau turn by the church then first left.
🚉 Carmarthen/Aberystwyth

CONWY
ABERGELE

Henllys Farm Camping & Touring Site, Henllys, Towyn, Abergele, Conwy, LL22 9UF
Tel: 01745 351208
www.henllys.com
Pitches For ▲ ⚑ 🚐 **Total** 280
Acreage 14 **Open** Mar **to** Octr
Access Good **Site** Level
Nearest Bus Stop (Miles) ¼
Level site adjoining farm land, yet close to attractions.
Facilities ♿ ⚡ 🏪 ♿ 🛒 ⊙ 🚠 ▢ ☎
🛟 🐕 🚮 🔌 ▢ 🔲
Nearest Town Rhyl
Directions 3 miles west of Rhyl on the A548 coast road.
🚉 Rhyl

ABERGELE

Hunters Hamlet Touring Caravan Park, Sirior Goch Farm, Betws-Yn-Rhos, Abergele, Conwy, LL22 8PL
Tel: 01745 832237
Email: huntershamlet@aol.com
www.huntershamlet.co.uk
Pitches For ⚑ 🚐 **Total** 30
Acreage 2½ **Open** Mar **to** Oct
Access Good **Site** Sloping
Nearest Bus Stop (Miles) ½
Within easy distance to Llandudno, Snowdonia, Anglesey.
Facilities ♿ ⚡ 🏪 🚿 🏪 ♿ 🛒 ⊙ 🚠 ▢ ☎
🛟 🐕 🚮 🔌 ▢ 📶
Nearest Town Abergele
Directions Junc 24 off A55. A547 into Abergele. turn left onto the A548 to Llanrwst. Right, B5381 towards Betws-yn Rhos we are on the left.
🚉 Abergele

ABERGELE

Owen's Caravan Park, Gainc Bach, Towyn Road, Towyn, Abergele, Conwy, LL22 9ES
Email: info@owenscp.co.uk
www.owenscaravanpark.co.uk
Pitches For ⚑ 🚐 **Total** 12
Open Mar **to** Oct
Access Good **Site** Level
Nearest Bus Stop (Miles) Outside
Near the coast, within walking distance of local amenities and entertainment.
Facilities ⚡ 🏪 🚿 🏪 ♿ 🛒 🔌 ▢ ☎
🐕 🔌 📶
Nearest Town Towyn
Directions From Rhyl, follow A548 coast road first park on right afterTowyn Church.
🚉 Rhyl

ABERGELE

Roberts Caravan Park, Waterloo Service Station, Penrefail Cross Roads, Abergele, Conwy, LL22 8PN
Tel: 01745 833265
Email: gailyroberts@btinternet.com
Pitches For ⚑ 🚐 **Total** 60
Open Mid Mar **to** Oct
Access Good **Site** Lev/Slope
Nearest Bus Stop (Miles) Outside
A quiet, tidy site with a well stocked shop. Near the beach and within easy reach of the Snowdonia mountain range.

CONWY

Facilities ♿ ⚡ 🚿 📶 ♨ ⌂ ⊙ 🚻 ☎
♿ 📶 ⊙ 🚿 ▣ 🅿 ⚡ ☼❄
Nearest Town Abergele
Directions From Abergele take the A548
Llanrwst road for 2 miles, at the crossroads
of the B5381 turn left towards St. Asaph, site
is 100 yards on the right of the junction.
≠ Rhyl

BETWS-Y-COED

Camp Snowdonia, Tan Aeldroch Farm,
Dolwyddelan, Conwy, LL25 0LZ
Tel: 01690 750225
Email: ruegg.peel@virgin.net
Pitches For ▲ 🚐 🚙 **Total** 34
Acreage 3 **Open** End March **to** Oct
Access Good **Site** Level
Nearest Bus Stop (Miles) ½
Tranquil, unspoilt site on a working hill farm
in Snowdonia National Park. In the stunning
Lledr Valley with pitches alongside the River
Lledr. Campfires allowed. Walks and
mountain biking from the site. Pub, restaurant
and shop 2 miles.
Facilities ▣ 🚻 🅿 ◫
Nearest Town Betws-y-Coed
Directions From the A5 before Betws Bridge
turn onto the A470. Pass under the railway
viaduct and turn left to the site after approx
¾ miles.
≠ Pont-y-Pant

BETWS-Y-COED

Cwmlanerch Caravan Park, Betws-y-
Coed, Conwy, LL24 0BG
Tel: 01492 642770
Email: food@delinorthwales.co.uk
www.cwmlanerch-snowdonia.co.uk
Pitches For ▲ 🚐 🚙 **Total** 40
Open Mar **to** Nov
Access Good **Site** Level
Nearest Bus Stop (Miles) 1
In the heart of the Snowdonia National Park
and alongside the River Conwy. Ideal location
for walking and mountain biking (Marin Trail
close by). Many attractions nearby.
Facilities ⚡ 🚿 🚻 🅿 ♨ ⊙ 🚽 ▣ ☎
🚮 ◫ 🚻 🅿 ✦ ☼❄
Nearest Town Betws-y-Coed
Directions From Betws-y-Coed take the
B5106 and the park is 1 mile on the right.
≠ Betws-y-Coed

BETWS-Y-COED

Rynys Farm Camping Site, Rynys Farm,
Nr Betws-y-Coed, Llanrwst, Conwy, LL26
0RU
Tel: 01690 710218
Email: carol@rynys-camping.co.uk
www.rynys-camping.co.uk
Pitches For ▲ 🚐 🚙
Acreage 6 **Open** All Year
Access Good **Site** Level
Nearest Bus Stop (Miles) ¼
Very scenic and peaceful site with excellent
clean facilities. Central for touring.
Facilities ⚡ 🚿 🅿 ⊙ ☎ 🚻 🅿
Nearest Town Betws-y-Coed
Directions 2 miles south of Betws-y-Coed
Left by Conway Falls, 200yds from A5.
≠ Betws-y-Coed

BETWS-Y-COED

Y Giler Arms, Rhydlydan, Pentrefoelas,
Conwy, LL24 0LL
Tel: 01690 770612
Email: gilerarms@hotmail.co.uk
www.giler.co.uk
Pitches For ▲ 🚐 🚙 🚙≀ **Total** 20
Acreage 4 **Open** All Year
Access Good **Site** Level

On the edge of Snowdonia National Park.
Facilities ⚡ 🚿 🅿 🚻 🅿 ♨ ▣ ☎
🚻 ✕ 🍴 ▲ ◫ 🚻 🅿 ✦ ☼❄ 📶
Nearest Town Betws-y-Coed
Directions On the A5 between Glasfryn and
Pentrefoelas.
≠ Betws-y-Coed

COLWYN BAY

Bron-Y-Wendon Touring Caravan Park,
Wern Road, Llanddulas, Colwyn Bay,
Conwy, LL22 8HG
Tel: 01492 512903
Email: stay@northwales-holidays.co.uk
www.northwales-holidays.co.uk
Pitches For 🚐 🚙 **Total** 130
Acreage 8 **Open** All Year
Access Good **Site** Lev/Slope
Nearest Bus Stop (Miles) ¼
Pitches have coastal views. Just a short walk
to the beach. Site is ideal for seaside and
touring. Visit Wales 5 Star Graded, AA 5
Pennants and Top 100 Park.
Facilities ♿ ⚡ 🚿 🅿 🚻 🅿 ♨ ⊙ 🚽 ☎
▣ ☎ ◫ 🚻 ⊙ 🚻 ▲ 🚻 🅿 ▣ ☼❄ 📶
Nearest Town Colwyn Bay
Directions Follow the A55 into North Wales
and take the Llanddulas junction (A547),
junction 23. Follow tourist information signs
to the park.
≠ Colwyn Bay

CONWY

Tyn Terfyn Touring Caravan Park, Tal Y
Bont, Conwy, LL32 8YX
Tel: 01492 660525
www.tynterfyn.co.uk
Pitches For ▲ 🚐 🚙 **Total** 15
Acreage 2 **Open** 14-Mar **to** Oct
Access Good **Site** Level
Nearest Bus Stop (Miles) Outside
Scenic views, good walking, fishing and
boating. Ideal touring location.
Facilities ⚡ 🚿 🚻 🅿 ♨ ⊙ 🚽 ☎ ▣
🚻 ⊙ ✦ 🚻 🅿
Nearest Town Conwy
Directions From Conwy travel approx 5
miles on the B5106 until road sign for Tal-y-
Bont. First house on the left after sign.

CONWY

Wern Farm Caravan Park, Wern Farm,
Tyn-Y-Groes, Conwy, LL32 8SY
Tel: 01492 650257
Email: gsutcliffe007@btinternet.com
Pitches For 🚐 🚙 **Total** 24
Acreage 2½ **Open** 15-Mar **to** Oct
Access Good **Site** Sloping
Nearest Bus Stop (Miles) Outside
Facilities ⚡ 🚿 🚻 🅿 ⊙ ☎ 🚻 🅿
Nearest Town Conwy
Directions Take the A55 to Conwy then the
B5106 signposted Trefriw. Site is 4 miles (1
mile past the Groes Inn).
≠ Llandudno Junction

LLANRWST

Bodnant Caravan Park, Nebo Road,
Llanrwst, Conwy Valley, LL26 0SD
Tel: 01492 640248
Email: ermin@bodnant-caravan-
park.co.uk
www.bodnant-caravan-park.co.uk
Pitches For ▲ 🚐 🚙 **Total** 54
Acreage 4 **Open** Mar **to** Oct
Access Good **Site** Level
Nearest Bus Stop (Miles) ¼
Small, quiet, pretty farm site. Ideal touring
centre. 26 times Winner of Wales in Bloom.
Multi serviced pitches. 2 holiday caravans for
hire. Rally field available.

Facilities ♿ ⚡ 🚿 🚻 🅿 ♨ ⊙ 🚽 ☎
🚻 ⊙ ☎ 🚻 🅿 ▣
Nearest Town Llanrwst
Directions At Traffic lights turn off the A470
south in Llanrwst onto the B5427 signposted
Nebo. Site is 300 yards on the right, opposite
the leisure centre.
≠ Llanrwst

LLANRWST

Bron Derw Touring Caravan Park, Bron
Derw, Llanrwst, Conwy, LL26 0YT
Tel: 01492 640494
Email: stay@aol.com
www.bronderw-wales.co.uk
Pitches For 🚐 🚙 **Total** 43
Acreage 4 **Open** Mar **to** Oct
Access Good **Site** Level
Nearest Bus Stop (Miles) ½
Ideal for exploring the Snowdonia mountain
range and the North Wales coast. Adults Only
field separate from the main touring site.
Facilities ♿ ⚡ 🚿 🚻 🅿 ♨ ⊙ 🚽 ☎ ▣ ☎
🚻 ⊙ 🚻 🅿 ☼❄ 📶
Nearest Town Llanrwst
Directions From the A5 or A55 take the A470
into Llanrwst. Tunr into Parry Road (sp
Llanddoged) and go to T-Junction, turn left
and the Park entrance is on the right.
≠ Llanrwst

PENMAENMAWR

Tyddyn Du Touring Park, Conwy Old
Road, Penmaenmawr, Conwy, LL34 6RE
Tel: 01492 622300
Email: stay@tyddyndutouringpark.co.uk
www.tyddyndutouringpark.co.uk
Pitches For ▲ 🚐 🚙 **Total** 100
Acreage 5 **Open** 22-Mar **to** Oct
Access Good **Site** Lev/Slope
Nearest Bus Stop (Miles) ½
ADULTS ONLY site overlooking Conwy Bay
to Llandudno and Anglesey. Heated toilet and
shower block with disabled facilities and
laundry. Close to the A55 so ideal for touring
Snowdonia.
Facilities ♿ ⚡ 🚿 🚻 🅿 ♨ ⊙ 🚽 ☎ ▣ ☎
🚻 ⊙ 🚻 🅿 ▣ ▲ 📶
Nearest Town Penmaenmawr
Directions 1 mile east of Penmaenmawr.
Take the A55 from Conwy and at junction 16
turn left at the roundabout after the Shell
Garage and sharp left again. Site access is
on the right after The Gladstone.
≠ Penmaenmawr

PENMAENMAWR

Woodlands Camping Park, Pendyffrin
Hall, Penmaenmawr, Conwy, LL34 6UF
Tel: 01492 623219
Email: admin@pendyffrinhall.co.uk
www.pendyffrinhall.co.uk
Pitches For ▲ 🚐 🚙 **Total** 21
Open Mar **to** Oct
Access Good **Site** Level
Nearest Bus Stop (Miles) Outside
In Snowdonia National Park, 5 miles from
the beach.
Facilities ⚡ 🚿 🚻 🅿 ♨ 🚽 ▣ ☎
🚻 ⊙ ▲ 🚻 🅿 ☼❄ 📶
Nearest Town Conwy
Directions 200yds off expressway A55, turn
off at junction 16A between Conwy and
Penmaenmawr.
≠ Penmaenmawr

TY-NANT

Glan Ceirw Caravan Park, Ty Nant,
Corwen, Conwy, LL21 0RF
Tel: 01490 420346
Email:
glanceirwcaravanpark@yahoo.co.uk
www.glanceirwcaravanpark.com
Pitches For ▲ ⊕ ⊕ **Total** 12
Acreage 5 **Open** Mar **to** Aug
Access Good **Site** Lev/Slope
Nearest Bus Stop (Miles) ½
Ideal for cycling, walking, canoeing, white
water rafting and sailing.
Facilities ⨍ 🗗 🖽 🕆 ⊙ ↵ 🗑 ☎
🏪 🕽 🛒 🦮 ↲ 🚿 ↰ ⚲
Nearest Town Corwen
Directions On the A5 between Corwen and
Betws-Y-Coed.
🚆 Betws-Y-Coed

DENBIGH
CORWEN

Hendwr Caravan Park, Llandrillo, Corwen,
Denbighshire, LL21 0SN
Tel: 01490 440210
Email: johnhendwr@btinternet.com
www.hendwrcaravanpark.co.uk
Pitches For ▲ ⊕ ⊕ 🚐 **Total** 40
Acreage 2¼ **Open** Apr **to** Oct
Access Good **Site** Level
Alongside a river, good walking and fishing.
Wonderful views and an excellent touring
centre for North Wales.
Facilities ⨍ 🗗 🖽 🕆 ⊙ ↵ 🗑 ☎
🏪 🕽 🛒 🖽 🎣 ↲ 🚿
Nearest Town Corwen/Bala
Directions From Corwen (A5) take the
B4401 for 4 miles, turn right at sign Hendwr.
Site is on the right in ¼ mile. From Bala take
the A494 for 1½ miles, turn right onto the
B4401 via Llandrillo. Site is 1 mile north on
the left.Follow brown tourism signs from
Corwen.
🚆 Ruabon

CORWEN

Llawr-Betws Caravan Park, Glanrafon,
Corwen, Denbighshire, LL21 0HD
Tel: 01490 460224
Email: david@llawrbetws.co.uk
Pitches For ▲ ⊕ ⊕ **Total** 35
Acreage 3 **Open** Mar **to** Oct
Access Poor **Site** Sloping
Nearest Bus Stop (Miles) ½
Quiet family run site
Facilities ⨍ 🗗 🖽 🕆 ⊙ ↵ 🗑 ☎
🕽 🛒 ♿ 🔔 ↲
Nearest Town Corwen
Directions A494 Corwen to Bala road 2nd
right after Thomas Motor Mart.
🚆 Wrexham

LLANGOLLEN

Ddol Hir Caravan Park, Pandy Road, Glyn
Ceiriog, Llangollen, Denbighshire, LL20
7PD
Tel: 01691 718681
www.ukparks.com
Pitches For ▲ ⊕ ⊕ **Total** 25
Acreage 6 **Open** Mar **to** Oct
Access Good **Site** Level
Nearest Bus Stop (Miles) ¼
Pretty riverside Park in a scenic valley with
mountain walks. Trout fishing and pony
trekking. Within walking distance of shops
and pubs.
Facilities ♿ ⨍ 🗗 🖽 🕆 ⊙ ↵ ☎
🕽 🛒 🖽 ↲ 🚿
Nearest Town Llangollen

Directions Turn off the A5 at Chirk onto the
B4500, park is on the left approx. 6 miles,
just through the village of Glyn Ceiriog.
🚆 Chirk

PRESTATYN

Nant Mill Farm Caravan & Tenting Park,
Nant Mill, Prestatyn, Denbighshire, LL19
9LY
Tel: 01745 852360
Email: nantmilltouring@aol.com
www.nantmilltouring.co.uk
Pitches For ▲ ⊕ ⊕ **Total** 150
Acreage 5 **Open** Easter **to** Oct
Access Good **Site** Lev/Slope
Nearest Bus Stop (Miles) Outside
Near town shops. ½ a mile from the beach.
Ideal for touring North Wales. Restaurant and
bar 200 yards away.
Facilities ♿ ⨍ 🖽 🕆 ⊙ ↵ 🗑 ☎ ▱ ♣
Nearest Town Prestatyn
Directions ½ mile east of Prestatyn on A548
coast road.
🚆 Prestatyn

RUTHIN

Dyffryn Ial Caravan Site, Troell Yr Alun,
Llanarmon-Yn-Ial, Near Mold,
Denbighshire, CH7 5TA
Tel: 01824 780286
Pitches For ⊕ ⊕ **Total** 18
Acreage ½ **Open** Mar **to** Oct
Access Good **Site** Level
Nearest Bus Stop (Miles) Outside
ADULTS ONLY SITE alongside the River
Alyn in an area of outstanding natural beauty.
Near Clwydian Hills, Offas Dyke walk and
Country Park Loggerheads. Over 100 walks
in the area. Ideal for touring North Wales.
Facilities ⨍ 🖽 🕆 ☎ 🏪 🔔 ↲ A
Nearest Town Mold/Ruthin
Directions 6 miles from both Mold and
Ruthin on the A494, take the B5430 towards
Llanarmon-Yn-Ial, site is on the right 1 mile
before Llanarmon Village.
🚆 Wrexham

ST. ASAPH

Penisar Mynydd Caravan Park, Caerwys
Road, Rhuallt, St Asaph, Denbighshire,
LL17 0TY
Tel: 01745 582227
Email: contact@penisarmynydd.co.uk
www.penisarmynydd.co.uk
Pitches For ▲ ⊕ ⊕ 🚐 **Total** 75
Acreage 6 **Open** Mar **to** 15-Jan
Access Good **Site** Lev/Slope
Quiet, rural park. Large flat tent area. Close
to Rhyl and Prestatyn. Ideal for touring the
main A55 coastal route to Holyhead. Adults
Only field. Superpitches available.
Facilities ♿ ⨍ 🗗 🖽 🕆 ⊙ ↵ 🗑 ☎
🕽 🛒 🖽 ↲ 🚿 ⚲ 🛜
Nearest Town Prestatyn
Directions Leave the A55 Chester to Bangor
road at junction 29, park is 500 yards on the
right.
🚆 Prestatyn

FLINTSHIRE
GRONANT

Greenacres Caravan Park, Shore Road,
Gronant, Flintshire, LL19 9SS
Tel: 01745 854061
Email: info@greenacrescaravanpark.co.uk
Pitches For ⊕ ⊕ **Total** 40
Open Mar **to** Oct
Access Good **Site** Level
Nearest Bus Stop (Miles) Outside

500 yards from the beach. Two licensed
premises with live entertainment. Health suite
and swimming pool.
Facilities ♿ ⨍ 🖽 🕆 ⊙ ↵ 🗑 ☎
🏪 🛒 ✗ 🕽 ↰ ↲ 🚿
Nearest Town Prestatyn
Directions 2 miles from Prestatyn off the
main A548 coast road.
🚆 Prestatyn

MOLD

Fron Farm Caravan Park, Fron Farm,
Rhes-Y-Cae Road, Hendre, Mold,
Flintshire, CH7 5QW
Tel: 01352 741482
Email: stay@fronfarmcaravanpark.co.uk
www.fronfarmcaravanpark.co.uk
Pitches For ▲ ⊕ ⊕ **Total** 70
Acreage 5 **Open** Apr **to** Oct
Access Good **Site** Level
Nearest Bus Stop (Miles) ½
Farm site with animals to see and scenic
views.
Facilities ♿ ⨍ 🖽 🕆 ⊙ ↵
🏪 🕽 🛒 🦮 🖽 ↲ 🚿
Nearest Town Mold
Directions From Mold take the A541 towards
Denbigh, pass through Rhydymwyn and
Hendre, turn right at the next crossroads for
Rhes-Y-Cae.
🚆 Flint

GWYNEDD
ABERDARON

Bryn Ffynnon Caravan Site,
Rhoshirwaun, Pwllheli, Gwynedd, LL53
8LF
Tel: 01758 730643
Pitches For ⊕ ⊕ **Total** 20
Open Mar **to** Oct
Access Good **Site** Level
Nearest Bus Stop (Miles) 1
Near to the beach and the village.
Facilities ⨍ 🗗 🖽 🕆 ⊙ ↵ 🗑 ☎
🕽 ↰ 🦮 🚿
Nearest Town Pwllheli
Directions From the A499 take the B4413,
go through Sarn and continue to Aberdaron.
🚆 Pwllheli

ABERDARON

Dwyros Campsite, Aberdaron, Pwllheli,
Gwynedd, LL53 8BS
Tel: 01758 760295
Email: dwyroscamp@aol.com
Pitches For ▲ ⊕ ⊕ **Total** 60
Acreage 4 **Open** Mar **to** Oct
Site Level
Nearest Bus Stop (Miles) ¼
Near the beach,within walking distance of
beach and village.
Facilities ♿ ⨍ 🗗 🖽 🕆 ⊙ ↵ 🗑 ☎ 🏪
Nearest Town Aberdaron
🚆 Pwllheli

ABERDARON

Mur Melyn Camping Site, Mur Melyn,
Aberdaron, Pwllheli, Gwynedd, LL53 8LW
Tel: 01758 760522
Email: murmelyn@hotmail.co.uk
www.murmelyncamping.co.uk
Pitches For ▲ ⊕ ⊕ **Total** 60
Acreage 2½ **Open** Easter **to** Oct
Access Good **Site** Level
Nearest Bus Stop (Miles) 1
Near the beach and a river with scenic views.
Ideal for touring Wales.
Facilities ⨍ 🖽 🕆 ☎ 🏪
Nearest Town Pwllheli

147

Directions Take A499 west from Pwllheli, then fork onto to B4413 at Llanbedrog about 3 miles before Aberdaron take Whistling Sand road. Turn left at Pen-y-Bont House to site ½ mile.
⚊ Pwllheli

ABERSOCH
Beach View Caravan Park, Bwlchtocyn, Abersoch, Gwynedd, LL53 7BT
Tel: 01758 712956
Pitches For Å ⚌ ⚌ **Total** 47
Acreage 5 **Open** Mid Mar **to** Mid Oct
Access Good **Site** Level
Nearest Bus Stop (Miles) ¼
Just a very short walk to the beach. Ideal touring area.
Facilities ⌕ ▨ ⌂ ⊙ ⌐ ▢
▯ ▨ ⌂ ⚑ ▢ ⚘
Nearest Town Abersoch
Directions Drive through Abersoch and Sarn Bach, go over the crossroads and turn next left signposted Bwlchtocyn and Porthtocyn Hotel. Go past the chapel and take left turn following signs for Porthtocyn Hotel, Beach View Park is on the left.
⚊ Pwllheli

ABERSOCH
Bryn Bach Caravan & Camping Site, Tyddyn Talgoch Uchaf, Bwlchtocyn, Abersoch, Gwynedd, LL53 7BT
Tel: 01758 712285
Email: brynbach@abersochcamping.co.uk
www.abersochcamping.co.uk
Pitches For Å ⚌ ⚌ ⚐ ⚘ **Total** 65
Acreage 3 **Open** Mar **to** Oct
Access Good **Site** Level
Nearest Bus Stop (Miles) ¼
Close to 2 sandy beaches, golf course and trekking centre.
Facilities ⅋ ⌕ ▨ ⌂ ⌐ ⊙ ⌐ ▢ ⚑
▯ ▢ ▨ ⌂ ⚑ ▢ ⚘ ⌕
Nearest Town Abersoch
Directions Take the Sarn Bach road from Abersoch, go through Sarn Bach and take the next left turn to Bwlchtocyn.
⚊ Pwllheli

ABERSOCH
Bryn Celyn Isaf Camping & Caravan Site, Bryn Celyn Isaf, Cilan, Abersoch, Pwllheli, Gwynedd, LL53 7DB
Tel: 01758 713583
Pitches For Å ⚌ ⚌ **Total** 25
Acreage 1½ **Open** Easter **to** Oct
Access Good **Site** Sloping
Nearest Bus Stop (Miles) Outside
Families only. Footpath runs through the farmyard to Hells Mouth beach.
Facilities ⅋ ▨ ⌂ ⌐ ⊙ ⚑ ⚑ ▢
Nearest Town Abersoch
Directions Travel through the villages of Abersoch and Sarn Bach on the Cilan main road. Pass the turning for Bwlchtocyn and then pass 6 houses on the left and turn sharp right by Tirlon.
⚊ Pwllheli

ABERSOCH
Deucoch Touring & Camping Park, Sarn Bach, Abersoch, Gwynedd, LL53 7LD
Tel: 01758 713293
Email: info@deucoch.com
www.deucoch.com
Pitches For Å ⚌ ⚌ **Total** 70
Acreage 5 **Open** Mar **to** Oct
Access Good **Site** Level
Nearest Bus Stop (Miles) Outside
Overlooking Abersoch beach and the Snowdonia mountain range. Within walking distance of Abersoch Village and the beach.

Facilities ⌕ ⅋ ▢ ⌂ ▨ ⌂ ⌐ ⊙ ⌐ ▢ ⚑
▨ ⚑ ▢
Nearest Town Abersoch
Directions Take the Bwlchtocyn road out of Abersoch, at the crossroads in Sarn Bach turn right, go past the school on the left and the Site is on the right.
⚊ Pwllheli

ABERSOCH
Nant-Y-Big, Cilan, Abersoch, Pwllheli, Gwynedd, LL53 7DB
Tel: 01758 712686
Email: nantybig@nantybig.co.uk
www.nantybig.co.uk
Pitches For Å ⚌ ⚌ **Total** 80
Acreage 10 **Open** Easter **to** Oct
200 metres from the beautiful sandy Porth Ceiriad beach.
Facilities ⅋ ▨ ⌂ ⊙ ⚒ ⊙ ⚑ ▢ ▢ ⚘ ⚘
Nearest Town Abersoch
Directions 2½ miles south of Abersoch. Go through the next village of Sarn Bach and follow signposts for Cilan. After approx. 500 metres turn left at No Through Road sign.
⚊ Pwllheli

ABERSOCH
Sarn Farm Caravan & Camping Site, Sarn Farm, Sarn Bach, Abersoch, Pwllheli, Gwynedd, LL53 7BG
Tel: 01758 713583
Email: sarnfarm@hotmail.com
Pitches For Å ⚌ ⚌ **Total** 40
Acreage 2 **Open** Easter **to** Oct
Access Good **Site** Level
Nearest Bus Stop (Miles) Outside
Within walking distance of the beach and 1 mile from Abersoch Village. Lovely views of Snowdon and Cardigan Bay.
Facilities ⚒ ⅋ ▨ ⌂ ⌐ ⊙ ⚑ ▢ ⚑ ▢
▨ ⚑ ▢
Nearest Town Abersoch
Directions On the main Abersoch to Cilan road, in the village of Sarn Bach, on the left.
⚊ Pwllheli

ABERSOCH
The Willows (Yr Helyg), Mynytho, Abersoch, Gwynedd, LL53 7RW
Tel: 01758 740676
Email: annamali2@aol.com
www.the-willows-abersoch.co.uk
Pitches For Å ⚌ ⚌ **Total** 42
Acreage 10 **Open** Mar **to** Nov
Access Good **Site** Level
Nearest Bus Stop (Miles) ¼
5 Star multi award winning site. Refined, quiet and charming with stunning views. Close to beaches. Suitable for the more discerning customer.
Facilities ⌕ ⅋ ▢ ⌂ ▨ ⌂ ⌐ ⊙ ⌐ ▢ ⚑
▯ ▢ ▨ ⌂ ⚑ ▢ ⚘ ⌕
Nearest Town Abersoch
Directions From Pwllheli take the A499 towards Abersoch. At Llanbedrog turn right onto the B4413. Once reaching Mynytho take the first right.
⚊ Pwllheli

ARTHOG
Garthyfog Camping Site, Garthyfog Farm, Arthog, Gwynedd, LL39 1AX
Tel: 01341 250338
Email: abcjohnson@btinternet.com
www.garthyfog.co.uk
Pitches For Å ⚌ ⚌ **Total** 20
Acreage 5 **Open** All Year
Site Lev/Slope

2 miles from Fairbourne, safe bathing, sandy beach and shops. Beautiful scenery, panoramic views. 300 yards from main road, sheltered from wind. Mains cold water. Plenty of room for children to play around the farm, rope-swing, little stream, etc. Two log cabins available to let.
Facilities ▨ ⌐ ⊙ ⚑ ▢
Nearest Town Barmouth/Dolgellau
Directions A493, 6 miles from Dolgellau, left by Village hall, look for signs on right hand side.
⚊ Morfa Mawddach

BALA
Bala Camping & Caravanning Club Site, Crynierth Caravan Park, Cefn-Ddwysarn, Bala, Gwynedd, LL23 7LN
Tel: 01678 530324
Email: bala.site@thefriendlyclub.co.uk
www.campingandcaravanning.co.uk/bala
Pitches For Å ⚌ ⚌ **Total** 50
Acreage 4 **Open** 15-Mar **to** 04-Nov
Access Good **Site** Level
Situated on the edge of Snowdonia National Park. 4 miles from Bala Lake. Good for watersports. Ideal touring site. WTB 4 Star Graded and AA 3 Pennants. Non members welcome. You can also call us on 0845 130 7633.
Facilities ⌕ ⅋ ⌂ ▨ ⌂ ⌐ ⊙ ⌐ ⚑ ▢ ▢
▯ ▢ ⌂ ▨ ⚑ ▢ ⚘
Nearest Town Bala
Directions From the A5 turn onto the A494 to Bala. At signpost Cefn-Ddwysarn turn right before the red phone box, site is 400 yards on the left.
⚊ Ruabon

BALA
Glanllyn-Lakeside Caravan & Camping Park, Bala, Gwynedd, LL23 7SS
Tel: 01678 540227
Email: info@glanllyn.com
www.glanllyn.com
Pitches For Å ⚌ ⚌ ⚐ **Total** 100
Acreage 14 **Open** Easter **to** Oct
Access Good **Site** Level
Nearest Bus Stop (Miles) Outside
Level parkland with trees. Alongside a lake and river, large launching area for sailing.
Facilities ⅋ ⌂ ▨ ⌂ ⌐ ⊙ ⌐ ⚑ ▢ ▢
▯ ▢ ⌂ ▨ ⚑ ▢ ⚘ ⌕
Nearest Town Bala
Directions 3 miles south west of Bala on the A494, situated on the left alongside Bala Lake.
⚊ Wrexham

BALA
Pen Y Bont Touring & Camping Park, Llangynog Road, Bala, Gwynedd, LL23 7PH
Tel: 01678 520549
Email: penybont-bala@btconnect.com
www.penybont-bala.co.uk
Pitches For Å ⚌ ⚌ ⚐ **Total** 95
Acreage 6 **Open** Mar **to** Oct
Access Good
Nearest Bus Stop (Miles) ½
100 yards from Bala Lake and just a 15 minute walk into Bala.
Facilities ⌕ ⅋ ▢ ⌂ ▨ ⌂ ⌐ ⊙ ⌐ ⚑ ▢ ▢
▯ ▢ ⌂ ▨ ⚑ ▢ ⚘ ⌕
Nearest Town Bala
Directions ½ a mile from Bala on the B4391 to Llangynog.
⚊ Wrexham

BALA

Ty-Isaf Camping Site, Llangynog Road, Bala, Gwynedd, LL23 7PP
Tel: 01678 520574
www.tyisafbala.co.uk
Pitches For ⚠ 🚐 🚍 **Total** 30
Acreage 2 **Open** April/Easter **to** Oct
Access Good **Site** Level
Working farm alongside a stream for fishing. Log fires. Ideal touring.
Facilities ⚡ 🌡 ⬢⬢ ⛽ 🏪 📞 📥
🍴 🛒 🖺 ⧖ 📥 ⬇ ⚡ 💈 🍴 🛒 📶
Nearest Town Bala
Directions 2½ miles southeast of Bala on the B4391, near the telephone kiosk and post box.
🚆 Ruabon

BALA

Tyn Cornel Camping & Caravan Park, Frongoch, Bala, Gwynedd, LL23 7NU
Tel: 01678 520759
Email: tyncornel@mail.com
www.tyncornel.co.uk
Pitches For ⚠ 🚐 🚍 **Total** 67
Acreage 10 **Open** Easter **to** Oct
Access Good **Site** Level
Nearest Bus Stop (Miles) ¼
Quiet and clean 4 Star site beside the River Tryweryn. Next door to the National White Water Centre, watch the thrills and spills of the white water rafting, or take part! Ideally situated for touring North Wales. Indoor swimming pool nearby.
Facilities ⚡ 🌡 ⬢⬢ ⛽ 📞 ⊙ 📥 🍴
🖺 🛒 📥 📥 📥 🖺 ⬇ ⚡ ✂
Nearest Town Bala
Directions 4 miles from Bala on the A4212 Porthmadog road.
🚆 Ruabon

BANGOR

Dinas Farm Camping & Touring Site, Dinas Farm, Halfway Bridge, Bangor, Gwynedd, LL57 4NB
Tel: 01248 364227
Email: dinasfarmcamping@btinternet.com
www.dinasfarmcamping.co.uk
Pitches For ⚠ 🚐 🚍 **Total** 35
Acreage 4 **Open** Easter **to** Oct
Access Good **Site** Level
Nearest Bus Stop (Miles) 50 yards
Sheltered site on the banks of the River Ogwen. Centrally situated for beaches and mountains. Fishing on site with a permit.
Facilities 🌡 ⬢⬢ ⛽ 📞 ⊙ 📥 🍴 ⬢ 📥 📥 ⬇ ✂
Nearest Town Bangor
Directions Leave the A55 at junc 11 and take the A5 towards Bethesda for 1 mile. Turn right at Halfway Bridge towards Tregarth then turn first left.
🚆 Bangor

BARMOUTH

Benar Beach Camping & Touring Site, Talybont, Barmouth, Gwynedd, LL44 2RX
Tel: 01341 247001/247571
Pitches For ⚠ 🚐 🚍 🚍
Acreage 9 **Open** Mar **to** Oct
Access Good **Site** Level
Nearest Bus Stop (Miles) 1
Friendly family site 100 yards from miles of golden sand dunes. By the Taith Ardudwy Way which is a 24 mile pathway. Ideal base for touring Snowdonia with its gardens, castles, caverns, railways and much more. On and by the all Wales coastal path.
Facilities ⚡ 🌡 🛒 📞 ⊙ ⬇ 🍴
🖺 ⬢ 📥 📥 🖺 ⬇ ✂ 📶
Nearest Town Barmouth
Directions 5 miles north of Barmouth on the A496 turn left by Llanddwywe Church ½ mile after Talybont Village, site is 100 yards from the beach on the left.
🚆 Dyffryn Ardudwy

BARMOUTH

Hendre Mynach Touring Caravan & Camping Park, Barmouth, Gwynedd, LL42 1YR
Tel: 01341 280262
Email: mynach@lineone.net
www.hendremynach.co.uk
Pitches For ⚠ 🚐 🚍 **Total** 240
Acreage 10 **Open** March **to** 09-Jan
Access Good **Site** Level
Nearest Bus Stop (Miles) Outside
100yds from a safe, sandy beach, 20 minutes walk down the promenade to Barmouth town centre. An excellent base for estuary and mountain walks. Pubs nearby with childrens room. Near to cycle route 8.
Facilities ⚡ 🌡 ⬢⬢ ⛽ 📞 ⊙ 📥 ⬇ ⚡ 🖺
🖺 🛒 ⬢ ✖ 📥 📥 📥 🖺 ⬇ ✂ 📶
Nearest Town Barmouth
Directions ½ a mile north of Barmouth on the A496 Barmouth to Harlech road.
🚆 Barmouth

BARMOUTH

Parc Isaf Farm, Dyffryn Ardudwy, Gwynedd, LL44 2RJ
Tel: 01341 247447
Email: post@parcisaf.co.uk
www.parcisaf.co.uk
Pitches For ⚠ 🚐 🚍 **Total** 30
Acreage 3 **Open** Mar **to** Oct
Access Good **Site** Lev/Slope
Nearest Bus Stop (Miles) ½
Overlooking Cardigan Bay. Plenty of mountain and woodland walks. Harlech Castle and Portmeirion (Italian village) close by.
Facilities ⚡ 🌡 🛒 📞 ⊙ ⬇ 🖺 📥 🍴
Nearest Town Barmouth
Directions From Barmouth take the A496 north for 5 miles, go through the small village of Talybont, ¼ mile on, opposite the church on the left there is a right hand turn through pillar gateway. Second farm on the right, signposted.
🚆 Dyffryn Ardudwy/Talybont

BARMOUTH

Trawsdir Touring Caravans & Camping Park, Llanaber, Barmouth, Gwynedd, LL42 1RR
Tel: 01341 280999
Email: enquiries@trawsdir.co.uk
www.barmouthholidays.co.uk
Pitches For ⚠ 🚐 🚍 🚍 **Total** 100
Access Good **Site** Level

Nearest Bus Stop (Miles) ¼
Near the beach and overlooking Cardigan Bay. Super Pitches for American RVs. State of the art toilets and facilities. Visit Wales 5 Star Grading. We have 5 Glamping pods.
Facilities ⚡ 🌡 ⬢⬢ ⛽ 📞 ⊙ 📥 ⚡ 🖺 🖺
🖺 ⬢ 🖺 📥 📥 🖺 📶
Nearest Town Barmouth
Directions 2½ miles north of Barmouth on the A496.
🚆 Barmouth

CAERNARFON

Bryn Gloch Caravan & Camping Park, Betws Garmon, Caernarfon, Gwynedd, LL54 7YY
Tel: 01286 650216
Email: eurig@bryngloch.co.uk
www.northwalescamping.co.uk
Pitches For ⚠ 🚐 🚍 🚍 **Total** 150
Acreage 28 **Open** Mar **to** Oct
Access Good **Site** Level
Nearest Bus Stop (Miles) Outside
Award winning site with scenic views. Plenty of flat and mountain walks in the area. Ideal touring centre and only 2 miles from Snowdon. AA 4 Pennants and AA Best Campsite in Wales 2005.
Facilities ⚡ 🌡 ⬢⬢ ⛽ 📞 ⊙ 📥 ⚡ 🖺 🖺
🖺 ⬢ 🛒 🌡 ⬢ 🖺 📥 📥 🖺 ⬇ ✂ 📶
Nearest Town Caernarfon
Directions 4½ miles south west of Caernarfon on A4085. Site on right opposite Betws Garmon church.
🚆 Bangor

CAERNARFON

Challoner Caravan Park, Erw Hywel Farm, Llanrug, Caernarfon, Gwynedd, LL55 2AJ
Tel: 01286 672985
Email: susanchalloner@btinternet.com
Pitches For ⚠ 🚐 🚍 **Total** 35
Open March **to** 10-Jan
Access Good **Site** Level
Nearest Bus Stop (Miles) Outside
Wetland and wild life meadow situated on site with Buzzards, Bats and Owls. Ideal for touring Snowdonia. 3 miles from Caernarfon Castle.
Facilities ⚡ 🌡 🛒 📞 ⊙ ⬇ 🍴
🖺 ⬢ 📥 📥 🖺
Nearest Town Caernarfon
Directions On the A4086 from Caernarfon towards Llanberis.
🚆 Bangor

CAERNARFON

Cwm Cadnant Valley Camping & Caravan Park, Llanberis Road, Caernarfon, Gwynedd, LL55 2DF
Tel: 01286 673196
Email: cades@cwmcadnant.co.uk
www.cwmcadnant.co.uk
Pitches For ⚠ 🚐 🚍 **Total** 69
Open Mar **to** Oct
Access Good **Site** Sloping
Nearest Bus Stop (Miles) Outside
Cafe/restaurant and indoor swimming pool nearby. You can also call us on FreePhone: 0800 043 5941.

Facilities 🚿 ⚡ 🚽 🔟 ♿ 📻 ⛽ ⊙ ◁ 🖭 ⊡ 🛒
🍴 🅿 🔥 🏊 ⊞ ⊠ ⛟ ⊡ 🖭 ❄ 📶
Nearest Town Caernarfon
Directions On the A4086, 1km from the town centre.
⚏ Bangor

CAERNARFON
Llys Derwen Camping & Caravan Site, Ffordd Bryngwyn, Llanrug, Nr Caernarfon, Gwynedd, LL55 4RD
Tel: 01286 673322
Email: llysderwen@aol.com
www.llysderwen.co.uk
Pitches For 🏕 ⊞ ⊟ **Total** 20
Acreage 4½ **Open** Mar **to** Oct
Access Good **Site** Level
Nearest Bus Stop (Miles) ¼
Small family run site. 2 miles from Llanberis and the foot of Mount Snowdon. Static caravans also available for hire.
Facilities 🚿 ⚡ 🔟 🚽 📻 ⊙ ◁ 🖭 🛒 🐾 🖭
Nearest Town Caernarfon
Directions From Caernarfon take the A4086 towards Llanberis. In the village of Llanrug turn right at the Glyntwrog Public House, site entrance is 100 yards on the right.
⚏ Bangor

CAERNARFON
Plas Gwyn Caravan & Camping Park, Plas Gwyn, Llanrug, Caernarfon, Gwynedd, LL55 2AQ
Tel: 01286 672619
Email: info@plasgwyn.co.uk
www.plasgwyn.co.uk
Pitches For 🏕 ⊞ ⊟ ⊟≲ **Total** 40
Acreage 4 **Open** Mar **to** Oct
Access Good **Site** Level
Nearest Bus Stop (Miles) Outside
Small, peaceful park. 3 miles from Snowdonia Mountains and 5 miles from the beach. Award winning hire caravans. En-suite bed and breakfast available in the house.
Facilities 🚿 ⚡ 🔟 🚽 ♿ 📻 ⊙ ⛽ 🖭 🛒
🅂 ⊙ 🔥 🖭 ⊡ 🖭 ❄ 📶
Nearest Town Caernarfon
Directions 3 miles from Caernarfon on the A4086, signposted on right.
⚏ Bangor

CAERNARFON
Rhyd-y-Galen Caravan & Camping Park, Bethel, Caernarfon, Gwynedd, LL55 1UL
Tel: 01286 650216
Email: info@copacamping.co.uk
www.wales-camping.co.uk
Pitches For 🏕 ⊞ ⊟ **Total** 56
Acreage 4 **Open** Mar **to** Oct
Access Good **Site** Level/Sloping
Nearest Bus Stop (Miles) Outside
1½ miles from Plas Menai Watersports Centre. Snowdon Footpath only 15 minutes away.
Facilities 🚿 ⚡ 🔟 🚽 📻 ⊙ ⛽ 🖭 🛒
🍴 ⊙ 🔥 🖭 🖭 ⊡ 🖭 ❄ ⛟ 📶
Nearest Town Caernarfon
Directions 2 miles east of Caernarfon on the B4366.
⚏ Bangor

CAERNARFON
Riverside Camping, Seiont Nurseries, Pontrug, Caernarfon, Gwynedd, LL55 2BB
Tel: 01286 678781
Email: brenda@riversidecamping.co.uk
www.riversidecamping.co.uk

Pitches For 🏕 ⊞ ⊟ **Total** 73
Acreage 5 **Open** Mar **to** Oct
Access Good **Site** Level
Nearest Bus Stop (Miles) Entrance
Secluded, landscaped site, bordered by a salmon river Mill Cafe with a spacious balcony, serving delicious home made meals. Plenty of space for childrens ball games. Wonderful place to relax after exploring Snowdonia. Permits available for fishing. 13 superb new delux pitches, hard standing fully serviced ideal for motorhomes.
Facilities 🚿 ⚡ 🔟 🚽 📻 ⊙ ◁ 🖭 🛒
🍴 🍽 🔥 🖭 🖭 ⛟ ❄ 📶
Nearest Town Caernarfon
Directions 2 miles out of Caernarfon on the right hand side of the A4086 (Llanberis road).
⚏ Bangor

CAERNARFON
Tyn Rhos Farm Caravan Park, Tyn Rhos Farm, Saron, Llanwnda, Caernarfon, Gwynedd, LL54 5UH
Tel: 01286 830362
www.tynrhosfarm.co.uk
Pitches For 🏕 ⊞ ⊟ **Total** 25
Acreage 2 **Open** Mar **to** Mid Jan
Access Good **Site** Level
Nearest Bus Stop (Miles) Outside
2½ miles from the beach, 1 mile from steam railway and cycle track. All pitches are hard standing.
Facilities 🚿 ⚡ 🔟 🚽 📻 ⊙ ⛽ 🖭 🔍
Nearest Town Caernarfon
Directions From Caernarfon take the A487, after passing Tesco go straight on at the roundabout, turn first right to Saron Llanfaglan, entrance is 3 miles on the left.
⚏ Bangor

CAERNARFON
White Tower Caravan Park, Llandwrog, Caernarfon, Gwynedd, LL54 5UH
Tel: 01286 830649
Email: whitetower@supanet.com
www.whitetowerpark.co.uk
Pitches For 🏕 ⊞ ⊟ **Total** 68
Acreage 6 **Open** Mar **to** Nov
Access Good **Site** Level
Nearest Bus Stop (Miles) Outside
2½ miles from the beach, 3¼ miles from Caernarfon. Splendid views of Snowdon. Central for touring Llyn Peninsula, Anglesey and Snowdonia.
Facilities 🚿 ♿ ⚡ 🔟 🚽 ♿ 📻 ⊙ ⛽ 🖭
⊙ 🛒
🍴 ⊙ ⚽ 📺 🔥 🖭 ⚒ 🍽 🖭 ⊡ 🖭 ❄
🔍 📶
Nearest Town Caernarfon
Directions From Caernarfon follow the A487 Porthmadog road for approx ¼ mile, go past McDonalds, straight ahead at the roundabout and take the first turning on the right. We are 3 miles on the right.
⚏ Bangor

CHWILOG
Tyddyn Heilyn Caravan Park, Chwilog, Pwllheli, Gwynedd, LL53 6SW
Tel: 01766 810441
Email: tyddynh@btinternet.com
Pitches For 🏕 ⊞ ⊟ **Total** 5
Access Good **Site** Level
Beautiful tree lined public footpath near the site to the beach. 15 minutes from Pwllheli, Porthmadog and Snowdonia. Wi-Fi available on request.
Facilities ⚡ 🔟 🚽 📻 ⊙ 🖭 ⊙ 🍴 🍽 📶
Nearest Town Pwllheli
Directions From the A497 take the B4354, in Chwilog Village turn right opposite Madryn

Arms, second site on the right, signpost at entrance.
⚏ Criccieth

CLYNNOG FAWR
Aberafon Camping & Caravan Site, Gyrn Goch, Caernarfon, Gwynedd, LL54 5PN
Tel: 01286 660295
Email: hugh@maelor.demon.co.uk
www.aberafon.co.uk
Pitches For 🏕 ⊞ ⊟ **Total** 65
Acreage 10 **Open** Apr **to** Oct
Access Poor **Site** Level
Nearest Bus Stop (Miles) Outside
Near the beach. Site shop only open during the summer holidays.
Facilities ⚡ 🔟 🚽 📻 ⊙ ⛽ 🖭 🛒
🍴 ⊙ 🔥 🖭 🖭 🖭 ⊡ 🍽 ❄
Nearest Town Caernarfon
Directions From Caernarfon take the A499 towards Pwllheli, site is 1 mile after Clynnog Fawr on the right hand side.
⚏ Bangor

CRICCIETH
Cae-Canol Caravan & Camping, Criccieth, Gwynedd, LL52 0NB
Tel: 01766 522351
Email: cae-carol@criccieth-holidays.com
www.criccieth-holidays.com
Pitches For 🏕 ⊞ ⊟ **Total** 25
Acreage 3 **Open** Apr **to** Oct
Access Very Good **Site** Level
Nearest Bus Stop (Miles) Outside
Fantastic touring,walking and cycling area.
Facilities ⚒ 🚿 ⚡ 🔟 🚽 📻 ⊙ ⛽ ⊙ 🖭 🖭
Nearest Town Criccieth
Directions Located on the B4411 between the picturesque Snowdonia National Park and the scenic Llyn Peninsula.
⚏ Criccieth

CRICCIETH
Eisteddfa Caravan & Camping Site, Eisteddfa Lodge, Pentrefelin, Criccieth, Gwynedd, LL52 0PT
Tel: 01766 522696
Email: eisteddfa@criccieth.co.uk
www.eisteddfapark.co.uk
Pitches For 🏕 ⊞ ⊟ **Total** 120
Acreage 22 **Open** Mar **to** Oct
Access Good **Site** Lev/Slope
Nearest Bus Stop (Miles) Outside
Spectacular views of Cardigan Bay and the mountains. Plenty of footpaths for walking.
Facilities 🚿 ⚡ 🔟 🚽 📻 ⊙ ⛽ 🖭 🛒
🍴 ⊙ 🔥 ⚽ 🔥 🖭 🖭 ⊡ 🖭 ⛟ ❄
Nearest Town Criccieth
Directions On the A497 Porthmadog to Criccieth road, 1½ miles north east of Criccieth. Entrance is at the west end of Pentrefelin beside the Plas Gwyn Nursing Home.
⚏ Criccieth

CRICCIETH
Llanystumdwy Camping & Caravanning Club Site, Tyddyn Sianel, Llanystumdwy, Criccieth, Gwynedd, LL52 0LS
Tel: 01766 522855
Email: llanystumdwy.site@thefriendlyclub.co.uk
www.campingandcaravanningclub.co.uk/ llanystumdwy
Pitches For 🏕 ⊞ ⊟ **Total** 70
Acreage 4 **Open** 21-Mar **to** 04-Nov
Access Good **Site** Sloping
Nearest Bus Stop (Miles) Outside
Situated just outside Criccieth with scenic coastal views. Nearby attractions include

Ffestiniog Railway and Snowdonia National Park. WTB 4 Star Graded and AA 3 Pennants. Non members welcome. You can also call us on 0845 130 7633.
Facilities ⚹ ⅃ 🍴 📶 ⚲ 🏧 ⌁ 🍴 🚿 🗑 ▣ ☎
🏧 🛁 ⚙ ✿➤🐾 🎦 ▣ 🛜
Directions From Criccieth take the A497 and turn second right signposted Llanstumdwy, site is on the right.
⚏ Criccieth

DINAS MAWDDWY
Tynypwll Caravan & Camping Site, Dinas Mawddwy, Machynlleth, Powys, SY20 9JF
Tel: 01650 531326
Pitches For 🛆 ⚌ ⚍
Open Apr **to** Sept
Access Good **Site** Level
Nearest Bus Stop (Miles) ¼
Riverside site with lovely scenery. Ideal for walking, fishing and touring.
Facilities ⅃ 🍴 ⌁ 🛁 ✦
Nearest Town Barmouth/Aberystwyth
Directions From the A470 turn right to the village of Dinas Mawddwy, turn right by The Red Lion, site is the first left, entrance over the bridge. 10 miles from Dolgellau and 12 miles from Machynlleth.
⚏ Machynlleth

DOLGELLAU
Dolgamedd Camping & Caravan Site, Dolgamedd, Bontnewydd, Dolgellau, Gwynedd, LL40 2DG
Tel: 01341 450221
Email: mair@dolgamedd.co.uk
www.midwalesholidays.co.uk
Pitches For 🛆 ⚌ ⚍ 🚲 ≷ **Total** 76
Acreage 12 **Open** Easter **to** Oct
Access Good **Site** Level
Nearest Bus Stop (Miles) ¼
Situated alongside the River Wnion, where campfires are allowed.The river allows for swimming, canoeing and fishing.
Facilities ⚹ ⅃ 🌫 🍴 🚿 ⌁ 🍴 🗑 ▣ ☎
🏧 🛁 ⌂ 🍴 🏧 ✦ ➤ ⚙ 🎦 🛜
Nearest Town Dolgellau
Directions 3 miles from Dolgellau on the A494 towards Bala, turn right at Bontnewydd onto the B4416 towards Brithdir. Continue over the bridge and Dolgamedd is on the left.
⚏ Machynlleth

DOLGELLAU
Dolserau Uchaf, Dolgellau, Gwynedd, LL40 2DE
Tel: 01341 422639
Pitches For ⚌ ⚍ **Total** 20
Acreage 1¼ **Open** Easter **to** Oct
Access Good **Site** Level
Nearest Bus Stop (Miles) Outside
Quiet site with open views of the Cader Idris Range. Ideal for walking and cycling.
Facilities ⅃ 🍴 ⚲ 🏧 ⌁ 🌫 ➤🐾 ▣
Nearest Town Dolgellau
Directions 2½ miles east of Dolgellau on the A494.
⚏ Barmouth

DOLGELLAU
Llwyn-Yr-Helm Farm, Brithdir, Dolgellau, Gwynedd, LL40 2SA
Tel: 01341 450254
Email: info@llwynyrhelmcaravanpark.co.uk
www.llwynyrhelmcaravanpark.co.uk
Pitches For 🛆 ⚌ ⚍ **Total** 25
Acreage 2½ **Open** Easter **to** Oct
Access Good **Site** Lev/Slope
Nearest Bus Stop (Miles) ¼

Seasides, hills, mountains, rivers, lakes and slate mines. Ideal for walking and mountain biking at Coed Y Brenin.
Facilities ⚹ ⅃ 🍴 🌫 🍴 🚿 ⌁ 🍴 🗑 ▣ ☎
🍴 🛁 🌫 🍴 🏧 ▣
Nearest Town Dolgellau
Directions Turn off the A470 or the A494 onto the B4416 to Brithdir. At the phonebox and village hall turn into a minor road, Park is ½ a mile on the left.
⚏ Machynlleth

DOLGELLAU
Pant-y-Cae, Arthog, Dolgellau, Gwynedd, LL39 1LJ
Tel: 01341 250892
Email: pantycaefarm@btconnect.com
www.pantycae.co.uk
Pitches For 🛆 ⚌ ⚍ **Total** 56
Acreage 5 **Open** All Year
Access Good **Site** Sloping
Nearest Bus Stop (Miles) 1
3 miles from the beach. Near Cregennan Lakes for fishing and Cadair Idris for mountain walking, bird watching and mountain biking.
Facilities ⅃ 🌫 🍴 ⚲➤🐾▣ ▣
Nearest Town Dolgellau/Fairbourne
Directions From Dolgellau take the A493, quarry on the left hand side then turn left for Cregennan Lakes, site is ¾ miles up the single track road.
⚏ Fairbourne

DOLGELLAU
Tyddyn Farm, Islawrdref, Dolgellau, Gwynedd, LL40 1TL
Tel: 01341 422472
Pitches For 🛆 ⚌ ⚍
Open All Year
Access Good **Site** Lev/Slope
Beautiful views of Cader Idris Mountain and alongside a river. Plenty of walks and fishing locally. ¼ of a mile from Lake Hotel.
Facilities ⚲➤🐾▣
Nearest Town Dolgellau
Directions 2 miles from Dolgellau on the Cader road. Pass Gwernan Lake Hotel, ¼ of a mile turn right through a wooden gate, go over the cattle grid and turn left.
⚏ Machynlleth

DOLGELLAU
Vanner Caravan & Camping Site, Vanner, Llanelltyd, Dolgellau, Gwynedd, LL40 2HE
Tel: 01341 422854
Email: enquiries@vanner.co.uk
www.vanner.co.uk
Pitches For 🛆 ⚌ ⚍ **Total** 30
Acreage 2 **Open** Apr **to** Oct
Access Good **Site** Level
Nearest Bus Stop (Miles) ½
Ancient monument (ruin), alongside river, ideal for walking and cycling.
Facilities ⚹ ⅃ 🌫 🍴 ⌁ 🍴 ✦
🍴 🏧 🌫 ▣ ⚙
Nearest Town Dolgellau
Directions Take A470 west towards Barmouth for 1½ miles turn right at Cymer Abbey sign and follow signs to site.
⚏ Barmouth

DYFFRYN ARDUDWY
Murmur-yr-Afon Touring Caravan & Camping Site, Dyffryn Ardudwy, Gwynedd, LL44 2BE
Tel: 01341 247353
Email: mills@murmuryrafon25.freeserve.co.uk
www.murmuryrafon.co.uk

Pitches For 🛆 ⚌ ⚍ **Total** 77
Acreage 4 **Open** Mar **to** Oct
Access Good **Site** Level
Nearest Bus Stop (Miles) Outside
1 mile from beach. Set in sheltered and natural surroundings, 100yds from village and shops, petrol stations and licensed premises.
Facilities ⚹ ⅃ 🍴 🌫 🍴 ⌁ 🍴 🗑 ▣ ☎
🍴 🏧 🛁 🏔 ▣ ⚙
Nearest Town Barmouth
Directions Take the A496 coast road from Barmouth towards Harlech. Caravan Site is located 100yds on the right after the Spar shop.
⚏ Dyffryn

FFESTINIOG
Llechrwd Riverside Campsite, Maentwrog, Blaenau Ffestiniog, Gwynedd, LL41 4HF
Tel: 01766 Maentwrog 590240
Email: llechrwd@hotmail.com
www.llechrwd.co.uk
Pitches For 🛆 ⚌ ⚍ **Total** 45
Acreage 5 **Open** Easter **to** Oct
Access Good **Site** Level
Nearest Bus Stop (Miles) Outside
Riverside camp within Snowdonia National Park, with meadow walk. Near Ffestiniog Railway.
Facilities ⚹ ⅃ 🌫 🍴 ⌁ 🍴 🗑 ➤🐾▣
Directions On the A496. Blaenau Ffestiniog 3 miles, Porthmadog 8 miles.
⚏ Blaenau Ffestiniog

HARLECH
Woodlands Caravan Park, Harlech, Gwynedd, LL46 2UE
Tel: 01766 780419
Email: info@woodlandparkharlech.com
www.woodlandsparkharlech.com
Pitches For 🛆 ⚌ ⚍ **Total** 18
Open Mar **to** Oct
Access Good **Site** Level
Nearest Bus Stop (Miles) ¼
Walking distance to Harlech town centre, beach,railway station, wonderful views of Harlech Castle.
Facilities ⅃ 🌫 🍴 ⌁ 🍴 🗑 ▣ ☎
🍴 ➤🐾▣ ⚙ 🛜
Nearest Town Harlech
⚏ Harlech

LLANBEDROG
Wern Newydd Tourer Park, Llanbedrog, Pwllheli, Gwynedd, LL53 7PG
Tel: 01758 740220
Email: office@wern-newydd.co.uk
www.wern-newydd.co.uk
Pitches For 🛆 ⚌ ⚍ 🚲 ≷ **Total** 25
Acreage 2½ **Open** Mar **to** Oct
Access Good **Site** Level
Nearest Bus Stop (Miles) ¼
Peaceful location on the beautiful Lleyn Peninsula. Near the beach and village with its country pubs and bistro. The area offers many walks, watersports activities and attractions.
Facilities ⅃ 🌫 🍴 ⚲ 🍴 ⌁ 🍴 🗑 ⌂ 🍴➤🐾 ▣ ⚙
🔧
Nearest Town Abersoch
Directions From Pwllheli take the A499 towards Abersoch, in Llanbedrog turn right onto B4413 sp Aberdaron. Continue through the village, go past the chemists (on the right) then take the first turning right onto an unclassified road, site is 700 yards on the right.
⚏ Pwllheli

MORFA NEFYN

Graeanfryn Farm, Morfa Nefyn, Gwynedd, LL53 6YQ
Tel: 01758 720455
Email: jan@campingnorthwales.co.uk
www.campingnorthwales.co.uk
Pitches For ▲ ⬜ ⬛ **Total** 40
Acreage 1½ **Open** Mar **to** Oct
Access Good **Site** Level
Nearest Bus Stop (Miles) ¼
Rural location, 1 mile from the beach. Barbecue area. Cafe/Restaurant nearby. One static caravan for hire. Camping and Caravan Club 3 Star Site and WTB 3 Star Graded. Jumbo tent pitches available.
Facilities ⬜⬜⬜⬜⬜⬜⬜⬜⬜
Nearest Town Pwllheli
Directions From Pwllheli take the A497 for 5 miles, at the roundabout turn left and then turn next left. Entrance to the site is 50 yards on the right.
⬛ Pwllheli/Bangor

PORTHMADOG

Black Rock Sands Camping & Touring Park, Morfa Bychan, Porthmadog, Gwynedd, LL49 9YH
Tel: 01766 513919
www.blackrocksands.webs.com
Pitches For ▲ ⬜ ⬛ **Total** 140
Acreage 9 **Open** Mar **to** Oct
Access Good **Site** Level
Nearest Bus Stop (Miles) ½
Adjacent to a 7 mile sandy beach.
Facilities ⬜⬜⬜⬜⬜⬜⬜⬜⬜⬜⬜⬜
Nearest Town Porthmadog
Directions From Porthmadog take the road to Morfa Bychan, turn right just before the beach.
⬛ Porthmadog

PORTHMADOG

Glan-Y-Mor Camping Park, Morfa Bychan, Porthmadog, Gwynedd, LL49 9YH
Tel: 01758 514640
www.glan-y-mor.webs.com
Pitches For ▲ ⬜ ⬛ **Total** 60
Acreage 5 **Open** Easter **to** Oct
Site Level
Nearest Bus Stop (Miles) ½
Adjacent to a 7 mile sandy beach.
Facilities ⬜⬜⬜⬜⬜⬜⬜⬜
Nearest Town Porthmadog
Directions From Porthmadog take the road to Morfa Bychan, continue to the beach, entrance is on the left.
⬛ Porthmadog

PORTHMADOG

Tyddyn Adi Caravan & Camping Park, Tyddyn Adi, Morfa Bychan, Nr Black Rock Sands, Porthmadog, Gwynedd, LL49 9YW
Tel: 01766 512933
Email: tyddynadi@btconnect.com
www.tyddynadi.co.uk
Pitches For ▲ ⬜ ⬛ ⬛⬛ **Total** 50
Acreage 28 **Open** Mar **to** Sept
Access Good **Site** Level
Nearest Bus Stop (Miles) Entrance
At the foot of Moel-y-Gest Mountain and near

Black Rock Sands. Perfect base from which to explore Snowdonia.
Facilities ⬜⬜⬜⬜⬜⬜⬜⬜⬜⬜⬜⬜
Nearest Town Porthmadog
Directions Take the A487 from Caernarfon, turn right at The Factory Shop and follow signs for Morfa Bychan. We are opposite Greenacres (Haven).
⬛ Porthmadog

PORTHMADOG

Tyddyn Llwyn Caravan Park, Morfa Bychan Road, Porthmadog, Gwynedd, LL49 9UR
Tel: 01766 512205
Email: info@tyddynllwyn.com
www.tyddynllwyn.com
Pitches For ▲ ⬜ ⬛ **Total** 153
Acreage 18 **Open** March **to** 01-Nov
Access Good **Site** Lev/Slope
Nearest Bus Stop (Miles) Entrance
⬛ Porthmadog

PWLLHELI

Abererch Sands Holiday Centre, Pwllheli, Gwynedd, LL53 6PJ
Tel: 01758 612327
www.abererch-sands.co.uk
Pitches For ▲ ⬜ ⬛
Open Mar **to** Oct **Access** Good **Site** Level
Nearest Bus Stop (Miles) ¼
Adjacent to the beach. Heated indoor swimming pool.
Facilities ⬜⬜⬜⬜⬜⬜⬜⬜⬜⬜⬜⬜⬜⬜⬜⬜⬜⬜⬜
Nearest Town Pwllheli
Directions From Pwllheli take the A497 towards Porthmadog for 1 mile, turn right at first roundabout and follow road to the Site.
⬛ Pwllheli

PWLLHELI

Bodwrog Farm, Bodwrog, Llanbedrog, Pwllheli, Gwynedd, LL53 7RE
Tel: 01758 740341
Email: enq@bodwrog.co.uk
www.bodwrog.co.uk
Pitches For ▲ ⬜ ⬛ **Total** 70
Acreage 5 **Open** Mar **to** Oct
Access Good **Site** Sloping
Nearest Bus Stop (Miles) ½
Superb coastal views. 1 miles from a sandy, sheltered beach. Quiet, scenic walks. Local restaurants and pubs within 1 mile.
Facilities ⬜⬜⬜⬜⬜⬜⬜⬜⬜⬜⬜⬜
Nearest Town Abersoch
Directions From Pwllheli take the A499 to Llanbedrog, turn right opposite Glyn-Y-Weddw Pub on the B4413. After 1 mile site is the third opening on the left after the Ship Inn, cattle grid inside entrance.
⬛ Pwllheli

PWLLHELI

Hendre Caravan Park, Efailnewydd, Near Pwllheli, Gwynedd, LL53 8TN
Tel: 01758 613416
Email: info@hendrecaravanpark.co.uk
www.hendrecaravanpark.co.uk

Pitches For ⬜ ⬛ **Total** 12
Acreage 10 **Open** Mar **to** Oct
Access Good **Site** Level
Nearest Bus Stop (Miles) ¼
Nefyn and Pwllheli beaches, Pwllheli marina, 1 mile from Abersoch.
Facilities ⬜⬜⬜⬜⬜⬜⬜⬜⬜⬜⬜⬜⬜⬜
Nearest Town Pwllheli
Directions From Pwllheli take the A497 after 1 mile turn left in Efailnewydd on B4415 we are 500 metres on left.
⬛ Pwllheli

PWLLHELI

Hirdre Fawr Caravan & Camping, Hirdre Fawr Farm, Edern, Pwllheli, Gwynedd, LL53 8YY
Tel: 01758 770309
Email: annwenw@yahoo.com
www.hirdrefawr.co.uk
Pitches For ▲ ⬜ ⬛ **Total** 80
Acreage 7 **Open** End Mar **to** Oct
Access Good **Site** Level
Nearest Bus Stop (Miles) Outside
Pebly beach on site which also adjoins the coastal path. Central to the Llyn Peninsula. 2 miles from a golf coarse and beach access. Fishing off the rocks.
Facilities ⬜⬜⬜⬜⬜⬜⬜⬜⬜⬜⬜⬜
Nearest Town Pwllheli
Directions On the B4417, 1½ miles out of Edern towards Tudweiliog.
⬛ Pwllheli

TALSARNAU

Barcdy Touring Caravan & Camping Park, Talsarnau, Gwynedd, LL47 6YG
Tel: 01766 770736
Email: anwen@barcdy.co.uk
www.barcdy.co.uk
Pitches For ▲ ⬜ ⬛ **Total** 98
Acreage 12 **Open** May **to** Sept
Access Good **Site** Lev/Slope
Nearest Bus Stop (Miles) Outside
Walks from site to nearby mountains and lakes. Ideal touring Snowdonia.
Facilities ⬜⬜⬜⬜⬜⬜⬜⬜⬜⬜⬜⬜⬜
Nearest Town Harlech
Directions From Bala A4212 to Trawsfynydd. A487 to Maentwrog. At Maentwrog left onto A496, signposted Harlech. Site 4 miles.
⬛ Talsarnau

TYWYN

Cwmrhwyddfor Campsite, T D Nutting, Talyllyn, Tywyn, Gwynedd, LL36 9AJ
Tel: 01654 761286/761380
Pitches For ▲ ⬜ ⬛ ⬛⬛ **Total** 30
Acreage 6 **Open** All Year
Access Good **Site** Level
Nearest Bus Stop (Miles) Outside
At the foot of Cader Idris and alongside a stream. Very central for Tywyn, Aberdovey and Barmouth. Ideal for the mountains and sea. All kept very clean, excellent reputation. Public telephone, pub and restaurant and a cafe within a 5 minute walk. Prices on application.

Facilities ⚡ ▣ Ⓗ Ⓦ ♨ ⌐ ☉ ⌐ ☎
▯ Ⓣ ⛃ ⊿ ⚡
Nearest Town Dolgellau
Directions Situated on the A487 between
Dolgellau and Machynlleth, at foot of Cader
Idris mountain, right at the bottom of Talyllyn
pass, a white house under the rocks.
⭢ Machynlleth

TYWYN

Dal Einion, Tal-y-Llyn, Tywyn, Gwynedd,
LL36 9AJ
Tel: 01654 761312
Email: marianrees@tiscali.co.uk
www.tal-y-llynheritagecentre.co.uk
Pitches For ⋏ ☗ ⊟
Acreage 3 **Open** All Year
Access Good **Site** Level
Nearest Bus Stop (Miles) ¼
Flat, grassy site with a stream in Snowdonia
National Park. At the start of the popular
Minffordd Path to the summit of Cader Idris.
Heritage Centre on site with full summer
programme on Welsh history, traditions and
music. Ideal for walking and touring. Fly fishing
½ mile, narrow gauge railway 3 miles and
beach 11 miles. B&B and self catering cottage
on site. Hotel restaurant and bar nearby. Public
telephone nearby. Good bus service.
Facilities ⚡ ▣ Ⓗ Ⓦ ♨ ⌐ ☉ ✦ ♨ ☚ ⚡
Nearest Town Dolgellau
Directions From Dolgellau take the A470 for
2 miles, turn right onto the A487 and continue
for 4 miles. Turn right onto the B4405, site is
300 metres.
⭢ Machynlleth

TYWYN

Glanywern, Dysefin, Llanegryn, Tywyn,
Gwynedd, LL36 9TH
Tel: 01654 782247
Pitches For ⋏ ☗ ⊟ **Total** 28
Acreage 4½ **Open** Apr to Oct
Access Good **Site** Level
Nearest Bus Stop (Miles) Outside
½ a mile from Bird Rock, 3 miles from Cader
Idris and 5 miles from the beach. Near a
Narrow Gauge Railway.
Facilities ⚡ ▣ Ⓗ Ⓦ ♨ ⌐ ☉ ✦ ➔ ⚡ ♨ �’
Nearest Town Tywyn
Directions From Tywyn take the road to
Llanegryn, 3 miles from Llanegryn to Bird Rock.
⭢ Tywyn

TYWYN

Pall Mall Farm Caravan Park, Pall Mall
Farm, Tywyn, Gwynedd, LL36 9RU
Tel: 01654 710384
Email: richardmvaughan@gmail.com
www.pallmallfarmcaravanpark.co.uk
Pitches For ⋏ ☗ ⊟ **Total** 50
Open Easter to Oct
Nearest Bus Stop (Miles) Outside
½ a mile to the town and safe sandy beach
which is ideal for watersports. Leisure centre
in the town plus a cinema, cafes, tennis
courts, bowling green and putting green. Tal-
y-Llyn Steam Railway nearby.
Facilities ♨ ⚡ ♨ ⌐ ☉ ⌐ ☚ ⌐ ☎
▯ ▯ ⌐ ⚡
Nearest Town Tywyn
Directions Park is the first on the left when
leaving Tywyn on the A493 Dolgellau road.
⭢ Tywyn

TYWYN

Tynllwyn Caravan & Camping Park,
Bryncrug, Tywyn, Gwynedd, LL36 9RD
Tel: 01654 710370
Email:
tynllwyncaravanpark@btconnect.com
www.tynllwyncaravanpark.co.uk

Pitches For ⋏ ☗ ⊟ **Total** 18
Open Mar to Oct
Site Level
Nearest Bus Stop (Miles) 1
Talyllyn Narrow gauge railway. Talyllyn beach
Aberdovey nearby.
Facilities ⚡ Ⓦ ♨ ⌐ ☉ ⌐ ☚ ☎
♨ ▯ ♨ ➔ ⌐ ⚡
Nearest Town Tywyn
Directions From Tywyn take the A493 into
Bryncrug then take the B4405. Take the first
left and follow signs up a lane to the site.
⭢ Tywyn

TYWYN

Waenfach Caravan Site, Waenfach,
Llanegryn, Tywyn, Gwynedd, LL36 9SB
Tel: 01654 711052
Email: waenfach@hotmail.co.uk
www.waenfach.com
Pitches For ⋏ ☗ ⊟ **Total** 10
Open Easter to Oct
Access Good
Small site on a working farm. 3 miles from
the sea.
Facilities ♨ ⚡ ⚡ ▣ Ⓗ Ⓦ ♨ ⌐ ☉ ⌐ ☚
▯ ▯ ⌐ ☚ ➔ ⌐ ⚡
Nearest Town Tywyn
Directions 4 miles north of Tywyn on the
A493.
⭢ Tywyn

TYWYN

Ynysymaengwyn Caravan Park, The
Lodge, Tywyn, Gwynedd, LL36 9RY
Tel: 01654 710684
Email: rita@ynysy.co.uk
www.ynysy.co.uk
Pitches For ⋏ ☗ ⊟ **Total** 80
Acreage 4 **Open** Apr to Oct
Access Good **Site** Level
Nearest Bus Stop (Miles) Outside
In the grounds of an old manor house with a
river at the bottom of the site for fishing. Near
to the beach and shops. Woodland walks
open to the public. Superpitches. Walkers
and Cyclists Award. Secure storage for
cycles. WTB 4 Star Grading and AA 4
Pennants.
Facilities ♨ ⚡ Ⓦ ♨ ⌐ ☉ ⌐ ☚ ⌐ ☎
♨ ▯ ▯ ⌐ ♨ ⌐ ➔ ⌐
Nearest Town Tywyn
Directions Take the A493 from Tywyn to
Dolgellau, we are the second caravan park
on the left.
⭢ Tywyn

MERTHYR TYDFIL
MERTHYR TYDFIL

Grawen Caravan & Camping Park, Cwm-
Taf, Cefn Coed, Merthyr Tydfil, CF48 2HS
Tel: 01685 723740
Email: grawen.touring@virgin.net
www.walescaravanandcamping.com
Pitches For ⋏ ☗ ⊟ **Total** 50
Acreage 3½ **Open** Apr to Oct
Access Good
Sityated inside the Brecon Beacons.
Facilities ♨ ⚡ ▣ Ⓗ Ⓦ ♨ ⌐ ☉ ⌐ ☚ ☉ ♨ ➔ ⌐
Nearest Town Merthyr Tydfil
Directions Located on the A470 Brecon
Beacons road, 4 miles north of Merthyr Tydfil.
2 miles off the A465 Heads of the Valleys
road.
⭢ Merthyr Tydfil

MONMOUTHSHIRE
ABERGAVENNY

Blossom Touring Park Tredillion,
Llantillio, Pertholey, Abergavenny,
Monmouthshire, NP7 8BG
Tel: 01873 850444
Email: james.harris27@btinternet.com
www.blossompark.co.uk
Pitches For ⋏ ☗ ⊟ ⌐ ⚄ **Total** 90
Acreage 7½ **Open** Mar to Oct
Access Good **Site** Sloping
Nearest Bus Stop (Miles) 1½
Set in a south facing pear and plum orchard
located 1.5 miles on the out skirts of
Abergavenny. With an abundance of
activities for all the family Abergavenny is a
fantastic choice for your well earned holiday.
Sugar Loaf Mountain. Skirrid Mountain walks.
Facilities ♨ ⚡ ▣ Ⓗ Ⓦ ♨ ⌐ ☉ ⌐ ☚ ☎
▯ ➔ ⌐ ⌐ ⚡ 📶
Nearest Town Abergavenny
Directions Hardwick Roundabout at
Abertale, take A465 towards Hereford for 1
mile. Turn right, then left in to Oldcross Road
(B4521), then right B4233.
⭢ Abergavenny

ABERGAVENNY

**Pyscodlyn Farm Caravan & Camping
Site,** Llanwenarth Citra, Abergavenny,
Monmouthshire, NP7 7ER
Tel: 01873 853271
Email: pyscodlyn.farm@virgin.net
www.pyscodlyncaravanpark.com
Pitches For ⋏ ☗ ⊟ **Total** 60
Acreage 4½ **Open** Apr to Oct
Access Good **Site** Level
Nearest Bus Stop (Miles) Outside
Ideal for walking, cycling and exploring the
Black Mountains and Brecon Beacons
National Park.
Facilities ♨ ⚡ Ⓦ ♨ ⌐ ☉ ⌐ ☚ ⌐ ☎
☉ ➔ ⌐ ⚡
Nearest Town Abergavenny
Directions Situated on A40 (Brecon road),
1½ miles from Nevill Hall Hospital, on the
left 50 yards past the telephone box.
⭢ Abergavenny

MONMOUTH

Bridge Caravan Park & Camping Site,
Dingestow, Monmouth, Monmouthshire,
NP25 4DY
Tel: 01600 740241
Email: info@bridgecaravanpark.co.uk
www.bridgecaravanpark.co.uk
Pitches For ⋏ ☗ ⊟ **Total** 123
Acreage 4 **Open** Easter to Oct
Access Good **Site** Level
Nearest Bus Stop (Miles) Outside
Riverside site. Easy access.
Facilities ♨ ⚡ ▣ Ⓗ Ⓦ ♨ ⌐ ☉ ⌐ ☚ ⌐ ☎
▯ ☉ ♨ ▯ ➔ ⌐ ⚡ ⊿ ⚡
Nearest Town Monmouth
Directions 4 miles west of Monmouth.
⭢ Abergavenny

MONMOUTH

Glen Trothy Caravan Park, Mitchel Troy,
Monmouth, Monmouthshire, NP25 4BD
Tel: 01600 712295
Email: enquiries@glentrothy.co.uk
www.glentrothy.co.uk
Pitches For ⋏ ☗ ⊟ **Total** 130
Acreage 6½ **Open** Mar to Oct
Access Good **Site** Level
Nearest Bus Stop (Miles) Outside
Quiet level Park set in beautiful countryside
on the edge of Forest of Dean and Wye
Valley. Alongside a river for fishing. 1½ miles

from the historic town of Monmouth. Plenty of castles and attractions nearby. No arrivals before 2pm.
Facilities ☆ � ⚇ Ⓗ ⽕ ♿ Ⓟ ☉ ⌂ ⌨ ▣ ☎
▣ 🅿 ✦ ♒
Nearest Town Monmouth
Directions From the North & North East M5, M50 to Ross on Wye then A40 to Monmouth. After traffic lights, 150yds, turn left
(before Tunnel), 150 yds to T junction. Turn left and follow signs to Mitchel Troy- 1½ miles The park ison the right as you enter village. From East & South Gloucester A4136 and Cheptow A466 to Monmouth over River Wye bridge. Turn left at traffic lights onto A40, then as above. From South West Newport M4 junction 24 then A3449 to Raglan. From West Abergavenny A40m to Raglan. From Raglam take Old Monmouth road signed Mitchel Troy. The park is on the left as you go through the village.
⇥ Newport

NEWPORT

NEWPORT

Pentre-Tai Farm, Rhiwderin, Newport, NP10 8RQ
Tel: 01633 893284
Email: sue@pentretai.f9.co.uk
www.pentretaifarm.co.uk
Pitches For ▲ ⊞ ➤ **Total** 5
Acreage 3 **Open** All Year
Access Good **Site** Lev/Slope
Nearest Bus Stop (Miles) ½
Ideal for visiting Cardiff and the Welsh castles. Useful stopover for Irish ferry. Good pub nearby. B&B also available (WTB 4 Star).
Facilities ℓ ⽕ ♿ ⌂ ☉ ☎ ⽘ ♒ ♒
Nearest Town Newport
Directions Leave the M4 at junction 28 and take the A467, at the next roundabout take the A468 for approx. 1 mile. Turn right immediately after Rhiwdden Inn and go straight through the village and straight down the lane to the Farm. Go past the farmhouse then turn into yard.
⇥ Newport

NEWPORT

Tredegar House Country Park Caravan Club Site, Coedkernew, Newport, NP10 8TW
Tel: 01633 815600
www.caravanclub.co.uk
Pitches For ▲ ⊞ ➤ **Total** 79
Acreage 7 **Open** All Year
Access Good **Site** Level
Nearest Bus Stop (Miles) ¼
Bordered by an ornamental lake by Tredegar House. Tea rooms on site. Adventure playground adjacent. 7 miles from Cardiff. Non members welcome. Booking essential.
Facilities ☆ ℓ ⚇ Ⓗ ⽕ ♿ ⌂ ☎
▣ ✦ ⽘ 🅿 ▣ ☎
Nearest Town Newport
Directions Leave the M4 at junction 28 and take the A48 signposted Tredegar House. At the roundabout turn left into the site entrance and follow site signs.
⇥ Newport

PEMBROKESHIRE

AMROTH

Little Kings Park, Amroth Road, Ludchurch, Narberth, Pembrokeshire, SA67 8PG
Tel: 01834 831330
Email: littlekingspark@btconnect.com
www.littlekings.co.uk
Pitches For ▲ ⊞ ➤ ➤⦚ **Total** 121
Acreage 16 **Open** Mar **to** Oct
Access Good **Site** Level
Quiet family park in a country setting with an excellent outlook towards the sea. Perfectly placed for easy access to explore all that Pembrokeshire has to offer.
Facilities ☆ ℓ ⚇ Ⓗ ⽕ ♿ ⌂ ☉ ⌨ ⌂ ▣ ☎
♒ ▣ ☎ ✗ ⽘ ⚑ ➤ ⽘ 🅿 ▣ ✦ ♒ ♒ ☎
Nearest Town Amroth
Directions 5 miles south east of Narberth. From the A477 in Llanteg Village, 2 miles after the petrol station turn left towards Amroth and Wisemans Bridge, turn first right signposted Ludchurch and the Park is 300 metres on the left.
⇥ Kilgetty

AMROTH

Pantglas Farm, Tavernspite, Pembrokeshire, SA34 0NS
Tel: 01834 831618
Email: pantglasfarm@btinternet.com
www.pantglasfarm.co.uk
Pitches For ▲ ⊞ ➤ ➤⦚ **Total** 86
Acreage 14 **Open** Mid Mar **to** Mid Oct
Access Good **Site** Lev/Slope
Nearest Bus Stop (Miles) ¼
A family caravan and camping park, quiet and secluded. Super play area for children. High standard toilet and shower facilities, disabled wet room facility. Year round caravan storage available. Within easy reach of Tenby, Saundersfoot and Amroth. Indoor swimming pool only 1 mile away.
Facilities ℓ ⚇ Ⓗ ⽕ ♿ ⌂ ☉ ⌨ ⌂ ▣ ☎
▣ ☎ ♒ ⽘ ⚑ ➤ ⽘ 🅿 ▣ ✦ ♒ ♒ ☎
Nearest Town Whitland/Narberth
Directions A477 towards Tenby take the B4314 at Red Roses crossroads to Tavernspite 1¼ miles, take the middle road at the village pump. Pantglas is ½ mile down on the left.
⇥ Whitland

ANGLE

Castle Farm Camping Site, Castle Farm, Angle, Nr Pembroke, Pembrokeshire, SA71 5AR
Tel: 01646 641220
Pitches For ▲ ⊞ ➤ **Total** 25
Acreage 2½ **Open** Easter **to** Oct
Access Good **Site** Lev/Slope
Overlooking East Angle Bay and directly behind the church in the village. Approx. 1 mile from a safe, sandy beach. Near to 2 public houses, Beach Cafe, a good shop and childrens play area. Pets are welcome if kept on leads.
Facilities ℓ ⽕ ♿ ⌂ ☉ ☎ ⽘ ▣ 🅿 ▣
Nearest Town Pembroke
Directions Approx. 10 miles from Pembroke.
⇥ Pembroke

BROAD HAVEN

Creampots Touring Caravan & Camping Park, Broadway, Broad Haven, Haverfordwest, Pembrokeshire, SA62 3TU
Tel: 01437 781776
Email: creampots@btconnect.com
www.creampots.co.uk

Pitches For ▲ ⊞ ➤ **Total** 72
Acreage 7 **Open** Mar **to** Nov
Access Good **Site** Level
Nearest Bus Stop (Miles) ¼
Family run park thats quiet, peaceful and well maintained. Ideal for couples and families. 1½ miles from safe sandy beach and coastal path at Broad Haven. 21 hardstanding pitches. Near Haverfordwest, Broad Haven and Littlehaven. WTB 5 Star Graded.
Facilities ☆ ℓ ⚇ Ⓗ ⽕ ♿ ⌂ ☉ ⌨ ⌂ ▣ ☎
▣ ☎ ♒ 🅿 ▣ ☎ ♒ ♒ ✦
Nearest Town Haverfordwest
Directions Take the B4131 Broad Haven road from Haverfordwest to Broadway (5 miles). Turn left and Creampots is 600 yards on the right.
⇥ Haverfordwest

FISHGUARD

Fishguard Bay Caravan Park, Garn Gelli, Fishguard, Pembrokeshire, SA65 9ET
Tel: 01348 811415
Email: enquiries@fishguardbay.com
www.fishguardbay.com
Pitches For ▲ ⊞ ➤ **Total** 50
Acreage 5 **Open** Mar **to** Dec
Access Good **Site** Lev/Slope
Superb cliff top location offering excellent views and walks along this Heritage coast of Pembrokeshire.
Facilities ℓ ⽕ ♿ ⌂ ☉ ⌨ ⌂ ▣ ☎
♒ ▣ ☎ ♒ ⽘ ⚑ ➤ ⽘ 🅿 ▣ ✦
Nearest Town Fishguard
Directions Take the A487 Cardigan road from Fishguard for 1½ miles, turn left at sign.
⇥ Fishguard

FISHGUARD

Gwaun Vale Touring Park, Llanychaer, Fishguard, Pembrokeshire, SA65 9TA
Tel: 01348 874698
Email: margaret.harries@talk21.com
www.gwaunvale.co.uk
Pitches For ▲ ⊞ ➤ **Total** 29
Acreage 1½ **Open** Apr **to** Oct
Access Good **Site** Level
Nearest Bus Stop (Miles) 1
Beautiful views of Gwaun Valley. Ideal for walking on Pembrokeshire Coast National Park.
Facilities ℓ ⚇ Ⓗ ⽕ ♿ ⌂ ☉ ⌨ ⌂ ▣ ☎
♒ ▣ ☎ ♒ ⚑ ➤ ⽘ 🅿
Nearest Town Fishguard
Directions From Fishguard take the B4313, site is 1½ miles on the right hand side.
⇥ Fishguard

FISHGUARD

Rosebush Caravan & Camping Park, Rhoslwyn, Rosebush, Narberth, Pembrokeshire, SA66 7QT
Tel: 01437 532206
Pitches For ▲ ⊞ ➤ **Total** 45
Acreage 15 **Open** Mar **to** Oct
Access Good **Site** Level
ADULTS ONLY PARK in the centre of Pembrokeshire, 800ft above sea level. 3 acre lake for coarse fishing. Mountain walks. David Bellamy Gold Award for Conservation.
Facilities ℓ ⚇ Ⓗ ⽕ ♿ ⌂ ☉ ⌨ ⌂ ▣ ☎
♒ ▣ ☎ ♒ ⚑ ➤ 🅿 ✦ ⽘ ⸝
Nearest Town Fishguard
Directions From the A40 take the B4313 near Narberth to Fishguard. 1 mile from the B4329 Haverfordwest to Cardigan road.
⇥ Clynderwen

HAVERFORDWEST

Brandy Brook Caravan & Camping Site,
Roch, Haverfordwest, Pembrokeshire,
SA62 6HE
Tel: 01348 840563
Email: a.daye@btopenworld.com
www.brandybrookcampsite.co.uk
Pitches For A **Total** 40
Acreage 5 **Open** Easter **to** Oct
Site Lev/Slope
Attractive quiet valley setting with The Brandy
Brook flowing alongside. Small motorhomes
also accepted.
Facilities 🔥 ▦ ⌐ ☺ 🚻 🕯
🏪 🅿 🛒 🔥 ♨ ⊬ 🔲
Nearest Town Haverfordwest
Directions From Haverfordwest take the
A487 west towards St Davids, turn right at
Roch, signposted.
⇌ Haverfordwest

HAVERFORDWEST

Nolton Cross Caravan Park, Nolton,
Haverfordwest, Pembrokeshire, SA62 3NP
Tel: 01437 710701
Email: info@noltoncross-holidays.co.uk
www.noltoncross-holidays.co.uk
Pitches For A ⊞ ♙ **Total** 15
Acreage 1½ **Open** Mar **to** Dec
Access Good **Site** Level
Nearest Bus Stop (Miles) 1½
Coarse fishing lake on site. 1½ miles from
sandy beaches. Central location for touring
Pembrokeshire.
Facilities 🔥 ▦ ⌐ ⌐ ☺ ↲ 🔲 🕯
🏪 ⛺ ⊟ 🛒 ✉ 🔲 ✈ ⊜
Nearest Town Haverfordwest
Directions Take the A487 from
Haverfordwest towards St Davids, after 5
miles at the village of Simpson Cross turn
left for Nolton, follow for 1 mile to the next
crossroads and turn left, entrance is 100
yards on the right.
⇌ Haverfordwest

HERMON

The Lamb Inn Touring Caravan Park,
Hermon, Glogue, Pembrokeshire, SA36
0DS
Tel: 01239 831864
Email: street867@btinternet.com
www.thelambinnhermon.co.uk
Pitches For ⊞ ♙ **Total** 28
Acreage 3 **Open** Easter **to** 03-Jan
Access Good **Site** Level
Nearest Bus Stop (Miles) Outside
Quiet and secluded ADULTS ONLY Park at
the rear of The Lamb Inn Pub. Ideal for
walking and cycling. Close to Cardigan.
Facilities ⅙ 🔥 ▦ ⌐ ☺ ↲ 🕯
🏪 🅿 🅾 ✗ ☗ 🔲 ♣ 🔲 🅵 ⊠ ✈ ⊬
Nearest Town Cardigan
Directions From Carmarthen take the A40
west, turn right onto the A478 Cardigan road.
At Crymmych turn right and follow signs to
Hermon for 2 miles.
⇌ Clunderwen

KILGETTY

Stone Pitt Caravan Park, Begelly, Kilgetty,
Pembrokeshire, SA68 0XE
Tel: 01834 811086
Email: info@stonepitt.co.uk
www.stonepitt.co.uk
Pitches For ⊞ ♙ **Total** 36
Acreage 6 **Open** 01-Mar **to** 09-Jan
Access Good **Site** Lev/Slope
Nearest Bus Stop (Miles) Outside
Quiet, peaceful, family run park. Within easy
reach of Pembrokeshires wonderful
beaches, Folly Farm, Heatherton, Oakwood,

Tenby and Saundersfoot. Ideal touring. All
pitches are hardstanding with grey water
waste.Online booking available.
Facilities 🔥 ▦ 🚻 ⌐ ⌐ ☺ ↲ 🚿 🔲 🕯
🅿 🅾 ▦ 🔲 🔲 ♣ ⊜
Nearest Town Saundersfoot/Tenby
Directions From St. Clears take the A477,
at the next roundabout turn onto the A478
for Narberth. Go over the next roundabout
in Begelly Village, site is ½ a mile on the left.
⇌ Kilgetty

LITTLE HAVEN

**Redlands Touring Caravan & Camping
Park,** Hasguard Cross, Nr Little Haven,
Haverfordwest, Pembrokeshire, SA62 3SJ
Tel: 01437 781300
Email: info@redlandscamping.co.uk
www.redlandstouring.co.uk
Pitches For A ⊞ ♙ ♙ ⌐ **Total** 60
Acreage 5 **Open** Mar **to** Dec
Access Good **Site** Level
Nearest Bus Stop (Miles) ¼
4 Star Park set in Pembrokeshire National
Park, within easy reach of coastal path and
superb sandy beaches.Sea views,
Immaculate facilities. Extra large tent pitches.
Special Offers for couples in Low Season.
Facilities 🔥 ▦ 🚻 ⌐ ☺ ↲ 🚿 🔲 🕯
🏪 🅿 🅾 🛒 🔲 ⊬
Nearest Town Little Haven
Directions 6½ miles southwest of
Haverfordwest, on B4327 Dale Road.
⇌ Haverfordwest

LITTLE HAVEN

South Cockett Caravan & Camping Park,
Broadway, Little Haven, Haverfordwest,
Pembrokeshire, SA62 3TU
Tel: 01437 781296
Email: esmejames@hotmail.co.uk
www.southcockett.co.uk
Pitches For A ⊞ ♙ **Total** 73
Acreage 6 **Open** Easter **to** Oct
Access Good **Site** Level
Nearest Bus Stop (Miles) ¼
1 mile from the beach. Ideal for touring.
Facilities 🔥 ▦ ⌐ ☺ ↲ 🚿 🔲 🕯
🏪 🅾 🛒 🔲 🔲
Nearest Town Broad Haven
Directions From Haverfordwest take the
B4341 for Broad Haven for about 6 miles,
turn left at sign post and the Site is ¼ of a
mile.
⇌ Haverfordwest

MANORBIER

Park Farm Holiday Park, Manorbier,
Tenby, Pembrokeshire, SA70 7SU
Tel: 01834 871273
Email: info@parkfarmholidaypark.co.uk
www.parkfarmholidaypark.co.uk
Pitches For A ⊞ ♙ **Total** 120
Acreage 7 **Open** Apr **to** Oct
Access Good **Site** Lev/Slope
Nearest Bus Stop (Miles) ¼
Just a 10 minute walk from Manorbier Beach
along a private foot path.
Facilities ⅙ 🔥 ▦ 🚻 ⌐ ☺ ↲ 🚿 🔲 🕯
🏪 🅿 🅾 🛒 🔲 ⊬ ♨ ⊜
Nearest Town Manorbier
Directions Take the A4139 from Tenby, take
second turn to Manorbier and follow brown
tourism signs.
⇌ Manorbier

MILFORD HAVEN

Sandy Haven Caravan Park,
Herbrandston, Nr Milford Haven,
Pembrokeshire, SA73 3ST
Tel: 01646 698844
www.sandyhavencampingpark.co.uk
Pitches For A ⊞ ♙ **Total** 26
Open Whitsun **to** Sept
Access Good **Site** Lev/Slope
Nearest Bus Stop (Miles) ¼
Very quiet and uncommercialised site,
alongside a beautiful beach and sea estuary.
Ideal for a family holiday.
Facilities ⌐ ⌐ ↲ 🕯 🔲 ▦ 🔲 ✈
Nearest Town Milford Haven
Directions Take the Dale Road from Milford
Haven, turn left at Herbrandston School and
follow the village road down to the beach.
⇌ Milford Haven

NARBERTH

Wood Office Caravan & Tent Park, Cold
Blow, Narberth, Pembrokeshire, SA67 8RR
Tel: 01834 860565
Email: barbara_morris@btconnect.com
Pitches For A ⊞ **Total** 30
Access Good **Site** Level
Nearest Bus Stop (Miles) Outside
Close to Oakwood Park, Bluestone & Blue
Lagoon and Folly Farm. Please telephone
prior to bringing a dog.
Facilities ⅙ 🔥 ▦ ⌐ ⌐ ☺ ↲ 🔲 🕯
🏪 🅾 🛒 🔲 ⊬
Nearest Town Saundersfoot
Directions Leave the M4 and take the A40,
then the A478, at the top of Templeton turn
left onto the B4315 to Cold Blow.
⇌ Narberth

NEWPORT

Llwyngwair Manor Holiday Park,
Newport, Pembrokeshire, SA42 0LX
Tel: 01239 820498
www.pembrokeshireholidaypark.co.uk
Pitches For A ⊞ ♙ **Total**
Acreage 55 **Open** Mar **to** 02-Jan
Access Good **Site** Level
Nearest Bus Stop (Miles) Outside
1 mile from a sandy beach. Alongside the
River Nevern in 55 acres of wood and
parkland in Pembrokeshire Coast National
Park.
Facilities ⅙ ✗ 🔥 ▦ ⌐ ⌐ ☺ ↲ 🔲 🕯
🏪 🅿 🅾 🛒 ✗ ☗ ♣ 🔲 🔲 🅵 ⊠ ✈ ⊬
Nearest Town Newport
Directions 1 mile from Newport on the A487
to Cardigan.
⇌ Fishguard

NEWPORT

Morawelon Caravan & Camping Site,
Morawelon, The Parrog, Newport,
Pembrokeshire, SA42 0RW
Tel: 01239 820565
Email: carreg@morawelon.fsnet.co.uk
Pitches For A ⊞ ♙ **Total** 90
Acreage 5 **Open** Mar **to** Oct
Access Good **Site** Sloping
Nearest Bus Stop (Miles) ½
Ideal family site. Near to the beach with a
slipway for boat launching just outside the
entrance. On the Pembrokeshire Coastal
Path.
Facilities 🔥 ▦ ⌐ ☺ ✉ ✗ 🔲 🔲
Nearest Town Newport
Directions A487 from Fishguard, 7 miles to
Newport. A487 from Cardigan, 12 miles to
Newport. Turn right after the garage, continue
into Newport, turn left down Parrog Road.
Go down to the bottom and Morawelon is
the house by the slipway.
⇌ Fishguard

NEWPORT

Tycanol Farm Camp Site, Newport, Pembrokeshire, SA42 0ST
Tel: 01239 820264
Email: sharonjackson70@hotmail,co.uk
www.caravancampingsites.co.uk
Pitches For ▲ ⊕ ⊞ �☰ **Total** 40
Acreage 6 **Open** All Year
Access Good **Site** Level
Nearest Bus Stop (Miles) ¼
Organic farm, situated on a coastal path with easy access to beaches and the town. barbecue nightly. Bunk house accommodation.
Facilities ⨍ ⌂ ⎘ ⌁ ⌽ ⊙⌐ ☎ ⟋⊣⊟ ⟋
Nearest Town Newport
⇌ Fishguard

PEMBROKE

Freshwater East Caravan Club Site, Trewent Hill, Freshwater East, Pembroke, Pembrokeshire, SA71 5LJ
Tel: 01646 672341
www.caravanclub.co.uk
Pitches For ▲ ⊕ ⊞ **Total** 130
Acreage 12½ **Open** Mar **to** Oct
Access Good **Site** Lev/Slope
Nearest Bus Stop (Miles) ¼
Situated at the bottom of a hill in Pembrokeshire Coast National Park. Just a few minutes from the beach with clifftop views and coastal walks. Close to the castles of Pembroke, Carew and Manorbier. Near Folly Farm and Oakwood Theme Park. Non members welcome. Booking essential.
Facilities ⬙ ⨍ ⌂ ⎘ ⌁ ⌽ ⌐ ☎
⎉ ⊙ ⊞ ⏁ ⟋⊣⊟ ⟋ ⟨
Nearest Town Pembroke
Directions From A477 take A4075 sp Pembroke. Immediately after passing under railway bridge turn left on A4139. In Lamphey at left hand bend continue onto B4584 sp Freshwater East. After 1¾ miles turn right sp Stackpole, at foot of hill turn right at Club site.
⇌ Pembroke

PEMBROKE

Windmill Hill Caravan Park, St Daniels Hill, Pembroke, Pembrokeshire, SA71 5BT
Tel: 01646 682392
Email: wjgibby@btconnect.com
www.windmillhillcaravanpark.co.uk
Pitches For ▲ ⊕ ⊞ **Total** 30
Open Mar **to** Dec
Access Good **Site** Level
Ideal base for surfing, hiking and rock climbing.
Facilities ⬙ ⨍ ⌂ ⎘ ⌁ ⌽ ⊙⌐ ⌑ ☎ ⊙⟋⊟
Nearest Town Pembroke
Directions From Pembroke take the B4319, site is ½ a mile on the right hand side.
⇌ Pembroke

REYNALTON

Croft Holiday Park, Reynalton, Kilgetty, Pembrokeshire, SA68 0PE
Tel: 01834 860315
Email: enquiries@croftholidaypark.com
www.celticholidaypark.com
Pitches For ▲ ⊕ ⊞ **Total** 55
Open Mar **to** Oct
Access Good **Site** Level
Close to the seaside resorts of Tenby and Saundersfoot, and Pembrokeshire National Park.
Facilities ⨍ ⌁ ⌁ ⌽ ⊙⌐ ⌑ ☎ ⌑
⎉ ⎉ ⊙ ☎ ⟊ ⟋⊣⊟ ⟋ ⟨
Nearest Town Saundersfoot

Directions From Narberth take the A478 following signs for Tenby. In Templeton turn second right at the Boars Head towards Yerbeston, turn second left to Reynalton and the park is ½ mile on the right hand side.
⇌ Kilgetty

SAUNDERSFOOT

Mill House Caravan Park, Pleasant Valley, Stepaside, Saundersfoot, Pembrokeshire, SA67 8LN
Tel: 01834 812069
Email: holiday@millhousecaravan.co.uk
www.millhousecaravan.co.uk
Pitches For ▲ ⊕ **Total** 12
Acreage 2½ **Open** Mar **to** Oct
Access Good **Site** Level
Nearest Bus Stop (Miles) Outside
Beautiful and sheltered setting in a wooded valley, next to an old water mill. 15 minute walk to the beach and coastal path. Holiday caravans for hire.
Facilities ⨍ ⌂ ⎘ ⌁ ⌽ ⊙⌐ ⌑ ☎
⎉ ⊙ ⌁ ⟋ ✿⟋
Directions 13 miles west of St. Clears on the A477 turn left signposted Stepaside. After crossing the bridge turn sharp left then immediately turn left again signed Pleasant Valley. Site is approx. 500 metres on the left hand side.
⇌ Kilgetty

SAUNDERSFOOT

Moysland Farm Camping Site, Narberth Road, Saundersfoot, Pembrokeshire, SA69 9DS
Tel: 01834 812455
Pitches For ▲ ⊕ **Total** 17
Acreage 2 **Open** July **to** 01-Sep
Access Good **Site** Level
Nearest Bus Stop (Miles) ¼
On cycle route for touring local area.
Facilities ⨍ ⌁ ⌽ ⊙⌐ ☎ ⊟ ⌑
Nearest Town Saundersfoot
Directions On A478 near Twycross roundabout, 1½ miles north of Tenby.
⇌ Tenby

ST. DAVIDS

Caerfai Bay Caravan & Tent Park, St Davids, Pembrokeshire, SA62 6QT
Tel: 01437 720274
Email: info@caerfaibay.co.uk
www.caerfaibay.co.uk
Pitches For ▲ ⊕ ⊞ **Total** 105
Acreage 10 **Open** Mar **to** Mid Nov
Site Lev/Slope
Nearest Bus Stop (Miles) 1
A family run park with panoramic coastal views. Adjacent to the Pembrokeshire Coastal Path and an award winning beach. Within walking distance of St Davids, Britains smallest city. Holiday hire caravans available. No dogs allowed in the tent fields during school summer holidays (July/August).
Facilities ⬙ ⨍ ⌂ ⎘ ⌁ ⌽ ⊙⌐ ⌑ ☎ ⌑
⎉ ⊙ ☎ ⟋⊣⊟ ⊟ ⟨
Nearest Town St. Davids
Directions Turn off the A487 (Haverfordwest to St. Davids road) at St. Davids Visitor Centre signposted Caerfai. At the end of the road, ¾ miles, turn right into park.
⇌ Haverfordwest

ST. DAVIDS

Hendre Eynon Camp Site, Hendre Eynon, St Davids, Pembrokeshire, SA62 6DB
Tel: 01437 720474
Email: hendreeynon@gmail.com
www.hendreeynon.co.uk
Pitches For ▲ ⊕ ⊞ **Total** 72

Open Apr **to** Sept
Access Good **Site** Level
Nearest Bus Stop (Miles) Outside
Ideal family site, spotlessly clean facilities, sheltered pitches, close to coast path.
Facilities ⨍ ⌂ ⎘ ⌁ ⌽ ⊙⌐ ⌑ ☎
⎉ ⊙ ☎⟋⊣⊟ ⟋
Nearest Town St Davids
Directions At St Davids take the Fishguard road and fork left at the rugby club signposted Llanrhian. Keep going straight and after approx. 2 miles Hendre Eynon is on the right hand side.
⇌ Haverfordwest

ST. DAVIDS

Nine Wells Caravan & Camping Park, Nine Wells, Solva, Nr Haverfordwest, Pembrokeshire, SA62 6UH
Tel: 01437 721809
Email: ocean6@clara.co.uk
www.ninewellscamping.com
Pitches For ▲ ⊕ ⊞ **Total** 70
Acreage 4½ **Open** Easter **to** Oct
Access Good **Site** Lev/Slope
Nearest Bus Stop (Miles) Outside
Sandy beach ¾ mile. Walk the coastal footpath to Solva. About 5 minute walk to cove and coastal footpath and Iron Age Fort, down National Trust Valley. You can also call us on Mobile 07974 516461.
Facilities ⨍ ⌂⎘ ⌁ ⌽ ⊙⌐ ⌑ ☎ ⎉⟋⊣⊟ ⟋ ⟨
Nearest Town Haverfordwest
Directions From Haverfordwest take A487 to Solva. ¼ mile past Solva turn left at Nine Wells. Site clearly signposted.
⇌ Haverfordwest

ST. DAVIDS

Park Hall Camping Park, Maerdy Farm, Penycwm, Haverfordwest, Pembrokeshire, SA62 6LS
Tel: 01437 721606/721282
Pitches For ▲ ⊕ ⊞ ⊟ᵣ☰ **Total** 100
Acreage 7 **Open** Mar **to** Oct
Access Good **Site** Level
Near the beach with scenic views. Ideal touring. Disabled toilet and shower. Dish washing facilities.
Facilities ⬙ ⨍ ⌂ ⎘ ⌁ ⌽ ⊙⌐ ⌑ ☎ ⌑
⎉ ⊙ ☎ ⟋⊣⊟ ⟨
Nearest Town Haverfordwest
Directions 12 miles from Haverfordwest on the A487 and 6 miles from St. Davids. Turn at the 14th Signal Regiment Brawdy.
⇌ Haverfordwest

ST. DAVIDS

St Davids Lleithyr Meadow Caravan Club Site, Whitesands, St Davids, Pembrokeshire, SA62 6PR
Tel: 01437 720401
www.caravanclub.co.uk
Pitches For ⊕ ⊞ **Total** 120
Acreage 8 **Open** Mar **to** Oct
Access Good **Site** Level
Nearest Bus Stop (Miles) ½
Just a short walk to Whitesands Bay. Shop adjacent. Non members welcome. Booking essential.
Facilities ⬙ ⨍ ⌂ ⎘ ⌁ ⌽ ⌐ ☎
⎉ ⊙ ☎⟋⊟ ⊟
Nearest Town St. Davids
Directions From Haverfordwest take A487, before entering St Davids t rt on B4583 sp Whitesands, t lt still on B4583. At second xroads (DO NOT follow Lleithyr Meadow signs at first xroads) t sharp right opposite St Davids Golf Club, site is 500 yards on left.
⇌ St. Davids

ST. DAVIDS
St. Davids Camping & Caravanning Club Site, Dwr Cwmwdig Berea, St Davids, Haverfordwest, Pembrokeshire, SA62 6DW
Tel: 01348 831376
Email: stdavids.site@thefriendlyclub.com
www.campingandcaravanningclub.co.uk/stdavids
Pitches For Å ⚏ ⚐ **Total** 40
Acreage 4 **Open** 30-Apr **to** Sept
Access Good **Site** Sloping
Nearest Bus Stop (Miles) Outside
Just 1 mile from the beach. Close to Britains smallest cathedral city. WTB 3 Star Graded and AA 2 Pennants. Non members welcome. You can also call us on 0845 130 7633.
Facilities ⚙ 🛁 📞 🛒 ⚸ 📷 🔌 ⚏
🏪 🚿 🛉 ▣ ⚷
Nearest Town Haverfordwest
Directions Travelling south on the A487, in Croesgoch turn right at Glyncheryn Farmers Stores. After approx. 1 mile turn right signposted Abereiddy, at the crossroads turn left and the site is 75 yards on the left hand side.
⚏ Fishguard

TENBY
Buttyland Camping Park, Manorbier, Tenby, Pembrokeshire, SA70 7SX
Tel: 01834 871278
Email: stay@buttyland.com
www.buttyland.com
Pitches For Å ⚏ ⚐ ⚏: **Total** 50
Acreage 10 **Open** 15-Mar **to** 15-Nov
Access Good **Site** Level
Nearest Bus Stop (Miles) ¼
Perfect location for Tenby, close to beach, 2 country pubs serving food, station next to park.
Facilities ⚙ 🛁 📞 🛒 ⚸ 📷 🔌 ⚏
🏪 🚿 ✕ ▽ 🛉 ▣ ▣ ⚸ 🌙 ⚷
Nearest Town Tenby
Directions After Tenby follow A4139 towards Pembroke, then after approx 4 miles, follow signs for Manorbier Railway station.
⚏ Manorbier

TENBY
Hazelbrook Caravan Park, Sageston, Nr Tenby, Pembrokeshire, SA70 8SY
Tel: 01646 651351
Email: hazbrook12@hotmail.co.uk
www.hazelbrookcaravanpark.co.uk
Pitches For Å ⚏ ⚐ **Total** 70
Acreage 7½ **Open** 14-Mar **to** 09-Jan
Access Good **Site** Level
Nearest Bus Stop (Miles) ¼
Quiet family site, 1 mile from Carew Castle and Mill, 2 miles from Dinosaur Park and 7

miles from Oakwood Theme Park.
Facilities ⚙ 🛁 📞 🛒 ⚸ 📷 🔌 ⚏ ⚐ 📷 ⚷
🏪 🛁 🛉 ▣ ▣ 🌙
Nearest Town Tenby
Directions Turn off the A477 at the roundabout turning onto the B4318 for Tenby. Caravan park is 20 yards on the right (60 foot entrance).
⚏ Tenby

TENBY
Kiln Park Holiday Centre, Marsh Road, Tenby, Pembrokeshire, SA70 7RB
Tel: 01834 844121
Email: kilnpark@haven.com
www.haventouring.com/tokilnpark
Pitches For Å ⚏ ⚐ **Total** 193
Acreage 150 **Open** Mid March **to** End Oct
Access Good **Site** Level
Nearest Bus Stop (Miles) Outside
Nearest Town Tenby
⚏ Tenby

TENBY
Lodge Farm Holiday Park, New Hedges, Tenby, Pembrokeshire, SA70 8TN
Tel: 01834 842468
Email: lodgefarm1@hotmail.co.uk
Pitches For Å ⚏ ⚐ **Total** 65
Acreage 5 **Open** Apr/Easter **to** Oct
Access Good **Site** Level
Nearest Bus Stop (Miles) Outside
Near the beach and coastal path.
Facilities ⚙ 📷 📞 ⚸ 📷 🔌 ⚏
🏪 🏪 ⚷ ✕ 🛁 🛉 ▣ ▣ 🌙
Nearest Town Tenby/Saundersfoot
Directions Approaching Tenby on the A478, turn left at New Hedges roundabout, turn first right, go through the village and Lodge Farm entrance is opposite the minimarket.
⚏ Tenby/Saundersfoot

TENBY
Masterland Farm Touring Park, Broadmoor, Kilgetty, Pembrokeshire, SA68 0RH
Tel: 01834 813298
Email: k.bonser@btconnect.com
www.ukparks.co.uk/masterland
Pitches For Å ⚏ ⚐ **Total** 38
Open 14-Feb **to** 02-Jan
Access Good **Site** Level
Nearest Bus Stop (Miles) Outside
Facilities ⚙ 🛁 📞 ⚸ 📷 🔌 ⚏
🏪 🏪 ⚷ ✕ ▽ 🛉 ▣ ▣ 🌙 ⚸ ⚷
Nearest Town Tenby
Directions After Carmarthen take the A477 to Broadmoor. Turn right at the Cross Inn Public House, Masterland is 400 yards on the right.
⚏ Kilgetty

TENBY
Milton Bridge Caravan Park, Milton, Nr Tenby, Pembrokeshire, SA70 8PH
Tel: 01646 651204
Email: enquiries@miltonbridgecaravanpark.co.uk
www.miltonbridgecaravanpark.co.uk
Pitches For ⚏ ⚐ **Total** 12
Acreage 3 **Open** Mar **to** Oct
Access Good **Site** Lev/Slope
Nearest Bus Stop (Miles) Outside
Small, friendly park situated on a tidal river. Ideal base for exploring the many attractions in the area.
Facilities ⚙ 🛁 🛉 📞 ⚸ 📷 🔌 ⚏ 📷 ⚷
🏪 ⚸ 🛉 ▣ ⚸ ⚷
Directions Half way between Kilgetty and Pembroke Dock on the A477.
⚏ Lamphey

TENBY
Red House Farm, Twy Cross, Tenby, Pembrokeshire, SA69 9DP
Tel: 01834 813918
Pitches For Å ⚏ ⚐ **Total** 10
Acreage 2 **Open** May **to** Sept
Access Good **Site** Lev/Slope
Nearest Bus Stop (Miles) ¼
Very quiet, small, ADULTS ONLY site. Most appreciated by those seeking peace rather than entertainment. Not suitable for small children. Sorry No pets.
Facilities ⚙ 🛁 📞 ⚸ 🏪 ⚷ 📷 A
Directions Situated just off the A478, 1½ miles from both Tenby and Saundersfoot. Regular bus service.
⚏ Tenby

TENBY
Rowston Holiday Park, New Hedges, Tenby, Pembrokeshire, SA70 8TL
Tel: 01834 842178
Email: rowston-hol-park@btconnect.com
www.rowston-holiday-park.co.uk
Pitches For Å ⚏ ⚐ **Total** 130
Open Apr **to** 01-Oct
Access Good **Site** Sloping
Nearest Bus Stop (Miles) Outside
Near beach.
Facilities ⚙ 🛁 🛉 📞 ⚸ 📷 🔌 ⚏ 📷 ⚷
🏪 🛁 🛉 ❄ ▣ 🌙
Directions 1½ miles from Tenby/Saundersfoot.
⚏ Tenby

TENBY
Tudor Glen Caravan Park, Jameston, Nr Tenby, Pembrokeshire, SA70 7SS
Tel: 01834 871417
Email: info@tudorglencaravanpark.com
www.tudorglencaravanpark.com

Pitches For 👤 🚐 🚍
Acreage 6 **Open** Mar **to** Oct
Access Good **Site** Lev/Slope
Nearest Bus Stop (Miles) ¼
1 mile from Manorbier.
Facilities 🚻 ⚑ 🛒 ♿ ▣ 🍴 ☎
⚙ 🏪 🔥 🐕 ▣
Nearest Town Tenby
Directions From Tenby take the A4139 Coast Road west for 6 miles. Site is on the right before entering village of Jameston.
➤ Tenby

TENBY
Well Park Caravans, Tenby, Pembrokeshire, SA70 8TL
Tel: 01834 842179
Email: enquiries@wellparkcaravans.co.uk
www.wellparkcaravans.co.uk
Pitches For 👤 🚐 🚍 🚍 **Total** 100
Acreage 10 **Open** Apr **to** Oct
Access Good **Site** Lev/Slope
Nearest Bus Stop (Miles) Outside
Ideally situated between Tenby 1 mile and Saundersfoot 1½. A family run Park with excellent facilities, very central and convenient for the beautiful beaches and places of interest, along the Pembrokeshire coast. AA 4 Pennant and Wales in Bloom award winning park.
Facilities ♿ ⚑ 🚻 ⚑ 🍴 ☎ 🛒 ☎
⚙ ▣ 🏪 🔥 🐕 ▣ 🔥
Nearest Town Tenby
Directions On righthand side of main Tenby (A478) road 1 mile north of Tenby.
➤ Tenby

TENBY
Windmills Camping Park, Tenby, Pembrokeshire, SA70 8TJ
Tel: 01834 842200
Pitches For 👤 🚐 🚍
Acreage 4 **Open** Easter **to** Oct
Access Good **Site** Level
Nearest Bus Stop (Miles) ½
Situated on a hill above Tenby with sea views. Footpath and cycle track down to the town and north beach.
Facilities ⚑ 🚻 ⚑ 🍴 ☎ ⚙ ▣ 🔥
Nearest Town Tenby
Directions Approaching Tenby turn left up the lane just past New Hedges Village.
➤ Tenby

TENBY
Wood Park Caravan Park, New Hedges, Tenby, Pembrokeshire, SA70 8TL
Tel: 01834 843414
Email: info@woodpark.co.uk
www.woodpark.co.uk
Pitches For 👤 🚐 🚍 **Total** 60
Acreage 2 **Open** Apr **to** Oct
Access Good **Site** Lev/Slope
Nearest Bus Stop (Miles) Outside
Quiet, family park ideally situated between Tenby and Saundersfoot. Advanced bookings are not taken for Motor Caravans. No Groups permitted. No dogs allowed Bank Holidays and school holidays, one small pet only at all other times. No dogs in hire caravans.
Facilities ⚑ 🚻 ⚑ 🍴 ☎ ⚙ ▣ 🔥
⚙ ▣ 🏪 🔥 ▣ 🔥
Nearest Town Tenby
Directions At the roundabout 2 miles north of Tenby, take the A478 towards Tenby. Take the second turn right and right again.
➤ Tenby

POWYS
BALA
Henstent Park, Llangynog, Nr Oswestry, Powys, SY10 0EP
Tel: 01691 860479
Email: henstent@mac.com
www.henstent.co.uk
Pitches For 👤 🚐 🚍 **Total** 35
Acreage 1½ **Open** All Year
Access Good **Site** Sloping
Nearest Bus Stop (Miles) Outside
Spectacular mountain views with frontage to the River Tanat. Rural location popular with bird watchers and walkers.
Facilities ⚑ 🚻 ⚑ 🍴 ☎ ⚙ ▣ 🔥
⚙ ▣ 🏪 🔥 ▣ 🔥 ✎ 🔥 🔥 📶
Nearest Town Bala
Directions Situated on the B4391. Follow signs for Bala from Oswestry. 18 miles from Oswestry, 12 miles from Bala.
➤ Gobowen

BRECON
Anchorage Caravan Park, Bronllys, Brecon, Powys, LD3 0LD
Tel: 01874 711246
www.anchoragecp.co.uk
Pitches For 👤 🚐 🚍 **Total** 110
Acreage 8 **Open** All Year
Access Good **Site** Lev/Slope
Nearest Bus Stop (Miles) Outside
Overlooking the Brecon Beacons National Park. Ideally situated for touring and walking mid and South Wales.
Facilities ♿ ⚑ 🚻 ⚑ 🍴 ☎ ⚙ ▣ 🔥
⚙ ▣ 🏪 🔥 ▣ 🔥 🔥
Nearest Town Brecon
Directions 8 miles north east of Brecon in the village of Bronllys.
➤ Abergavenny

BRECON
Lakeside Caravan Park, Llangorse Lake, Llangorse, Brecon, Powys, LD3 7TR
Tel: 01874 658226
Email: lakesidereception@tiscali.co.uk
www.llangorselake.co.uk
Pitches For 👤 🚐 🚍 🚍 **Total** 80
Open 20-Mar **to** Oct
Access Good **Site** Level
Llangorse Lake, mountains and beautiful scenery.
Facilities ⚑ 🚻 ⚑ 🍴 ☎ ⚙ ▣ 🔥
⚙ ▣ ✗ 🔥 ▣ 🔥 📶
Nearest Town Brecon
Directions From Brecon take the B4560 and follow signs to Llyn Lake. 6 miles from Brecon.
➤ Abergavenny

BRECON
Mill Field Caravan Park, Mill Service Station, Three Cocks, Brecon, Powys, LD3 0SL
Tel: 01497 847381
Pitches For 👤 🚐 🚍 **Total** 40
Acreage 2¼ **Open** All Year
Access Good **Site** Level
Nearest Bus Stop (Miles) ¼
Near to Hay-on-Wye the Town of Books. Easy access to the Black Mountains and Brecon Beacons.
Facilities ⚑ 🚻 ⚙ 🔥 ▣ 🔥 🔥
Directions On the A438 between Brecon and Hay-on-Wye, 5 miles from Hay-on-Wye.
➤ Hereford

BRECON
Pencelli Castle Caravan & Camping Park, Pencelli Castle, Pencelli, Brecon, Powys, LD3 7LX
Tel: 01874 665451
Email: pencelli@tiscali.co.uk
www.pencelli-castle.com
Pitches For 👤 🚐 🚍 🚍 **Total** 80
Acreage 10 **Open** Feb **to** 28-Nov
Access Good **Site** Level
Nearest Bus Stop (Miles) Outside
Multi award winning park in the heart of the Brecon Beacons and adjoining Brecon Canal. Plenty of good walking and cycling in the area.
Facilities ⚑ 🚻 ⚑ 🍴 ☎ ⚙ ▣ 🔥
⚙ ▣ 🏪 🔥 ▣ 🔥 📶
Nearest Town Brecon
Directions Leave Brecon on the A40 heading east, after 2 miles turn onto the B4558 signposted Pencelli and follow brown tourism signs.
➤ Abergavenny

BUILTH WELLS
Fforest Fields Camping & Caravan Park, Hundred House, Builth Wells, Powys, LD1 5RT
Tel: 01982 570406
Email: office@fforestfields.co.uk
www.fforestfields.co.uk
Pitches For 👤 🚐 🚍
Acreage 12 **Open** Mar **to** 10-Jan
Access Good **Site** Level
Adjacent fishing and boating/swimming lakes. extensive hill and woodland walking direct from site.
Facilities ♿ ⚑ 🚻 ⚑ 🍴 ☎ ⚙ ▣ 🔥
⚙ ▣ 🏪 🔥 ▣ 🔥 🔥 📶
Nearest Town Builth Wells
Directions 4 miles east of Builth Wells on the A481, ½ mile before the village of Hundred House.
➤ Builth Road

BUILTH WELLS
White House Campsite, Hay Road, Builth Wells, Powys, LD2 3BP
Tel: 01982 552255
Email: info@whitehousecampsite.co.uk
www.whitehousecampsite.co.uk
Pitches For 👤 🚐 🚍
Acreage 3 **Open** Apr **to** Sept
Access Good **Site** Level
Nearest Bus Stop (Miles) ¼
On the banks of the River Wye. Just a ten minute walk from the Royal Welsh Showground. WTB 3 Star Graded.
Facilities ♿ ⚑ 🚻 ⚑ 🍴 ☎ ⚙ 🏪 🔥 ▣
Nearest Town Builth Wells
Directions Adjacent to the A470 at the eastern edge of Builth Wells.
➤ Builth Road

CLYRO
Borders Hideaway Holiday Home Park, Painscastle Road, Clyro, Hay-on-Wye, Herefordshire, HR3 5SG
Tel: 01497 820156
Email: bhhhp@hotmail.co.uk
www.bhhhp.co.uk
Pitches For 👤 🚐 🚍 🚍
Acreage 4 **Open** Mar **to** 07-Jan
Access Good **Site** Lev/Slope
Nearest Bus Stop (Miles) ½
Close to Hay-on-Wye, the second hand book capital of the world! Near to Golden Valley, Brecon Beacons and the Black Mountains.
Facilities ⚑ 🚻 ⚑ 🍴 ☎ ⚙ ▣ 🔥
⚙ ▣ 🔥 ▣ 🔥 🔥

Nearest Town Hay-on-Wye
Directions Upon entering Clyro on the A438 (Leominster to Brecon road), turn at the brown tourism caravan sign and follow the road and signs for 1 mile.
➤ Hereford

CRICKHOWELL
Cwmdu Campsite, Cwmdu, Crickhowell, Powys, NP8 1RU
Tel: 01874 730741
Email: cwmducampsite@btconnect.com
www.campingbreconbeacons.com
Pitches For ▲ ⊕ ⊟ **Total** 50
Acreage 4 **Open** Easter **to** Oct
Access Good **Site** Lev/Slope
Nearest Bus Stop (Miles) ¾
Quiet, peaceful location at the foot of the Black Mountains in the centre of Brecon Beacons National Park. Perfect for walking.
Facilities ∮ 🅷 🆄🅱 ⌁ ⌢ ⊙ ↲ ◻ ➤
🖲 🅾 🅱 ╋🖅 🅴 ⅍ 🛜
Nearest Town Crickhowell
Directions Situated 4 miles north of Crickhowell on the A479. Turn off at the Farmers Arms Pub in Cwmdu Village, and the site is 300 metres.
➤ Abergavenny

CRICKHOWELL
Riverside Caravan & Camping Park New Road, Crickhowell, Powys, NP8 1AY
Tel: 01873 810397
www.riversidecaravanscrickhowell.co.uk
Pitches For ▲ ⊕ ⊟ **Total** 65
Acreage 3½ **Open** Mar **to** Oct
Access Good **Site** Level
Nearest Bus Stop (Miles) ¼
River, mountain and canal walks.
Facilities ∮ 🅷 🆄🅱 ⌁ ⌢ ⊙ ➤ 🅾 🅿🅰
Nearest Town Crickhowell
Directions Between the A40 and the A4077 at Crickhowell.
➤ Abergavenny

LLANBRYNMAIR
Cringoed Caravan Park, The Birches, Llanbrynmair, Powys, SY19 7DR
Tel: 01650 521237
Email: enquiries@cringoed.co.uk
www.cringoed.co.uk
Pitches For ▲ ⊕ ⊟ **Total** 35
Acreage 10 **Open** Mar **to** Nov
Site Level
Nearest Bus Stop (Miles) 1
nearest beaches Aberbovey, Twywn, Barmouth, Borth, all within 45 minutes.
Facilities ∮ 🅷 🅱 ⌁ ⌢ ⊙ ➤ 🅴
🖲 🅾 🅰 🅽 🅱 ╋🖅 🅴 ⅍ 🅰 🛜
Nearest Town Machynlleth
Directions 12 miles inland towards Newtown.
➤ Machynlleth

LLANBRYNMAIR
Gwern-y-Bwlch Caravan Club Site, Llanbrynmair, Powys, SY19 7EB
Tel: 01650 521351
www.caravanclub.co.uk
Pitches For ⊕ ⊟ **Total** 37
Acreage 5 **Open** Mar **to** Oct
Access Good **Site** Lev/Slope
Lovely setting with views to the mountains across a valley. Bird hide and feeding station on site, watch for Red Kites. Own sanitation required. Non members welcome. Booking essential.
Facilities ∮ 🅷 🖲 🅾 ╋🖅 🅴 ⅍
Nearest Town Llanbrynmair

Directions From the A470, 1 mile past Llanbrynmair turn right at Caravan Club sign, site is 50 yards up the hill on the left.
➤ Llanbrynmair

LLANDRINDOD WELLS
Bryncrach Farm Caravan Site, Bryncrach, Hundred House, Llandrindod Wells, Powys, LD1 5RY
Tel: 01982 570291
Email: stella@bryncrachcaravans.co.uk
www.bryncrachcaravans.co.uk
Pitches For ▲ ⊕ ⊟ **Total** 15
Acreage 1¾ **Open** All Year
Access Good **Site** Level
Nearest Bus Stop (Miles) ¼
Quiet site with splendid views and walks. Fishing and riding can be arranged. River nearby. You can also contact us on Mobile: 07534 509104.
Facilities ∮ 🅷 🆄🅱 ⌁ ⌢ ⊙ ↲ ➤
🖲 🅾 🅱 🅴 ⅍
Nearest Town Builth Wells
Directions Hundred House is on the A481 between Builth Wells and the A44. Turn left signposted Franks Bridge immediately before the public house, after 250 yards turn left into farm road.
➤ Llandrindod Wells

LLANDRINDOD WELLS
Dalmore Caravan Park, Howey, Llandrindod Wells, Powys, LD1 5RG
Tel: 01597 822483
Pitches For ▲ ⊕ ⊟ **Total** 20
Acreage 2 **Open** Mar **to** Oct
Access Good **Site** Lev/Gentle Slope
Nearest Bus Stop (Miles) Outside
EXCLUSIVELY FOR ADULTS. Ideal base for hiking and touring Mid Wales, scenic views.
Facilities ∮ 🅷 🆄🅱 ⌁ ⌢ ⊙ ↲ ➤
🖲 🅾 🅱 🅰 ⅍ 🅰
Nearest Town Llandrindod Wells
Directions 2½ miles south of Llandrindod Wells, adjoining the main A483, at the top of the hill and towards Builth Wells.
➤ Llandrindod

LLANDRINDOD WELLS
Disserth Caravan & Camping Park, Howey, Llandrindod Wells, Powys, LD1 6NL
Tel: 01597 860277
Email: disserthcaravan@btconnect.com
www.disserth.biz
Pitches For ▲ ⊕ ⊟ **Total** 30
Acreage 4 **Open** Mar **to** Oct
Access Good **Site** Level
Small, tranquil, riverside park with wildlife for neighbours.
Facilities ⅋ ∮ 🅵 🅷 🆄🅱 ⌁ ⌢ ⊙ ↲ 🅴 ◻ ➤
🖲 🅾 🍴 🅱 🅴 ⅍ 🅰 🛜
Nearest Town Llandrindod Wells
Directions Follow brown tourism signs from the A483 or the A470. Park entrance is by the church.
➤ Llandrindod Wells

LLANGAMMARCH WELLS
Riverside Park, Llangammarch Wells, Powys, LD4 4BY
Tel: 01591 620465
Email: sales@riversidecaravans.com
www.riversidecaravans.com
Pitches For ▲ ⊕ ⊟ **Total** 26
Acreage 4 **Open** Apr **to** Oct
Access Good **Site** Level
Nearest Bus Stop (Miles) ¼
Builth Wells show ground.

Facilities ∮ 🅷 🆄🅱 ⌁ ⌢ ⊙ ↲ ◻ ➤
🖲 🅾 🅰 🅱 ╋🖅 🅴 ⅍ 🅰 🛜
Nearest Town Builth Wells
Directions From Builth Wells 5 miles on A483 towards Llandovery road, turn to the left.
➤ Llangammarch Wells

LLANSANTFFRAID
Vyrnwy Caravan Park, Llansantffraid, Powys, SY22 6SY
Tel: 01691 828217
Email: info@vyrnwycaravansldt.co.uk
www.vyrnwycaravanpark
Pitches For ▲ ⊕ ⊟ **Total** 40
Acreage 40 **Open** Apr **to** Sept
Access Good **Site** Level
Nearest Bus Stop (Miles) Outside
Alongside a river.
Facilities ∮ 🅷 🆄🅱 ⌢ ⊙ 🅾 🅱 ╋🖅 🅴 ⅋
Nearest Town Oswestry
Directions Take the A483 then the B4393 to Llansantffraid.
➤ Gobowen

MACHYNLLETH
Morben Isaf Holiday Home & Touring Park, Derwenlas, Machynlleth, Powys, SY20 8SR
Tel: 01654 781473
Email: manager@morbenisaf.co.uk
www.morbenisaf.co.uk
Pitches For ▲ ⊕ ⊟ **Total** 35
Open Mid Mar **to** Oct
Access Good **Site** Level
Nearest Bus Stop (Miles) Outside
Next door to Dyfi Osprey Project at Cors Dyfi. 8 miles from Ynyslas Beach and 3 miles from Ynys-Hir Nature Reserve.
Facilities ♿ ∮ 🅵 🆄🅱 ⌢ ⊙ ↲ ◻ ➤
🅱 🅽🅷╋🅱 🅴 ⅍ 🛜
Nearest Town Machynlleth
Directions 2½ miles south of Machynlleth on the A487 Aberystwyth road.
➤ Machynlleth

MIDDLETOWN
Bank Farm Caravan Park, Middletown, Welshpool, Powys, SY21 8EJ
Tel: 01938 570526
Email: bankfarmcaravans@yahoo.co.uk
www.bankfarmcaravans.co.uk
Pitches For ▲ ⊕ ⊟ **Total** 20
Acreage 2 **Open** Mar **to** Oct
Access Good **Site** Lev/Slope
Nearest Bus Stop (Miles) ¼
Scenic views, ideal touring area.
Facilities ♿ ➤ ∮ 🅵 🆄🅱 ⌢ ⊙ ↲ ◻ ➤
🅾 🅰 🅽🅷╋🅱 🅴 ⅍
Nearest Town Welshpool
Directions On A458 5½ miles east of Welshpool and 13¼ miles west of Shrewsbury.
➤ Welshpool

NEW RADNOR
Old Station Caravan Park, New Radnor, Powys, LD8 2SS
Tel: 01544 350543
Email: info@oldstationcaravanpark.co.uk
www.oldstationcaravanpark.co.uk
Pitches For ▲ ⊕ ⊟ **Total** 12
Acreage 1¾ **Open** All Year
Access Good **Site** Level
Nearest Bus Stop (Miles) ¼
Ideal base for walking and cycling. Easy access to Offa's Dyke, Elan Valley Dams and the attractions of Mid Wales. You can also contact us on Mobile: 07917 846508. Field available for small rallies.

Facilities
Nearest Town Kington
Directions 6 miles from Kington on the A44 to Rhayader.
⚞ Leominster

NEWTOWN

Smithy Park, Abermule, Newtown, Montgomery, Powys, SY15 6ND
Tel: 01584 711280
Email: info@smithypark.co.uk
www.smithypark.co.uk
Pitches For ⚞ ⚞ ⚞ **Total** 30
Acreage 5 **Open** Mar to Oct
Access Good **Site** Level
Nearest Bus Stop (Miles) Outside
Set between the River Mule and the River Severn, with a branch of the Shropshire Union Canal nearby.
Facilities
Nearest Town Newtown
Directions Abermule is off the A483 between Welshpool and Newtown.
⚞ Newtown

PENYBONTFAWR

Parc Farm, Penybontfawr, Powys, SY10 0PD
Tel: 01691 860204
Email: deal@tinyworld.co.uk
www.parcfarm-minafon.co.uk
Pitches For ⚞ ⚞ **Total** 12
Open Easter to Oct
Access Good **Site** Level
Nearest Bus Stop (Miles) Outside
River frontage with beautiful scenery.
Facilities
Nearest Town Oswestry/Welshpool
Directions On the B4391.
⚞ Welshpool

PRESTEIGNE

Rockbridge Park, Presteigne, Powys, LD8 2NF
Tel: 01568 708326
Email: info@bestparks.co.uk
www.rockbridgepark.co.uk
Pitches For ⚞ ⚞ ⚞ **Total** 53
Acreage 13 **Open** Mar to Nov
Access Good **Site** Level
Nearest Bus Stop (Miles) Outside
Picturesque and peaceful site alongside the River Lugg.
Facilities
Nearest Town Presteigne
Directions 1 mile west of Presteigne on the B4356.
⚞ Knighton

PRESTEIGNE

Walton Court Caravan Site, Walton Court, Walton, Presteigne, Powys, LD8 2PY
Tel: 01544 350259
Email: jeanandglyn@hotmail.co.uk
www.waltoncourtcaravanandcampingsite.co.uk
Pitches For ⚞ ⚞ ⚞ **Total** 30
Acreage 7 **Open** Mar to Oct
Access Good **Site** Level
Nearest Bus Stop (Miles) Outside
Many walks and rides into the hills. The Harp Inn (15 mins walk) serves excellent food.
Facilities
Nearest Town Kington

Directions On the A44 Kington to Aberystwyth road, in the village of Walton opposite the Crown Hotel.
⚞ Knighton

RHAYADER

Gigrin Farm, South Street, Rhayader, Powys, LD6 5BL
Pitches For ⚞ ⚞ ⚞ ⚞ **Total** 15
Acreage 2 **Open** All Year
Access Good **Site** Level
Nearest Bus Stop (Miles) Outside
Ideal touring, Red Kite feeding centre Gigrin Farm.
Facilities
Nearest Town Rhayader
Directions Just off the A470 mile south of Rhayader.
⚞ Llandrindod Wells

WELSHPOOL

Carmel Caravan Park, Tynewydd, Cefncoch, Welshpool, Powys, SY21 0AJ
Tel: 01938 810542
Email: carmelcaravanpk@aol.com
www.carmelcaravanpark.com
Pitches For ⚞ ⚞ ⚞ ⚞ **Total** 120
Open 15-Mar to Oct
Access Good **Site** Level
Farm site set alongside a river for walks.
Facilities
Nearest Town Newtown
Directions From Welshpool take the A458 to Llanfair Caereinion, turn left over the bridge and follow signs for Cefncoch. Turn left at the pub and follow caravan signs.
⚞ Newtown

WELSHPOOL

Henllan Caravan Park, Llangyniew, Welshpool, Powys, SY21 9EJ
Tel: 01938 810554
Email: sue@henllancaravanpark.co.uk
www.henllancaravanpark.co.uk
Pitches For ⚞ ⚞ ⚞ **Total** 10
Acreage ½ **Open** Mar to Dec
Access Good **Site** Level
Alongside the River Banwy. Ideal touring, 9 hole golf course and bowling green on site. You can also telephone us on Mobile 07909 531331. Contact Sue Round.
Facilities
Nearest Town Welshpool
Directions 6 miles from Welshpool on the A458.
⚞ Welshpool

WELSHPOOL

Rhyd-Y-Groes Touring Caravan & Camping Park, Pont Rhyd-Y-Groes, Marton, Welshpool, Powys, SY21 8JJ
Tel: 01938 561228
Email: hldavies@hotmail.co.uk
www.rhyd-y-groes.co.uk
Pitches For ⚞ ⚞ ⚞ ⚞ **Total** 40
Acreage 4½ **Open** All Year
Access Good **Site** Lev/Slope
ADULTS ONLY PARK set among natural beauty with outstanding views. Near Offas Dyke footpath. Ideal for touring and bird watching. Some fully serviced pitches available.
Facilities
Nearest Town Welshpool
Directions From the A490 Welshpool to Churchstoke road, turn left for Marton approx 5 miles from Welshpool.
⚞ Welshpool

WELSHPOOL

Riverbend Caravan Park, Llangadfan, Nr Welshpool, Powys, SY21 0PP
Tel: 01938 820356
Email: riverbend@hillandale.co.uk
www.hillandale.co.uk
Pitches For ⚞ ⚞ ⚞ **Total** 50
Acreage 4 **Open** All Year
Access Good **Site** Level
Nearest Bus Stop (Miles) ½
The best of both worlds! - In unspoilt rural Wales, yet close to the Welsh coast. On the River Banwy with 1 mile of private fishing. Local pub.
Facilities
Nearest Town Llanfair Caereinion
Directions Take the A458 from Welshpool westbound towards the coast. After 17 miles you enter the village of Llangadfan, turn left at Gann Office (pub), and the Park is 300 metres on the right.
⚞ Welshpool

WELSHPOOL

Severn Caravan Park, Cilcewydd, Welshpool, Powys, SY21 8RT
Tel: 01938 580238
Email: severncp@tiscali.co.uk
www.severncaravans.co.uk
Pitches For ⚞ ⚞ ⚞ **Total** 70
Open Apr to Oct
Access Good **Site** Level
Nearest Bus Stop (Miles) Outside
On the banks of the River Severn.
Facilities
Nearest Town Welshpool
Directions From Welshpool take the A483 towards Newtown, turn onto the A490 sp Forden, then turn first left onto the B4331 for Leighton and site is 500 yards on the left.
⚞ Welshpool

SWANSEA
GOWERTON

Gowerton Caravan Club Site, Pont-y-Cob Road, Gowerton, Swansea, SA4 3QP
Tel: 01792 873050
www.caravanclub.co.uk
Pitches For ⚞ ⚞ **Total** 135
Acreage 17 **Open** Mar to Nov
Access Good **Site** Level
Nearest Bus Stop (Miles) ½
Easy drive to many safe sandy beaches. Inland theres the Vale of Neath and Aberdulais Falls. Non members welcome. Booking essential.
Facilities
Nearest Town Swansea
Directions Leave M4 at junc 47 take A483 sp Swansea. At r/about t rt on A484, at next r/about go straight over, next r/about t lt on B4296 sp Gowerton. After passing under railway bridge at lights t rt, next lights t rt into Pont-y-Cob Rd, site ¼ mile on rt.
⚞ Swansea

HORTON

Bank Farm, Horton, Gower, Swansea, SA3 1LL
Tel: 01792 390228
Email: bankfarmleisure@aol.com
www.bankfarmleisure.co.uk
Pitches For ▲ ⚏ ⚏ **Total** 230
Acreage 80 **Open** Mar **to** 18-Nov
Access Good **Site** Sloping
Nearest Bus Stop (Miles) ¼
Overlooking the beach. Heated swimming pool.
Facilities ⎓ ⏦ ⬚⬚ ⌁ ⊙⌣ ⬚ ◻ ⬚
⬚⬚ ⬚⬚⬚ ⬚ ⬚ ⬚ ⬚
Nearest Town Swansea
Directions Take the A4118 from Swansea towards Port Eynon, turn left for Horton 1 mile before Port Eynon, turn right at the site entrance after 200 yards.
⇇ Swansea

LLANGENNITH

Kennexstone Camping & Touring Park, Kennexstone Farm, Llangennith, Gower, Swansea, SA3 1HS
Tel: 01792 386790
Email: gowercamping@btconnect.com
www.gowercamping.co.uk
Pitches For ▲ ⚏ ⚏ **Total** 240
Acreage 10 **Open** Apr **to** Sept
Access Good **Site** Level
Nearest Bus Stop (Miles) ½
Friendly, family run site, ideal for a relaxing holiday. 1½ miles from one of Wales best surfing beaches.
Facilities ⎓ ⏦ ⬚⬚ ⌁ ⊙⌣ ⬚ ◻ ⬚
⬚⬚ ⬚ ⬚ ⬚ ⬚ ⬚
Nearest Town Swansea
Directions Leave the M4 at junction 47 and take the A483/A484 to Gowerton, then take

---

the B4295 for 8 miles to Llanrhidian. Follow signs to Llangennith for approx. 2½ miles, at T-junction ½ mile after Burry Green turn right, site is 200 yards.
⇇ Gowerton

RHOSSILI

Pitton Cross Caravan & Camping Park, Rhossili, Swansea, SA3 1PT
Tel: 01792 390593
Email: admin@pittoncross.co.uk
www.pittoncross.co.uk
Pitches For ▲ ⚏ ⚏ **Total** 100
Acreage 6 **Open** All Year
Access Good **Site** Level
Nearest Bus Stop (Miles) Outside
Quiet, family friendly park, with a mix of sea views and sheltered areas. Within walking distance of beaches. Ideal for surfing and kiting.
Facilities ⎓ ⬚ ⬚⬚ ⌁ ⊙⌣ ⬚ ◻ ⬚
⬚⬚ ⬚ ⬚ ⬚ ⬚ ⬚
Nearest Town Swansea
Directions Leave the M4 at junc 42 and take the A483 to Swansea. Follow signs for A4067 to Mumbles, turn right onto the B4436 to South Gower and follow to Kittle, turn right at Pennard Church. Turn left at the T-Junction onto the A4118, go through Scurlage and turn right, Park is 2 miles.
⇇ Swansea

WREXHAM

WREXHAM

Plassey Leisure Park, Eyton, Wrexham, LL13 0SP
Tel: 01978 780277
Email: enquiries@plassey.com
www.plassey.com

Pitches For ▲ ⚏ ⚏ **Total** 120
Acreage 10 **Open** All Year
Access Good **Site** Level
Nearest Bus Stop (Miles) ½
On site facilities include a 9 hole golf course, a craft centre with 16 workshops and boutiques, garden centre, hair and beauty studio, restaurant and coffee shop. We even have our own on-site mini real ale brewery!
Facilities ⎓ ⬚ ⏦ ⬚ ⬚⬚ ⌁ ⊙⌣ ⬚ ⬚
◻ ⬚
⬚⬚ ⬚⬚ ⬚ ⬚ ⬚ ⬚ ⬚ ⬚ ⬚ ⬚ ⬚ ⬚ ⬚ ⬚ ⬚
⬚ ⬚
Nearest Town Wrexham
⇇ Wrexham

WREXHAM

Trench Farm Touring Caravan Park & Fisheries, Trench Farm, Redhall Lane, Penley, Wrexham, LL13 0NA
Tel: 01978 710098
Email: mail@trenchfarmfisheries.co.uk
www.trenchfarmfisheries.co.uk
Pitches For ▲ ⚏ ⚏ **Total** 6
Acreage 5 **Open** Mar **to** Nov
Access Good **Site** Level
Nearest Bus Stop (Miles) ½
Set in 160 acres of farmland. Lovely long country walks. Fishing on site.
Facilities ⎓ ⏦ ⬚ ⬚⬚ ⌁ ⊙⌣ ⬚ ◻ ⬚
⬚ ⬚
Nearest Town Ellesmere
Directions Appeox 3 miles from Ellesmere on the A528 towards Wrexham. On the Shropshire and Wrexham border.
⇇ Wrexham

SCOTLAND

ABERDEENSHIRE

ABERDEEN

Deeside Holiday Park, South Deeside Road, Maryculter, Aberdeen, Aberdeenshire, AB12 5FX
Tel: 01224 733860
Email: deeside@holiday-parks.co.uk
www.holiday-parks.co.uk
Pitches For ▲ ⚏ ⚏ ⚏ **Total**
Acreage 10 **Open** All Year
Access Good **Site** Level
Nearest Bus Stop (Miles) ¼
A tranquil retreat set in the southern valley of the River Dee, yet only a few miles from the lively city of Aberdeen, and at the gateway to the spectacular scenery of Royal Deeside.
Facilities ⏦ ⬚ ⬚⬚ ⌁ ⊙⌣ ⬚ ◻ ⬚
⬚⬚ ⬚ ⬚ ⬚ ⬚ ⬚ ⬚ ⬚
Nearest Town Aberdeen
Directions From Aberdeen take the B9077 at Bridge of Dee roundabout for 6 miles. From Stonehaven take the B979.
⇇ Aberdeen

ABOYNE

Aboyne Loch Caravan Park, Aboyne, Royal Deeside, Aberdeenshire, AB34 5BR
Tel: 013398 86244
Email: heatherreid24@yahoo.co.uk
Pitches For ▲ ⚏ ⚏ **Total** 32
Open Mar **to** Oct
Access Good **Site** Level

Nearest Bus Stop (Miles) Outside
By Aboyne Loch. Beside two golf courses and within walking distance of two restaurants. Boats available to hire. Good area for walking. Dog walk. David Bellamy Gold Award.
Facilities ⎓ ⏦ ⬚ ⬚⬚ ⌁ ⊙⌣ ⬚ ◻ ⬚
⬚⬚ ⬚ ⬚ ⬚ ⬚⬚ ⬚ ⬚
Nearest Town Banchory
Directions Take the A96 to Ballater.

ABOYNE

Tarland Camping & Caravanning Club Site, Tarland By Deeside, Tarland By Aboyne, Aberdeenshire, AB34 4UP
Tel: 01339 881388
Email: tarland.site@thefriendlyclub.co.uk
www.campingandcaravanningclub.co.uk/tarland
Pitches For ▲ ⚏ ⚏ **Total** 58
Acreage 8 **Open** 01-Mar **to** 05-Jan
Access Good **Site** Level
Nearest Bus Stop (Miles) ¼
Close to the village of Tarland and approx. 6 miles from Aboyne. STB 5 Star Graded and AA 3 Pennants. Non members welcome. You can also call us on 0845 130 7633.
Facilities ⏦ ⬚ ⬚⬚ ⌁ ⊙⌣ ⬚ ◻ ⬚
⬚⬚ ⬚ ⬚ ⬚ ⬚ ⬚⬚ ⬚
Nearest Town Aboyne
Directions Take the A93 from Aberdeen, in Aboyne turn right at the Struan Hotel onto the B9094. After 6 miles take the next turn right and then fork left before the bridge, site is on the left in 600 yards.
⇇ Aberdeen

BANCHORY

Feughside Caravan Park, Mount Battock, Strachan, Banchory, Aberdeenshire, AB31 6NT
Tel: 01330 850669
Email: info@feughsidecaravanpark.co.uk
www.feughsidecaravanpark.co.uk
Pitches For ▲ ⚏ ⚏ ⚏ **Total** 27
Open Apr **to** Oct
Access Good **Site** Level
Set in the heart of Royal Deeside. Relax in this beautiful and picturesque part of the Scottish countryside.
Facilities ⏦ ⬚ ⬚⬚ ⌁ ⊙⌣ ⬚ ◻ ⬚
⬚⬚ ⬚ ⬚ ⬚ ⬚ ⬚ ⬚
Nearest Town Banchory
Directions From Banchory take the B974 for 3 miles to Strachan, then take the B976 for 2 miles to the Feughside Inn, turn right and the Park entrance is 100 metres.
⇇ Stonehaven

BRAEMAR

Braemar The Invercauld Caravan Club Site, Glenshee Road, Braemar, Ballater, Aberdeenshire, AB35 5YQ
Tel: 01339 741373
www.caravanclub.co.uk
Pitches For ▲ ⚏ ⚏ **Total** 97
Acreage 9½ **Open** Dec **to** Oct
Access Good **Site** Level
Nearest Bus Stop (Miles) ¼
Abundant wildlife can be seen at this gateway to the Cairngorms, ideal for walking and cycling. Near a dry ski slope. Open in December for winter sports. Ski racks, drying room and community room (winter only) on

161

site. Non members welcome. Booking
essential.
Facilities ♿ ⚡ 🚻 ♨ 🚾 ┌ ☺ 🍴
🅿 🛒 🏪 🔌 ➡ 🔲 ➲ ☼ 📶
Nearest Town Braemar
Directions Just off the A93 on the outskirts
of Braemar Village.

CRUDEN BAY

Craighead Caravan & Camping Park,
Cruden Bay, Peterhead, Aberdeenshire,
AB42 0PL
Tel: 01779 812251
Email: stephen@craigheadcamping.com
www.craigheadcamping.com
Pitches For ⚡ 🚐 🚕 **Total** 17
Acreage 5 **Open** All Year
Nearest Bus Stop (Miles) ½
1 mile from the beach. Close to castles and
the Whisky Trail.
Facilities ♿ ⚡ 🚾 ♨ ┌ ☺ ➡ 🔲 ☎
🅿 🛒 🏪 ➡ 🔲 ➲ ☼
Nearest Town Peterhead
Directions 6 miles south of Peterhead on
the A90, signposted from main road.
🚄 Aberdeen

LAURENCEKIRK

Brownmuir Caravan Park, Fordoun,
Laurencekirk, Aberdeenshire, AB30 1SJ
Tel: 01561 320786
Email:
brownmuircaravanpark@talk21.com
www.brownmuircaravanpark.co.uk
Pitches For ⚡ 🚐 🚕 🚕 **Total** 10
Acreage 7 **Open** Apr to Oct
Access Good **Site** Level
Nearest Bus Stop (Miles) Outside
Quiet site. Ideal for cycling and walking. Golf
course in the village.
Facilities ♿ ⚡ 🚻 ♨ ┌ ☺ ➡ 🔲 ☎
🅿 🏪 ➡ 🔌 ☼ 📶
Nearest Town Laurencekirk
Directions On the A90, 4 miles north of
Laurencekirk, turn left at the junction marked
Fordoun and Auchenblae. After 150 yards
turn left and go over the bridge, the Park is 1
mile on the right.
🚄 Stonehaven

LAURENCEKIRK

Dovecot Caravan Park, Northwaterbridge,
By Laurencekirk, Aberdeenshire, AB30
1QL
Tel: 01674 840630
Email: adele@dovecotcaravanpark.co.uk
www.dovecotcaravanpark.co.uk
Pitches For ⚡ 🚐 🚕 **Total** 25
Acreage 6 **Open** Apr to 28-Oct
Access Good **Site** Level
Nearest Bus Stop (Miles) ¼
Alongside the River North Esk. 8 miles from
a sandy beach and 10 miles from the Angus
Glens. Static caravans and a cottage
available for hire.
Facilities ♿ ⚡ 🚻 ♨ ┌ ☺ ➡ ➡ 🔲
🅿 🛒 🏪 ➡ 🔌 ☼
Nearest Town Laurencekirk
Directions From the A90 at
Northwaterbridge, turn to Edzell Woods and
the Site is signposted 300 metres on the left.
🚄 Laurencekirk

PORTSOY

Sandend Caravan Park, Sandend,
Portsoy, Aberdeenshire, AB45 2UA
Tel: 01261 842660
Email: sandendholidays@aol.com
www.sandendcaravanpark.co.uk

Pitches For ⚡ 🚐 🚕 **Total** 52
Acreage 4½ **Open** Apr to 04-Oct
Access Good **Site** Level
Nearest Bus Stop (Miles) ¼
In a conservation village overlooking a sandy
beach. Ideal for touring and The Whisky Trail.
Facilities ♿ ⚡ 🚻 🚾 ♨ ┌ ☺ ➡ 🔲 ☎
🅿 🛒 🔌 ☼
Nearest Town Portsoy
Directions 3 miles from Portsoy on the A98.
🚄 Keith

ST. CYRUS

East Bowstrips Holiday Park, St Cyrus,
Nr Montrose, Aberdeenshire, DD10 0DE
Tel: 01674 850328
Email: tully@bowstrips.freeserve.co.uk
www.ukparks.co.uk/eastbowstrips
Pitches For ⚡ 🚐 🚕 **Total** 33
Acreage 4 **Open** Apr to Oct
Access Good **Site** Lev/Slope
Nearest Bus Stop (Miles) ½
Quiet park by the coast. Ideal touring base.
Excellent facilities. Beautiful sandy beach
and nature reserve approx 1 mile. Tourist
Board 4 Star Graded and AA 4 Pennants.
Facilities ♿ ⚡ 🚻 ♨ ┌ ☺ ➡ 🔲 ☎
🅿 🛒 🏪 ➡ 🔲 ☼
Nearest Town Montrose
Directions Approx 6 miles north of Montrose.
Follow A92, enter village of St. Cyrus, first
left after Hotel, second right.
🚄 Montrose

TURRIFF

East Balthangie Caravan Park, East
Balthangie, Cuminestown, Turriff,
Aberdeenshire, AB53 5XY
Tel: 01888 544261/544280
Email: ebc@4horse.co.uk
www.eastbalthangie.co.uk
Pitches For ⚡ 🚐 🚕 🚕 **Total** 12
Acreage 5 **Open** Mar to Oct
Access Good **Site** Level
Nearest Bus Stop (Miles) 5
Good base for touring, Banff and Buchan.
Facilities ⚡ 🚻 🚾 ♨ ┌ ☺ ➡ 🔲 ☎
🅿 🅿 🛒 🏪 ❀ ➡ 🔲 ➲ ☼ 📶
Nearest Town Turriff
Directions From Ellon take New Deer Road,
pass New Deer and take 1st road to right.
🚄 Inverurie

ANGUS

ARBROATH

Elliot Caravan Park, Dundee Road,
Arbroath, Angus, DD11 2PH
Tel: 01241 873466
Pitches For 🚐 🚕 **Total** 8
Acreage 2 **Open** Apr to Sept
Access Good **Site** Level
Nearest Bus Stop (Miles) Outside
Near the beach, across from a golf club. Ideal
for touring and sea fishing.
Facilities ⚡ 🚾 ┌ ☺ ➡ 🔲 ☎
🅿 🛒 🏪 ➡ ☼
Nearest Town Arbroath
Directions On the A92, ½ a mile from town.
🚄 Arbroath

FORFAR

Foresterseat Caravan Park, Arbroath
Road, Forfar, Angus, DD8 2RY
Tel: 01307 818880
Email: emma@foresterseat.co.uk
www.foresterseat.co.uk
Pitches For ⚡ 🚐 🚕 🚕 **Total** 76
Acreage 16 **Open** Mar to Nov
Access Good **Site** Level

Nearest Bus Stop (Miles) Outside
Modern Park on the edge of Forfar, with 42
Super Pitches. Ideal base for touring the
Angus Glens and scenic coast. 1 mile from
a golf course and fishing loch. Walking path
networks from the site. Fully licensed
restaurant on site.
Facilities ♿ ⚡ 🚻 🚾 ♨ ┌ ☺ ➡ ➡ 🔲 ☎
🅿 ✕ 🛒 ➡ 🔲 ☼ 📶
Nearest Town Forfar
Directions From Forfar take the A932
towards Arbroath, Foresterseat is 1 mile after
Cunninghill Golf Course on the right.
🚄 Arbroath

KIRRIEMUIR

Drumshademuir Caravan Park, Roundyhill,
By Glamis, Forfar, Angus, DD8 1QT
Tel: 01575 573284
Email: info@drumshademuir.com
www.drumshademuir.com
Pitches For ⚡ 🚐 🚕 **Total** 60
Acreage 15 **Open** All Year
Access Good **Site** Level
Nearest Bus Stop (Miles) Outside
Panoramic views. Central location for towns,
cities and Angus Glens.
Facilities ♿ ⚡ 🚻 🚾 ♨ ┌ ☺ ➡ 🔲 ☎
🅿 🅿 🛒 🏪 ✕ 🍴 ➡ 🔲 ➲ ☼ 📶 🔧
Nearest Town Kirriemuir
Directions From the A94 or the A90 take the
A928, park is 3 miles north of Glamis Castle.
🚄 Dundee

ARGYLL & BUTE

CAMPBELTOWN

Peninver Sands Holiday Park, Peninver,
By Campbeltown, Argyll & Bute, PA28 6QP
Tel: 01586 552262
Email: info@peninver-sands.com
www.peninver-sands.com
Pitches For 🚐 **Total** 25
Acreage 2¾ **Open** 15-Mar to 15-Jan
Access Poor **Site** Lev/Slope
Nearest Bus Stop (Miles) Outside
Situated right on the beach.
Facilities ⚡ 🚾 ┌ ☺ ➡ 🔲 ☎
🅿 🛒 ➡
Nearest Town Campbeltown
Directions From Campbeltown take the
B842 north for 4½ miles. Park is on the right
as you enter the village of Peninver.
🚄 Oban

CONNEL

**Oban Camping & Caravanning Club
Site,** Barcaldine By Connel, Argyll & Bute,
PA37 1SG
Tel: 01631 720348
Email: oban.site@thefriendlyclub.co.uk
www.campingandcaravanningclub.co.uk/
oban
Pitches For ⚡ 🚐 🚕 **Total** 75
Acreage 4½ **Open** 21-Mar to 28-Oct
Access Good **Site** Level
Nearest Bus Stop (Miles) Outside
Set in a delightful walled garden. Superb
forest walks are just 5 minutes from the site.
A perfect base to explore the Highlands and
Islands. STB 4 Star Graded and AA 3
Pennants. Non members welcome. You can
also call us on 0845 130 7633.
Facilities ♿ ⚡ 🚻 🚾 ♨ ┌ ☺ ➡ 🔲 ☎
🅿 🅿 🛒 ✕ 🍴 ➡ 🔲 ☼ 📶 🔧
Nearest Town Loch Lomond
Directions Heading North on the A828, 7
miles from the Connel bridge turn right at the
Camping & Caravanning Club sign opposite
the Marine Resource Centre, proceed
through the large iron gates.
🚄 Oban

DUNOON

Cot House Caravan Park, Sandbank Road, Kilmun By Dunoon, Argyll & Bute, PA23 8QS
Tel: 01369 840351
Pitches For Å ⚏ ⚏ ⚏≶ **Total** 14
Acreage 1 **Open** Mar **to** Oct
Access Good **Site** Level
Nearest Bus Stop (Miles) Outside
Alongside river.
Facilities ⚏ 🚻 🚿⚏🚻 ⚏ ⚏ ⚏ 🛒🚮⚏ ⚏
Nearest Town Dunoon
Directions A815 Dunoon to Strachur road.
⚏ Gourock

GLENBARR

Killegruer Caravan Site, Woodend, Glenbarr, Tarbert, Argyll & Bute, PA29 6XB
Tel: 01583 421241
Email: anne.littleson@btinternet.com
www.ukcampsites.co.uk
Pitches For Å ⚏ ⚏ **Total** 25
Acreage 1¼ **Open** Apr **to** Oct
Access Good **Site** Level
Nearest Bus Stop (Miles) Outside
Overlooking a sandy beach with views of the Inner Hebrides and the Mull of Kintyre. Site facilities have recently been upgraded. Hair dryers available. Close to the ferry link to Arran and Islay Jura & Gigha.
Facilities ⚏ ⚏ 🚻🚿⚏⚏⚏ ⚏
🛒⚏⚏⚏🚮⚏⚏
Nearest Town Campbeltown
Directions 12 miles north of Campbeltown on the A83.
⚏ Oban

GLENDARUEL

Glendaruel Caravan Park, Glendaruel, Argyll & Bute, PA22 3AB
Tel: 01369 820267
Email: mail@glendaruelcaravanpark.com
www.glendaruelcaravanpark.com
Pitches For Å ⚏ ⚏
Acreage 6 **Open** Apr **to** Oct
Access Good **Site** Level
Nearest Bus Stop (Miles) 1
Peaceful rural setting, mature woodland home to Red Squirrels and other rare wildlife.
Facilities ⚏ 🚻 🚿⚏🚻 ⚏ ⚏ ⚏ ⚏
🛒⚏⚏⚏⚏⚏ ⚏ ≋ 📶
Nearest Town Strachur
Directions 13 miles south Strachur on A886 park is signposted on right.
⚏ Arrochar

ISLE OF COLL

Garden House Camp Site, Garden House, Isle of Coll, Argyll, Argyll & Bute, PA78 6TB
Tel: 01879 230374
Email: collcampsite@hotmail.com
www.visitcoll.com
Pitches For Å ⚏ ⚏ **Total** 25
Acreage 2 **Open** Apr **to** 15-Sep
Access Good **Site** Level
In the middle of a nature reserve and only 5 minutes to the beach.
Facilities ⚏ 🚻🚿 ⚏ 🛒⚏
Nearest Town Arinagour
Directions Take the airport road west and before the airport take the track on the left at Uig to Walled Garden.
⚏ Oban

ISLE OF MULL (CRAIGNURE)

Shieling Holidays, Craignure, Isle of Mull, Argyll & Bute, PA65 6AY
Tel: 01680 812496
Email: sales@shielingholidays.co.uk
www.shielingholidays.co.uk

Pitches For Å ⚏ ⚏ ⚏≶ **Total** 90
Acreage 7 **Open** 08-Mar **to** 04-Nov
Access Good **Site** Level
Nearest Bus Stop (Miles) ¼
Enchanting beside the sea, great for fishing. Self Catering Shielings and hostel beds. 5 Star Graded.
Facilities ⚏ 🚻🚿⚏🚻⚏⚏⚏ ⚏ ⚏ ⚏
🛒⚏⚏⚏⚏⚏⚏⚏⚏⚏⚏⚏ ≋
Nearest Town Craignure
Directions From Craignure Ferry turn left on A849 to Iona for 400 metres, then left again at church.Follow site signs towards sea.
⚏ Oban

KILBERRY

Port Ban Holiday Park, Kilberry, Tarbert, Argyll & Bute, PA29 6YD
Tel: 01880 770224
Email: info@portban.com
www.portban.com
Pitches For Å ⚏ ⚏ **Total** 35
Acreage 10 **Open** Apr **to** Oct
Access Poor **Site** Level
Nearest Bus Stop (Miles) Outside
Coastal with beaches, remote views of Jura.
Facilities ⚏ 🚻🚿⚏🚻⚏⚏ ⚏ ⚏ ⚏
🛒⚏⚏✕⚏⚏⚏🚮⚏⚏ ≋ 📶
Nearest Town Lochgilphead
Directions Head south on A83 after 4 miles turn right onto B8024 follow for 15 miles.
⚏ Oban

LOCHGILPHEAD

Tayvallich Caravan Site, Leachive Farm, Tayvallich, By Lochgilphead, Argyll & Bute, PA31 8PL
Tel: 01546 870206
Email: fiona@leachive.co.uk
www.leachive.co.uk
Pitches For Å ⚏ ⚏ **Total** 15
Acreage 4 **Open** Apr **to** Oct
Access Good **Site** Level
Nearest Bus Stop (Miles) ¼
Set beside a sheltered sea loch, ideal for canoeing and sailing. Nearby the Beaver Trail Loch and nature reserve.
Facilities ⚏ ⚏ 🚻🚿⚏🚻⚏⚏ ⚏ ⚏
🛒⚏🚮⚏ ≋
Nearest Town Lochgilphead
Directions From Lochgilphead follow signs for Oban for 3 miles, then follow signs for Tayvallich.
⚏ Oban

LUSS

Luss Camping & Caravanning Club Site, Luss, Loch Lomond, Alexandria, Nr Glasgow, Argyll & Bute, G83 8NT
Tel: 01436 860658
Email: luss.site@thefriendlyclub.co.uk
www.campingandcaravanningclub.co.uk/
luss
Pitches For Å ⚏ ⚏ **Total** 90
Acreage 12 **Open** 21-Mar **to** 28-Oct
Access Good **Site** Level
Nearest Bus Stop (Miles) ¼
On the banks of Loch Lomond with good views of Ben Lomond. Fishing (permit required) and watersports. STB 4 Star Graded, AA 3 Pennants, Loo of the Year Award and Babychange Winner 2002. CLUB MEMBER CARAVANNERS & MOTORHOMES ONLY. Non member tents welcome. You can also call us on 0845 130 7633.
Facilities ⚏ ⚏ 🚻🚿⚏🚻⚏⚏ ⚏ ⚏ ⚏
🛒⚏⚏⚏🚮⚏⚏ 📶

Nearest Town Luss
Directions Take the A82 from the Erkside Bridge and head north towards Tarbet. Ignore first signpost for Luss. After the bagpipe and kiltmakers workshop take the next turn right sp Lodge of Loch Lomond and international camping sign, site approx. 200 yards.
⚏ Balloch

MUASDALE

Muasdale Holiday Park, Muasdale, Tarbert, Argyll & Bute, PA29 6XD
Tel: 01583 421207
Email: enquiries@muasdaleholidays.com
www.muasdaleholidays.com
Pitches For Å ⚏ ⚏ **Total** 10
Open Apr **to** 23-Oct
Access Good
Nearest Bus Stop (Miles) 100 Yards
Adjoining the beach with stunning views of Islay, Jura and Gigha. Sea fishing on site (bring your own equipment). Convenient for ferries to Islay, Jura, Gigha and Arran.
Facilities ⚏ 🚻🚿⚏🚻⚏⚏ ⚏ ⚏ ⚏
🛒⚏⚏🚮⚏⚏ ≋ 📶
Nearest Town Campbeltown/Tarbert
Directions On the A83 at the southern end of Muasdale Village, approx. 22 miles from Tarbert.

OBAN

Caravans at Highfield, 3 Kiel Croft, Benderloch, Oban, Argyll & Bute, PA37 1QS
Tel: 01631 720262
Email: elaine.clsite@gmail.com
www.clsite.co.uk
Pitches For ⚏ ⚏ **Total** 10
Acreage 1 **Open** Apr **to** Oct
Access Good **Site** Level
Nearest Bus Stop (Miles) ½
Country location only 500 metres from Tralee beach. 1 mile to the village for shop and cafe. Ideal for walking and touring, only 10 miles from Oban. Fort William and Inveraray within 1 hours drive.
Facilities ⚏ 🚻 ⚏ 🚮
Nearest Town Oban
Directions Turn off the A828 in Benderloch signposted Tralee and South Shian. Highfield is approx 800 metres on the right (its the second gate on the right after Hawthorn Cottage Restaurant).
⚏ Connel

OBAN

Oban Caravan & Camping Park, Gallanachmore Farm, Gallanach Road, Oban, Argyll & Bute, PA34 4QH
Tel: 01631 562425
Email: info@obancaravanpark.com
www.obancaravanpark.com
Pitches For Å ⚏ ⚏ ⚏≶ **Total** 150
Acreage 15 **Open** Apr **to** 07-Oct
Access Good **Site** Level
Nearest Bus Stop (Miles) Outside
On the coast with beautiful views. Close to a diving centre and ferry to islands.
Facilities ⚏ 🚻🚿⚏🚻⚏⚏ ⚏ ⚏ ⚏
🛒⚏⚏⚏⚏⚏⚏🚮⚏⚏⚏⚏ ⚏ ≋
Nearest Town Oban
Directions 2½ miles south of Obanon Gallanach road.
⚏ Oban

SOUTHEND

Machribeg Caravan Site, Southend, By Campbeltown, Argyll & Bute, PA28 6RW
Tel: 01586 830249
Pitches For ⋏ ⊕ ⇔ **Total** 80
Acreage 4 **Open** Easter **to** Sept
Access Good **Site** Level
Nearest Bus Stop (Miles) Outside
Near the beach with good views, very quiet location. 18 hole golf course.
Facilities 🖟⊡↑⊙🧺🖃🔲🍴
🎇🏦⊙🔵⊷🖃✐
Nearest Town Campbeltown
Directions Take the B843 from Campbeltown for 10 miles. Site is situated 250yds through Southend Village on the left by the beach.

TAYINLOAN

Point Sands Holiday Park, Tayinloan, Argyll & Bute, PA29 6XG
Tel: 01583 441263
Email: info@pointsands.co.uk
www.pointsands.co.uk
Pitches For ⋏ ⊕ ⇔ ⋨ **Total** 30
Acreage 15 **Open** Apr **to** Oct
Access Good **Site** Level
Nearest Bus Stop (Miles) Outside
Peaceful site on a safe sandy beach with terrific scenery. Near to island ferries. Ideal for touring and visiting the Isles of Gigha, Arran and Islay. Holiday homes to let.
Facilities 🕭⎕ 🖟⊡↑⊙🧺🖃🔲🍴
🎇⊙🛇🖃⊷🖃✐🌤🔆
Nearest Town Tarbert
Directions On the A83 Glasgow to Campbeltown road, 17 miles south of Tarbert.
🚆 Arrochar

AYRSHIRE (NORTH)
ISLE OF ARRAN

Lochranza Caravan & Camping Site, Lochranza, Isle of Arran, North Ayrshire, KA27 8HL
Tel: 01770 830273
Email: info@arran-campsite.com
www.arran-campsite.com
Pitches For ⋏ ⊕ ⇔ **Total** 60
Acreage 2½ **Open** Mar **to** Oct
Access Good **Site** Level
Nearest Bus Stop (Miles) Outside
Beautiful mountain scenery and abundant wildlife. Red Deer and Red Squirrels are often seen on site, aswell as Golden Eagles overhead. Adjacent to a golf course.
Facilities 🕭⎕ 🖟⊡🖟↑⊙🧺🖃🔲🍴
🎇⊙✕⊷🖃
Nearest Town Brodick

Directions Follow the road north for 14 miles to the north end of the island. Site entrance is opposite the Isle of Arran Distillery.
🚆 Ardrossan

Isle of Arran

Seal Shore Camping & Touring, Seal Shore, Kildonan, Isle of Arran, North Ayrshire, KA27 8SE
Tel: 01770 820320
Email: enquiries@campingarran.com
www.campingarran.com
Pitches For ⋏ ⊕ ⇔ **Total** 43
Acreage 2¾ **Open** Mar **to** Oct
Access Good **Site** Sloping
Nearest Bus Stop (Miles) Outside
Situated on our own private beach.
Facilities 🕭⎕ 🖟⊡🖟↑⊙🧺🖃🔲🍴
🎇✕⎕🔺🏦⊹⇔🖃🔲🔆
Nearest Town Whiting Bay
Directions From the Brodick ferry turn left, we are situated 12 miles, along the coast.
🚆 Ardrossan

LARGS

South Whittlieburn Farm, Brisbane Glen, Largs, North Ayrshire, KA30 8SN
Tel: 01475 675881
Email:
largsbandb@southwhittlieburnfarm.freeserve.co.uk
www.smoothhound.co.uk/hotels/whittlie
Pitches For ⋏ ⊕ ⇔ **Total** 5
Acreage 5 **Open** All Year
Access Good **Site** Level/Sloping
Nearest Bus Stop (Miles) ½
Situated on a working sheep farm with 4 Star Farmhouse B&B accommodation also available. Great for hill walking. Close to Largs for ferries, shops, restaurants, pubs, swimming pool, putting green and theatre.
Facilities 🖟 ⎕🖿🖟⊡🖟↑⊙🧺🖃⊷🖃
Nearest Town Largs
Directions From the A78 in Largs, turn off just past Vikingar Complex (sp Brisbane Glen), Park is approx 2¼ miles on the left.
🚆 Largs

AYRSHIRE (SOUTH)
AYR

Ayr Craigie Gardens Caravan Club Site, Craigie Road, Ayr, South Ayrshire, KA8 0SS
Tel: 01292 264909
www.caravanclub.co.uk
Pitches For ⊕ ⇔ **Total** 90
Acreage 7 **Open** 23-Mar **to** 07-Jan
Access Good **Site** Level
Nearest Bus Stop (Miles) ½
Situated in a beautiful park, just a ten minute

walk from Ayr seaside resort. Open March then all year. 40 golf courses in the area. Close to Burns Heritage Trail, Culzean Castle, Vikingar and The Tam OShanter Experience. Non members welcome. Booking essential.
Facilities 🖟⎕ 🖟⊡🖿🖟↑ 🔲🍴
🎇⊙🛇🏦⊷🖃🔲🔆
Nearest Town Ayr
Directions From the A77 Ayr bypass take the A719 signposted Ayr. Just past the racecourse at the traffic lights turn left into Craigie Road, on right bend turn left into Craigie Gardens, keep right and site is 400 yards.
🚆 Ayr

AYR

Sundrum Castle Holiday Park, By Ayr, South Ayrshire, KA6 5JH
Tel: 0844 335 3731
Email:
touringandcamping@parkdeanholidays.com
www.parkdeantouring.com
Pitches For ⋏ ⊕ ⇔ **Total** 45
Acreage 32 **Open** March **to** Oct
Access Good **Site** Level
Nearest Bus Stop (Miles) Â½
Four Star Park set in rolling Ayrshire countryside, just 4 miles from the beach. Indoor pool. FREE kids clubs and live family entertainment.
Facilities 🖟 🖟⊡🖿🖟↑⊙🧺 🔲🍴
🎇🕭⊙🛇✕⎕🔺🏦🌤⊹⇔🖃🔲🔆
Nearest Town Ayr
Directions From Glasgow head south on the A77 to Ayr, then take the A70 to Cumnock. The park is 3 miles along the A70, before Coylton Village.
🚆 Ayr

BARRHILL

Barrhill Holiday Park, Millers Holiday Parks, Barrhill, Girvan, South Ayrshire, KA26 0PZ
Tel: 01465 821355
Email: barrhillholidaypark@gmail.com
www.barrhillholidaypark.com
Pitches For ⋏ ⊕ ⇔ ⋨ **Total** 30
Acreage 1 **Open** Mar **to** Jan
Access Good **Site** Level
Nearest Bus Stop (Miles) Outside
Close to the border of Dumfries & Galloway and Ayrshire, Ideal for exploring both counties and SW Scotland.
Facilities 🖟⎕ 🖿🖟⊡🖿🖟↑⊙🧺🖃🔲🍴
🎇🕭⊙🔵⊷🖃🌤
Nearest Town Girvan
Directions Situated on the A714 between Newton Stewart and Girvan, 1 mile north of Barrhill.
🚆 Barrhill

BARRHILL

Queensland Holiday Park, Barrhill, Girvan, South Ayrshire, KA26 0PZ
Tel: 01465 821364
Email: info@queenslandholidaypark.co.uk
www.queenslandholidaypark.co.uk
Pitches For Å ⊞ ⊞ **Total** 64
Acreage 9 **Open** Mar **to** Jan
Access Good **Site** Level
Nearest Bus Stop (Miles) Outside
Ideal location for walking and cycling in Galloway Forest, or for touring South Scotland. Good local rivers.
Facilities ⬧ ⚡ ⊡ ⊞ ⩗ ⌂ ⊙ ⬦ ⬛ ⊡ ☕
⬒ ⬓ ⊙ ⊠ ⏃ ◄⊞ ⬀ ⬥
Nearest Town Girvan
Directions 10 miles south east of Girvan on the A714.
⬆ Barrhill

MAYBOLE

Culzean Castle Camping & Caravanning Club Site, Culzean Castle, Maybole, South Ayrshire, KA19 8JX
Tel: 01655 760627
Email:
culzean.castlesite@thefriendlyclub.co.uk
www.campingandcaravanningclub.co.uk
Pitches For Å ⊞ ⊞ **Total** 90
Acreage 10 **Open** 21-Mar **to** 04-Nov
Access Good **Site** Lev/Slope
Nearest Bus Stop (Miles) Outside
Set in the grounds of historic Culzean Castle with excellent views and country walks. STB 4 Star Graded and AA 3 Pennants. Non members welcome. You can also call us on 0845 130 7633.
Facilities ⬧ ⚡ ⊡ ⊞ ⩗ ⌂ ⊙ ⬦ ⬛ ⊡ ☕
⊙ ⊠ ⏃ ◄⊞ ⊡ ⬥ ⬀ ☕
Nearest Town Maybole
Directions In Maybole turn right onto the B7023 signposted Culzean and Maidens. After 100 yards turn left, site is 4 miles on the right.
⬆ Maybole

TROON

St Meddans Caravan Site, Low St Meddans, Troon, South Ayrshire, KA10 6NS
Tel: 01292 312957
www.ukparks.co.uk/stmeddans
Pitches For Å ⊞ ⊞ **Total** 25
Acreage 1 **Open** 1st Fri Mar **to** Last Sun Oct
Nearest Bus Stop (Miles) Outside
Just a 5 minute walk from beaches, golf courses and the town centre.
Facilities ⚡ ⬚ ⩗ ⌂ ⊙ ⬦ ☕
⬒ ⊙ ⬛◄⊞ ⊡ ⬥
Nearest Town Troon
⬆ Troon

TURNBERRY

Balkenna Caravan Park, Girvan Road (A77), Turnberry, South Ayrshire, KA26 9LN
Tel: 01655 331692
Email: balkenna@aol.com
www.balkenna.co.uk
Pitches For Å ⊞ ⊞ **Total** 15
Acreage 1½ **Open** All Year
Access Good **Site** Level
Nearest Bus Stop (Miles) Outside
Magnificent sea views looking towards the Isle of Arran. Close to Turnberry Golf Course.
Facilities ⚡ ⬚ ⩗ ⌂ ⊙ ⬦
⬒ ⊙ ✕◄⊞ ⊡ ⬥
Nearest Town Girvan
Directions From Girvan take the A77 north, site is 5 miles on the right, just before Turnberry Golf Course.
⬆ Girvan

CLACKMANNAN

DOLLAR

Riverside Caravan Park, Dollarfield, Dollar, Clackmannan, FK14 7LX
Tel: 01259 742896
www.riverside-caravanpark.co.uk
Pitches For Å ⊞ ⊞ **Total** 90
Acreage 6 **Open** Mar **to** Feb
Access Good **Site** Level
Nearest Bus Stop (Miles) ½
Alongside river, ideal base for exploring Central Scotland.
Facilities ⬧ ⚡ ⊡ ⩗ ⌂ ⊙ ⬦
⊡◄⊞ ⊡ ⬛ ⧸ ⬥
Nearest Town Dollar
Directions From Stirling take the A91, in Dollar take the B913 and follow for a mile, Park is on the left.
⬆ Alloa

DUMFRIES & GALLOWAY

BORGUE

Brighouse Bay Holiday Park, Borgue, Kirkcudbright, D & G, DG6 4TS
Tel: 01557 870267
Email: info@gillespie-leisure.co.uk
www.gillespie-leisure.co.uk
Pitches For Å ⊞ ⊞ ⊞⸴ **Total** 180
Acreage 25 **Open** All Year
Access Good **Site** Lev/Slope
Nearest Bus Stop (Miles) At Entrance
Beautifully situated on a quiet peninsula with its own sandy beach, family park with exceptional on-site recreational facilities including an indoor pool complex, jacuzzi, fitness room, family room, bowling green, quad bikes, pony trekking centre, 18 hole par 73 golf course and driving range, 9 hole par 3 golf course, fishing, nature trails, boating, pond canoes and slipway.
Facilities ⬧ ⚡ ⊡ ⊞ ⬚ ⩗ ⌂ ⊙ ⬦ ⬛ ⊡ ☕
⬒ ⊙ ⊠ ✕ ⬛ ♦ ⏃ ⬟ ◄⊞ ⊡ ⧸ ⬥ ☕
Directions Off the B727 Kirkcudbright to Borgue road. Or take the A755 (Kirkcudbright) off the A75 2 miles west of Twynholm, clear signposting for 8 miles.
⬆ Dumfries

DALBEATTIE

Glenearly Caravan Park, Dalbeattie, Dumfries & Galloway, DG5 4NE
Tel: 01556 611393
Email: glenearlycaravan@btconnect.com
Pitches For ⊞ ⊞ **Total** 39
Acreage 10 **Open** All Year
Access Good **Site** Level
Nearest Bus Stop (Miles) ¼
Peaceful site situated centrally for all local attractions.
Facilities ⬧ ⚡ ⊡ ⊞ ⩗ ⌂ ⊙ ⬦ ⬛ ⊡ ☕
⬒ ⊙ ⊠ ♦ ◄⊞ ⊡ ⬥
Nearest Town Dalbeattie
Directions From Dumfries take the A711 towards Dalbeattie. On approaching Dalbeattie see signs for Glenearly on the right.
⬆ Dumfries

DALBEATTIE

Islecroft Caravan & Camping Site, Mill Street, Dalbeattie, D & G, DG5 4HE
Tel: 01556 612236/612645
Email: wahsong@gmail.com
www.islecroft.co.uk
Pitches For Å ⊞ ⊞ **Total** 25
Acreage 1½ **Open** mid Mar **to** Oct
Access Good **Site** Level
Nearest Bus Stop (Miles) ¼
Adjacent to 10 acre public park with childrens playground, ask about our accoustic week-end singalongs.

Facilities ⬧ ⚡ ⊡ ⊞ ⬚ ⩗ ⌂ ⊙ ⬦ ⬛ ⊡ ☕
◄⊞ ⊡ ⬥ ⬀ ☕
Nearest Town Dalbeattie
Directions 500yds from town centre.
⬆ Dumfries

DALBEATTIE

Mossband Caravan Park, Kirkgunzeon, Dumfries, Dumfries & Galloway, DG2 8JP
Tel: 01387 760208
Email: mossbandcp@btconnect.com
www.mossbandcaravanpark.co.uk
Pitches For ⊞ ⊞ **Total** 37
Acreage 5 **Open** Mar **to** Oct
Access Good **Site** Level
Nearest Bus Stop (Miles) Outside
Ideal touring, mountain biking,walking.
Facilities ⚡ ⊡ ⩗ ⌂ ⊙ ⬦ ⬛ ⊡
⊙ ◄⊞ ⊡ ⬥
Nearest Town Dalbeattie
Directions From Dumfries take the A711 Dalbeattie road for approx. 10 miles. We are on the right hand side at Kirgunzeon.
⬆ Dumfries

DALBEATTIE

Sandyhills Bay Leisure Park, Sandyhills, Dalbeattie, Dumfries & Galloway, DG5 4NY
Tel: 01557 870267
Email: info@gillespie-leisure.co.uk
www.gillespie-leisure.co.uk
Pitches For Å ⊞ ⊞ **Total** 20
Acreage 15 **Open** Easter **to** Oct
Access Good **Site** Level
Cliff top walk to Rockcliffe from Sandyhills. Adventure play area by the beach, shop and small take-away.
Facilities ⬧ ⚡ ⊡ ⩗ ⌂ ⊙ ⬦ ⬛ ⊡
⬒ ⊙ ⊠ ✕ ⏃◄⊞ ⊡ ⬥
Nearest Town Dalbeattie
Directions From Dumfries take the A710 Solway Coast road for approx 16 miles. Park is on the left just after signs for Sandyhills.
⬆ Dumfries

DUMFRIES

Barnsoul Caravan Park Barnsoul Caravan Park, Shawhead, Dumfries, Dumfries & Galloway, DG2 9SQ
Tel: 01557 814351
Email: info@barnsoulcaravanpark.co.uk
www.barnsoulcaravanpark.co.uk
Pitches For Å ⊞ ⊞ **Total** 60
Acreage 40 **Open** Mar **to** Nov
Access Good **Site** Sloping
Nearest Bus Stop (Miles) 1
Surrounded by woodland and farms very quite site.
Facilities ⬧ ⚡ ⊡ ⊞ ⬚ ⩗ ⌂ ⊙ ⬦ ⬛ ⊡ ☕
⬒ ⊙ ⏃ ♦◄⊞ ⊡ ⧸ ⬥
Nearest Town Dumfries
⬆ Dumfries

ECCLEFECHAN

Cressfield Caravan Park, Ecclefechan, Lockerbie, Dumfries & Galloway, DG11 3LG
Tel: 01576 300702
Email: info@cressfieldcaravanpark.co.uk
www.cressfieldcaravanpark.co.uk
Pitches For Å ⊞ ⊞ ⊞⸴ **Total** 200
Acreage 40 **Open** All Year
Access Good **Site** Level
Nearest Bus Stop (Miles) Outside
Lovely rural Scottish countryside.
Facilities ⬧ ⚡ ⊡ ⊞ ⬚ ⩗ ⌂ ⊙ ⬦ ⬛ ⊡ ☕
⬒ ⊙ ⊠ ♦◄⊞ ⊡ ⬥
Nearest Town Lockerbie
Directions From the M6 head north on the M74 to junction 19, then follow signs for Cressfield.
⬆ Lockerbie

ECCLEFECHAN

Hoddom Castle Caravan Park, Hoddom, Lockerbie, Dumfries & Galloway, DG11 1AS
Tel: 01576 300251
Email: hoddomcastle@aol.com
www.hoddomcastle.co.uk
Pitches For ▲ ⊕ ⊟ **Total** 89
Open Apr **to** Oct
Access Good **Site** Lev/Slope
Nearest Bus Stop (Miles) ¼
Facilities ⅙ ∱ ⌂ Ⓗ ☒ ♐ ⌒ ☉ ⏁ ◢ ◻ ☎
℠ ☺ ◨ ☓ ♠ Ⓜ ⊣ ⊡ ◢ ⅍ ⚓
Nearest Town Annan
Directions Signposted 4 miles from Annan 2 miles from Ecclefechan junction 19 M74.
⇻ Annan

GATEHOUSE OF FLEET

Anwoth Holiday Park, Garden Street, Gatehouse of Fleet, Castle Douglas, Dumfries & Galloway, DG7 2JU
Tel: 01557 814333
Email: paul@auchenlarie.co.uk
www.anwothholidaypark.co.uk
Pitches For ▲ ⊕ ⊟ **Total** 28
Open Mar **to** Oct
Access Good **Site** Level
Nearest Bus Stop (Miles) ¼
Quiet 5 Star Park in the village of Gatehouse of Fleet.
Facilities ⅙ ∱ ⌂ Ⓗ ☒ ♐ ⌒ ☉ ⏁ ◢ ◻ ☎
℠ ☺ ◨ ⊣ ⊡ ◢ ⚓
Nearest Town Gatehouse of Fleet
Directions From Dumfries take the A75 towards Stranraer, 16 miles from Castle Douglas.
⇻ Dumfries

GATEHOUSE OF FLEET

Auchenlarie Holiday Park, Gatehouse of Fleet, Castle Douglas, Dumfries & Galloway, DG7 2EX
Tel: 01556 506200
Email: enquiries@auchenlarie.co.uk
www.swalwellholidaygroup.co.uk
Pitches For ▲ ⊕ ⊟ **Total** 109
Acreage 20 **Open** Mar **to** Oct
Access Good **Site** Sloping
Nearest Bus Stop (Miles) Outside
Our own sandy cove. Restaurant, 3 bars on site, as well as a pool, gym, crazy golf and a shop. Good centre for touring.
Facilities ⅙ ∱ ⌂ Ⓗ ☒ ♐ ⌒ ☉ ⏁ ◢ ◻ ☎
℠ ☺ ◨ ☓ ☖ ♠ Ⓜ ☼ ⊣ ⊡ ◢ ⅍ ☎
Nearest Town Gatehouse of Fleet
Directions On the main A75 5 miles west of Gatehouse of Fleet heading towards Stranraer, Park is on the left hand side.
⇻ Dumfries

GATEHOUSE OF FLEET

Mossyard Caravan Park, Mossyard, Gatehouse of Fleet, Castle Douglas, Dumfries & Galloway, DG7 2ET
Tel: 01557 840226
Email: enquiry@mossyard.co.uk
www.mossyard.co.uk
Pitches For ▲ ⊕ ⊟ **Total** 30
Open Apr **to** Oct
Access Good **Site** Level
Nearest Bus Stop (Miles) ½
Situated on a working farm and set in a coastal location with a back drop of the Galloway Hills. Family run business.
Facilities ⅙ ∱ ⌂ Ⓗ ☒ ♐ ⌒ ☉ ⏁ ◢ ◻ ☎
℠ ☺ ⊣ ⊡ ◢ ☎
Nearest Town Gatehouse of Fleet
Directions 4 miles west of Gatehouse of Fleet on the A75, turn left at Mossyard sign and follow for 800 yards to reception.
⇻ Dumfries

GLENLUCE

Glenluce Caravan Park, Balkail Avenue, Glenluce, Dumfries & Galloway, DG8 0QR
Tel: 01581 300412
Email: enquiries@glenlucecaravans.co.uk
www.glenlucecaravans.co.uk
Pitches For ▲ ⊕ ⊟ **Total** 18
Acreage 4 **Open** All Year
Access Good **Site** Level
Nearest Bus Stop (Miles) ¼
Secluded suntrap in the centre of the village. Set in mature grounds. Ideal for walking, beaches, fishing, mountain biking, UK Dark Skies Park, golfing and watersports.
Facilities ⅙ ∱ ⌂ Ⓗ ☒ ♐ ⌒ ☉ ⏁ ◢ ◻ ☎
℠ ☺ ◨ Ⓜ ☼ ⊣ ⊡ ◢ ⅍ ⚓
Nearest Town Stranraer
⇻ Stranraer

GLENLUCE

Whitecairn Holiday Park, Glenluce, Newton Stewart, Dumfries & Galloway, DG8 0NZ
Tel: 01581 300267
Email: enquiries@whitecairncaravans.co.uk
www.whitecairncaravans.co.uk
Pitches For ▲ ⊕ ⊟ **Total** 10
Acreage 22 **Open** All Year
Access Good **Site** Level
Nearest Bus Stop (Miles) ½
Central location for touring Wigtownshire. Very peacful park, away from the main road. Ideal for beaches, walking, fishing, mountain biking, UK Dark Skies Park, golfing and watersports.
Facilities ∱ ⌂ Ⓗ ☒ ♐ ⌒ ☉ ⏁ ◢ ◻ ☎
℠ ☺ ◨ Ⓜ ☼ ⊣ ⊡ ◢ ⅍
Nearest Town Stranraer
Directions 1½ miles north of Glenluce Village and 2 miles from the A75.
⇻ Stranraer

GRETNA

Braids Caravan Park, Annan Road, Gretna, Dumfries & Galloway, DG16 5DQ
Tel: 01461 337409
Email: enquiries@thebraidscaravanpark.co.uk
www.thebraidscaravanpark.co.uk
Pitches For ⊕ ⊟ **Total** 84
Acreage 5 **Open** All Year
Access Good **Site** Lev/Slope
Nearest Bus Stop (Miles) ¼
Ideal touring centre. Good area for bird watching. On board tank waste disposal point. Small rallies welcome, rally building available. STB 4 Star Graded Park.
Facilities ⅙ ∱ ⌂ Ⓗ ☒ ♐ ⌒ ☉ ⏁ ◢ ◻ ☎
℠ ☺ ⊣ ⊡ ⚓
Directions From the M6 run straight onto the A74. Take the A75 signposted Dumfries/Stranraer. In 1 mile take the second left for Gretna (B721), park is 600yds on the left.
⇻ Gretna Green

ISLE OF WHITHORN

Burrowhead Holiday Village, Tonderghie Road, Isle of Whithorn, Newton Stewart, Dumfries & Galloway, DG8 8JB
Tel: 01988 500252
Email: burrowheadhv@aol.com
www.burrowheadholidayvillage.co.uk
Pitches For ▲ ⊕ ⊟ ⊟ **Total** 90
Acreage 20 **Open** Mar **to** 01-Nov
Access Good **Site** Level
Beathtaking views over the Solway Firth and across to the Isle of Man.
Facilities ∱ ⌒ ☉ ⏁ ☎
℠ ☺ ◨ ☓ ☖ ⊓ ♠ Ⓜ ☼ ⊣ ⊡ ◢ ⅍

Newton Stewart (right column)

Nearest Town Newton Stewart
Directions From the A75 at Newton Stewart take the A714 to Wigtown, then take the A746 to Whithorn. Then take the B7004 to the Isle of Whithorn and Burrowhead is signposted.
⇻ Stranraer

KIPPFORD

Kippford Holiday Park, Kippford, Dalbeattie, Kirkcudbrightshire, DG5 4LF
Tel: 01556 620636
Email: info@kippfordholidaypark.co.uk
www.kippfordholidaypark.co.uk
Pitches For ▲ ⊕ ⊟ **Total** 50
Acreage 8 **Open** All Year
Access Good **Site** Lev/Slope
Nearest Bus Stop (Miles) Outside
Just ½ a mile from the truly beautiful seaside village and pubs. Level pitches, many separately screened. Enjoy woodland walks to the sea and watch the Red Squirrels. Golf, fishing, biking, childrens play area and a shop on site. No on site entertainment.
Facilities ⅙ ∱ ⌂ Ⓗ ☒ ♐ ⌒ ☉ ⏁ ◢ ◻ ☎
℠ ℡ ☺ ◨ ☖ ☼ ⊣ ⊡ ◻ ⚓
Nearest Town Kippford
Directions From Dumfries take the A711 to Dalbeattie, then turn left onto the A710 signposted Colvend Coast. In 3½ miles, just beyond Kippford road end, turn right.
⇻ Dumfries

KIRKCUDBRIGHT

Seaward Caravan Park, Dhoon Bay, Kirkcudbright, Dumfries & Galloway, DG6 4TJ
Tel: 01557 331079
Email: info@gillespie-leisure.co.uk
www.gillespie-leisure.co.uk
Pitches For ▲ ⊕ ⊟ **Total** 20
Acreage 23 **Open** March **to** Oct
Access Good **Site** Level
Nearest Bus Stop (Miles) At Entrance
Exceptional panoramic views over the bay. Heated outdoor pool and beach picnic area. Beach and sea angling nearby.
Facilities ∱ ⌂ Ⓗ ⌒ ☉ ⏁ ◢ ◻ ☎
℠ ℡ ☺ ◨ ⊓ ⊣ ⊡ ⅍
Nearest Town Kirkcudbright
Directions From Kirkcudbright take the A755 west, then take the B727 Borgue road. Seaward is on the right after approx 3 miles.
⇻ Dumfries

KIRKPATRICK FLEMING

King Robert the Bruces Cave Caravan & Camping Site, Cove Farm, Kirkpatrick Fleming, By Lockerbie, Dumfries & Galloway, DG11 3AT
Tel: 01461 800285
Email: jan534@btinternet.com
www.brucescave.co.uk
Pitches For ▲ ⊕ ⊟ **Total** 40
Acreage 80 **Open** All Year
Access Good **Site** Level
Nearest Bus Stop (Miles) ¼
In the grounds of an 80 acre estate, peaceful, quiet and secluded. Famous ancient monument of King Robert the Bruce cave in the grounds. Free fishing on 3 miles of river for Trout and Salmon, or fish on the pond. Disabled toilet block and family shower rooms. Under 5's park. Holiday apartments available.
Facilities ⅙ ∱ ⌂ Ⓗ ☒ ♐ ⌒ ☉ ⏁ ◢ ◻ ☎
℠ ℡ ☺ ◨ ☓ ⊓ ⊣ ⊡ ◢ ⅍
Nearest Town Gretna
Directions Turn off A74 M74 at Kirkpatrick Fleming, then in Kirkpatrick follow all signs to Bruces Cave.
⇻ Annan

LANGHOLM

Whitshiels Caravan Park, Langholm, Dumfries & Galloway, DG13 0HG
Tel: 01387 380494
Email: whitshielscafe@btconnect.com
Pitches For **Total** 4
Acreage ½ **Open** All Year
Access Good **Site** Level
Nearest Bus Stop (Miles) Outside
Ideal area for fishing, golf, Hadrians Wall, Gretna Green, Borders region and Armstrong Clan Museum. Scenic route to Edinburgh. 3 x 6 berth holiday caravans available to let.
Facilities
Nearest Town Langholm
Directions 200 yards north of Langholm on the A7.
Carlisle

MOFFAT

Craigielands Country Park, Beattock, Moffat, Dumfries & Galloway, DG10 9RB
Tel: 01683 300591
Email: admin@craigielandspark.com
www.craigielands.com
Pitches For **Total** 100
Acreage 4 **Open** All Year
Access Good **Site** Lev/Slope
Nearest Bus Stop (Miles) ¼
Facilities
Nearest Town Moffat
Directions Leave the M74 at junction 15 Beattock turn off, go to the south end of the village.
Lockerbie

MOFFAT

Moffat Camping & Caravanning Club Site, Hammerlands Farm, Moffat, Dumfries & Galloway, DG10 9QL
Tel: 01683 220436
Email: moffat.site@thefriendlyclub.co.uk
www.campingandcaravanningclub.co.uk/moffat
Pitches For **Total** 180
Acreage 8 **Open** All Year
Site Level
Nearest Bus Stop (Miles) ¼
Set in the Scottish lowlands, the site is perfect for touring Scotland. The local village of Moffat has won awards for The Best Kept Village in Scotland. STB 4 Star Graded and AA 3 Pennants. Non members welcome. You can also call us on 0845 130 7633.
Facilities
Nearest Town Moffat
Directions Take the Moffat sign off the A74, in 1 mile turn right by the Bank of Scotland, right again in 200 yards, signposted on the right, follow road round to the site.
Lockerbie

MONREITH

Knock School Caravan Park, Monreith, Newton Stewart, Dumfries & Galloway, DG8 8NJ
Tel: 01988 700414
Email: pauline@knockschool.co.uk
www.knockschool.co.uk
Pitches For **Total** 15
Acreage 1 **Open** Easter **to** Oct
Access Good **Site** Lev/Slope
Nearest Bus Stop (Miles) Outside
Near sandy beaches and golf. Four hard standing pitches available.
Facilities
Nearest Town Port William
Directions 3 miles south on the A747 at crossroads to golf course.

NEWTON STEWART

Glentrool Holiday Park, Glentrool, Nr Newton Stewart, Dumfries & Galloway, DG8 6RN
Tel: 01671 840280
Email: enquiries@glentroolholidaypark.co.uk
www.glentroolholidaypark.co.uk
Pitches For **Total** 14
Acreage 7½ **Open** Mar **to** Oct
Access Good **Site** Level
Nearest Bus Stop (Miles) Outside
On the edge of a forest, ideal touring.
Facilities
Nearest Town Newton Stewart
Directions Situated off the A714, 9 miles north of Newton Stewart, ½ mile south of Glentrool Village.
Barhill

NEWTON STEWART

Kings Green Caravan Park, South Street, Port William, Newton Stewart, Dumfries & Galloway, DG8 9SH
Tel: 01988 700489
Email: kingsgreencaravanpark@gmail.com
www.portwilliam.com/kingsgreen
Pitches For **Total** 30
Open Mid-Mar **to** Oct
Access Good **Site** Level
Nearest Bus Stop (Miles) ¼
Located on the sea shore, sandy beaches within a mile of site.
Facilities
Nearest Town Newton Stewart
Directions Leave A75 at Newton Stewart on to A714 for approx 9 miles then B7085 to Port William.
Stranraer

PALNACKIE

Barlochan Caravan Park, Palnackie, By Castle Douglas, Dumfries & Galloway, DG7 1PF
Tel: 01556 600256
Email: info@gillespie-leisure.co.uk
www.gillespie-leisure.co.uk
Pitches For **Total** 20
Acreage 9 **Open** Easter **to** Oct
Access Good **Site** Level
Nearest Bus Stop (Miles) At Entrance
Games and TV rooms, outdoor heated pool, small shop, mini golf and play area. Pub and coarse fishing loch nearby.
Facilities
Nearest Town Dalbeattie
Directions Barlochan is 2½ miles south west of Dalbeattie on the A711, by the village of Palnackie.
Dumfries

PARTON

Loch Ken Holiday Park, Parton, Castle Douglas, Dumfries & Galloway, DG7 3NE
Tel: 01644 470282
Email: office@lochkenholidaypark.co.uk
www.lochkenholidaypark.co.uk
Pitches For **Total** 90
Acreage 15 **Open** Feb **to** Nov
Access Good **Site** Level
Nearest Bus Stop (Miles) Entrance
On a lochside for excellent fishing, water skiing, boating and sailing. Near an RSPB Nature Reserve.
Facilities
Nearest Town Castle Douglas
Directions From Dumfries take the A75 towards Castle Douglas, then take the A713 towards Ayr and continue for 7 miles.
Dumfries

PORT LOGAN

New England Bay Caravan Club Site, Port Logan, Stranraer, Dumfries & Galloway, DG9 9NX
Tel: 01776 860275
www.caravanclub.co.uk
Pitches For **Total** 159
Acreage 17 **Open** Mar **to** Nov
Access Good **Site** Level
Set on the edge of Luce Bay with sea views. Direct access to a shingle and sand beach. Boat storage on site. Near a sports centre, bowling green and swimming pool. Close to Mull of Galloway RSPB Sanctuary, Castle Kennedy, Ardwell House and Port Logan Botanic Gardens. Non members welcome. Booking essential.
Facilities
Nearest Town Stranraer
Directions Approaching Stranraer on the A77 follow signs for Portpatrick A77, approx. 1½ miles past Stranraer continue on the A716 sp Drummore. Site is 2½ miles past Ardwell on the left.
Stranraer

PORTPATRICK

Castle Bay Holiday & Residential Park, Portpatrick, Stranraer, Dumfries & Galloway, DG9 9AA
Tel: 01776 810462
Email: castle.bay@btconnect.com
www.castlebayholidaypark.co.uk
Pitches For **Total** 40
Access Good **Site** Lev/Slope
Nearest Bus Stop (Miles) ½
Fine views across the Irish Sea. Coastal walk to nearby Portpatrick.
Facilities
Nearest Town Stranraer
Directions From Stranraer take the A77 south. In Portpatrick turn first left after the 30mph sign, the Park is ¾ miles on the right after the railway bridge.
Stranraer

PORTPATRICK

Sunnymeade Caravan Park, Portpatrick, Nr Stranraer, Dumfries & Galloway, DG9 8LN
Tel: 01776 810293
Email: info-sunnymeade@btconnect.com
www.sunny-meade.co.uk
Pitches For
Open May **to** Sept
Access Good **Site** Lev/Slope
Nearest Bus Stop (Miles) ¼
Near the beach, a golf course, bowling and fishing.
Facilities
Nearest Town Portpatrick
Directions A77 to Portpatrick. First left on entering village, park is ¼ mile on the left.
Stranraer

SANDHEAD

Sands of Luce Holiday Park, Sandhead, Stranraer, Dumfries & Galloway, DG9 9JN
Tel: 01776 830456
Email: info@sandsofluceholidaypark.co.uk
www.sandsofluceholidaypark.co.uk
Pitches For Å ⊕ ⊟ **Total** 12
Acreage 8 **Open** Mar **to** Jan
Access Good **Site** Level
Nearest Bus Stop (Miles) Outside
Our spectacular beach and facilities.
Facilities ⬚⬚⬚⬚⬚⬚⬚
Directions Follow directions to Mull of Galloway, ¼ mile before the village of Sandhead.
⇌ Stranraer

SOUTHERNESS

Lighthouse Leisure, Southerness, Nr Dumfries, Dumfries & Galloway, DG2 8AZ
Tel: 01387 880277
Email: lighthouseleis@aol.com
Pitches For Å ⊕ ⊟ **Total** 20
Open Mar **to** Oct **Access** Good **Site** Level
Nearest Bus Stop (Miles) Outside
Near beach.
Facilities ⬚⬚⬚⬚⬚⬚
Nearest Town Dumfries
Directions From Dumfries take the A710 coast road to Southerness. 15 miles from Dumfries and 9 miles from Dalbeattie.
⇌ Dumfries

SOUTHERNESS

Southerness Holiday Village,
Southerness, By Dumfries, Dumfries & Galloway, DG2 8AZ
Tel: 0844 335 3731
Email:
touringandcamping@parkdeanholidays.com
www.parkdeantouring.com
Pitches For Å ⊕ ⊟ **Total** 100
Acreage 58 **Open** March **to** Oct
Access Good **Site** Level
Nearest Bus Stop (Miles) Outside
Beside 2 miles of sandy beach on the Solway Firth. Superb touring and camping facilities plus a choice of nearby golf courses. Indoor pool. FREE kids clubs and live family entertainment.
Facilities ⬚⬚⬚⬚⬚⬚
Nearest Town Dumfries
Directions From Dumfries follow the Solway coast road through New Abbey and follow signs to Southerness Holiday Village for 10 miles.
⇌ Dumfries

STRANRAER

Aird Donald Caravan Park, Stranraer, Dumfries & Galloway, DG9 8RN
Tel: 01776 702025
Email: enquiries@aird-donald.co.uk
www.aird-donald.co.uk
Pitches For Å ⊕ ⊟ **Total** 75
Acreage 12 **Open** All Year
Access Good **Site** Level
Only 1 mile east of Stranraer town centre. Ideal touring. Tarmac hard standing for touring caravans in wet weather. Ideal site for ferry to Ireland. Good toilets and facilities. Leisure centre nearby.
Facilities ⬚⬚⬚⬚⬚⬚
Nearest Town Stranraer
Directions Off A75 entering Stranraer. Signposted.
⇌ Stranraer

EDINBURGH (CITY)

EDINBURGH

Drum Mohr Caravan Park, Levenhall, Musselburgh, Edinburgh, EH21 8JS
Tel: 0131 665 6867
Email: admin@drummohr.org
www.drummohr.org
Pitches For Å ⊕ ⊟ ⊟≀ **Total** 120
Acreage 10 **Open** All Year
Access Good **Site** Lev/Slope
Nearest Bus Stop (Miles) ¼
Camping Bothy and Octolodges now available for hire by the night! Close to Edinburgh with an excellent bus service. 12 holiday lodges available to rent some with hot tub.
Facilities ⬚⬚⬚⬚⬚⬚
Directions From south on the A1, take the A199 to Musselburgh then the B1361 and follow park signs. From west on the A1, exit at the Wallyford slip road and follow park signs.
⇌ Wallyford

EDINBURGH

Mortonhall Caravan & Camping Park, 38 Mortonhall Gate, Frogston Road, Edinburgh (City), EH16 6TJ
Tel: 0131 664 1533
Email: mortonhall@meadowhead.co.uk
www.meadowhead.co.uk
Pitches For Å ⊕ ⊟ **Total** 250
Open All year
Access Good **Site** Level
Nearest Bus Stop (Miles) Outside
Set in 200 acres of parkland with views to the Pentland Hills. Arboretum with specimen trees. 15 minutes to the city centre.
Facilities ⬚⬚⬚⬚⬚⬚
Nearest Town Edinburgh
Directions Five minutes from the A720 city by-pass. Exit the by-pass at Straiton or Lothianburn junctions and follow signs for Mortonhall.
⇌ Edinburgh

FIFE

LEVEN

Monturpie Caravan Park, Monturpie, Upper Largo, By Leven, Fife, KY8 5QS
Tel: 01333 360254
Email: enquiries@monturpie.co.uk
www.monturpie.co.uk
Pitches For Å ⊕ ⊟≀ **Total** 28
Open 31-Mar **to** October
Access Good **Site** Level
Nearest Bus Stop (Miles) Outside
ADULTS ONLY SITE ideally situated for access to the East Neuk of Fife. Numerous golf courses in the area. Excellent for the Fife coastal path and St Andrews.
Facilities ⬚⬚⬚⬚⬚⬚
Nearest Town Leven
Directions From Leven take the A915, when in Upper Largo follow signs for St Andrews, the Park is on the left after approx ¾ miles.
⇌ Markinch

ST. ANDREWS

Craigtoun Meadows Holiday Park, Mount Melville, St Andrews, Fife, KY16 8PQ
Tel: 01334 475959
Email: craigtoun@aol.com
www.craigtounmeadows.co.uk
Pitches For Å ⊕ ⊟ ⊟≀ **Total** 58
Open 15-Mar **to** Oct
Access Good **Site** Level
Nearest Bus Stop (Miles) Outside
Only 1½ miles from beaches and golf course. Large childrens play area also with putting green, football pitch and Flying Fox slide. Woodland walks.
Facilities ⬚⬚⬚⬚⬚⬚
Nearest Town St Andrews
Directions 1½ miles south west of St Andrews town centre. Head westwards from West Port along Hepburn Gardens.
⇌ Leuchars

HIGHLAND

ACHARACLE

Resipole Holiday Park, Loch Sunart, Acharacle, Highlands, PH36 4HX
Tel: 01967 431235
Email: info@resipole.co.uk
www.resipole.co.uk
Pitches For Å ⊕ ⊟≀ **Total** 60
Acreage 8 **Open** Apr **to** Oct
Access Good **Site** Level
Nearest Bus Stop (Miles) Outside
Loch side location, spectacular views, central for touring.
Facilities ⬚⬚⬚⬚⬚⬚
Nearest Town Acharacle
Directions From Fort William take the A82 south for 8 miles, across Corran Ferry, then take the A861 to Strontian and Salen. Site is 8 miles west of Strontian on the roadside.
⇌ Fort William

APPLECROSS

Applecross Campsite, Applecross, Strathcarron, Highlands, IV54 8ND
Tel: 01520 744268
Email: enquiries@applecross-campsite.co.uk
www.visitapplecross.com
Pitches For Å ⊕ ⊟ **Total** 60
Acreage 6 **Open** Mar **to** Oct
Access Good **Site** Level
Near beaches, river, mountains, archaeolgy.
Facilities ⬚⬚⬚⬚⬚⬚
Directions From the A9 take the A86 and follow signs to Lochcarron then Applecross.
⇌ Strathcarron

AVIEMORE

High Range Touring Caravan Park, Grampian Road, Aviemore, Highlands, PH22 1PT
Tel: 01479 810636
Email: info@highrange.co.uk
www.highrange.co.uk
Pitches For Å ⊕ ⊟≀ **Total** 72
Acreage 2 **Open** Dec **to** Oct
Access Good **Site** Level
Nearest Bus Stop (Miles) ¼
Winter ski resort 9 miles from village/River Spey nearby/within the Cairngorms National Park.
Facilities ⬚⬚⬚⬚⬚⬚
Nearest Town Aviemore
Directions Off the B9152 at the south end of Aviemore, directly opposite the B970.
⇌ Aviemore

BALLACHULISH

Glencoe Camping & Caravanning Club Site, Glencoe, Ballachulish, Argyll, Highlands, PH49 4LA
Tel: 01855 811397
Email: glencoe.site@thefriendlyclub.co.uk
www.campingandcaravanningclub.co.uk/glencoe
Pitches For ⅄ ⬛ ⬛ **Total** 120
Acreage 11 **Open** 21-Mar **to** 28-Oct
Access Good **Site** Lev/Slope
Surrounded by mountains, this quiet site is situated next to forests. Non members welcome. You can also call us on 0845 130 7633.
Facilities ⬛ ⬛ ⬛ ⬛ ⬛ ⬛ ⬛ ⬛ ⬛ ⬛ ⬛
⬛ ⬛ ⬛ ⬛ ⬛ ⬛
Nearest Town Fort William
Directions On the A82, 1 mile south east of Glencoe Village, follow signs for Glencoe Visitor Centre.
⭍ Fort William

BALMACARA

Reraig Caravan Site, Balmacara, Kyle of Lochalsh, Highlands, IV40 8DH
Tel: 01599 566215
Email: warden@reraig.com
www.reraig.com
Pitches For ⅄ ⬛ ⬛ **Total** 45
Acreage 2 **Open** May **to** Sept
Access Good **Site** Level
Forest walks and a hotel adjacent to the site. Dishwashing sinks and hairdryers. No bookings. No large tents. Not suitable for units longer than 7½ metres. No awnings during July and August.
Facilities ⬛ ⬛ ⬛ ⬛ ⬛ ⬛ ⬛ ⬛ ⬛ ⬛ ⬛
Nearest Town Kyle of Lochalsh
Directions On the A87, 1¾ miles west of junction with A890. 4 miles east of the bridge to the Isle of Skye.
⭍ Kyle of Lochalsh

BRORA

BroraCaravan Club Site, Brora, Highlands, KW9 6LP
Tel: 01408 621479
www.caravanclub.co.uk
Pitches For ⅄ ⬛ ⬛ **Total** 52
Acreage 5 **Open** Apr **to** Oct
Access Good **Site** Level
300 yards from a safe, sandy beach where Arctic Tern nest and you can see seals and dolphins. Play golf directly from the site. Many picturesque lochs and mountains nearby. Close to the Clynelish Distillery. Non members welcome. Booking essential.
Facilities ⬛ ⬛ ⬛ ⬛ ⬛ ⬛ ⬛
⬛ ⬛ ⬛ ⬛ ⬛
Nearest Town Brora
Directions From south on the A9, in Brora 1½ miles past the bridge, ignore Dalchalm sign and turn right at brown caravan sign. After 350 yards at the T-junction turn left, site is 150 yards on the right.
⭍ Brora

CANNICH

Cannich Caravan Park, Cannich, By Beauly, Inverness-Shire, IV4 7LN
Tel: 01456 415364
Email: enquiries@highlandcamping.co.uk
www.highlandcamping.co.uk
Pitches For ⅄ ⬛ ⬛ ⬛ **Total** 43
Acreage 6½ **Open** Dec **to** Oct
Access Good **Site** Level
Nearest Bus Stop (Miles) Outside
Set in the heart of Strathglass, at the head of Glen Affric Nature Reserve. Superb

highland and lowland, walking and cycling. Disabled shower room. Also open winter by arrangement only.
Facilities ⬛ ⬛ ⬛ ⬛ ⬛ ⬛ ⬛ ⬛ ⬛ ⬛
⬛ ⬛ ⬛ ⬛ ⬛ ⬛ ⬛ ⬛ ⬛ ⬛ ⬛ ⬛ ⬛
Nearest Town Drumnadrochit
Directions From Inverness take the A82 towards Fort William, at Drumnadrochit take the A831 signposted Cannich and Strathglass.
⭍ Beauly

CULLODEN

Culloden Moor Caravan Club Site, Newlands, Culloden Moor, Inverness, Highlands, IV2 5EF
Tel: 01463 790625
www.caravanclub.co.uk
Pitches For ⅄ ⬛ ⬛ **Total** 97
Acreage 7 **Open** Mar **to** Jan
Access Good **Site** Lev/Slope
Nearest Bus Stop (Miles) Outside
Breathtaking views over the Nairn Valley. 1 mile from the Culloden battlefield. Only 6 miles from Inverness with its superb shopping, Whisky trails and Loch Ness. Basic provisions available on site. Non members welcome. Booking essential.
Facilities ⬛ ⬛ ⬛ ⬛ ⬛ ⬛ ⬛
⬛ ⬛ ⬛ ⬛ ⬛ ⬛
Nearest Town Inverness/Culloden
Directions From south on the A9 turn off signposted Hilton (ignoring previous signs for Culloden Moor), at roundabout turn left onto the B9006, site is 5 miles on the left.
⭍ Inverness

DINGWALL

Dingwall Camping & Caravanning Club Site, Jubilee Park Road, Dingwall, Highlands, IV15 9QZ
Tel: 01349 862236
Email: dingwall.site@thefriendlyclub.co.uk
www.campingandcaravanningclub.co.uk/dingwall
Pitches For ⅄ ⬛ ⬛ **Total** 85
Acreage 6½ **Open** 21-Mar **to** 28-Oct
Access Difficult **Site** Level
Nearest Bus Stop (Miles) ½
Central for touring the Highlands. Train and ferry links to the Isle of Skye. Close to the city of Inverness. STB 4 Star Graded and AA 3 Pennants. Non members welcome. You can also call us on 0845 130 7633.
Facilities ⬛ ⬛ ⬛ ⬛ ⬛ ⬛ ⬛ ⬛ ⬛ ⬛ ⬛
⬛ ⬛ ⬛ ⬛ ⬛ ⬛
Nearest Town Dingwall
Directions From the northwest on the A862 in Dingwall turn right into Hill Street (past the Shell Filling Station), turn right into High Street then turn first left after the railway bridge, site is ahead.
⭍ Dingwall

DORNIE

Ardelve, Dornie, Kyle, Ross-Shire, IV40 8DY
Tel: 01599 555231
www.ardelvecaravanandcampingpark.co.uk
Pitches For ⅄ ⬛ ⬛ **Total** 35
Open Easter **to** Oct
Access Good **Site** Lev/Slope
Nearest Bus Stop (Miles) ¼
Overlooking a loch with views of Eilean Donan Castle. Static caravans for hire.
Facilities ⬛ ⬛ ⬛ ⬛ ⬛ ⬛ ⬛
Nearest Town Dornie
Directions Just off the A87.
⭍ Kyle

DORNOCH

Dornoch Caravan & Camping Park, The Links, Dornoch, Highlands, IV25 3LX
Tel: 01862 810423
Email: info@dornochcaravans.co.uk
www.dornochcaravans.co.uk
Pitches For ⅄ ⬛ ⬛ **Total** 130
Acreage 25 **Open** Apr **to** 30-Oct
Access Good **Site** Level
Nearest Bus Stop (Miles) ¼
Beach, championship golf course, cathedral town. Scenic views, ideal touring.
Facilities ⬛ ⬛ ⬛ ⬛ ⬛ ⬛ ⬛ ⬛ ⬛ ⬛
⬛ ⬛ ⬛ ⬛ ⬛ ⬛ ⬛ ⬛ ⬛ ⬛ ⬛ ⬛
Nearest Town Dornoch
Directions From A9, 6 miles north of Tain, turn right into Dornoch. Turn right at the bottom of the square.
⭍ Tain

DORNOCH

Dornoch Links Caravan and Camping Park River Street,
Tel: 01862 810423
Email: info@dornochcaravans.co.uk
www.dornochcaravans.co.uk
Pitches For ⅄ ⬛ ⬛ ⬛ **Total** 120
Acreage 25 **Open** Apr **to** 22-Oct
Access Good
Nearest Bus Stop (Miles) ¼
Adjacent to famous Royal Dornoch Golf Course, sandy safe beaches.
Facilities ⬛ ⬛ ⬛ ⬛ ⬛ ⬛ ⬛ ⬛ ⬛ ⬛
⬛ ⬛ ⬛ ⬛ ⬛ ⬛ ⬛ ⬛ ⬛ ⬛ ⬛ ⬛
Nearest Town Dornoch
Directions Bottom of town Square signposted to right 450yds
⭍ Tain

DORNOCH

Grannie's Heilan' Hame Holiday Park, Embo, Dornoch, Highlands, IV25 3QD
Tel: 0844 0
Email: touringandcamping@parkdeanholidays.com
www.parkdeantouring.com
Pitches For ⅄ ⬛ ⬛ **Total** 160
Acreage 60 **Open** March **to** Oct
Access Good **Site** Level
Nearest Bus Stop (Miles) Outside
Overlooking Embo Beach and close to the village of Dornoch with its Heritage Centre. Dial-A-Bus service. Indoor pool. FREE kids clubs and live family entertainment.
Facilities ⬛ ⬛ ⬛ ⬛ ⬛ ⬛ ⬛ ⬛ ⬛ ⬛
⬛ ⬛ ⬛ ⬛ ⬛ ⬛ ⬛ ⬛ ⬛ ⬛ ⬛ ⬛ ⬛
Nearest Town Dornoch
Directions Take the A9 north from Inverness. After approx. 45 minutes turn right onto the A949 to Dornoch and Embo, after 3 miles turn right for Embo.
⭍ Tain

DUNBEATH

Inver Caravan Park, Houstry Road, Dunbeath, Highlands, KW6 6EH
Tel: 01593 731441
Email: rhonagwillim@yahoo.co.uk
www.inver-caravan-park.co.uk
Pitches For ⅄ ⬛ ⬛ ⬛ **Total** 15
Acreage 1 **Open** All Year
Access Good **Site** Sloping
Nearest Bus Stop (Miles) ½
Quiet small site. Excellent location for exploring the far north of Scotland, walking and cycling. Visit Scotland 4* site.
Facilities ⬛ ⬛ ⬛ ⬛ ⬛ ⬛ ⬛ ⬛ ⬛ ⬛
⬛ ⬛ ⬛ ⬛ ⬛
Nearest Town Wick

Directions Adjacent to the A9, just north of Dunbeath. Take the turning signposted Houstry 3, Park entrance is 40 metres on the left hand side. 21 miles south west of Wick and 16 miles north east of Helmsdale.
≠ Helmsdale

DUNDONNELL

Badrallach Bothy & Campsite, Croft 9, Badrallach, Dundonnell, Highlands, IV23 2QP
Tel: 01854 633281
Email: mail@badrallach.com
www.badrallach.com
Pitches For Å ⬛ ⬛ **Total** 15
Acreage 1 **Open** All Year
Access Poor **Site** Level
Lochshore site on a working croft, overlooking Anteallach on the Scoraig Peninsular. Bothy, peat stove. Otters, porpoises, Golden Eagles and wild flowers galore. Total peace and quiet - Perfect! Caravans by prior booking only. Airstream for hire. STB 4 Star Graded.
Facilities ⬛ ⬛ ⬛ ⬛ ⬛ ⬛ ⬛ ⬛ ⬛ ⬛ ⬛ ⬛ ⬛
Nearest Town Ullapool/Gairloch
Directions Off the A832, 1 mile east of the Dundonnell Hotel take a left turn onto a single track road to Badrallach, 7 miles to lochshore site.
≠ Garve/Inverness

DUNDONNELL

Northern Lights Campsite, Croft 9, Badcaul, Dundonnell, Highlands, IV23 2QY
Tel: 01697 371379
Pitches For Å ⬛ ⬛ **Total** 12
Acreage 2 **Open** Apr to Aug
Nearest Bus Stop (Miles) ½
Overlooking Loch Broom and in close proximity of several Muras.
Facilities ⬛ ⬛ ⬛ ⬛ ⬛ ⬛ ⬛ ⬛ ⬛
Nearest Town Ullapool
Directions On the A832, 19 miles south west of the junction with the A835 and 12 miles south east of Ullapool.
≠ Garve

DURNESS

Sango Sands Caravan & Camping Site, Durness, Sutherland, Highlands, IV27 4PP
Tel: 01971 511262/511222
Email: keith.durness@btinternet.com
Pitches For Å ⬛ ⬛ **Total** 82
Acreage 12 **Open** Apr to 15-Oct
Access Good **Site** Level
Nearest Bus Stop (Miles) ¼
Overlooking Sango Bay.
Facilities ⬛ ⬛ ⬛ ⬛ ⬛ ⬛ ⬛ ⬛ ⬛ ⬛ ⬛ ⬛ ⬛ ⬛ ⬛ ⬛ ⬛ ⬛ ⬛
Directions On the A838 in the centre of Durness Village.
≠ Lairg

DUROR

Achindarroch Touring Park, Duror, Highlands, PA38 4BS
Tel: 01631 740329
Email: stay@achindarrochtp.co.uk
www.achindarrochtp.co.uk

Pitches For Å ⬛ ⬛ ⬛ ⬛
Acreage 5 **Open** 24-Jan to 16-Jan
Access Good **Site** Level
Friendly, family run site in a quiet, well sheltered, picturesque location at the foot of Glen Duror. Camping Pods available for hire.
Facilities ⬛ ⬛ ⬛ ⬛ ⬛ ⬛ ⬛ ⬛ ⬛ ⬛ ⬛ ⬛ ⬛ ⬛ ⬛
Nearest Town Fort William
Directions Off the A828 north of Appin and south of Fort William and Ballachulish, signposted.
≠ Fort William

EDINBANE

Skye Camping & Caravanning Club Site, Borve, Arnisort, Edinbane, Portree, Isle of Skye, Highlands, IV51 9PS
Tel: 01470 582230
Email: skye.site@thefriendlyclub.co.uk
www.campingandcaravanningclub.co.uk/skye
Pitches For Å ⬛ ⬛ **Total** 105
Acreage 7 **Open** 21-Mar to 04-Nov
Access Good **Site** Lev/Slope
Nearest Bus Stop (Miles) Outside
Situated on a working croft with Highland cows, sheep, ducks and chickens. Within easy reach of a variety of attractions including boat trips and a distillery. Restaurants and pubs close by. Camping Pods available for hire. Non members welcome. You can also call us on 0845 130 7633.
Facilities ⬛ ⬛ ⬛ ⬛ ⬛ ⬛ ⬛ ⬛ ⬛ ⬛ ⬛ ⬛ ⬛
Nearest Town Inverness
Directions From Inverness head NW on A82 towards Fairfield Lane. At Telford Street roundabout take the third exit onto A82, go over 3 roundabouts at Longman roundabout take the first exit onto A9. Do a slight left at Millbank, at the roundabout take second exit, turn left, turn left again, then turn left again.
≠ Kyle of Lochalsh

EVANTON

Black Rock Caravan Park, Balconie Street, Evanton, Highlands, IV16 9UN
Tel: 01349 830917
Email: enquiries@blackrockscotland.co.uk
www.blackrockscotland.co.uk
Pitches For Å ⬛ ⬛ **Total** 56
Acreage 4½ **Open** Apr to Oct
Access Good **Site** Level
Nearest Bus Stop (Miles) Outside
Central location with a river beside the site. Ideal for fishing and forest walks.
Facilities ⬛ ⬛ ⬛ ⬛ ⬛ ⬛ ⬛ ⬛ ⬛ ⬛ ⬛ ⬛ ⬛ ⬛ ⬛ ⬛
Nearest Town Dingwall
Directions From Dingwall take the A862 then the A9 to Evanton, approx 5 miles.
≠ Dingwall

FORT WILLIAM

Linnhe Lochside Holidays, Corpach, Fort William, Highlands, PH33 7NL
Tel: 01397 772376
Email: relax@linnhe-lochside-holidays.co.uk
www.linnhe-lochside-holidays.co.uk

Pitches For Å ⬛ ⬛ ⬛ ⬛ **Total** 65
Acreage 14 **Open** Dec to Oct
Access Good **Site** Level
Nearest Bus Stop (Miles) Outside
Lochside with fantastic views and free fishing. 50 years open this year.
Facilities ⬛ ⬛ ⬛ ⬛ ⬛ ⬛ ⬛ ⬛ ⬛ ⬛ ⬛ ⬛ ⬛ ⬛ ⬛ ⬛ ⬛ ⬛
Nearest Town Fort William
Directions On the A830, 1 mile west of Corpach village, 5 miles from Fort William.
≠ Fort William

FORTROSE

Fortrose Caravan Park, Wester Greengates, Fortrose, Highlands, IV10 8RX
Tel: 01381 621927
Email: fortrosecaravanpark@hotmail.co.uk
www.fortrosecaravansite.co.uk
Pitches For Å ⬛ ⬛ ⬛ ⬛ **Total** 50
Acreage 4 **Open** Apr to Oct
Access Good **Site** Level
Nearest Bus Stop (Miles) ¼
On the shores of the Black Isle, overlooking Moray Firth. Near to Chanonry Point, one of the best places to view bottlenose dolphins.
Facilities ⬛ ⬛ ⬛ ⬛ ⬛ ⬛ ⬛ ⬛ ⬛ ⬛ ⬛
Nearest Town Inverness
Directions From the A9 follow signs to Fortrose. Turn right into Academy Street and the Park is on the right hand side.
≠ Inverness

FORTROSE

Rosemarkie Camping & Caravanning Club Site, Ness Road East, Rosemarkie, Fortrose, Highlands, IV10 8SE
Tel: 01381 621117
Email: rosemarkie.site@thefriendlyclub.co.uk
www.campingandcaravanningclub.co.uk/rosemarkie
Pitches For Å ⬛ ⬛ **Total** 60
Acreage 4 **Open** 21-Mar to 28-Oct
Access Good **Site** Level
Nearest Bus Stop (Miles) 1
On the shores of the Black Isle, overlooking Moray and Cromarty Firths. The spectacular coastline is famous for its bottle nosed dolphins. STB 4 Star Graded, AA 3 Pennants and Loo of the Year Award. Non members welcome. You can also call us on 0845 130 7633.
Facilities ⬛ ⬛ ⬛ ⬛ ⬛ ⬛ ⬛ ⬛ ⬛ ⬛ ⬛ ⬛ ⬛
Nearest Town Rosemarkie
Directions From the A9 at Tore roundabout take the A832 Fortrose to Cromarty road. Go through Avoch, in Fortrose turn right at the Police House into Ness Road signposted golf course and leisure centre. Turn first left and the site is 400 yards.
≠ Inverness

GLENCOE

Invercoe Caravan & Camping Park, Glencoe, Ballachulish, Highlands, PH49 4HP
Tel: 01855 811210
Email: holidays@invercoe.co.uk
www.invercoe.co.uk

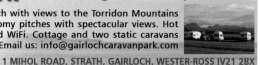
Pitches For Å ⊞ 🚐 **Total** 60
Acreage 5 **Open** All Year
Access Good **Site** Level
Nearest Bus Stop (Miles) ¼
Lochside site with beautiful scenery. Slipway access to the loch. Ideal centre for touring West Highlands. Wi-Fi available for a charge.
Facilities ᕼ ✦ 🖰 🖾 ♪ ⊓ ☺ ↵ ▱ ◻ 🛜
⅀ ⦿ 🛆 ☇ ↤⊟ ✦ 🛜
Nearest Town Fort William
Directions Heading north on the A82 turn right at Glencoe crossroads onto the B863.
⚒ Fort William

GLENCOE

Red Squirrel Campsite, Leacantuim Farm, Glencoe, Highlands, PH49 4HX
Tel: 01855 811256
www.redsquirrelcampsite.co.uk
Pitches For Å 🚐
Acreage 20 **Open** All Year
Site Lev/Slope
Casual and very different Two Star Site in the centre of the mountains. River for swimming and fishing (salmon, permit, must bring your own rods). Kids under 12 years £1, adults £9. Gazebos during July and August for £7 per night. Group discounts available.
Facilities 🖰 🖾 ♪ ⊓ ☺ ↵ ▱ 🛆 ↤⊬ ✦
Nearest Town Fort William
Directions Turn off the main A82 into Glencoe Village, turn up main street, go over the humpback bridge and park is 1½ miles.
⚒ Fort William

GRANTOWN-ON-SPEY

Grantown-on-Spey Caravan Park, Seafield Avenue, Grantown-on-Spey, Highlands, PH26 3JQ
Tel: 01479 872474
Email: warden@caravanscotland.com
www.caravanscotland.com
Pitches For Å ⊞ 🚐 🚐₤ **Total** 160
Acreage 23 **Open** 05-Jan **to** Oct
Access Good **Site** Lev/Slope
Nearest Bus Stop (Miles) ¼
A bird lovers mecca and a dogs paradise! Easy level walk into town. Salmon fishing on the River Spey. Loads of walks in beautiful countryside.
Facilities ᕼ ✦ 🖰 🖾 ♪ ⊓ ☺ ↵ ▱ ◻ 🛜
⅀ ⦿ 🛆 ♠ 🛆 🛜
Nearest Town Grantown-on-Spey
Directions From Aviemore take the A9, approx. 1½ miles past Aviemore turn right onto the A95. When in Grantown high street go through the traffic lights and turn left by the Bank of Scotland, site is ¼ a mile on the right.
⚒ Aviemore

INVERGARRY

Faichemard Farm Caravan & Camping Park, Faichemard Farm, Invergarry, Highlands, PH35 4HG
Tel: 01809 501314
Email: dgrant@faichemard-

caravancamping.co.uk
www.faichemard-caravancamping.co.uk
Pitches For Å ⊞ 🚐 **Total** 35
Acreage 10 **Open** Apr **to** Oct
Access Good **Site** Lev/Slope
Nearest Bus Stop (Miles) 1
ADULTS ONLY SITE with plenty of space and quiet. Ideal for hill walking and bird watching. Pitch price £6.50-£14.50. Every pitch has its own picnic table.
Facilities ✦ 🖰 🖾 ♪ ⊓ ☺ ↵ ▱ ◻ 🛜
🖫 ↤🛆 ☺ 🛆 🛜
Nearest Town Fort William
Directions Take A82 to Invergarry (25 miles) travel west on A87 for 1 mile, take side road on right at sign for Faichem, proceed to the sign for A & D Grant Faichemard Farm.
⚒ Spean Bridge

INVERMORISTON

Loch Ness Holiday Park, Invermoriston, Highlands, IV63 7YE
Tel: 01320 351207
Email:
enquiries@lochnessholidaypark.co.uk
www.lochnessholidaypark.co.uk
Pitches For ⊞ 🚐 🚐₤ **Total** 50
Open Feb **to** Oct
Access Good **Site** Lev/Slope
Nearest Bus Stop (Miles) 1
Lochside location with a stoney beach and small jetties. Licensed bar during peak season.
Facilities ✦ 🖰 🖾 ♪ ⊓ ☺ ↵ ▱ ◻ 🛜
🖫 ♈ 🛆 ⅏ ↤⊟ ◻ ✦
Nearest Town Fort Augustus
Directions 5 miles west of Fort Augustus on the A82.
⚒ Inverness

INVERNESS

Auchnahillin Holiday Park, Daviot East, Inverness, Highlands, IV2 5XQ
Tel: 01463 772286
Email: info@auchnahillin.co.uk
www.auchnahillin.co.uk
Pitches For Å ⊞ 🚐 **Total** 50
Acreage 10 **Open** Apr **to** Oct
Access Good **Site** Level
Nearest Bus Stop (Miles) Outside
Ideal touring area for the Highlands, many attractions within easy reach.
Facilities ᕼ ✦ 🖰 🖾 ♪ ⊓ ☺ ↵ ▱ ◻ 🛜
⅀ ⦿ 🛆 🛆 ↤⊟
Nearest Town Inverness
Directions Approx. 8 miles south of Inverness off the A9 take the turning onto the B9154 towards Daviot East and Moy.
⚒ Inverness

INVERNESS

MacDonalds Bught Caravan & Tent Park, Bught Lane, Inverness, Highlands, IV3 5SR
Tel: 01463 236920
Email: john@invernesscaravanpark.com

www.invernesscaravanpark.com
Pitches For Å ⊞ 🚐 🚐₤ **Total** 140
Acreage 4¾ **Open** Easter **to** 01-Oct
Access Good **Site** Level
Nearest Bus Stop (Miles) Outside
Alongside the River Ness and canal, and next to an Aquadome. Just a 20 minute walk into the town centre. Kitchen shed in the tent area. Ice rink and childrens park in the immediate vacinity and two sports stadiums.
Facilities ᕼ ✦ 🖫 🖾 ♪ ⊓ ☺ ↵ ▱ ◻ 🛜
⅀ ♏ 🛆 ⦿ ☒ ♤ ↤⊟ ◻
Nearest Town Inverness
Directions Situated inside Inverness city limits on the A82 Loch Ness road, beside the canal bridge and Aquadome.
⚒ Inverness

ISLE OF SKYE

Glen Brittle Camping Park, Glen Brittle, via Sleachan, Isle of Skye, Highlands,
Tel: 01478 640404
Pitches For ⊞ 🚐 **Total** 220
Acreage 10 **Open** Apr **to** Sept
Access Poor **Site** Lev/slope
Nearest Bus Stop (Miles) 7
Beach
Facilities ✦ 🖰 🖾 ♪ ⊓ ☺ ⅀ 🛆↤⊟ ◻
Nearest Town Carbost
Directions From Carbost take small road signed Glenbrittle Campsite, follow single track road 7 miles.
⚒ Kyle of Lochalsh

ISLE OF SKYE

Sligachan Campsite, Sligachan, Isle of Skye, Highlands, IV47 8SW
Tel: 07786 435294
Pitches For Å ⊞ 🚐 🚐₤ **Total** 80
Acreage 2 **Open** May **to** Sept
Access Good **Site** Level
Nearest Bus Stop (Miles) Outside
Mountains ,river,ideal touring, walking ,climbing.
Facilities ᕼ ✦ 🖰 🖾 ♪ ⊓ ☺ ↵ ▱ ☒ 🛆 ↤⊬
Nearest Town Portree
Directions On A87.
⚒ Kyle of Lochalsh

JOHN O'GROATS

John O'Groats Caravan & Camping Site, John O'Groats, Nr Wick, Highlands, KW1 4YR
Tel: 01955 611329
Email: info@johnogroatscampsite.co.uk
www.johnogroatscampsite.co.uk
Pitches For Å ⊞ 🚐 **Total** 90
Acreage 4 **Open** Apr **to** Sept
Access Good **Site** Level
Nearest Bus Stop (Miles) Outside
On sea shore with clear view of Orkney Islands. Day trips to Orkney by passenger ferry, jetty nearby. Hotel and snack bar 600 yards. Cliff scenery and sea birds 1½ miles. STB 3 Star Graded.
Facilities ᕼ ✦ 🖰 🖾 ♪ ⊓ ☺ ↵ ▱ ◻ 🛜
🖫 ⦿ 🛆↤⊟ ◻
Nearest Town John O'Groats
Directions End of A99 beside last house.
⚒ Wick

KINLOCHEWE

Kinlochewe Caravan Club Site,
Kinlochewe, Achnasheen, Highlands, IV22 2PA
Tel: 01445 760239
www.caravanclub.co.uk
Pitches For 🚐 🚏 **Total** 56
Acreage 5 **Open** Mar **to** Oct
Access Good **Site** Level
Peaceful location at the foot of Ben Eighe, surrounded by lochs, woodland and mountains. Close to Victoria Falls and Inverewe Gardens. Butcher calls into site twice a week. Adjacent to a service station and theres a general shop and cafe in the village. Non members welcome. Booking essential.
Facilities 👶 🍴 🎪 🚾 🛁 🍴 🍽 🔥
🏧 🛒 🍴 🏤 🖃
Directions From Inverness take A9, in Tore at roundabout turn onto A835 sp Maryburgh, in Maryburgh at roundabout continue on A835 sp Ullapool. In Gorstan turn left onto A832, in Achnasheen at roundabout follow signs for Kinlochewe, site is 10 miles on the left.

KINLOCHLEVEN

Caolasnacon Caravan & Camping Park,
Caolasnacon, Kinlochleven, Highlands, PH50 4RJ
Tel: 01855 831279
Email:
enquiry@kinlochlevencaravans.com
www.kinlochlevencaravans.com
Pitches For ⛺ 🚐 🚏 **Total** 50
Acreage 7½ **Open** Apr **to** Oct
Access Good **Site** Lev/Slope
Nearest Bus Stop (Miles) Outside
Lochside location with breathtaking mountain scenery. Ideal for touring the west coast.
Facilities 🍴 🚾 🍴 🏤 ⊙ 🍴 🍽 🔥
🏧 🛒 🏤 🖃 🍴 🌲🌲
Nearest Town Fort William
Directions From Glencoe on the A82, turn onto the B863, Park is 3 miles.
🚉 Fort William

LAIDE

Gruinard Bay Caravan Park, Laide, Ross-Shire, IV22 2ND
Tel: 01445 731225
Email: gruinard@ecosse.net
www.gruinardbay.co.uk
Pitches For ⛺ 🚐 🚏 **Total** 35
Acreage 3 **Open** Apr **to** Oct
Access Good **Site** Level
Nearest Bus Stop (Miles) ¼
Beach front location.
Facilities 🍴 🚾 🏤 ⊙ 🍴 🍽 🔥
🍴 🏧 🛒 🖃 🍴 🍽 🌲🌲

Nearest Town Gairloch
Directions On the A832, 15 miles north of Gairloch.
🚉 Inverness

LAIRG

Woodend Caravan & Camping Park,
Woodend, Achnairn, Lairg, Highlands, IV27 4DN
Tel: 01549 402248
Pitches For ⛺ 🚐 🚏 **Total** 45
Acreage 4 **Open** Apr **to** Sept
Access Good **Site** Lev/Slope
Overlooking Loch Shin for fishing and scenic views. Campers Kitchen is a small building where campers can take their cooking stores to prepare food, with table, chairs and a dish washing area. Ideal touring centre for north west. AA 3 Pennants and a Gold Award for Quality & Service from International Caravan & Camping Guide.
Facilities 🍴 🚾 🏤 ⊙ 🍴 🍽 🔥 🏧 🛒 🖃
Nearest Town Lairg
Directions From Lairg take the A836, then take the A838 and follow site signs.
🚉 Lairg

LOCHINVER

Clachtoll Campsite, Croft 134, Clachtoll, Lochinver, Highlands, IV27 4JD
Tel: 01571 855377
Email: mail@clachtollbeachcampsite.co.uk
www.clachtollbeachcampsite.co.uk
Pitches For ⛺ 🚐 🚏 **Total** 40
Acreage 3 **Open** Easter **to** Sept
Access Good **Site** Level
200 yards from a sandy beach. Beautiful scenery. Ideal location for hillwalkers and children who enjoy rockpools.
Facilities 👶 🍴 🎪 🚾 🏤 ⊙ 🍴 🍽 🔥
🏧 🛒 🏤 🖃 🍴
Nearest Town Lochinver
Directions 5 miles outside of Lochinver.
🚉 Inverness

MELVICH

Halladale Inn Caravan Park, Halladale Inn, Melvich, Sutherland, KW14 7YJ
Tel: 01641 531282
Email: mazfling@tinyworld.co.uk
www.halladaleinn.co.uk
Pitches For ⛺ 🚐 🚏 **Total** 11
Acreage ½ **Open** Apr **to** Oct
Access Good **Site** Level
Nearest Bus Stop (Miles) 1
10 minutes walk from a lovely sandy beach. Ideal for surfers. 14 miles from Forsinard RSPB Reserve. Fishing on the Halladale River.
Facilities 🍴 🎪 🚾 🏤 ⊙ 🍴 🍽 🔥
🏧 ✕ 🍴 🏤 🖃 🍴

Nearest Town Thurso
Directions 16 miles west of Thurso on the A836 following the North Highlands Tourist Route.
🚉 Forsinard

NAIRN

Nairn Camping & Caravanning Club Site, Delnies Wood, Nairn, Inverness, Highlands, IV12 5NX
Tel: 01667 455281
Email: nairn.site@thefriendlysite.co.uk
www.campingandcaravanningclub.co.uk/nairn
Pitches For ⛺ 🚐 🚏 **Total** 75
Acreage 14 **Open** Mar **to** 28-Oct
Access Good **Site** Level
Nearest Bus Stop (Miles) Outside
Wooded setting just 2 miles from the beach, close to the town of Nairn. STB 4 Star Graded and AA 3 Pennants. Non members welcome. You can also call us on 0845 130 7633.
Facilities 🍴 🚾 🏤 ⊙ 🍴 🍽 🔥 🏧 🛒 🍴
🏧 🛒 🍴 🏤 🖃 🌲🌲 🛜
Nearest Town Nairn
Directions Off the A96 Inverness to Aberdeen road 2 miles west of Nairn.
🚉 Nairn

NAIRN

Nairn Lochloy Holiday Park, East Beach, Nairn, Highlands, IV12 4PH
Tel: 0844 0
Email: touringandcamping@parkdeanholidays.com
www.parkdeantouring.com
Pitches For ⛺ 🚐 🚏 **Total** 10
Acreage 15 **Open** March **to** Nov
Access Good **Site** Level
Nearest Bus Stop (Miles) ½
Situated next to the harbour, East Nairn Beach and the lovely village of Nairn. Indoor pool. FREE kids clubs and live family entertainment.
Facilities 🍴 🚾 🏤 ⊙ 🍴 🍽 🔥
♿ 🏧 🛒 ✕ 🍴 🍴 🍴 🏤 🖃 🌲🌲 🛜
Nearest Town Nairn
Directions Take the A96 from Inverness or Aberdeen. In Nairn follow signs, adjacent to the harbour.
🚉 Nairn

NEWTONMORE

Invernahavon Caravan Site, Glentruim, Newtonmore, Highlands, PH20 1BE
Tel: 01540 673534/673219
www.caravanclub.co.uk
Pitches For ⛺ 🚐 🚏 **Total** 67

Acreage 10 **Open** Mar **to** Oct
Access Good **Site** Level
Tranquil and spacious family run site with spectacular views of the Monarch of the Glen country. Heather covered mountains, ideal for walking and wildlife spotting. Adjacent to the Rivers Spey and Truim, fishing permits available. Booking essential.
Facilities 🚿 🏋 🔌 🎖 🚻 ♿ 🅿 ⊙ ⌁ ▭ 🔲 🛎
🛒 🔥 ⛽ 🏧 ⚙ 🛒 ☼ 📶
Nearest Town Newtonmore
Directions 2 miles south of Newtonmore on the A9 turn right onto Glentruim road, site is 400 yards on the right.
🚉 Newtonmore

ONICH

Bunree Caravan Club Site, Onich, Fort William, Highlands, PH33 6SE
Tel: 01855 821283
www.caravanclub.co.uk
Pitches For 🚎 🚐 **Total** 99
Acreage 7 **Open** Mar **to** Jan
Access Good **Site** Level
Nearest Bus Stop (Miles) ¼
Situated at the edge of Loch Linnhe with mountain views. Visit Ben Nevis or take a cable car 2300 feet to Aonach Mor Mountain for fabulous views of the whole mountain range, the Great Glen and islands of Skye and Rhum. Non members welcome. Booking essential.
Facilities 🚿 🏋 🔌 🎖 🚻 🅿 ⊙ ⌁ 🔲 🛎
🛒 🔥 🏧 🔔 🔥 ⊹ 🔲 📶
Nearest Town Onich
Directions From south east on the A82, just past Onich turn left at Caravan Club sign into a narrow track with traffic lights and passing places, site is in ¼ mile.

POOLEWE

Inverewe Gardens Camping & Caravanning Club Site, Inverewe Gardens, Poolewe, Achnasheen, Highlands, IV22 2LF
Tel: 01445 781249
Email:
inverewe.site@thefriendlyclub.co.uk
www.campingandcaravanningclub.co.uk/inverewe
Pitches For 🚎 🚐 **Total** 55
Acreage 3 **Open** 18-Apr **to** 28-Oct
Site Level
Nearest Bus Stop (Miles) Outside
Close to Inverewe Gardens and Loch Ewe. National Trust Ranger Walks ¼ mile. Diving nearby. STB 4 Star Graded and AA 3 Pennants. Non members welcome. You can also call us on 0845 130 7633.
Facilities 🚿 🏋 🔌 🎖 🚻 ♿ 🅿 ⊙ ⌁ ▭ 🔲 🛎
🛒 🔥 🏧 🔔 🔲 📶
Directions Site entrance is on the A832, north of the village of Poolewe.
🚉 Achnasheen

PORTREE

Torvaig Caravan & Campsite, 8 Torvaig, Portree, Isle of Skye, Highlands, IV51 9HU
Tel: 01478 611849
Email: torvaigcampsite@aol.com
www.portreecampsite.co.uk
Pitches For 🚎 🚐 **Total** 90
Acreage 4½ **Open** April **to** 20-Oct
Access Good **Site** Sloping
Nearest Bus Stop (Miles) Outside
Ideal for touring the Isle of Skye.
Facilities 🏋 🔌 🎖 🚻 🅿 ⊙ 🔲 🛎 🔔 📶
Nearest Town Portree
Directions 1 mile north of Portree on the main A855, on the right.
🚉 Kyle of Lochalsh

ROY BRIDGE

Bunroy Camping & Caravanning Site,
Bunroy Park, Roy Bridge, Highlands, PH31 4AG
Tel: 01397 712332
Email: info@bunroycamping.co.uk
www.bunroycamping.co.uk
Pitches For 🚎 🚐 🚐 **Total** 25
Acreage 7 **Open** Apr **to** Oct
Access Good **Site** Level
Nearest Bus Stop (Miles) ½
Peaceful, secluded, riverside site. Ideal for touring the Highlands and outdoor pursuits.
Facilities 🏋 🔌 🎖 🚻 🅿 ⊙ ⌁ ▭ 🔲 🛎
🛒 🔥 🔔 🔲 🔲 ⚙ 📶
Nearest Town Fort William
Directions From the A86 in Roy Bridge, turn off opposite the Stronlossit Inn, go past the school on the left, over the railway bridge and go straight on.
🚉 Roy Bridge

SHIEL BRIDGE

Morvich Caravan Club Site, Inverinate, Shiel Bridge, Kyle, Highlands, IV40 8HQ
Tel: 01599 511354
www.caravanclub.co.uk
Pitches For 🚎 🚐 🚐 **Total** 106
Acreage 7 **Open** Mar **to** Nov
Access Good **Site** Level
Set on a valley floor surrounded by hills and mountains on National Trust land. Daily guided walks July and August. Close to Eilean Castle, Dunvegan Castle, Falls of Glomach, Talisker Distillery and Isle of Skye. Non members welcome. Booking essential.
Facilities 🚿 🏋 🔌 🎖 🚻 🅿 ⌁ 🔲 🛎
🛒 🔥 🏧 🔔 🔲 📶
Directions From the A87, 1¼ miles past Shiel Bridge at the head of Loch Duich, turn right by the restaurant into loop road signposted Morvich, after 1 mile turn right into road to the site.

SHIEL BRIDGE

Shiel Bridge Caravan Park, Shiel Bridge, Glenshiel, Kyle of Lochalsh, Ross-Shire, IV40 8HW
Tel: 01599 511221
Email: johnfivesisters@btinternet.com
www.shielbridgecaravanpark.co.uk
Pitches For 🚎 🚐 🚐 **Total** 75
Acreage 3 **Open** 16-Mar **to** 16-Oct
Access Good **Site** Level
Nearest Bus Stop (Miles) ¼
Alongside a river with spectacular scenery. Ideal for walking and touring the Isle of Skye and the North West Highlands.
Facilities 🚿 🏋 🔌 🎖 🚻 🅿 ⊙ ⌁ 🛎
🛒 🔥 🔲 🔲 ☼
Nearest Town Kyle of Lochalsh
Directions 16 miles east of Kyle of Lochalsh on the A87.
🚉 Kyle of Lochalsh

SPEAN BRIDGE

Gairlochy Holiday Park, Old Station, Gairlochy Road, Spean Bridge, Highlands, PH34 4EQ
Tel: 01397 712711
Email: theghp@talk21.com
www.theghp.co.uk
Pitches For 🚎 🚐 🚐 **Total** 10
Acreage 1½ **Open** Apr **to** Oct **Site** Level
Ideal touring area.
Facilities 🏋 🔌 🎖 🚻 🅿 ⊙ ⌁ ▭ 🔲 🛎
🛒 🔔 🔥 🔲 🔲 ☼
Nearest Town Spean Bridge
Directions 1 mile north of Spean Bridge on the A82 turn onto the B8004 signposted Gairlochy
🚉 Spean Bridge

SPEAN BRIDGE

Stronaba Caravan Camp Site, Stronaba, Spean Bridge, Inverness-Shire, PH34 4DX
Tel: 01397 712259
Pitches For 🚎 🚐 🚐 **Total** 20
Acreage 3 **Open** Apr **to** Oct
Access Good **Site** Lev/Slope
Nearest Bus Stop (Miles) Outside
Outdoor activities, mountain bike trails and mountain gondola all nearby.
Facilities 🏋 🔌 🎖 🚻 🅿 ⊙ 🛎 🔲 🔲
Nearest Town Fort William
Directions On the main A82, 2 miles north of Spean Bridge, on the left hand side (if travelling north).
🚉 Spean Bridge

STAFFIN

Staffin Caravan & Camping Site, Staffin, Isle of Skye, Highlands, IV51 9JX
Tel: 01470 562213
Email: staffincampsite@btinternet.com
www.staffincampsite.co.uk
Pitches For 🚎 🚐 🚐 **Total** 50
Acreage 2½ **Open** Apr **to** Oct
Access Good **Site** Lev/Slope
Nearest Bus Stop (Miles) Outside
Near a sandy beach. Ideal for touring the area and the Western Isles. Campers Kitchen and information room on site.
Facilities 🏋 🔌 🎖 🚻 🅿 ⊙ ⌁ 🔲 🛎
🛒 🔥 🏧 🔔 🔲
Nearest Town Portree
Directions 16 miles north of Portree on the A855.
🚉 Kyle of Lochalsh

STRONTIAN

Sunart Camping Park Strontian, Highlands, PH36 4HZ
Tel: 01967 402080
Email: sunartcamping@orangehome.co.uk
www.sunartcamping.co.uk
Pitches For 🚎 🚐 🚐 🚐 **Total** 29
Acreage 3 **Open** Mar **to** 01-Nov
Access Good **Site** Level
Nearest Bus Stop (Miles) ¼
On Loch Sunart at the edge of small village with shop, resturants.
Facilities 🏋 🔲 🔌 🎖 🚻 🅿 ⊙ ⌁ ▭ 🔲 🛎
🛒 🔥 🔔 🔲 📶
Nearest Town Fort William
Directions From A82 Corran Ferry turn left 12 miles to Strontian.
🚉 Fort William

THURSO

Dunnet Bay Caravan Club Site, Dunnet, Thurso, Highlands, KW14 8XD
Tel: 01847 821319
www.caravanclub.co.uk
Pitches For 🚎 🚐 🚐 **Total** 57
Acreage 5 **Open** Apr **to** Oct
Access Good **Site** Level
Nearest Bus Stop (Miles) Outside
Situated on the beach above the sand dunes. Ideal for bird watching, walking, guided walks and day trips to the Orkney Islands. Climb Dunnet Head for magnificent views over Pentland Firth to Orkney and the north coast to Ben Loyal and Ben Hope. Non members welcome. Booking essential.
Facilities 🏋 🔌 🎖 🚻 🅿 ⊙ 🛎 🛒 🔔 🔥 🔲
Nearest Town Thurso
Directions From Thurso take the A836, site is on the left approx. 2½ miles past Castletown Village.
🚉 Thurso

UIG

Uig Bay Camping & Caravan Site, 10 Idrigill, Uig, Isle of Skye, Highlands, IV51 9XU
Tel: 01470 542714
Email: lisa.madigan@btopenworld.com
www.uig-camping-skye.co.uk
Pitches For Å ⊕ 🚐 **Total** 50
Acreage 2¼ **Open** All Year
Access Good **Site** Level
Nearest Bus Stop (Miles) Outside
Close to a pebble beach. Near ferry terminal to the Western Isles. Ideal for touring the Highlands. Cycle hire locally.
Facilities ⑤ ♪ 🖬 Ⅲ 🖿 Г ⊙⌿ 🔺 ◎ 🛱
🍴 🚿 🕈 🖪 ∕ 🛜
Nearest Town Uig
Directions From Portree take the A87 to Uig, pass the ferry terminal and turn right just before the pier to the site.
🚲 Fort William

ULLAPOOL

Broomfield Holiday Park, Shore Street, Ullapool, Highlands, IV26 2UT
Tel: 01854 612020
Email: sross@broomfieldhp.com
www.broomfieldhp.com
Pitches For Å ⊕ 🚐 **Total** 140
Acreage 11 **Open** Easter **to** Sept
Access Good **Site** Level
Nearest Bus Stop (Miles) ¼
On the sea front. Beside a cafe/restaurant and adjacent to a golf course.
Facilities ⑤ ♪ 🖬 Ⅲ Г ⊙⌿ 🔺 ◎ 🛱
🍴 🚿 🕈 🕏 Ⅹ 🗚 🖺 🕈 🖪 🛜
Nearest Town Ullapool
Directions Turn right past Ullapool Harbour.
🚲 Garve

WICK

Wick Caravan & Camping Site, Riverside Drive, Janetstown, Wick, Highlands, KW1 5SP
Tel: 01955 605420
Email: wickcaravansite@hotmail.co.uk
www.wickcaravansite.co.uk
Pitches For Å ⊕ 🚐 **Total** 90
Acreage 6½ **Open** Mid Apr **to** Mid Oct
Access Good **Site** Level
Nearest Bus Stop (Miles) ¼
Sheltered site overlooking the River Wick and surrounded by trees. Just a 10 minute walk to the town centre and 3 miles from the beach.
Facilities ♪ 🖬 Ⅲ 🖿 Г ⊙⌿ 🔺 🍴 🕏 🗚 🖪
Nearest Town Wick
Directions From the A99, turn left into Thurso Street (A882), after ½ a mile turn right into Riverside Drive.
🚲 Wick

LANARKSHIRE (NORTH)
GLASGOW

Craigendmuir Caravan & Camping Site, Red Deer Village Complex, Clayhouse Road, Cardowan, Stepps, Glasgow, North Lanarkshire, G33 6AF
Tel: 0141 779 4159
Email: info@craigendmuir.co.uk
www.craigendmuir.co.uk
Pitches For Å ⊕ 🚐 **Total** 40
Open All Year
Access Good **Site** Level
Nearest Bus Stop (Miles) ½
Ideal for Glasgow (15 mins), Edinburgh, Stirling and Loch Lomond.
Facilities ⑤ ♪ 🖬 Ⅲ 🖿 Г ⊙⌿ 🔺 🛱
🍴 🕏 🚿 🕈 🖪 🖺
Nearest Town Glasgow
Directions Leave the M8 (Glasgow North) at junction 11 and take the A80 sp Stepps, Cumbernauld and Stirling. At Buchanaw Business Park turn into Cardowan Road, take the third road on the right (Clayhouse Road) and the Park entrance is at the roundabout.
🚲 Stepps

LANARKSHIRE (SOUTH)
ABINGTON

Mount View Caravan Park, Abington, South Lanarkshire, ML12 6RW
Tel: 01864 502808
Email: info@mountviewcaravanpark.co.uk
www.mountviewcaravanpark.co.uk
Pitches For Å ⊕ 🚐 **Total** 50
Acreage 5½ **Open** Mar **to** Oct
Access Good **Site** Lev/Slope
Nearest Bus Stop (Miles) ¼
Ideal for walking, touring and a quiet family holiday. Well situated for exploring Clyde Valley. One hour from Glasgow, Edinburgh and the Ayrshire coast.
Facilities ⑤ ♪ 🖬 Ⅲ 🖿 Г ⊙⌿ 🔺 ◎ 🛱
🍴 🕏 🖿 🗚 🖪 🖺
Nearest Town Biggar
Directions Leave the M74 at junction 13 and take the A702 south into Abington Village, then follow signs down Station Road.
🚲 Lanark

LOTHIAN (EAST)
ABERLADY

Aberlady Caravan Park, Aberlady Station, Haddington Road, Aberlady, Lothian (East), EH32 0PZ
Tel: 01875 870666
Email: aberladycaravanpark@hotmail.co.uk
www.aberladycaravanpark.co.uk
Pitches For Å ⊕ 🚐 ⊞┊ **Total** 20
Acreage 2 **Open** Mar **to** Oct
Access Good **Site** Level
Nearest Bus Stop (Miles) ¼
Ideal for touring East Lothian, Edinburgh 15 minutes by train.
Facilities ⑤ ♪ 🖬 Ⅲ 🖿 Г ⊙⌿ 🔺 ◎ 🛱
🍴 🕏 🗚 🕈 🕏 🛜
Nearest Town Aberlady
Directions From Haddington take the A6137 to Aberlady site is approx 4½ on the left hand side.
🚲 Longniddry

DUNBAR

Belhaven Bay Caravan & Camping Park, Edinburgh Road, Dunbar, East Lothian, EH42 1TS
Tel: 01368 865956
Email: belhaven@meadowhead.co.uk
www.meadowhead.co.uk
Pitches For Å ⊕ 🚐 **Total** 128
Open 08-Mar **to** 31-Oct
Access Good **Site** Level
Nearest Bus Stop (Miles) Outside
Set within the John Muir Country Park, and right on one side of East Lothians beautiful sandy beaches.
Facilities ⑤ ♪ 🖬 Ⅲ 🖿 Г ⊙⌿ 🔺 ◎ 🛱
🍴 🕏 🗚 🕈 🖪 🖺 🛜
Nearest Town Dunbar
Directions From the A1 north or south, exit at Thistly Cross roundabout west of Dunbar and take the A1087 towards Dunbar, Park is approx. 1 mile.
🚲 Dunbar

NORTH BERWICK

Station Park Caravan Site East Fortune Farm, East Fortune, North Berwick, East Lothian, EH39 5JU
Tel: 01620 880231
Email: jane@brandleisure.co.uk
www.brandleisure.co.uk
Pitches For ⊕ 🚐 **Total** 15
Acreage 2 **Open** All Year
Access Good **Site** Level/Sloping
Facilities ♪ 🖬 🛱 🗚 🖪
Nearest Town North Berwick
Directions Turn off A1 at Haddington-Abbotsview junction on to A199. Turn left on to B1347. At T-junction turn right on to B1377. Site on left at farm entrance.
🚲 Drem

NORTH BERWICK

Tantallon Caravan & Camping Park, Dunbar Road, North Berwick, East Lothian, EH39 5NJ
Tel: 01620 893348
Email: tantallon@meadowhead.co.uk
www.meadowhead.co.uk
Pitches For Å ⊕ 🚐
Open 08-Mar **to** Oct
Access Good **Site** Level
Nearest Bus Stop (Miles) ¼
Spectacular views over the Firth of Forth to the Bass Rock. Scotlands golfing capital.
Facilities ⑤ ♪ 🖬 Ⅲ 🖿 Г ⊙⌿ 🔺 ◎ 🛱
🍴 🕏 🖿 🖩 🗚 🖺 🖪 ∕ 🛜
Nearest Town North Berwick
Directions From the A1, 3 miles west of Dunbar take the A198 and follow to North Berwick. Tantallon Park is on the right.
🚲 North Berwick

NORTH BERWICK

Yellowcraig Caravan Club Site, Dirleton, North Berwick, East Lothian, EH39 5DS
Tel: 01620 850217
www.caravanclub.co.uk
Pitches For ⊕ 🚐 **Total** 116
Acreage 7½ **Open** Mar **to** Nov
Access Good **Site** Level
Attractive site with grass covered sandy dunes and shrubs. Golden sands and rock pools nearby. Close to the Scottish Seabird Centre, Hailes Castle and East Fortune Museum of Flight. Non members welcome. Booking essential.
Facilities ⑤ ♪ 🖬 Ⅲ 🖿 Г ◎ 🛱
🍴 🕏 🖿 🗚 🖪 ∕
Nearest Town North Berwick

Directions From A1 approaching East Linton turn right onto A198. After approx. 8¾ miles turn left past railway station, at junction turn left (still on A198). After 2½ miles turn right signposted Dirleton, turn right at site sign, site is 1 mile.
☒ North Berwick

LOTHIAN (WEST)
BLACKBURN
Mosshall Farm Caravan Park, Mosshall Farm, Blackburn, West Lothian, EH47 7DB
Tel: 01501 762318
Pitches For Å ⊒ ⊒ **Total** 25
Acreage ¾ **Open** All Year
Access Good **Site** Level
Nearest Bus Stop (Miles) ¼
Situated half way between Edinburgh and Glasgow.
Facilities ⅙ ⨍ ⊞ ⑫ ☂ ⌐ ☉ ☎ ⌷⨼
Directions Leave the M8 at junction 4 and take the road for Whitburn. At T-Junction A705 take a left turn towards Blackburn, we are 300 yards on the right.
☒ Bathgate

EAST CALDER
Linwater Caravan Park, West Clifton, East Calder, West Lothian, EH53 0HT
Tel: 0131 333 3326
Email: linwater@supanet.com
www.linwater.co.uk
Pitches For Å ⊒ ⊒ **Total** 60
Acreage 5 **Open** 18-Mar **to** Oct
Access Good **Site** Level
Lovely amenities and walks nearby. Ideal for visiting Edinburgh, Royal Highland Showground and Falkirk Wheel.
Facilities ⅙ ⨍ ⊞ ⑫ ☂ ⌐ ☉ ⌷ ☎
⏚ ⌷ ⋒ ⨼ ⌦ ⊞ ⌕ ☎
Nearest Town Edinburgh
Directions From junction 1, Newbridge on the M9 or Wilkieston on the A71, park is signposted along the B7030.
☒ Kirknewton

LINLITHGOW
Beecraigs Caravan & Camping Site, Beecraigs Country Park, Nr Linlithgow, West Lothian, EH49 6PL
Tel: 01506 844516
Email: mail@beecraigs.com
www.beecraigs.com
Pitches For Å ⊒ ⊒ ⊒ ⅝ **Total** 48
Acreage 6½ **Open** All Year
Access Good **Site** Level
Within a 913 acre Country Park which offers a wide range of leisure and recreational interests - fly fishing, play area, Red Deer attraction, Highland cattle, restaurant and many woodland walks.
Facilities ⅙ ⨍ ⊞ ⑫ ☂ ⌐ ☉ ⌐ ⌦ ⌷ ☎
⏚ ⌷ ⋒ ⨯ ⋒ ⌦ ⌦ ⊞ ⌕ ⨍
Nearest Town Linlithgow
Directions From Linlithgow High Street follow signs for Beecraigs Country Park, taking you approx. 2 miles up Preston Road. At the top of the hill turn left and then first right, take the next right into reception within the Beecraigs Restaurant.
☒ Linlithgow

LINLITHGOW
Loch House Caravan & Camping Park, Loch House Farm, Linlithgow, Lothian, (West), EH49 7RG
Tel: 01506 848283
Email: dotanddonj@btinternet.com
www.lochhousefarmcaravanpark

Pitches For Å ⊒ ⊒
Open Jan **to** Oct
Access Good **Site** Sloping
Facilities ⨍ ⊞ ⑫ ☂ ⌐ ☉ ⌐ ☎ ☉ ⌷⨼
Nearest Town Linlithgow
Directions A706 Bo'ness road from Linlithgow High Street.
☒ Linlithgow

MORAY
ABERLOUR
Aberlour Gardens Caravan Park, Aberlour on Spey, Moray, AB38 9LD
Tel: 01340 871586
Email: info@aberlourgardens.co.uk
www.aberlourgardens.co.uk
Pitches For Å ⊒ ⊒ **Total** 20
Acreage 2 **Open** Mar **to** Oct
Access Good **Site** Level
Nearest Bus Stop (Miles) ¼
Ideal for touring East Lothian, Edinburgh 15 minutes by train.
Facilities ⅙ ⨍ ⊞ ⑫ ☂ ⌐ ☉ ⌐ ⌦ ⌷ ☎
⌷ ⌷ ⌦ ⊞ ⌕ ☎
Nearest Town Charlestown/Aberlour
Directions 1 mile north of Aberlour on the A95, between Aberlour and Craigellachie. Vehicles over 10' 6" must use the A941 (due to bridge) and follow signs.
☒ Elgin

ABERLOUR
Speyside Camping & Caravanning Club Site, Speyside, Archiestown, Aberlour, Moray, AB38 9SL
Tel: 01340 810414
Email:
speyside.site@thefriendlyclub.co.uk
www.campingandcaravanningclub.co.uk/ speyside
Pitches For Å ⊒ ⊒ **Total** 75
Acreage 7 **Open** 25-Apr **to** 28-Oct
Access Good **Site** Level
Nearest Bus Stop (Miles) Outside
The surrounding area has historic castles, National Trust properties and gardens to visit. Salmon and Whisky are the specialities of this area of Scotland. STB 4 Star Graded and AA 3 Pennants. Non members welcome. You can also call us on 0845 130 7633.
Facilities ⅙ ⨍ ⊞ ⑫ ☂ ⌐ ☉ ⌐ ⌦ ⌷ ☎
⌷ ⏚ ⌷ ⋒ ⌦ ⊞ ⌕ ☎
Nearest Town Aberlour
Directions From the A9 at Carbridge turn onto the A95 to Grantown-on-Spey then on to Aberlour. Take the A941 then turn left onto the B9102 signposted Archiestown, site is on the left after 3 miles.
☒ Elgin

BUCKIE
Strathlene Caravan Park, Great Western Road, Portessie, Buckie, Moray, AB56 1SR
Tel: 01542 834851
Email: frasercoln@aol.com
Pitches For Å ⊒ ⊒ **Total** 60
Acreage 9 **Open** Mar **to** Oct
Access Good **Site** Level
Nearest Bus Stop (Miles) Outside
Small beach and cafe/resturant across the road. Golf course adjoins the caravan park.
Facilities ⨍ ⊞ ⑫ ⌐ ☉ ⌐ ⌦ ⌷ ☎
⌷ ⏚ ⌕
Nearest Town Buckie
Directions On the coast road from Cullen to Buckie.
☒ Keith

ELGIN
Riverside Caravan Park, West Road, Elgin, Moray, IV30 8UN
Tel: 01343 542813
Pitches For Å ⊒ ⊒ **Total** 44
Open Apr **to** Oct
Access Good **Site** Level
Elgin is near to beaches and alongside the River Lossie. Ideal fun touring base. Fishing, golfing and plenty of of shops, restaurants and entertainment for children nearby.
Facilities ⅙ ⨍ ⊞ ⑫ ☂ ⌐ ☉ ⌐ ⌦ ⌷ ☎
⌷⏚ ⌷ ⋒ ⌦ ⌦ ⨍ ⌕ ☎
Nearest Town Elgin
Directions Situated off the A96 Aberdeen to Inverness road. On the western outskirts of Elgin, 3 minutes drive from the town centre.
☒ Elgin

FORRES
The Old Mill Caravan Park, Brodie, Forres, Moray, IV36 2TD
Tel: 01309 641244
Email: admin@theoldmillbrodie.com
www.theoldmillbrodie.com
Pitches For Å ⊒ ⊒ **Total** 27
Acreage 1 **Open** Apr **to** Oct
Access Good **Site** Level
Brodie castle, beach 10 minutes by car, local fishing and golf course 10 minutes by car.
Facilities ⨍ ⊞ ⑫ ☂ ⌐ ☉ ⌐ ⌦ ⌷ ☎
⌷ ⌯ ⌦ ⊞ ⌕ ☎ ☎
Nearest Town Forres
Directions Brodie is on the A96 main road from Inverness to Aberdeen, 3 miles west of Forres and 7 miles east of Nairn.
☒ Forres

HOPEMAN
Station Caravan Park, Hopeman, Nr Elgin, Moray, IV30 5RU
Tel: 01343 830880
Email:
enquiries@stationcaravanpark.co.uk
www.stationcaravanpark.co.uk
Pitches For Å ⊒ ⊒ **Total** 37
Acreage 13 **Open** Mar **to** Nov
Access Good **Site** Level
Nearest Bus Stop (Miles) ¼
On a beach on Moray Firth coast.
Facilities ⨍ ⊞ ⑫ ☂ ⌐ ☉ ⌐ ⌦ ⌷ ☎
⌷ ⏚ ⌷ ⋒ ⌦ ⌦ ⊞ ⌕
Nearest Town Elgin
☒ Elgin

SPEY BAY
Spey Bay Caravan Park, Spey Bay, Nr Fochabers, Moray, IV32 7PJ
Tel: 01343 820424
Email: info@speybay.co
www.speybay.co
Pitches For Å ⊒ ⊒ ⊒ ⅝ **Total** 30
Open Apr **to** Oct
Access Good **Site** Level
Nearest Bus Stop (Miles) Outside
Own golf course on site. Near the beach, historic sites and the Scottish Dolphin Centre.
Facilities ⅙ ⨍ ⊞ ⑫ ☂ ⌐ ☉ ⌐
⏚ ⌯ ⌷ ⋒ ⌦ ⊞ ⌕ ☎ ☎
Nearest Town Elgin
Directions From the A96 Aberdeen to Inverness road, take the B9104, turn off at Baxters Visitor Centre.
☒ Elgin

ORKNEY ISLES

KIRKWALL

Pickaquoy Caravan & Camping Park,
Pickaquoy Road, Kirkwall, Orkney Isles,
KW15 1LR
Tel: 01856 888741
Email: enquiries@pickaquoy.com
www.pickaquoy.co.uk
Pitches For Å ♊ 🚐 🚃 ⊰ **Total** 80
Acreage 5¼ **Open** Apr **to** Oct
Access Good **Site** Level
Nearest Bus Stop (Miles) ¼
Within walking distance of Pickaquoy town
centre and St Magnus Cathedral. Next to a
leisure centre. 10 minutes away from the
harbour for ferries to the North Isles.
Facilities ♿ ⨍ 🚻 ⤬ 🕭 ⌕ ⊙ ⌁ ▱ 🖂 ☎
🏋 ⛴ ✕ ⚑ 🛆 ✿ ♨ 🐟 🖃
Nearest Town Kirkwall
⚘ Thurso (Mainland)

PERTH & KINROSS

ALYTH

Five Roads Caravan Park, Alyth,
Blairgowrie, Perth & Kinross, PH11 8NB
Tel: 01828 632255
Email: steven.ewart@btopenworld.com
www.fiveroads-caravan-park.co.uk
Pitches For Å ♊ 🚐 🚃 ⊰ **Total** 28
Acreage 3 **Open** All Year
Access Good **Site** Level
Nearest Bus Stop (Miles) Outside
Three golf courses within a 1 mile radius.
Facilities ♿ ⨍ 🚻 ⤬ 🕭 ⌕ ⊙ ⌁ ▱ 🖂 ☎
🏋 ⛴ 🛆 ⚑ 🖃 ♨ ✿ 🛜
Nearest Town Alyth
Directions From Blairgowrie take the A926,
after 4½ miles at the Blackbird Inn turn left.
⚘ Dundee

BLAIR ATHOLL

Blair Castle Caravan Park, Blair Atholl,
Pitlochry, Perth & Kinross, PH18 5SR
Tel: 01796 481263
Email: mail@blaircastlecaravanpark.co.uk
www.blaircastlecaravanpark.co.uk
Pitches For Å ♊ 🚐 🚃 **Total** 275
Acreage 35 **Open** March **to** Nov
Access Good **Site** Level
Nearest Town -
⚘ Blair Atholl

BLAIRGOWRIE

Blairgowrie Holiday Park, Rattray,
Blairgowrie, Perth & Kinross, PH10 7AL
Tel: 01250 876666
Email: blairgowrie@holiday-parks.co.uk
www.holiday-parks.co.uk

Pitches For ♊ 🚐
Acreage 15 **Open** All Year
Access Good **Site** Level
Nearest Bus Stop (Miles) Outside
Ideal base for touring the hills, lochs and
glens of scenic Perthshire.
Facilities ⨍ 🚻 🕭 ⌕ ⊙ ⌁ ▱ 🖂 ☎
🏋 ⛴ 🛆 ⚑ 🖃 ♨ ✿ ✕ 🛜
Nearest Town Blairgowrie
Directions 1 mile north of Blairgowrie town
centre. Turn right off the A93 at caravan sign
after ½ a mile on Balmoral Road within the
town boundary, Park is 500 yards on the left.
⚘ Perth

BRIDGE OF CALLY

Corriefodly Holiday Park, Bridge of Cally,
Perth & Kinross, PH10 7JG
Tel: 01250 876666
Email: corriefodly@holiday-parks.co.uk
www.holiday-parks.co.uk
Pitches For ♊ 🚐 **Total** 20
Acreage 17½ **Open** All Year
Access Good **Site** Level
Riverside setting with scenic views. Level
hardstanding pitches. Lounge bar and TV
lounge. Ideal touring base.
Facilities ♿ ⨍ 🚻 🕭 ⌕ ⊙ ⌁ ▱ 🖂 ☎
🏋 ⛴ ♛ ✕ ⚑ 🛆 ✿ ♨ 🖃 🚭 ✕ 🛜
Nearest Town Blairgowrie
Directions From Blairgowrie take A93 north
for 6 miles. Turn onto A924 Pitlochry road,
site approx 200yds from junction of A93 and
A924.
⚘ Perth

COMRIE

Twenty Shilling Wood Caravan Park, St
Fillans Road, Comrie, Perth & Kinross,
PH6 2JY
Tel: 01764 670411
Email: alowe20@aol.com
www.ukparks.co.uk/twentyshilling
Pitches For ♊ 🚐 **Total** 10
Acreage 10¼ **Open** Late Mar **to** 20-Oct
Access Good **Site** Level
Nearest Bus Stop (Miles) Outside
Family run, spotless all season, peaceful,
sheltered, sunny south facing park set in
woodlands that are visited by deer and many
woodland birds. Individual pitches. Sorry, NO
tents. Pets permitted. David Bellamy Gold
Award for Conservation. Booking essential.
Facilities ♿ ⨍ 🚻 🕭 ⌕ ⊙ ⌁ ▱ 🖂 ☎
🏋 ⛴ ♛ ✕ ⚑ 🖃 ♨ ✕ 🛆
Nearest Town Crieff
Directions ½ mile west of Comrie on A85.
⚘ Perth

COMRIE

West Lodge Caravan Park, Comrie,
Perth, Perthshire, PH6 2LS
Tel: 01764 670354
www.westlodgecaravanpark.co.uk
Pitches For Å ♊ 🚐 **Total** 20
Acreage 3 **Open** April **to** Oct
Access Good **Site** Level
Nearest Bus Stop (Miles) Outside
Sheltered friendly park, set in beautiful
country area. Ideal for touring. Caravans for
hire nightly or weekly.
Facilities ♿ ⨍ 🚻 🕭 ⌕ ⊙ ⌁ ▱ 🖂 ☎
🏋 ⛴ ⚑ 🛆 🖃 ♨ ✕ ✿ 🛆
Nearest Town Comrie
Directions On A85, 5 miles from Crieff. 1
mile east of Comrie.
⚘ Perth

CRIEFF

Braidhaugh Park, South Bridgend, Crieff,
Perth & Kinross, PH7 4DH
Tel: 01764 652951
Email: info@braidhaugh.co.uk
www.braidhaugh.co.uk
Pitches For ♊ 🚐 🚃 ⊰
Open All year
Access Good **Site** Level
Nearest Bus Stop (Miles) ¼
Riverside park 10 minutes walk into Crieff
centre.
Facilities ♿ ⨍ 🚻 🕭 ⌕ ⊙ ⌁ ▱ 🖂 ☎
🏋 ⛴ ♛ 🛆 ⚑ 🖃 ♨ ✕ 🚭 ✕
Nearest Town Crieff
Directions From Crieff main street, turn left
onto A822 (Stirling). Cross bridge and turn
right and immediatly right again.
⚘ Perth

DUNKELD

Inver Mill Farm Caravan Park, Inver,
Dunkeld, Perth & Kinross, PH8 0JR
Tel: 01350 727477
Email: invermill@talk21.com
www.invermillfarm.com
Pitches For Å ♊ 🚐 **Total** 65
Acreage 5 **Open** End Mar **to** Mid/End Oct
Access Good **Site** Level
Nearest Bus Stop (Miles) ½
Riverside setting. 1 mile from Dunkeld which
has many tourist attractions along with
walking, fishing, golf and cycling.
Facilities ♿ ⨍ 🚻 🕭 ⌕ ⊙ ⌁ ▱ 🖂 ☎
🖃 🚭 ⚑ 🖃 ✕
Nearest Town Dunkeld
Directions From the A9 turn onto the A822
signposted Crieff, turn immediately right
following signs to Inver.
⚘ Dunkeld

KINROSS

Gallowhill Caravan & Camping Park,
Gallowhill Farmhouse, Kinross, Perth &
Kinross, KY13 0RD
Tel: 01577 862364
Email: jpaterson21@hotmail.com
Pitches For A ⚐ ⚑ ⚑ **Total** 50
Acreage 6 **Open** Apr **to** Oct
Access Good **Site** Lev/Slope
Nearest Bus Stop (Miles) ½
Situated in central Scotland. Near to a
swimming pool, Loch Leven, two golf
courses, boat trips to the castle and a walking
and cycling track.
Facilities ⚙ ⚑ ⚑ 🚿 🏪 ⚑ ⊙ ⚑ ⚑ ⚑ ⚑
⚑ ⚑ ⚑ 🔌 ⚑ ⚑
Nearest Town Kinross
Directions Leave the M90 at junction 6 or 7
and head to Kinross following brown tourism
signs to the site.
⚑ Inverkeithing

PERTH

**Scone Camping & Caravanning Club
Site,** Scone Palace Caravan Park, Scone,
Perth & Kinross, PH2 6BB
Tel: 01738 552323
Email: scone.site@thefriendlyclub.co.uk
www.campingandcaravanningclub.co.uk/
scone
Pitches For A ⚐ ⚑ **Total** 150
Acreage 16 **Open** 01-Mar **to** 05-Nov
Site Lev/Slope
Nearest Bus Stop (Miles) ½
Trout and salmon fishing is available from
the nearby River Tay. Just to the north of
Perth. Ideal for touring central Scotland. STB
4 Star Graded, David Bellamy Gold Award
and AA 3 Pennants. Non members welcome.
You can also call us on 0845 130 7633.
Facilities ⚙ ⚑ ⚑ 🏪 ⚑ ⊙ ⚑ ⚑ ⚑
⚑ ⚑ ⚑ ⚑ ⚑ ⚑ ⚑ ⚑ ⚑ ⚑
Nearest Town Perth
Directions From the Motorway follow signs
for Scone Palace, after Scone Palace
continue for 2 miles then turn left following
camp site signs or signs for Stormontfield.
After 1 mile turn left into Racecourse Road,
site entrance is through the car park.
⚑ Perth

PITLOCHRY

Milton of Fonab Caravan Site, Bridge
Road, Pitlochry, Perth & Kinross, PH16 5NA
Tel: 01796 472882
Email: info@fonab.co.uk
www.fonab.co.uk
Pitches For A ⚐ ⚑ **Total** 154
Acreage 15 **Open** End Mar **to** Beg Oct
Access Good **Site** Level
Nearest Bus Stop (Miles) ¼
On the banks of the River Tummel. 5 minute
walk to Pitlochry Festival Theatre and a 10
minute walk to Dam and Fish Ladder.
Facilities ⚙ ⚑ ⚑ ⚑ ⚑ ⊙ ⚑ ⚑ ⚑
⚑ ⚑ ⚑ ⚑ ⚑ ⚑ ⚑
Nearest Town Pitlochry
Directions ½ a mile south of Pitlochry,
opposite Bells Distillery.
⚑ Pitlochry

TUMMEL BRIDGE

Tummel Valley Holiday Park, Tummel
Bridge, Nr Pitlochry, Perth & Kinross, PH16
5SA
Tel: 0844 335 3731
Email:
touringandcamping@parkdeanholidays.com
www.parkdeantouring.com
Pitches For ⚐ ⚑ **Total** 34
Acreage 52 **Open** March **to** Nov
Access Good **Site** Lev/Slope

Nearest Bus Stop (Miles) Outside
Set on the banks of the River Tummel in the
stunning Perthshire countryside. Indoor pool.
FREE kids clubs and live family entertainment.
Facilities ⚑ ⚑ ⚑ ⚑ ⚑ ⊙ ⚑ ⚑ ⚑
⚑ ⚑ ⚑ 🏪 🍴 ⚑ ⚑ ⚑ ⚑ ⚑ ⚑ ⚑ ⚑
Nearest Town Pitlochry
Directions From Perth take the A9 to
Pitlochry, park is 13 miles along this road.
⚑ Pitlochry

SCOTTISH BORDERS

ETTRICK

Honey Cottage Caravan Park, Hope
House, Ettrick Valley, Selkirk, Borders, TD7
5HU
Tel: 01750 62246
www.honeycottagecaravanpark.co.uk
Pitches For A ⚐ ⚑
Open All Year
Access Good **Site** Level
Alongside a river for fishing. Golf courses
within easy reach. Ideal for walking, cycling
or just relaxing in open countryside. Pub and
restaurant 1 mile.
Facilities ⚑ ⚑ ⚑ ⚑ ⚑ ⊙ ⚑ ⚑ ⚑
⚑ ⚑ ⚑ ⚑ ⚑ ⚑ ⚑
Nearest Town Hawick/Selkirk

HAWICK

Riverside Caravan Park, Hornshole
Bridge, Hawick, Borders, TD9 8SY
Tel: 01450 373785
Email: info@bordercaravans.co.uk
www.riversidehawick.co.uk
Pitches For A ⚐ ⚑ **Total** 40
Open Mar **to** Oct
Access Good **Site** Level
Nearest Bus Stop (Miles) Outside
On the banks of a river.
Facilities ⚙ ⚑ ⚑ ⚑ ⚑ ⊙ ⚑ ⚑ ⚑
⚑ ⚑ ⚑ ⚑ ⚑ ⚑
Nearest Town Hawick
Directions 1 mile from Hawick on the A698.
⚑ Carlisle

JEDBURGH

**Jedburgh Camping & Caravanning Club
Site,** Elliot Park, Jedburgh, Borders, TD8
6EF
Tel: 01835 863393
Email: jedburgh.site@thefriendlyclub.co.uk
www.campingandcaravanningclub.co.uk/
jedburgh
Pitches For A ⚐ ⚑ **Total** 60
Acreage 3 **Open** 21-Mar **to** 28-Oct
Access Good **Site** Level
Nearest Bus Stop (Miles) ¼
Quiet, secluded site bounded by the River
Jed. Ideal site for picturesque walks. STB 4
Star Graded and AA 3 Pennants. Non
members welcome. You can also call us on
0845 130 7633.
Facilities ⚑ ⚑ ⚑ ⚑ ⚑ ⊙ ⚑ ⚑ ⚑
⚑ ⚑ ⚑ ⚑ ⚑ ⚑
Nearest Town Jedburgh
Directions On the A68 Newcastle to
Edinburgh road, drive to the northern side of
Jedburgh and the entrance is opposite the
Edinburgh & Jedburgh Woollen Mills.
⚑ Berwick-upon-Tweed

JEDBURGH

**Lilliardsedge Holiday Park & Golf
Course,** Jedburgh, Scottish Borders, TD8
6TZ
Tel: 01835 830271
Email: bordercaravans@btconnect.com
www.lilliardsedgepark.co.uk

Pitches For A ⚐ ⚑ **Total** 40
Open Mar **to** 06-Nov
Access Good **Site** Level
Nearest Bus Stop (Miles) Outside
On St Cuthberts Way with a 9 hole golf
course on site. Fishing available locally.
Small tents only
Facilities ⚑ ⚑ ⚑ ⚑ ⚑ ⊙ ⚑ ⚑ ⚑
⚑ ⚑ ⚑ ⚑ ⚑ ⚑ ⚑ ⚑ ⚑
⚑
Nearest Town Jedburgh
Directions 5 miles north of Jedburgh on the
A68.
⚑ Berwick

KELSO

Kirkfield Caravan Park, Grafton Road,
Yetholm, Kelso, Scottish Borders, TD5
8RU
Tel: 01573 420346
Email: fiona@frankgibsonatv.co.uk
www.kirkfieldcaravansite.co.uk
Pitches For A ⚐ ⚑ **Total** 20
Open Apr **to** Oct
Access Good **Site** Level
Nearest Bus Stop (Miles) ¼
Situated in the Yetholm Loch Bird Nature
Reserve at the end of Penine Way and on St
Cuthberts Walk. Near a river and the Cheviot
Hills.
Facilities ⚑ ⚑ ⚑ ⚑ ⊙ ⚑ ⚑ ⚑ ⚑
Nearest Town Kelso
Directions From Kelso take the B6352 to
Yetholm
⚑ Berwick Upon Tweed

LAUDER

**Lauder Camping & Caravanning Club
Site,** Carfraemill, Oxton, Lauder, Borders,
TD2 6RA
Tel: 01578 750697
Email: lauder.site@thefriendlyclub.co.uk
www.campingandcaravanningclub.co.uk/
lauder
Pitches For A ⚐ ⚑ **Total** 60
Acreage 5 **Open** 18-Apr **to** 28-Oct
Access Good **Site** Level
Nearest Bus Stop (Miles) Outside
Situated 24 miles south of the vibrant city of
Edinburgh. Close to Thirlestane Castle and
a good fishing area. Self catering chalets also
available to let. STB 4 Star Graded and AA 3
Pennants. Non members welcome. You can
also call us on 0845 130 7633.
Facilities ⚑ ⚑ ⚑ ⚑ ⚑ ⊙ ⚑ ⚑ ⚑
⚑ ⚑ ⚑ ⚑ ⚑ ⚑ ⚑
Nearest Town Edinburgh
Directions From Lauder, at the roundabout
turn right onto the A697, at the Lodge Hotel
turn left and the site is on the right behind
Carfraemill Hotel.
⚑ Edinburgh

LAUDER

Thirlestane Castle Caravan Park,
Thirlestane Castle Park, Lauder, Borders,
TD2 6RU
Tel: 01578 718884
Email: thirlestanepark@btconnect.com
www.thirlestanecastlepark.co.uk
Pitches For A ⚐ ⚑ **Total** 60
Acreage 5 **Open** Apr **to** Sept
Access Good **Site** Lev/Slope
Nearest Bus Stop (Miles) ½
Ideal location for exploring the Border towns
and Edinburgh.
Facilities ⚑ ⚑ ⚑ ⚑ ⚑ ⊙ ⚑ ⚑ ⚑ ⚑ ⚑ ⚑
Nearest Town Lauder
Directions Well signposted off the A68.
⚑ Edinburgh

177

PEEBLES

Crossburn Caravan Park, Edinburgh Road, Peebles, Scottish Borders, EH45 8ED
Tel: 01721 720501
Email: enquiries@crossburncaravans.co.uk
www.crossburn-caravans.co.uk
Pitches For **Total** 50
Acreage 6 **Open** April/Easter **to** Oct
Access Good **Site** Level
Nearest Bus Stop (Miles) ¼
River nearby. Ideal touring base.
Facilities
Nearest Town Peebles
Directions ½ mile north of Peebles on the A703.
Edinburgh

STIRLING

ABERFOYLE

Trossachs Holiday Park, By Aberfoyle, Stirling, FK8 3SA
Tel: 01877 382614
Email: info@trossachsholidays.co.uk
www.trossachsholidays.co.uk
Pitches For **Total** 48
Open Mar **to** Oct
Access Good **Site** Level
Nearest Bus Stop (Miles) Outside
Stunning views in the heart of the Trossachs. USRVs by arrangement.
Facilities
Nearest Town Aberfoyle
Directions On the east side of the A81, 3 miles south of Aberfoyle.
Stirling

CALLANDER

Gart Caravan Park, Stirling Road, Callander, Stirling, FK17 8LE
Tel: 01877 330002
Email: enquiries@theholidaypark.co.uk
www.theholidaypark.co.uk
Pitches For **Total** 131
Acreage 26 **Open** Apr **to** 15-Oct
Access Good **Site** Level
Nearest Bus Stop (Miles) Outside
The ideal centre for walking, golf, fishing and exceptional for off-road cycling. Or you can simply relax and enjoy the scenery.
Facilities
Nearest Town Callander
Directions Situated on the main A84, 1 mile east of Callander.
Stirling

CALLANDER

Keltie Bridge Caravan Park, Callander, Stirling, FK17 8LQ
Tel: 01877 330606
Email: stay@keltiebridge.co.uk
Pitches For **Total** 50
Acreage 12 **Open** Apr **to** Oct
Access Good **Site** Level
Nearest Bus Stop (Miles) ¼
Well situated for exploring Loch Lomond and Trossachs National Park.
Facilities
Nearest Town Callander
Directions Well signposted just off the A84 from Doune towards Callander, 1 mile before Callander.
Dunblane

CALLANDER

Mains Farm Campsite, Mains Farm, Thornhill, Stirling, FK8 3QR
Tel: 01786 850605
www.mainsfarmwigwams.com
Pitches For **Total** 35
Acreage 5 **Open** 15-Mar **to** Oct
Access Good **Site** Lev/Slope
Nearest Bus Stop (Miles) ¼
Near to Loch Lomond National Park. Heated wooden Wigwams and real tepees available for hire.
Facilities
Nearest Town Stirling
Directions Leave the M9 at junc 10 and take the A84 sp Callander. After 3¾ miles fork left onto the A873 sp Aberfoyle & Thornhill. After 3¾ miles, in the village, turn left onto the B822 sp Kippen, the Site entrance is 300 yards on the right.
Stirling

CRIANLARICH

Glendochart Holiday Park, Luib, Crainlarich, Stirling, FK20 8QT
Tel: 01567 820637
Email: info@glendochart-caravanpark.co.uk
www.glendochart.co.com
Pitches For
Open Mar **to** Nov
Access - **Site** Level
Ideal for touring central highlands.
Facilities
Nearest Town Syirling
Directions Situated on A85 between Killin and Crianlarich.
Crianlarich

DRYMEN

Milarrochy Bay Camping & Caravanning Club Site, Milarrochy Bay, Balmaha, Near Drymen, Stirling, G63 0AL
Tel: 01360 870236
Email: milarrochy.bay.site@thefriendlyclub.co.uk
www.campingandcaravanningclub.co.uk/milarrochybay
Pitches For **Total** 150
Acreage 12 **Open** 21-Mar **to** 28-Oct
Access Good **Site** Level
On the east bank of Loch Lomond, in the heart of Rob Roy country. Near Queen Elizabeth Forest Park. Boat launching available from site. STB 4 Star Graded and AA 4 Pennants. Non members welcome. You can also call us on 0845 130 7633.
Facilities
Nearest Town Loch Lomond
Directions From the A811 Balloch to Stirling road, take the Drymen turnoff. In Drymen turn onto the B837 (junction is by the War Memorial) to Balmaha. After approx. 5 miles the road turns sharp right up a steep hill, the site is approx. 1½ miles.
Balloch

FINTRY

Balgair Castle Holiday Park, Overglinns, Fintry, Stirling, G63 0LP
Tel: 01360 860399
Email: balgaircastle@holiday-parks.co.uk
www.holiday-parks.co.uk
Pitches For **Total** 33
Acreage 28 **Open** Apr **to** Oct
Access Good **Site** Level
On the banks of the River Endrick. Close to Blair Drummond Safari Park and Stirling Castle.
Facilities
Nearest Town Balfron
Directions From Stirling take the A811 west towards Drymen, then take the B822 south to Fintry. After Balgair Castle Holiday Park sign turn right and follow road down into Park reception, on right hand side as you enter.
Stirling

KILLIN

Cruachan Caravan Park, Killin, Stirling, FK21 8TY
Tel: 01567 820302
Email: enquiries@cruachanfarm.co.uk
www.cruachanfarm.co.uk
Pitches For **Total** 55
Acreage 10 **Open** 15-Mar **to** Oct
Access Good **Site** Lev/Slope
Working farm set in countryside. Central location for touring, climbing, golf and fishing. Octolodges now available for rent.
Facilities
Nearest Town Killin
Directions 3 miles east of Killin on the A827.
Crianlarich

KILLIN

High Creagan Caravan Park, Killin, Stirling, FK21 8TX
Tel: 01567 820449/07786880016
Pitches For **Total** 30
Acreage 7 **Open** Mar **to** Oct
Access Good **Site** Level
Nearest Bus Stop (Miles) Outside
Facilities
Directions 2½ miles east of Killin on the left of the A827.
Crianlarich

KILLIN

Maragowan Caravan Club Site, Aberfeldy Road, Killin, Stirling, FK21 8TN
Tel: 01567 820245
www.caravanclub.co.uk
Pitches For **Total** 100
Acreage 8½ **Open** Mar **to** Nov
Access Good **Site** Level
Nearest Bus Stop (Miles) ½
On the banks of the River Lochay for salmon and trout fishing. Ideal for walkers and wildlife lovers. Close to Archray Forest, Scottish Wool Centre and two Visitor Centres. Non members welcome. Booking essential.
Facilities
Nearest Town Killin
Directions Just off the A827 just outside Killin Village.
Killin

LOCHEARNHEAD

Balquhidder Braes Holiday Park, Balquhidder Station, Lochearnhead, Stirling, FK19 8NX
Tel: 01567 830293
Email: enquiries@balquhidderbraes.co.uk
www.balquhidderbraes.co.uk
Pitches For **Total** 4
Acreage 2 **Open** Mar **to** Oct
Access Good **Site** Level
Nearest Bus Stop (Miles) Outside
Nature trail on site.
Facilities

Nearest Town Lochearnhead
Directions From Stirling take the A84 and follow signs for Callander. 1 mile south of Lochearnhead.
≠ Stirling

STIRLING

Witches Craig Caravan & Camping Park, Blairlogie, Stirling, Stirling, FK9 5PX
Tel: 01786 474947
Email: info@witchescraig.co.uk
www.witchescraig.co.uk
Pitches For ▲ ⚲ ⛺ ⛺ Total 60
Acreage 5 **Open** Apr **to** Oct
Access Good **Site** Level
Nearest Bus Stop (Miles) Outside
Situated at the foot of the Ochil Hills with beautiful scenery and many local historical sites. Good hill walking. Ideal touring centre.
Facilities 🛁 ⚷ 🚽 ▥ ⤳ ⊙ ⤴ ⚑ ⛽
🏪 🎯 🛝 🔥 ⤳ ⊟ ⋇ ⚓ ☎
Nearest Town Stirling
Directions 3 miles east of Stirling town centre on the A91 Stirling to St. Andrews road.
≠ Stirling

WESTERN ISLES
BENBECULA

Shell Bay Caravan & Camping Park, Liniclate, Creagorry, Benbecula, Outer Hebrides, Western Isles, HS7 5PJ
Tel: 01870 602447
Email: shellbaylin@aol.com
Pitches For ▲ ⚲ ⛺ ⛺ Total 25
Acreage 3½ **Open** Apr **to** Oct
Access Good **Site** Level
Nearest Bus Stop (Miles) Outside
Near beach, Birds, Otters, Seals, Flowers.
Facilities 🛁 ⚷ 🚽 ▥ ⤳ ⊙ ⤴ ⊟ ⚑ ⛽

HARRIS

Minch View Campsite 10 Drinishader, Isle of Harris, Western Isles, HS3 3DX
Tel: 01859 511207
Email: cath.macdonald@btinternet.com
Pitches For ▲ ⚲ ⛺ Total 8
Acreage 3 **Open** Apr **to** Sept
Access Good **Site** Level
Nearest Bus Stop (Miles) Outside
Friendly, family run site, situated between the sea and a fresh water loch. Beautiful beaches, excellent walking. Central for touring the Western Isles.
Facilities ⚷ ▣ ▥ ⤳ ⤴ ⊙ ⤴ ⚑ ⛽
🏪 ☎⤴✔ ⋇ ⚓
Nearest Town Tarbert
Directions 5 miles south east of Tarbert Ferry Port. Turn off the A859 into Golden Road to Drinishader. Site is well signposted.

ISLE OF LEWIS

Uig Sands Campsite, 6 Ardoil, Timsgearraidh, Isle of Lewis, Western Isles, HS2 9EU
Pitches For ▲ ⚲ Total 20
Acreage 1 **Open** -
Access Good **Site** l
Nearest Bus Stop (Miles) ½
Ideal touring.
Facilities 🛁 ⚷ ▥ ▣ ⤳ ⊟ ⚑ ⛽ ⚓⤴
Nearest Town Stornoway
Directions 38 miles from Stornoway.

NORTH SHAWBOST

Eilean Fraoich Caravan & Camping Park, North Shawbost, Isle of Lewis, Western Isles, HS2 9BQ
Tel: 01851 710504
Email: eileanfraoich@btinternet.com
www.eileanfraoich.co.uk
Pitches For ▲ ⚲ ⛺ Total 25
Open May **to** Oct
Access Good **Site** Level
Nearest Bus Stop (Miles) Outside
Nera to beaches and historical sites. Ideal for hill walking.
Facilities 🛁 ⚷ ▣ ▥ ⤳ ⊙ ⤴ ⚑ ⛽
🏪 🎯 🛝 ☎⤴⊟ ⋇
Nearest Town Stornoway
Directions From Stornoway take the A857 to Barvas, turn left onto the A858 for approx. 6 miles, turn left at Shawbost School.

NORTHERN IRELAND
ANTRIM
BALLYCASTLE

Watertop Farm, 188 Cushendall Road, Ballycastle, Co. Antrim, BT54 6RN
Tel: 028 2076 2576
Email: watertopfarm@aol.com
www.watertopfarm.co.uk
Pitches For ▲ ⚲ ⛺ ⛺ Total 17
Open 10-Apr **to** Oct
On a working farm (open July and August) with pony trekking, fishing, boating, pedal go-karts, quad train, assault course, museum, small animals and farm tours on the paddiwagon. Opposite Ballypatrick Forest, ideal for walking and birdwatching. Positioned 4th in the Top 50 Campsites in the UK.
Facilities ⚷ ▥ ▣ ⤳ ⊙ ⤴ ⚑
⋇ ⚓⤴⊟ ⋇
Directions 18 miles east of Giants Causeway on the A2 between Ballycastle and Cushendall. 6 miles from Ballycastle, signposted.

BALLYMONEY

Drumaheglis Marina & Caravan Park, 36 Glenstall Road, Ballymoney, Co. Antrim, BT53 7QN
Tel: 028 2766 0280/2766 0227
Email: drumaheglis@ballymoney.gov.uk
www.ballymoney.gov.uk
Pitches For ▲ ⚲ ⛺ Total 65
Open 17-Mar **to** Oct

Situated on a boat park and 32 berth marina on the Causeway coastal route. Volley Ball, picnic areas, table tennis and nature walk on site.
Facilities
⚷ ▥ ⤳ ⊙ ⤴ ⊟ 🛝 🎯 ⚑ ⋇⤴⊟ ☎
Directions Off the A26 between Ballymoney and Coleraine. Turn left at Seacon crossroads and follow signs for Drumaheglis Marina.

BUSHMILLS

Ballyness Caravan Park, 40 Castlecatt Road, Bushmills, Co. Antrim, BT57 8TN
Email: info@ballynesscaravanpark.com
www.ballynesscaravanpark.com
Pitches For ⚲ ⛺ ⛺ Total 48
Acreage 16 **Open** Mar **to** Oct
Access Good **Site** Lev/Slope
Multi award winning Park on the spectacular North Coast. Well maintained, quiet Park in a beautiful location. Close to Giants Causeway and Old Bushmills Distillery. AA 5 Pennants, 5 Stars and David Bellamy Gold Award.
Facilities 🛁 ⚷ ▣ ▥ ⤳ ⤴ ⊙ ⤴ ⚑ ⛽
🏪 🎯 🛝 ☎⤴⊟ ☎
Nearest Town Bushmills
Directions On the B66, ½ a mile south of Bushmills.
≠ Coleraine

LARNE

Carnfunnock Country Park, Coast Road, Ballygally, Larne, Co. Antrim, BT40 2QG
Tel: 028 2827 0541/2826 0088
Email: carnfunnock@larne.gov.uk
www.larne.gov.uk/carnfunnock
Pitches For ▲ ⚲ ⛺ Total 39
Open 15-Mar **to** 03-Nov
Set within a country park with a walled garden, a maze, family fun zone (mini golf, bouncy castle, bungee run, laser clay pigeon shooting and miniature railway), outdoor adventure playground, mini cars, trampolines and golfing activities, professional driving range and golf acadamy, Picnic and barbecue areas, gift and coffee shop. Regular weekend events.
Facilities 🛁 ⚷ ▣ ▥ ⤳ ⊙ ⊟ ⚑
⚓⋇ ⚓⤴⊟
Nearest Town Larne
Directions On the A2 Coast Road, 3½ miles north of Larne between Drains Bay and Ballygally.

PORTRUSH

Ballymacrea Touring Caravan Park, 220 Ballybogey Road, Portrush, Co. Antrim, BT56 8NE
Tel: 028 7082 4507
Email:
info@ballymacreacaravanpark.co.uk
www.ballymacreacaravanpark.co.uk
Pitches For ⚲ ⛺ Total 45
Acreage 3½ **Open** Mar **to** Oct
Access Good **Site** Level
Nearest Bus Stop (Miles) 1

Rural location, close to all tourist amenities and places of interest on the Causeway Coast.
Facilities ⬚⬚⬚⬚⬚⬚⬚⬚⬚⬚⬚
⬚⬚⬚⬚⬚⬚⬚⬚⬚
Nearest Town Portrush
Directions On the B62 Ballymoney to Portrush road, approx 1½ miles from Portrush, signposted.
⚇ Portrush

ARMAGH
LURGAN
Kinnego Marina Caravan Park, Kinnego Marina, Oxford Island, Lurgan, Co. Armagh, BT66 6WJ
Tel: 02838 32 7573
Email: kinnego.marina@craigavon.gov.uk
Pitches For 🅰 ⬚ ⬚ **Total** 20
Open April **to** Oct
Access Good **Site** Level
Nearest Bus Stop (Miles) ½
On the shores of Lough Neagh within the National Nature Reserve.
Facilities ⬚⬚⬚⬚⬚⬚⬚⬚⬚
⬚⬚⬚⬚⬚⬚⬚
Nearest Town Lurgan
Directions Signposted Oxford Island from the M1 junction 10.
⚇ Lurgan

DOWN
HILLSBOROUGH
Lakeside View Caravan & Camping Park, 71 Magheraconluce Road, Hillsborough, Co. Down, BT26 6PR
Tel: 028 9268 2098
Email: lakeside-view@hotmail.co.uk
www.lakeside-view.8m.com
Pitches For 🅰 ⬚ ⬚ **Total** 30
Open Easter **to** Oct
Quiet countryside park with views of lake and mountains. Half hours drive to Belfast. Caravans available for rent.
Facilities ⬚⬚⬚⬚⬚⬚⬚⬚⬚⬚
Directions From the M1 and A1 travel to Hillsborough Village. Take the B177 Ballynahinch road for 3 miles, signposted.

KILLYLEAGH
Delamont Country Park Camping & Caravanning Club Site, Delamont Country Park, Downpatrick Road, Killyleagh, Co. Down, BT30 9TZ
Tel: 028 4482 1833
Email:
delamont.site@thefriendlyclub.co.uk
www.campingandcaravanningclub.co.uk/delamont
Pitches For 🅰 ⬚ ⬚ ⬚ **Total** 63
Acreage 4 **Open** 15-Mar **to** 12-Nov
Access Good **Site** Level
Nearest Bus Stop (Miles) ¼
On the shores of Strangford Lough within a country park (free entry for campers). Many walks, historical sites and cultural landmarks. David Bellamy Silver Award. Non members welcome. You can also call us on 0845 130 7633.
Facilities ⬚⬚⬚⬚⬚⬚⬚⬚⬚
⬚⬚⬚⬚⬚⬚
Nearest Town Downpatrick
Directions On the A22 1 mile south of Killyleagh and 4 miles north of Downpatrick.

NEWCASTLE
Murlough Cottage Caravan Park, 180-182 Dundrum Road, Newcastle, Co. Down, BT33 0LN
Tel: 028 4372 2906/4372 3184
Email: info@murloughcottage.com
www.murloughcottage.com
Pitches For ⬚ ⬚ **Total** 26
Open March **to** Oct
Idyllic location in an area of outstanding natural beauty. A warm and friendly welcome awaits you!
Facilities ⬚⬚⬚⬚⬚⬚⬚⬚⬚
⬚⬚⬚⬚⬚⬚⬚⬚
Directions On the A24 2 miles north of Newcastle. Signposted.

FERMANAGH
LISNARICK
Castle Archdale Caravan Park, Lisnarick, Irvinestown, Co. Fermanagh, BT94 1PP
Tel: 028 6862 1333
Email: bookings@castlearchdale.com
www.castlearchdale.com
Pitches For 🅰 ⬚ ⬚ **Total** 158
Open April **to** Oct
Situated on the shores of Lough Erne and set amongst thousands of acres of forest park on a former WWII airbase. Close to Donegal and Sligo. Licensed restaurant, take-away, shop and play park. Seasonal opening times.
Facilities ⬚⬚⬚⬚⬚⬚⬚⬚⬚⬚⬚⬚
Directions Signposted off the B82 Enniskillen to Kesh road, 10 miles north of Enniskillen.

LISNARICK
Drumhoney Caravan Park, Lisnarick, Irvinestown, Co. Fermanagh, BT94 1NB
Tel: 028 6862 1892
Email: info@drumhoneyholidaypark.com
www.drumhoneyholidaypark.com
Pitches For 🅰 ⬚ ⬚ ⬚ **Total** 40
Acreage 30 **Open** Apr **to** Oct
Access Good **Site** Sloping
Nearest Bus Stop (Miles) ½
Millenium Forest walk beside Lough Erne ½ mile from site, ideal family base for childrens open farm train on park.
Facilities ⬚⬚⬚⬚⬚⬚⬚⬚⬚⬚
⬚⬚⬚⬚⬚⬚⬚⬚⬚⬚⬚
Nearest Town Irvinestone
Directions Off the B82, 10 miles north of Enniskillen, signposted.

LONDONDERRY
BENONE
Benone Tourist Complex, 53 Benone Avenue, Limavady, Co. Londonderry, BT49 0LQ
Tel: 028 7775 0555
Email: benone.complex@limavady.gov.uk
www.limavady.gov.uk
Pitches For 🅰 ⬚ ⬚ ⬚ **Total** 101
Acreage 11 **Open** Apr **to** Sept
Access Good **Site** Level
Nearest Bus Stop (Miles) ½
Two outside heated splash pools (seasonal), golf practice range, putting and bowling greens (admission fee per activity). Cafe (seasonal).
Facilities ⬚⬚⬚⬚⬚⬚⬚⬚⬚
⬚⬚⬚⬚⬚⬚⬚⬚
Nearest Town Limavady
Directions On the A2 coast road, 12 miles from Limavady and 10 miles from Coleraine.
⚇ Castlerock

TYRONE
OMAGH
Sperrin Mountains Caravan Park, 1 Lisnaharney Road, Omagh, Co. Tyrone, BT79 7UG
Tel: 028 8166 2288
Email: mail@sperrincottages.com
www.sperrincottages.com
Pitches For 🅰 ⬚ ⬚ ⬚ **Total** 24
Acreage 3 **Open** Easter **to** Sept
Access Good **Site** Level
Nearest Bus Stop (Miles) Outside Ulster American Folk Park.
Facilities ⬚⬚⬚⬚⬚⬚⬚⬚
⬚⬚⬚⬚⬚⬚⬚
Nearest Town Omagh
Directions On the B48, signposted between Omagh and Gorin.

REPUBLIC OF IRELAND
CAVAN
VIRGINIA
Lough Ramor Caravan & Camping Park, Ryefield, Virginia, Co. Cavan,
Tel: 00 87 282 5976
Email: loughramor@eircom.net
Pitches For 🅰 ⬚ ⬚ **Total** 22
Acreage 5½ **Open** 19-Jun **to** 01-Sep

On the shores of the scenic Lough Ramor for fishing and boating (boat hire on site). Pubs, restaurants and shops close by. Historical Newgrange, Loughcrew and Hill of Tara nearby.
Facilities ⬚⬚⬚⬚⬚⬚⬚⬚
Directions Just off the N3 south of Virginia.

CLARE
COROFIN
Corofin Village, Main Street, Corofin, Co. Clare,
Tel: 00 65 683 7683
Email: corohost@iol.ie
www.corofincamping.com
Pitches For 🅰 ⬚ ⬚ **Total** 20
Acreage 1¼ **Open** 10-Apr **to** Sept

Family run, sheltered site near to Burren and the Cliffs of Moher. 7 fishing lakes in the area, also good walking and cycling.
Facilities ⬚⬚⬚⬚⬚⬚⬚⬚
Directions From Shannon Airport take the N18, N85 and R476.

DOOLIN
Nagles Doolin Camping & Caravan Park, Doolin, Co. Clare,
Tel: 00 65 707 4458
Email: ken@doolincamping.com
www.doolincamping.com
Pitches For 🅰 ⬚ ⬚ ⬚ **Total** 99
Acreage 9¾ **Open** Mid Mar **to** Mid Oct
Situated on the edge of the Atlantic between the Cliffs of Moher and the Burren. Only 100 metres from Doolin Pier, ferry port for boats to Aran Islands. Shop only open from June BH weekend to the end of August. Lovely coastal walks and pot holing in the area.
Facilities ⬚⬚⬚⬚⬚⬚⬚⬚
⬚⬚⬚⬚⬚⬚⬚⬚
Directions From Lisdoonvarna go towards Cliffs of Moher, turn right for Doolin and follow signs to Doolin Pier. Park is situated 100m from Doolin Pier.

DOOLIN

O'Connors Riverside Camping & Caravan Park, Doolin, Co. Clare,
Tel: 00 65 707 4498
Email: joan@oconnorsdoolin.com
www.oconnorsdoolin.com
Pitches For ▲ ⊞ ⚏ ⛺ ⛌ **Total** 100
Acreage 6¼ **Open** Apr **to** Sept
In the heart of Doolin in a unique setting overlooking the Aille River. Small and friendly family run Park on a farm. 3 Star Graded Park. Guesthouse on site (3 Stars).
Facilities ♿ ∮ ⊟ ⊞ ᴪ ℙ ⊙ ⌷ ⊸ ◨ ▣ ☂
⊠ ᛚ ⊞ ♠ ⛌ ▤ ✓ ☂
Directions From the N67 turn for Doolin, go straight across the main crossroads (Hotal Doolin on the right), go over the Aille River Bridge and the Park is on the left behind O'Connors Guesthouse.

KILKEE

Green Acres Caravan & Camping Park, Doonaha, Kilkee, Co. Clare,
Tel: 00 65 905 7011
Pitches For ▲ ⊞ ⚏ ⛺ ⛌ **Total** 40
Acreage 17 **Open** Apr **to** Sept
Delightful setting on the shores of the River Shannon, with lovely beaches and spectacular coastal views. Dolphin watch at Carrigaholt (5 minutes drive).
Facilities ∮ ⎕ ⊟ ⊞ ᴪ ℙ ⊙ ⌷ ⊸ ◨ ▣ ☂
✦⛌
Directions From Kilrush take the N67 to Kilkee, then follow signs from the R487.

MOUNTSHANNON

Lakeside Holiday Park, Dooras, Mountshannon, Co. Clare,
Tel: 00 61 927225
Email: lakesidecamping@eircom.net
www.lakesideireland.com
Pitches For ▲ ⊞ ⚏ ⛺ ⛌ **Total** 45
Acreage 17¾ **Open** May **to** 01-Oct

Unique, spacious Park situated on the shores of Lough Derg, Irelands finest lake. Motor boats, rowing boats, kayaks, swimming, fishing, tennis, soccer and table tennis on site. NO dogs during July and August.
Facilities ∮ ⊞ ᴪ ℙ ⊙ ◨ ⊖ ⊠ ⊞ ᴪ ☂
Directions On the R352, go through Mountshannon Village and take the first turn right (signposted).

CORK

BANTRY

Dunbeacon Camping Site, Durrus, Bantry, Co. Cork,
Tel: 00 27 62851
Email: julaclem@gmail.com
Pitches For ▲ ⊞ ⚏ **Total** 20
Acreage 2½ **Open** June **to** Sept
Overlooking Dunmanus Bay. Trees and shrubs create individual private pitches. Ideal for exploring Mizen and Sheep's Head Peninsulas.
Facilities ∮ ⊞ ᴪ ℙ ⊸ ⊖⛌
Directions From Bantry take the R591 through Durras Village, Site is 3 miles on the left hand side.

BANTRY

Eagle Point Camping, Ballylickey, Bantry, West Cork, Co. Cork,
Tel: 00 27 50630
Email: eaglepointcamping@eircom.net
www.eaglepointcamping.com
Pitches For ▲ ⊞ ⚏ **Total** 125
Acreage 19¾ **Open** 24-Apr **to** 28-Sep

On a peninsula with a safe and sheltered coastline. Pebbled beaches suitable for watersports, swimming and fishing. Tennis on site. Shop and petrol station at park entrance. No commercial vehicles. Booking essential.
Facilities ∮ ⊞ ᴪ ℙ ⊙ ◨
⊠ ◨ ⊞ ♠ ⛌ ☑ ⛌ ☂
Directions Take the N71 from Cork towards Bandon to Glengarriff, then take the R586 to Bantry. Opposite Cronins Petrol Station.

BEARA

Hungry Hill Camping Site, Adrigole Harbour, Beara, Co. Cork,
Tel: 00 27 60228
Email: info@hungryhilllodge.com
www.hungryhilllodge.com
Pitches For ▲ ⊞ ⚏ ⛺ ⛌ **Total** 23
Acreage 7½ **Open** Mar **to** Oct

At the foot of Healy Pass in a rural setting at Adrigole, the jewel of Beara Peninsula. Pub on site, shop adjacent.
Facilities ∮ ⊞ ᴪ ℙ ⊸ ◨ 𝄋 ⚑ ☒ ♈⛌◨
Directions West of Glengarriff on the R572.

BLARNEY

Blarney Caravan & Camping Park, Stone View, Blarney, Co. Cork,
Tel: 00 21 451 6519
Email: conquill@camping-ireland.ie
www.blarneycaravanpark.com
Pitches For ▲ ⊞ ⚏ ⛺ ⛌ **Total** 40
Acreage 3 **Open** April **to** 29-Oct
Award winning Park only 5 miles from the city of Cork. Sheltered, secluded and gently sloping family run park with views towards the famous Blarney Castle. 18 hole pitch 'n' putt on site. Plenty of attractions nearby. NO commercial vehicles.
Facilities ∮ ⊟ ⊞ ᴪ ℙ ⊸
⊠ ◨ ⊖ ⊞ ⛌◨
Directions From the N25 take the N8 towards Cork. Turn onto the N20 and then turn right onto the R617.

CARRIGTWOHILL

Jasmine Villa Caravan & Camping Park, Carrigtwohill, Co. Cork,
Tel: 00 21 488 3234
Pitches For ▲ ⊞ ⚏ **Total** 17
Acreage 1¼ **Open** All Year

Close to all amenities and beaches.
Facilities ∮ ⛌
Directions On the N25 Cork to Rosslare road, 1 mile from Carrigtwohill and 4 miles from Midleton.

CASTLETOWNBERE

Berehaven Camper & Amenity Park, Filane, Castletownbere, Co. Cork,
Tel: 00 27 71957/70700
Email: info@berehavengolf.com
www.berehavengolf.com
Pitches For ▲ ⊞ ⚏ **Total** 22
Acreage 2½ **Open** All Year

Set amidst mountain scenery on the shores of Bantry Bay, breathtakingly beautiful. Ideal for fishing, hill walking, canoeing and golf. Very short walk to the ferry for Bere Island.
Facilities ∮ ⊞ ᴪ ℙ ⊸ ◨ 𝄋 ⚑ ☒ ✗ ⛌ ⛌

CLONAKILTY

Desert House Caravan & Camping Park, Coast Road, Clonakilty, Co. Cork,
Tel: 00 23 883 3331
Email: deserthouse@eircom.net
Pitches For ▲ ⊞ ⚏ ⛺ ⛌ **Total** 36

Acreage 4 **Open** May **to** Sept
Small, family run Park on a dairy farm overlooking Clonakilty Bay. Sandy beaches and model railway village nearby. Take-away food available.
Facilities ∮ ⊞ ᴪ ℙ ⊸ ◨ 𝄋 ⊞ ▤⛌◨
Directions Take the N71 from Cork and follow signs.

FERMOY

Blackwater Valley Caravan & Camping Park, Mallow Road, Fermoy, Co. Cork,
Tel: 00 25 32147
Email: blackwatervalleycaravanpark@gmail.com
www.blackwatervalleycaravanpark.ie
Pitches For ▲ ⊞ ⚏ **Total** 30
Acreage 2 **Open** 15-Mar **to** Oct
Adjacent to Fermoy Town Park with its swimming pool and childrens play area. Fishing on site. No commercial vehicles.
Facilities ∮ ⊞ ᴪ ℙ ⊸ ◨ ⊙ ⊞ ♠ ⛌ ⛌
Directions From the M8/N8 take the R639 to Fermoy Town. Park is 100 metres from the town on the N72.

GLANDORE

The Meadow Camping Park, Glandore, Co. Cork,
Tel: 00 28 33280
Email: meadowcamping@eircom.net
Pitches For ▲ ⊞ ⚏ **Total** 19
Acreage 2½ **Open** Easter **to** 15-Sep
Family run park providing peace and tranquility, yet only 1 mile from the village. Three environmental awards. Near the beach. 10 minute drive to Union Hall for fresh fish, fishing or a whale watching trip.
Facilities ∮ ⊟ ⊞ ᴪ ℙ ⊸ ◨ 𝄋⛌
Directions From the N71 take the R597 to Glandore.

GLENGARRIFF

Dowlings Caravan & Camping Park, Castletownbere Road, Glengarriff, Co. Cork,
Tel: 00 27 63154
Email: nickydee@eircom.net
Pitches For ▲ ⊞ ⚏ ⛺ ⛌ **Total** 90
Acreage 12 **Open** Apr **to** Oct

Spacious, well maintained Park situated between mountains and the sea. Top standard amenities. Take-away food available. Abundant leisure pursuits in the area. Ideal for touring West Cork and South Kerry.
Facilities ∮ ⊟ ⊞ ᴪ ℙ ⊸
⊠ ᛚ ⊙ ▤ ⊞ ♠ ▤⛌◨
Directions Leave Glengarriff on the R572 towards Castletownbere, Park is 1 mile.

KINSALE

Garrettstown House Holiday Park, Kinsale, Co. Cork,
Tel: 00 21 477 8156
Email: reception@garrettstownhouse.com
www.garrettstownhouse.com
Pitches For ▲ ⊞ ⚏ **Total** 60
Acreage 19¾ **Open** May **to** 06-Sep

Set within the grounds of an 18th Century Estate with top class facilities. Childrens Club and family discos. Crazy golf, snooker and tennis on site. Close to two Blue Flag beaches. Take-away food available. Seal, dolphin and whale watching locally. 6 miles from Kinsale with its numerous attractions
Facilities ∮ ⊟ ⊞ ᴪ ℙ ⊸ ◨
⊠ ᛚ ⊙ ⊖ ⊞ ⊞ ▤⛌
Directions 6 miles from Kinsale on the R600.

ROSSCARBERY

O'Riordans Caravan Park, Owenahincha, Rosscarbery, Co. Cork,
Tel: 00 21 454 1825
Pitches For A ⛺ 🚐 **Total** 16
Acreage 3¾ **Open** All Year
Family run Park beside a sandy beach. Adjacent to Castlefreke Woods. Modern mobile home available for hire.
Facilities ∮ ⬚⬚ 🚻 🛉 🅿 ⬚
Directions Take the N71 to Clonakilty then to Rosscarbery.

SKIBBEREEN

The Hideaway Camping & Caravan Park, Skibbereen, Co. Cork,
Tel: 00 28 21254 28 33280
Email: skibbereencamping@eircom.net
Pitches For A ⛺ 🚐 🚐 **Total** 60
Acreage 5 **Open** Easter **to** 15-Sep
Rural setting, just a 10 minute walk to the market town of Skibbereen.
Facilities ∮ ⬚⬚ 🛉 🅿 🚿 ⬚ ⬚ ⬚ ⬚ ⬚ ⬚ ⬚
Directions ½ a mile from Skibbereen town centre on the R596 towards Castletownsend.

TIMOLEAGUE

Sexton's Caravan & Camping Park, R600 Clonakilty Road, Timoleague, Co. Cork,
Tel: 00 88 46347/87 220 8088
Email: info.sextons@gmail.com
www.sextonscamping.com
Pitches For A ⛺ 🚐 🚐 **Total** 30
Acreage 4 **Open** 15-Mar **to** 30-Oct
Situated in countryside, yet only a 5 minute drive to beaches and family activities. Dog friendly site. Breakfast available. Free Wi-Fi. Groups welcome. Find us on Facebook.
Facilities ∮ 🅵 ⬚⬚ 🛉 🅿 ⊙ 🍴 🚻 ⬚ ⬚
🚿 ⬚ ⬚ ⬚ ⬚ ⬚ ⬚ ⬚ ⬚ ⬚ ⬚ ⬚ ⬚ ⬚ 🚲 ⬚ ⬚
Directions Just off the R600.

DONEGAL

CARRIGART

Caseys Caravan Site, Downings, Letterkenny, Carrigart, Co. Donegal,
Tel: 00 74 915 5376
Pitches For A ⛺ 🚐 🚐 **Total** 78
Acreage 19¾ **Open** Apr **to** Sept
On the edge of Sheephaven Bay in the fishing village of Downings. Bordered by a safe sandy beach. 200 yards from shops, pubs and a hotel. Two 18 hole links championship golf courses in ¼ mile. Interesting walks and drives.
Facilities ⬚ ∮ ⬚⬚ 🛉 🅿 ⊙ ⬚ ⬚ ⬚ 🚻

DUNGLOE

Dungloe Touring Caravan Park, Carnmore Road, Dungloe, Co. Donegal,
Tel: 00 74 95 21021
Email: chasg14@gmail.com
www.dungloecaravanpark.com
Pitches For ⛺ 🚐 **Total** 25
Acreage 2 **Open** Easter Weekend **to** Mid Sept
Access Good **Site** Level
Nearest Bus Stop (Miles) ¼
In the village of Dungloe with pubs, restaurants and supermarkets all just a ten minute walk away. Dungloe is on a coastal bay with beaches within 5km.
Facilities ∮ 🅵 ⬚⬚ 🛉 🅿 ⊙ ⬚ ⬚ 🍴 ⬚ ⬚ ⬚ ⬚
Nearest Town Dungloe
Directions In the town, at the N56 roundabout junction, 200 metres from Main Street.

DUBLIN

CLONDALKIN

Camac Valley Tourist Caravan & Camping Park, Green Isle Road, Clondalkin, Co. Dublin,
Tel: 00 1464 0644
Email: info@camacvalley.com
www.camacvalley.com
Pitches For A ⛺ 🚐 🚐 🚐 **Total** 163
Acreage 37 **Open** All Year
Spacious premier park with top class facilities. Adjoining Corkagh Park with 300 acres of fishing lakes and playgrounds, and is ideal for walking.
Facilities ∮ 🅷 ⬚⬚ 🛉 🅿 ⬚
⬚ 🚿 ⬚ ⬚ ⬚ ⬚ ⬚ 🍴 ⬚ ⬚ 🛜
Directions Off the N7 beside Corkagh Park near Clondalkin Village.

RUSH

North Beach Caravan & Camping Park, North Beach, Rush, Co. Dublin,
Tel: 00 1843 7131
Email: info@northbeach.ie
www.northbeach.ie
Pitches For A ⛺ 🚐 🚐 🚐 **Total** 64
Acreage 4½ **Open** Apr **to** Sept
Plenty of amenities in the village. Ideal base for visiting Dublin.
Facilities ∮ ⬚⬚ 🛉 🅿 ⬚ ⬚ 🍴
Directions Leave the M1 signposted Rush. Leave the R132 at the Esso, drive along Rush main street and at the third set of traffic lights turn left, after 100 metres turn right.

GALWAY

CLIFDEN

Shanaheever Campsite & Caravan Park, Shanaheever, Westport Road, Clifden, Co. Galway,
Tel: 00 95 22150/95 21078
Email: info@clifdencamping.com
www.clifdencamping.com
Pitches For A ⛺ 🚐 **Total** 42
Acreage 2½ **Open** 14-Apr **to** Sept
In a sheltered valley at the foot of Twelve Bens but within a few minutes drive of the sea. 15 minute walk to Clifden, the capital of Connemara.
Facilities ∮ ⬚⬚ 🛉 🅿 ⬚ 🍴 🚿 ⬚ 🍴 🛉
Directions From Galway take the N59 through Clifden to Westport. Turn right at the AIB Bank (on the left), Park is first turn right after the lake.

GALWAY CITY

Galway City East Caravan & Camping Park, Ballyloughane Beach, Renmore, Co. Galway,
Tel: 00 91 752029
Email: galwcamp@iol.ie
Pitches For A ⛺ 🚐 🚐 **Total** 45
Acreage 4 **Open** 15-May **to** 01-Sep
Quiet, family run park with a high standard of cleanliness and security. Beside a sandy beach with scenic walks and panoramic views of Galway Bay. Close to the city centre and all amenities.
Facilities ∮ ⬚⬚ 🛉 🅿 ⬚ ⬚ 🍴 🛉
Directions Approaching the city, at the first roundabout take exit for 'Galway City East - Merlin Park'. At Skerritt roundabout follow city centre route and take next turn left at Dawn Dairies.

LEENANE CONNEMARA

Connemara Caravan & Camping Park, Lettergesh Renvyle, Leenane, Connemara, Co. Galway,
Tel: 00 95 43406

Pitches For A ⛺ 🚐 **Total** 36
Acreage 5 **Open** May **to** Sept
Dolphins often seen from the site. Sandy beaches. National Park & Adventure Centre and a diving centre close by.
Facilities ⬚⬚ 🛉 🅿 ⬚ ⬚ 🚿 ⬚ 🍴 ⬚ 🛉
Directions 5 miles south of Leenane, turn right off the main Westport to Clifden road.

RENVYLE

Renvyle Beach Caravan & Camping Park, Renvyle Peninsula, Connemara, Co. Galway,
Tel: 00 95 43462
Email: renvylebeachcaravanpark@gmail.com
www.renvylebeachcaravanpark.com
Pitches For A ⛺ 🚐 **Total** 36
Acreage 6¼ **Open** Apr **to** Sept
Scenic park with direct access to the beach. High standard of cleanliness. 10 minute walk to shops, pubs and restaurants. Holiday Cottages available for hire. NO Dogs July and August.
Facilities ∮ ⬚⬚ 🛉 🅿 ⬚ ⬚ 🍴 🛉
Directions Signposted in Tullycross.

SALTHILL

Salthill Caravan Park, Salthill, Co. Galway,
Tel: 00 91 523972
Email: info@salthillcaravanpark.com
www.salthillcaravanpark.com
Pitches For A ⛺ 🚐 🚐 **Total** 70
Acreage 19¾ **Open** Easter **to** Sept
Family run Park on the shores of Galway Bay with stunning views of of the Burren and Clare Hills. 1½ miles from Galway City. NO Commercial vehicles.
Facilities ∮ ⬚⬚ 🛉 🅿 ⬚ ⬚ 🍴 🛉
Directions Approaching Galway on the N17, to avoid the city centre stay on the N6 which will take you to Dunnes Stores and onto Bodkin roundabout, turn right and continue straight on the N6 to Deane roundabout, just past at the traffic lights turn right onto the R3

KERRY

ARDFERT

Sir Rogers Caravan Park, Banna, Ardfert, Tralee, Co. Kerry,
Tel: 00 66 713 4730
Email: sirrogerscaravanpark@eircom.net
www.sirrogerscaravanpark.com
Pitches For A ⛺ 🚐 🚐 **Total** 56
Acreage 3½ **Open** Feb **to** Dec

Modern family run park with state of the art childrens playground. Pleasant, safe and secure for families. 200 metres from the beach.
Facilities ∮ ⬚⬚ 🛉 🅿 ⬚ ⬚ 🍴 ⬚ 🛉
Directions Approx 6 miles north west of Tralee on the R551.

CAHERDANIEL

Wave Crest Caravan & Camping Park, Caherdaniel, Co. Kerry,
Tel: 00 66 947 5188
Email: wavecrest@eircom.net
www.wavecrestcamping.com
Pitches For A ⛺ 🚐 🚐 **Total** 100
Acreage 5½ **Open** 15-Mar **to** 15-Oct
Elevated, landscaped Park with views of beaches, coves and the majestic mountains of the Beara Peninsula. Dolphins and basking sharks are familiar sights. A haven for outdoor enthusiasts. Take-away food available. NO commercial vehicles.
Facilities ⬚ ∮ ⬚⬚ ⬚
⬚ 🚿 ⬚ ⬚ ⬚ 🍴 🛉 🍴 🛉

CAHIRCIVEEN

Mannix Point Camping & Caravan Park, Cahirciveen, Ring of Kerry Coast, Co. Kerry,
Tel: 00 66 947 2806
Email: mortimer@campinginkerry.com
www.campinginkerry.com
Pitches For Å ♣ ♠ ♠⌇ **Total** 42
Acreage 6¼ **Open** 15-Mar **to** 15-Oct
On the waterfront in the spectacular Gulf Stream coast of South West Kerry with wonderful views in every direction. 15 minute walk to the town and amenities. Ideal for hill, mountain and foreshore walks. Pre-booking is essential for the music festival and there is a minimum of a 3 night stay for that weekend (first weekend in August).
Facilities ƒ ⬚ ♠ ♠ ⬚ ◯ ☒ 🕏
Directions 300 metres from the N70, just west of Cahirciveen.

CASTLEGREGORY

Anchor Caravan Park, Castlegregory, Tralee, Co. Kerry,
Tel: 00 66 713 9157
Email: anchorcaravanpark@eircom.net
www.anchorcaravanpark.com
Pitches For ♣ ♠ **Total** 30
Acreage 5 **Open** Easter **to** Sept
Sheltered Park with direct access to sandy beach for safe bathing. Ideal for the Dingle Peninsula, Killarney and the Ring of Kerry.
Facilities ƒ ⬚ ♠ ♠ ⬚ ◯ ⬚ ♠ 🅿 ⬚
Directions 12 miles from Tralee on the coast road to Dingle, signposted.

DINGLE

Campail Teach an Aragail, Gallarus, Baile na Gall, Dingle, Co. Kerry,
Tel: 00 66 915 5143
Email: info@gaeilgebeo.com
www.gaeilgebeo.com
Pitches For Å ♣ ♠ **Total** 42
Acreage 3 **Open** Apr **to** 20-Sep

On the tranquil, pure and beautiful Dingle Peninsula, a Gaelic speaking area. Ideal for walking with the Way of the Saints to Mount Brandon, or the Dingle Way to visit the Blasket Islands. Pub and restaurant in the nearby village.
Facilities ⬚ ƒ ⬚ ♠ ♠ ⬚ ◯ ⬚ ⬚ ⬚
Directions From Dingle (An Daingean) take the R559 to Baile an Fheirtearaigh and follow signs.

GLENBEIGH

Glenross Caravan & Camping Park, Glenbeigh Village, Ring of Kerry, Co. Kerry,
Tel: 00 66 976 8451 (April
Email: glenross@eircom.net
www.campingkerry.com
Pitches For Å ♣ ♠ ♠⌇ **Total** 40
Acreage 4½ **Open** 06-Apr **to** 24-Sep
On the spectacular Ring of Kerry with fine views of Rossbeigh Strand. 5 minutes from the beach. Telephone number for Oct to April: 00 353 87 137 6865.
Facilities ƒ ⬚ ♠ ♠ ◯ ⌣ ⬚ ◯ ☒
♘ ◯ ⬚ ✕ ♠ ♠ ⬚ 🕏
Directions From Killarney take the N70, park is on the right just before the village.

KILLARNEY

Beech Grove Caravan & Camping Park, Fossa, Killarney, Co. Kerry,
Tel: 00 64 663 1727
www.beechgrovecamping.net
Pitches For Å ♣ ♠ ♠⌇ **Total** 46
Acreage 3½ **Open** 04-Apr **to** 03-Oct

Family run site with a woodland background and panoramic views overlloking Killarneys lower lake.
Facilities ƒ ⬚ ♠ ♠ ⬚
◯ ♘ ⬚ ⬚ ♠ ⬚ ⬚
Directions On the N72, 3 miles west of Killarney, right after the Golden Nugget Pub.

KILLARNEY

Donoghues White Villa Farm Caravan & Camping Park, Lissivigeen, Killarney-Cork Road (N22, Killarney, Co. Kerry,
Tel: 00 64 662 0671
Email: killarneycamping@eircom.net
www.killarneycaravanpark.com
Pitches For Å ♣ ♠ ♠⌇ **Total** 24
Acreage 11 **Open** Easter **to** 01-Oct
Award winning, well landscaped, sheltered Park in the countryside, yet only minutes from Killarney town. The River Flesk runs through the farm for fishing. Coach trips from the Park. Self catering holiday apartments available for hire.
Facilities ⬚ ƒ ⬚ ⬚ ⬚ ♠ ◯ ⌣ ⬚ ◯ ⬚
♘ ◯ ⬚ ♠ ⬚ ⬚ ⬚ ⬚ ✕ 🕏
Directions 2 miles east of Killarney on the N22, 300 metres from the N22/N72 roundabout.

KILLARNEY

Fleming's White Bridge Caravan & Camping Park, White Bridge, Ballycasheen Road, Killarney, Co. Kerry,
Tel: 00 64 663 1590
Email: info@killarneycamping.com
www.killarneycamping.com
Pitches For Å ♣ ♠ ♠⌇ **Total** 92
Acreage 24½ **Open** 09-Apr **to** 05-Oct
Multi award winning riverside Park, in a prime location away from all the busy road, yet only a short walk to the town. Coach trips from the site. Pool, gym and fitness centre nearby. Fishing and cycle hire on site.
Facilities ƒ ⬚ ♠ ♠ ⬚
◯ ⬚ ◯ ⬚ ♠ ♠ ✕ ⬚ 🕏
Directions 300 metres off the N22 south east of Killarney.

KILLARNEY

Fossa Caravan & Camping Park, Fossa, Killarney, Co. Kerry,
Tel: 00 64 663 1497
www.fossacampingkillarney.com
Pitches For Å ♣ ♠ **Total** 120
Acreage 8 **Open** Apr **to** Sept
Nearest Bus Stop (Miles) Outside
Beautiful wooded area overlooking the famous MacGillycuddy Reeks and only a 5 minute walk to Lough Leane. Ideal for touring the Kingdom of Kerry, and only 7 miles from Carrantuohill which is Irelands highest mountain. Tennis and take-away food on site. Mobile homes available for hire.
Facilities ƒ ⬚ ⬚ ♠ ♠ ⬚
◯ ⬚ ◯ ⬚ ♠ ♠ ✕ ⬚ ⬚
Directions On the N72 3 miles west of Killarney.

KILLARNEY

Killarney Flesk Caravan & Camping Park, Flesk, Muckross Road, Killarney, Co. Kerry,
Tel: 00 64 31704
Email: info@campingkillarney.com
www.campingkillarney.com
Pitches For Å ♣ ♠ ♠⌇ **Total** 72
Acreage 5 **Open** Apr **to** Sept
Situated at the gateway to the National Park and lakes. At the start of the Kerry Walk for enjoying the magnificent woodlands and mountains, and our native deer!

Entertainment in high season. Cycle hire and take-away food available.
Facilities ⬚ ƒ ⬚ ♠ ♠
◯ ⬚ ✕ ♠ ♠ ⬚ 🕏
Directions From Killarney take the N71, adjacent to Irelands National Events Centre.

KILLORGLIN

West's Caravan Park, Killarney Road, Killorglin, Ring of Kerry, Co. Kerry,
Tel: 00 66 976 1240
Email: enquiries@westcaravans.com
www.westcaravans.com
Pitches For ♣ ♠ **Total** 60
Acreage 3½ **Open** Easter **to** Oct
Access Good **Site** Level
Alongside a river and overlooked by Irelands highest mountain. Only 1 mile from the town. Close to Killarney National Park, Skellig Rock and Dingle. Mobile home sales and hire.
Facilities ƒ ⬚ ♠ ♠ ◯ ⌣ ⬚
♘ ♠ ⬚ ⬚ ♠ ♠ ⬚ ✕
Nearest Town Killorglin
Directions Take the Ring of Kerry road from Killarney to Killorglin, 1 mile from Killorglin town.
✈ Killarney

LAURAGH

Creveen Lodge Caravan Park, Healy Pass Road, Lauragh Village, Co. Kerry,
Tel: 00 64 668 3131
Email: info@creveenlodge.com
www.creveenlodge.com
Pitches For Å ♣ ♠ **Total** 20
Acreage 4 **Open** Easter **to** Oct
Small, well sheltered Park in the beautiful Ring of Beara with excellent amenities. The perfect place for a quiet holiday. Cottages and caravans available to hire.
Facilities ƒ ⬚ ⬚ ♠ ♠ ⬚ ◯ ⬚ ♠ ⬚ ♠ ✕
Directions From the R571 in Lauragh, take the R574 Healy Pass Road and look for signs.

TRALEE

Woodlands Park, Dan Spring Road, Tralee, Co. Kerry,
Tel: 00 66 712 1235
Email: wdlands@eircom.net
www.kingdomcamping.com
Pitches For Å ♣ ♠ ♠⌇ **Total** 135
Acreage 15 **Open** Mid Mar **to** Sept
Multi award winning Park situated in a quiet parkland setting at the gateway to Dingle Peninsula. Just a short walk through a rose garden to Tralee town centre. Close to a greyhound stadium, Aqua Dome, Aqua Golf, a museum, the National Folk Theatre and a cinema.
Facilities ⬚ ƒ ⬚ ♠ ♠ ⬚
◯ ⬚ ◯ ⬚ ♠ ♠ ✕ ⬚ 🕏
Directions From the N21, N22 or N70, follow signs for Dingle N86.

KILKENNY

BENNETTSBRIDGE

Nore Valley Park, Annamult, Bennettsbridge, Kilkenny, Co. Kilkenny,
Tel: 00 56 772 7229
Email: norevalleypark@eircom.net
www.norevalleypark.com
Pitches For Å ♣ ♠ ♠⌇ **Total** 60
Acreage 5 **Open** Mar **to** Oct
Quiet, family run Park in a peaceful, rural setting on a farm where children can feed the animals. Lovely walks in the area. High standard of cleanliness. Delicious home baked food available. Fly fishing (extra charge), crazy golf, pedal go-karts, 3D maze, trailer rides and pool table on site.

Facilities ⫯ ⫯⫯⫯⫯ ⫯
⫯⫯⫯⫯⫯⫯⫯⫯⫯⫯⫯
Directions From Kilkenny take the R700 to Bennettsbridge. Just before the bridge turn right at the sign, then after approx 3km turn left at the sign.

KILKENNY

Tree Grove Caravan & Camping Park,
Danville House, New Ross Road, Kilkenny, Co. Kilkenny,
Tel: 00 56 777 0302
Email: treecc@iol.ie
www.treegrovecamping.com
Pitches For ▲ ⛺ ⛺ ⛺ **Total** 30
Acreage 4¼ **Open** Mar to Mid Nov
Perfectly situated for Medieval Kilkenny and South East. 25 minute easy walk along a river pathway to Kilkenny. Cycle hire on site. Also open weekends from Nov to March by prior arrangement only.
Facilities ⫯ ⫯⫯⫯⫯
⫯⫯⫯⫯⫯⫯⫯⫯
Directions Approx 1 mile from Kilkenny, after the roundabout on the R700 in the direction of New Ross.

LEITRIM

CARRICK-ON-SHANNON

Battlebridge Caravan & Camping Park,
Leitrim Village, Carrick-on-Shannon, Co. Leitrim,
Tel: 00 71 965 0824
Email: battlebridge@eircom.net
www.beirnesofbattlebridge.com
Pitches For ▲ ⛺ ⛺ ⛺ **Total** 20
Acreage 2 **Open** All Year
On the banks of the River Shannon with a traditional Irish pub on site serving food. Cast a fishing line from your pitch or enjoy our private marina with slipway for boating. Miles of forest and canal walks in the area, good bird watching. Take-away food available.
Facilities
⫯⫯⫯⫯⫯⫯⫯⫯⫯⫯⫯⫯⫯⫯
Directions From Carrick-on-Shannon take the R280 to Leitrim, turn left onto the R284 to Keadue, Park is ½ a mile.

MOHILL

Lough Rynn Caravan & Camping Park,
Lough Rynn, Mohill, Co. Leitrim,
Tel: 00 86 825 4428
Email: cbohan@leitrimcoco.ie
www.leitrimcoco.ie
Pitches For ▲ ⛺ ⛺ ⛺ **Total** 20
Acreage 19 **Open** 08-Apr to Sept
On the shores of Lough Rynn and adjacent to Lough Rynn House & Gardens. Host of friendly pubs and restaurants and a childrens play area close by.
Facilities ⫯ ⫯⫯⫯⫯ ⫯⫯
Directions 1¼ miles south of Mohill on the road to Drumlish.

LIMERICK

ADARE

Adare Camping & Caravan Park, Adare, Co. Limerick,
Tel: 00 61 395376
Email: dohertycampingadare@eircom.net
www.adarecamping.com
Pitches For ▲ ⛺ ⛺ ⛺ **Total** 28
Acreage 5 **Open** 12-Mar to Sept
Family run Park with a high standard throughout. Newly developed farm walk. Outdoor hot tub on site.
Facilities ⫯ ⫯⫯⫯⫯ ⫯⫯⫯⫯⫯⫯⫯
Directions From Limerick take the N21 for Tralee and continue through Adare, turn left onto the R519 to Balingarry and follow signs.

KILCORNAN

Curragh Chase Caravan & Camping,
Coillte Forest Park, Kilcornan, Co. Limerick,
Tel: 00 61 396349
Email: eileen.okeeffe@coillte.ie
www.coillteoutdoors.ie
Pitches For ▲ ⛺ ⛺ **Total** 80
Acreage 8½ **Open** Easter then May to Sept
Located within the 773 acres of Coillte Forest Park with its arboretum, picnic sites, childrens playground, forest walks and cycle trails, as well as multi-use trails which are suitable for all users.
Facilities ⫯ ⫯⫯⫯⫯ ⫯⫯⫯⫯⫯
Directions Take the N69 from Limerick for Foynes, in Kilcornan Village turn left and the Site is 2 miles.

LOUTH

DUNDALK

Gyles Quay Caravan Park, Riverstown, Dundalk, Co. Louth,
Tel: 00 42 937 6262
Pitches For ▲ ⛺ ⛺ **Total** 139
Open 31-May to 01-Sep
Licensed pub on site with live entertainment.
Facilities ⫯ ⫯⫯⫯⫯ ⫯
⫯⫯⫯⫯⫯⫯⫯⫯⫯
Directions From the M1 take the R173 for Dundalk. Follow signs for Carlingford for approx 7 miles then turn right for Gyles Quay. The Park is towards the end of the road on the right.

MAYO

ACHILL

Lavelles Golden Strand Caravan & Camping Park, Golden Strand, Dugort, Achill, Co. Mayo,
Tel: 00 86 231 4596/87 616 5
Pitches For ▲ ⛺ ⛺ **Total** 37
Acreage 3¾ **Open** Apr to Oct
Set beside one of Mayos finest Blue Flag beaches (direct access form the Park). Scenic walks in the area.
Facilities ⫯ ⫯⫯⫯⫯ ⫯⫯⫯⫯⫯⫯⫯
Directions From Achill Sound take the R319 to Bunnacurry T-Junction, turn right onto the crossroads at the valley, turn left and the Park is 1 mile.

ACHILL ISLAND

Keel Sandybanks Caravan & Camping Park, Achill Island, Keel, Co. Mayo,
Tel: 00 98 43211
Email: info@achillcamping.com
www.achillcamping.com
Pitches For ▲ ⛺ ⛺ ⛺ **Total** 100
Acreage 15 **Open** Mid May to Mid Sept
Set spectacularly below Slievemore Mountain, the Minaun Cliffs and Keel beach on Achill Island. Plenty of activities locally. Tennis on site.
Facilities ⫯ ⫯⫯⫯⫯ ⫯
⫯⫯⫯⫯⫯⫯⫯⫯⫯

BALLINA

Belleek Park Caravan & Camping,
Belleek, Ballina, Co. Mayo,
Tel: 00 96 71533
Email: lenahan@belleekpark.com
www.belleekpark.com
Pitches For ▲ ⛺ ⛺ ⛺ **Total** 58
Acreage 9¾ **Open** Mar to Oct
Award winning park in a tranquil and sheltered location with excellent facilities and high standards. Close to the town and the River Moy (one of Europes most prolific

salmon rivers). Ten minute walk to a forest park and riverside walks.
Facilities ⫯ ⫯⫯⫯⫯⫯⫯⫯⫯⫯⫯⫯⫯
⫯⫯⫯⫯⫯⫯⫯⫯⫯⫯⫯⫯⫯⫯⫯⫯
Directions Take the R314 from Ballina towards Ballycastle, Park is just outside the town boundary, look for signs to Belleek on your right, turn right and the Park entrance is 300 metres on the right.

CASTLEBAR

Carra Caravan & Camping Park,
Belcarra, Castlebar, Co. Mayo,
Tel: 00 94 903 2054
Email: post@mayoholidays.com
www.horsedrawncaravan.com
Pitches For ▲ ⛺ ⛺ **Total** 20
Acreage 1¾ **Open** May to Late Sept
Village centre site. Horsedrawn holidays and country walks are a speciality from this site. Close to all amenities and attractions.
Facilities ⫯ ⫯⫯⫯⫯ ⫯⫯⫯⫯⫯⫯⫯
Directions Take the N84 from Castlebar towards Ballinrobe, immediately turn left for Ballycarra (Belcarra).

CASTLEBAR

Carrowkeel Camping & Caravan Park,
Ballyvary, Castlebar, Co. Mayo,
Tel: 00 94 903 1264
Email: info@carrowkeelpark.ie
www.carrowkeelpark.ie
Pitches For ▲ ⛺ ⛺ **Total** 58
Acreage 5 **Open** Apr to Sept
Well maintained Park in the heart of Mayo. Clubhouse with live entertainment in high season. Small shop with basic food supplies. Take-away food available. Just a few miles from the famous River Moy for salmon fishing.
Facilities ⫯ ⫯⫯⫯⫯ ⫯
⫯⫯⫯⫯⫯⫯⫯⫯⫯⫯
Directions 5 miles from Castlebar, just off the N5.

CASTLEBAR

Lough Lannagh Caravan Park, Castlebar, Co. Mayo,
Tel: 00 94 902 7111
Email: info@loughlannagh.ie
www.loughlannagh.ie
Pitches For ▲ ⛺ ⛺ **Total** 20
Acreage 2½ **Open** Mid Apr to Sept
Lakeside setting just a 10 minute walk from Castlebar. Kids activities July and August. Breakfast caf, B&B, tennis and table tennis on site. Also for the over 18's, gym, sauna and steam rooms.
Facilities ⫯ ⫯⫯⫯⫯ ⫯⫯⫯
Directions On the N5 at the edge of Castlebar going towards Westport, straight over two roundabouts, at the third take the second exit then turn immediately left.

CONG

Cong Caravan & Camping Park,
Lisloughrey, Quay Road, Cong, Co. Mayo,
Tel: 00 94 954 6089
Email: info@quietman-cong.com
www.quietman-cong.com
Pitches For ▲ ⛺ ⛺ **Total** 40
Acreage 3 **Open** All Year
Situated between Lough Mask and Lough Corrib, 1 mile from the fascinating Cong Village. Fisherman and boatsmans paradise! Lakeside and forest walks. Bike and boat rental on site.

Facilities ⌗ 🏠🚿🚻 📷🛠️🔥🏪🎣🛒🔌⚡
Directions From Cong head out on the Galway road, go past Ashford Castle entrance and take the next turn right, the Park is on your right after the cemetary.

KNOCK
Knock Caravan & Camping Park, Main Street, Knock, Co. Mayo,
Tel: 00 94 938 8100
Email: info@knock-shrine.ie
www.knock-shrine.ie
Pitches For ⛺ 🚐 🚎 **Total** 88
Acreage 7¼ **Open** Mar to Oct
Sheltered, landscaped park. 5 minute walk from Our Lady's Shrine and Knock Museum. Ideal base for touring Mayo and the West of Ireland. Mobile homes for hire.
Facilities ⌗ 🏠🚿🚻 📷
🛒🔥🍴🔥🏪🎣🔌
Directions At Knock roundabout take Main Street for 1 mile, Park is on the left.

WESTPORT
Westport House Parkland Caravan & Camping Park, Westport House & Adventure Pk, Westport, Co. Mayo,
Tel: 00 98 27766/98 27780
Email: camping@westporthouse.ie
www.westporthouse.ie
Pitches For ⛺ 🚐 🚎 🚎⚡ **Total** 95
Acreage 9¾ **Open** May to 06-Sep
Situated in the grounds of Westport House & Gardens with tennis, pitch n putt, fishing, swan pedaloes, mini railway, log flume ride, bouncy castle, Pirate Queen Ships Galleon, and indoor Jungle World (soft play). Easy drive to beaches.
Facilities ⌗ 🏠🚿🚻 🛒📷 ❓🛠🔥🔌
Directions On the R335 2 miles from Westport, turn right at Westport Quay.

ROSCOMMON
ATHLONE
Hodson Bay Caravan & Camping Park, Kiltoom, Athlone, Co. Roscommon,
Tel: 00 90 649 2448
Pitches For ⛺ 🚐 🚎 **Total** 34
Acreage 2½ **Open** June to Aug
Quiet lakeside location beside a hotel, marina and golf course.
Facilities ⌗ 🏠🚿🚻 🛒📷📷
Directions From Athlone take the N61 Roscommon road for 3 miles, turn right for Hodson Bay and the Park is ½ a mile past the Hotel.

BALLAGHADERREEN
Willowbrook Caravan & Camping Park, Killtybranks, Ballaghaderreen, Co. Roscommon,
Tel: 00 94 986 1307
Email: info@willowbrookpark.com
www.willowbrookpark.com
Pitches For ⛺ 🚐 🚎 **Total** 29
Acreage 2 **Open** All Year
Warm and friendly atmosphere in the Lung Valley, an unspoilt and beautiful landscaped area. Walking, archery and course fishing on site. We also offer the relaxing techniques of meditation, Tai Chi and Chi Kung.
Facilities ⌗ 🏠🚿🚻 🛒📷🔥🛠🔥🛒
Directions Take the R293 towards Castlerea, then take the R325. Go over the bridge and turn left, after approx ½ a mile turn right at Park sign and continue for 500 metres, Park on the left.

BOYLE
Lough Key Forest & Activity Park, Caravan & Camping Dept., Boyle, Co. Roscommon,
Tel: 00 71 966 2212
www.loughkey.ie
Pitches For ⛺ 🚐 🚎 **Total** 72
Acreage 13½ **Open** -
Situated in Lough Key Forest Park with a legendary backdrop of water, parkland and forest encompassing a landmark cluster of unique attractions offering gentle pursuits or energetic activities. Boda Borg Technology House and Adventure Play Kingdom.
Facilities ⌗ 🏠🚿🚻 📷🛒❌🛠🔥
Directions On the N4, approx 2½ miles east of Boyle.

GAILEY BAY
Gailey Bay Caravan & Camping Park, Gailey Bay, Knockcroghery, Co. Roscommon,
Tel: 00 90 666 1058
Email: gaileybay@hotmail.com
www.gaileybay.com
Pitches For ⛺ 🚐 🚎 🚎⚡ **Total** 27
Acreage 2¾ **Open** Mid April to Oct
Fishing tackle and boat hire on site.
Facilities ⌗ 🏠🚿🚻 🛒📷🛠🔥🏪🎣
Directions Take the N61 from Roscommon towards Athlone. After Knockcroghery Village turn right then immediately left after the railway crossing, at first crossroads turn right.

SLIGO
BOYLE
Lough Arrow Touring Park, Ballynarry, Riverstown, Boyle, Co. Sligo,
Tel: 00 71 966 6018
Email: latp@eircom.net
www.homepage.eircom.net/~latp
Pitches For ⛺ 🚐 🚎 🚎⚡ **Total** 30
Acreage 8½ **Open** Mid Mar to Oct
Award winning, landscaped site in a conservation area of stunning natural beauty overlooking Lough Arrow. Boules pitch, golf practice nets and boat hire on site.
Facilities ⌗ 🏠🏠🚿🚻 🛒📷❓🔥
Directions Take the N4 north, pass Boyle and turn first right sp Ballyfarnon and follow signs.

ROSSES POINT
Greenlands Caravan & Camping Park, Rosses Point, Co. Sligo,
Tel: 00 71 917 7113
Pitches For ⛺ 🚐 🚎 🚎⚡ **Total** 120
Acreage 6¼ **Open** Mid Apr to Mid Sept
Overlooking the Atlantic Ocean with magnificent views of Coney Island, Oyster Island, Blackrock Lighthouse and Benbulben and Knocknarea Mountains. Two bathing beaches. Adjacent to s golf club.
Facilities ⌗ 🏠🚿🚻 ⛱🛠🚿🏠📷❓
Directions On the R29, 5 miles west of Sligo.

STRANDHILL
Strandhill Caravan & Camping Park, Strandhill, Co. Sligo,
Tel: 00 71 916 8111
Pitches For 🚐 🚎 🚎⚡ **Total** 100
Acreage 14¾ **Open** Mid Apr to Sept
Beside Strandhill beach.
Facilities ⌗ 🏠🏠🚿🚻 🛒📷
📷🛠🔥🏪🎣🔌
Directions 5 miles west of Sligo City on the R292, on Airport Road.

TIPPERARY
AHERLOW
Ballinacourty House Caravan & Camping Park, Glen of Aherlow, Co. Tipperary,
Tel: 00 62 56559
Email: info@camping.ie
www.camping.ie
Pitches For ⛺ 🚐 🚎 **Total** 50
Acreage 5 **Open** Mid Apr to End Sept
Quiet and unique family run Park set in the beautiful Glen of Aherlow in the grounds of an 18th Century estate with the restored stable block as our main building. Wonderful views of the Galtee Mountains and the Sliebh na Much Hills. Tennis on site.
Facilities ⌗ 🏠🏠🚿🚻 😊🛒🍴
🚿🛒📷❌🛠🔥🏪🎣🔌🛒❄️
Directions Take the N24 from Cahir roundabout towards Tipperary, after 4 miles turn left to Glen of Aherlow Scenic Route, turn next right over the railway crossing and follow road through Rossadrehid Village, after approx 8½ miles turn right and follow signs to the

CAHIR
The Apple Camping & Caravan Park, Moorstown, Cahir, Co. Tipperary,
Tel: 00 52 744 1459
Email: con@theapplefarm.com
www.theapplefarm.com
Pitches For ⛺ 🚐 🚎 🚎⚡ **Total** 32
Acreage 3½ **Open** May to Sept
Well maintained, nicely landscaped, unique park on a fruit farm. Succession of fruits to try all summer from strawberries and raspberries to apples and plums. Tennis on site.
Facilities ♿ ⌗ 🏠🏠🚿🚻 😊🍴
🚿📷🔥🔌
Directions On the N24 between Cahir and Clonmel.

CLOGHEEN
Parson's Green, Clogheen, Co. Tipperary,
Tel: 00 52 65290
Email: kathleennoonan@oceanfree.net
www.clogheen.com
Pitches For ⛺ 🚐 🚎 **Total** 40
Acreage 27 **Open** All Year

Small family run Park with excellent facilities including coffee shop and take-away, farm museum, indoor and outdoor playgrounds, pet field, pony and pony n trap rides, boat rides and tennis court. Garden and river walks. Close to many places of interest.
Facilities ⌗ 🏠🚿🚻 🛒📷❓🛒🔥🏪🎣
Directions From Cahir take the R668.

CLONMEL
Powers The Pot Camping & Caravan Park, Harneys Cross, Clonmel, Co. Tipperary,
Tel: 00 52 612 3085
Email: info@powersthepot.net
www.powersthepot.net
Pitches For ⛺ 🚐 🚎 **Total** 20
Acreage 3¾ **Open** May to Sept
A beautiful spot on the side of the Comeragh Mountains with a wonderful ambiance and breathtaking views on a clear day. Ideal for walking with Munster Way passing by the site. Take-away food available.
Facilities ⌗ 🏠🚿🚻 🛒📷
🛒🔥🛠❓🛠🔥🏪
Directions From the East on the N24, in Clonmel turn left at the first set of traffic lights, go straight and continue past the golf club.

ROSCREA

Streamstown Caravan & Camping Park, Roscrea, Co. Tipperary,
Tel: 00 50 521519
Email: streamstowncaravanpark@eircom.net
www.tipperarycaravanpark.com
Pitches For **Total** 30
Acreage 2½ **Open** Easter **to** Sept
Beautifully landscaped family run Park on a dairy farm in quiet surroundings. Ideal for walking the Slieve Bloom Mountains. Mobile homes for hire.
Facilities
Directions Just off the N7. From Roscrea take the R491 to Shinrone for 1½ miles, signposted.

WATERFORD

DUNGARVAN

Bayview Caravan & Camping Park, Gold Coast Golf Resort, Dungarvan, Co. Waterford,
Tel: 00 58 45100/58 45050
Email: info@bayviewcaravancamping.com
www.bayviewcaravancamping.com
Pitches For **Total** 32
Acreage 6 **Open** Feb **to** Nov
Award winning Park adjacent to The Gold Coast Golf Hotel & Leisure Centre with its 18 hole golf course which overlooks Dungarvan Bay. Bike hire and ten pin bowling. 1 mile from Clonea Beach.
Facilities
Directions Turn south off the N25 or the R675 onto the Gold Coast road and follow signs.

DUNGARVAN

Casey's Caravan & Camping Park, Clonea, Dungarvan, Co. Waterford,
Tel: 00 58 41919
Pitches For **Total** 284
Acreage 19¾ **Open** 09-Apr **to** 13-Sep
Award winning Park with direct access to a golden sands beach. Crazy golf on site. Wet World Kids Club during July and August. Hotel with leisure centre adjacent. Whilst here why not visit the famous Waterford Crystal Factory.
Facilities
Directions From Waterford take the N25 towards Dungarvan, turn left after the Clonea Strand & Gold Coast Amenity sign. Pass Dungarvan Golf Club and turn first left, go straight over crossroads and roundabout onto Clonea.

TRAMORE

Newtown Cove Caravan & Camping Park, Newtown Road, Tramore, Co. Waterford,
Tel: 00 51 381979/51 381121
Email: info@newtowncove.com
www.newtowncove.com
Pitches For **Total** 40
Acreage 5½ **Open** 11-Apr **to** 28-Sep
Superbly kept, multi award winning, family run Park in a peaceful setting. Short distance from Tramore with its sandy beach, and just a 5 minute walk from the picturesque cove of Newtown. Plenty of attractions nearby. Mobile homes for hire. No commercial vehicles. Booking is advisable.
Facilities

WESTMEATH

ATHLONE

Lough Ree (East) Caravan & Camping Park, Ballykeeran, Athlone, Co. Westmeath,
Tel: 00 90 647 8561
Email: athlonecamping@eircom.net
Pitches For **Total** 40
Acreage 5 **Open** Apr **to** Sept
Set on wonderful countryside on the shores of Lough Ree and bordered by the Breensford trout river. Ideal for fishing, canoeing, boating, windsurfing and sailing. Jetty and boat slip. Beside a pub and 2 miles from Athlone.
Facilities
Directions Take the N55 off the Athlone Bypass and head north for 1¾ miles. Park is directly behind the srone clad house in Ballykeeran Village.

WEXFORD

FETHARD-ON-SEA

Ocean Island, Fethard-on-Sea, New Ross, Co. Wexford,
Tel: 00 51 397148
Pitches For **Total** 42
Acreage 3 **Open** Mid Apr **to** Sept

1¼ miles to the beach.
Facilities
Directions From Wexford take the R733 to Duncannon Road roundabout and turn left sp Wellington Bridge. Follow signs for Fethard-on-Sea.

KILMUCKRIDGE

Morriscastle Strand Caravan & Camping Park, Morriscastle, Kilmuckridge, Co. Wexford,
Tel: 00 53 913 0124
Email: info@morriscastlestrand.com
www.morriscastlestrand.com
Pitches For **Total** 100
Acreage 39½ **Open** Mid Mar **to** Sept
Beside the soft sand dunes with 12 miles of Blue Flag beach. Close to many attractions.
Facilities
Directions From Wexford take the R741 and follow signs for Kilmuckridge Village. Park is clearly signposted.

ROSSLARE

St Margarets Beach, Lady's Island, Rosslare Harbour, Co. Wexford,
Tel: 00 53 913 1169
Email: stmarg@eircom.net
Pitches For **Total** 38
Acreage 5 **Open** Mid Mar **to** Sept

Quiet, rural park in an area of natural beauty. 500 metres from a sandy beach. 15 minutes from Rosslare Ferry Port.
Facilities
Directions From Rosslare take the N25, approaching Tagoat, turn left just after the roundabout towards Lady's Island and Carne. Continue past Butlers Bar on the left and turn next left. Signposted from the N25.

WEXFORD

Ferrybank Caravan & Camping, Ferrybank, Wexford, Co. Wexford,
Tel: 00 53 918 5256
Email: info@wexfordswimmingpool.ie
www.wexfordswimmingpool.ie
Pitches For **Total** 97
Acreage 10 **Open** All Year
Overlooking Wexford Harbour. Within 9 miles of Blue Flag beaches, heritage sites and nature reserves. Booking essential for May and September.
Facilities
Directions ½ a mile east of Wexford Town on the R741 (over the bridge).

WEXFORD

The Trading Post, Ballaghkeen, Co. Wexford,
Tel: 00 53 912 7368
Email: info@wexfordcamping.com
www.wexfordcamping.com
Pitches For **Total** 21
Acreage 3 **Open** Apr **to** Sept
4 Star family run Park. Beside a traditional thatched pub, a shop and a service station (open 24 hours for fuel). 5km from the beach and only 25km from Rosslarf Ferry Port.
Facilities
Directions From Enniscorthy take the Blackwater/Oulart road for approx 4km then turn right onto the R744. Go through Ballaghkeen and at the R741 intersection turn right, Park is approx 2km beside the Emo petrol station. ENTRANCE FROM THE FORECOURT.

WICKLOW

DONARD

Moat Farm Caravan & Camping Park, Donard, Co. Wicklow,
Tel: 00 45 404727
Email: moatfarm@ireland.com
Pitches For **Total** 40
Acreage 2½ **Open** Mid Mar **to** Sept
Small, quiet and secluded family run Park set in a tranquil, rural area in the foothills of Wicklow Mountains. Short stroll to Donard Village. Painters, walkers and photographers paradise. No commercial vehicles.
Facilities
Directions From the N81 in Doinard, turn at The Old Toll House Pub and follow signs.

RATHDRUM

Hidden Valley Caravan & Camping Park, Rathdrum, Co. Wicklow,
Tel: 00 86 727 2872
Email: info@irelandholidaypark.com
www.irelandholidaypark.com
Pitches For **Total** 60
Acreage 18 **Open** 09-Apr **to** 20-Sep
Serene haven of tranquility and relaxation. Set in a beautiful valley overlooking the cascading waters of the Avonmore River and our very own lake for fishing, swimming, kayaking and rowboats. Abundance of wildlife. NEW fun park on site. 10 minute walk to Rathdrum and its amenities. Numerous walks in the Wicklow Mountains and Clara Vale National Park.
Facilities
Directions From Dublin take the N11/M50 South to the R752 exit and go into Rathnew. Follow signs to Rathdrum and on passing Glanbia (on the left) take the next right turn.

INDEX TO PARKS OPEN ALL YEAR

ESSEX
COLCHESTER, Colchester Holiday Park Ltd.,

GLOUCESTERSHIRE
CHELTENHAM, Briarfields Motel & Touring Park,
CIRENCESTER, Mayfield Touring Park,
DURSLEY, Hogsdown Farm C & C,
GLOUCESTER, The Red Lion Inn C & C Park,
MORETON-IN-MARSH, Moreton-In-Marsh C.C. ,
SLIMBRIDGE, Tudor C & C Park,

HAMPSHIRE
ANDOVER, Wyke Down Touring C & C Park,
FAREHAM, Dibles Park,
SOUTHSEA, Southsea Leisure Park,

HEREFORDSHIRE
HEREFORD, Cuckoos Corner,
LEOMINSTER, Home Farm Caravan Site,
PETERCHURCH, Poston Mill Park,

HERTFORDSHIRE
HERTFORD, Hertford C & C Club Site,

ISLE OF WIGHT
SANDOWN, Village Way C & C Park,

KENT
ASHFORD, Broadhembury C & C Park,
CANTERBURY, Canterbury C & C Club Site,
FOLKESTONE, Black Horse Farm C.C. Site,
MARDEN, Tanner Farm Touring C & C Park,
RAMSGATE, Nethercourt Touring Park,
ROCHESTER, Woolmans Wood Tourist C P,

LANCASHIRE
LANCASTER, Wyreside Lakes Fishery,
MORECAMBE, Venture Caravan Park,

LEICESTERSHIRE
LEICESTER, Hill Top Caravan Park,
LUTTERWORTH, Stanford Hall Caravan Park,
MARKET BOSWORTH, Bosworth Water Trust,

LINCOLNSHIRE
BOSTON, Orchard Park,
BOSTON, Pilgrims Way C & C Park,
HORNCASTLE, Greetham Retreat Holidays (CL)
LINCOLN, Oakhill Leisure,
LINCOLN, Shortferry Caravan Park,
MARKET DEEPING, The Deepings Cara Park,
MARKET RASEN, Lincolnshire Lanes C & C ,
SCUNTHORPE, Brookside C & C Park,
SKEGNESS, Ronam Cottage,
SPILSBY, Meadowlands,

LONDON
ABBEY WOOD, Abbey Wood C.C. Site,
CRYSTAL PALACE, Crystal Palace C.C. Site,

NORFOLK
BURGH ST. PETER, Waveney River Centre,
FAKENHAM, Crossways C & C Park,
GREAT HOCKHAM, Thetford Forest C & C Site,
GREAT YARMOUTH, Rose Farm T & C Park,
KINGS LYNN, Kings Lynn C & C Park,
KINGS LYNN, Narborough Trout & Coarse Lakes,
KINGS LYNN, Pentney Park,
NORWICH, Swans Harbour C & C Park,
NORWICH, The Willows,
SANDRINGHAM, Sandringham Estate C.C. Site,
SWAFFHAM, Breckland Meadows Touring Park,
THETFORD, Lowe Caravan Park,
WYMONDHAM, Rose Cottage Caravan Site

NORTHAMPTONSHIRE
KETTERING, Kestrel Caravans,

NORTHUMBERLAND
ALNWICK, Railway Inn Caravan Park,
BERWICK-UPON-TWEED, Ord House Country Park,

NOTTINGHAMSHIRE
HOLME PIERREPONT, NWS C & C Park,
MANSFIELD, Tall Trees Park,
NEWARK, Milestone Caravan Park,
NOTTINGHAM, Manor Farm Caravan Site,
NOTTINGHAM, Thorntons Holt Camping Park,
RATCLIFFE ON SOAR, Red Hill Marina,
SUTTON-IN-ASHFIELD, Teversal C & C Site,
WORKSOP, Clumber Park C.C. Site,
WORKSOP, Riverside Caravan Park,

OXFORDSHIRE
BANBURY, Barnstones C & C Site,
BLETCHINGDON, Greenhill Leisure Park,
OXFORD, C & C Club Site,

SHROPSHIRE
BISHOPS CASTLE, Daisy Bank Caravan Park,
BRIDGNORTH, Woodend Farm,
OSWESTRY, Oswestry C & C Club Site,
SHREWSBURY, Beaconsfield Farm Holiday Park,
TELFORD, Severn Gorge Park,
WEM, Lower Lacon Caravan Park,
WHITCHURCH, Roden View C & C,

SOMERSET
BATH, Bath Chew Valley Caravan Park,
BATH, Bury View Farm,
BRIDGWATER, Mill Farm C & C Park,

188

CHARD, Barleymows Farm Shop & Restaurant,
CHARD, South Somerset Holiday Park,
EXFORD, Westermill Farm,
LANGPORT, Bowdens Crest C & C Park,
MARTOCK, Southfork Caravan Park,
SPARKFORD, Long Hazel Park,
TAUNTON, Cornish Farm Touring Park,
TAUNTON, Waterrow Touring Park,
WELLINGTON, Cadeside C.C. Site,
WESTON-SUPER-MARE, West End Farm C P,
WILLITON, Home Farm Holiday Centre,

STAFFORDSHIRE
BURTON-ON-TRENT, Willowbrook Farm,
LEEK, Leek C & C Club Site,
LICHFIELD, Cathedral Grange T C Park,

SUFFOLK
BURY ST EDMUNDS, The Dell Touring Park,
IPSWICH, Low House Touring Caravan Centre,
STOWMARKET, Stonham Barns Holiday Park,

SURREY
CHERTSEY, Chertsey C & C Club Site,
LINGFIELD, Long Acres C & C Park,
REDHILL, Alderstead Heath C.C. Site,

SUSSEX (EAST)
BEXHILL-ON-SEA, Kloofs Caravan Park,
BRIGHTON, Brighton Valley C.C. Site,
UCKFIELD, Heaven Farm,
UCKFIELD, Honeys Green Caravan Park,

SUSSEX (WEST)
ARUNDEL, Maynards C & C Park,
CHICHESTER, Stubcroft Farm Campsite,
HORSHAM, Honeybridge Park,
HORSHAM, Sumners Ponds Fishery & Campsite,
LITTLEHAMPTON, Daisyfields Touring Park,

WARWICKSHIRE
LEAMINGTON SPA, Lairhillock Touring Park
STRATFORD-UPON-AVON, Dodwell Park,
WOLVEY, Wolvey C & C Park,

WEST MIDLANDS
MERIDEN, Somers Wood Caravan Park,
SUTTON COLDFIELD,
        Kingsbury Water Park C & C Club Site,
SUTTON COLDFIELD, Marston C & C Park,

WILTSHIRE
CALNE, Blackland Lakes,
DEVIZES, Devizes C & C Club Site,
MARLBOROUGH, Postern Hill C & C Site,
ORCHESTON, Stonehenge Touring Park,

SALISBURY, Alderbury C & C Park,
SALISBURY, Green Hill Farm C & C Park,
TILSHEAD, Brades Acre,
WESTBURY, Brokerswood Country Park,

WORCESTERSHIRE
BEWDLEY, Bank Farm Holiday Parks Ltd.,
GREAT MALVERN, Blackmore C & C Club Site,
STOURPORT-ON-SEVERN, Lickhill Manor C P,
WYTHALL, Chapel Lane C.C. Site,

YORK (COUNTY OF)
YORK, York Rowntree Park C.C. Site,
YORK, York Touring Caravan Site,
GOOLE, Dobella Lane Farm,

YORKSHIRE (NORTH)
BOROUGHBRIDGE, Boroughbridge C & C Site,
HARROGATE, Shaws Trailer Park,
KNARESBOROUGH, Spen House Caravan Site,
MUKER, Usha Gap Caravan & Camp Site,
RICHMOND, Swale View Caravan Park,
SKIPTON, Eshton Road Caravan Site,
THORNABY-ON-TEES,
        White Water Park C.C. Site,
YORK (Near), Cawood Park,
YORK (Near), The Ponderosa Caravan Park,
YORK (Near), Willow House Caravan Park,

YORKSHIRE (SOUTH)
ROTHERHAM, Thrybergh Country Park,
THORNE, Elder House Touring Park,

YORKSHIRE (WEST)
LEEDS, Glenfield Caravan Park,
LEEDS, Moor Lodge Caravan Park,
SILSDEN, Lower Heights Farm,

WALES
ANGLESEY
RHOSNEIGR, Tyn Llidiart Camping Site,

CARMARTHENSHIRE
LLANDDEUSANT, Black Mountain Caravan Park,

CONWY
BETWS-Y-COED, Rynys Farm Camping Site,
BETWS-Y-COED, Y Giler Arms,
COLWYN BAY, Bron-Y-Wendon Touring Caravan Park,

INDEX TO PARKS OPEN ALL YEAR

ALWAYS CHECK DIRECTLY

WITH THE SITE THAT

ANY FACILITY

YOU PARTICULARLY REQUIRE

WILL BE AVAILABLE

AT THE TIME OF YOUR VISIT

WEST MIDLANDS
MERIDEN, Somers Wood Caravan Park,

WILTSHIRE
CHIPPENHAM, Plough Lane Caravan Site,

WORCESTERSHIRE
STOURPORT-ON-SEVERN, Lincomb Lock Caravan Park,

YORK (COUNTY OF)
YORK, Moorside Caravan Park,
YORK, Naburn Lock Caravan Park,

YORKSHIRE (EAST)
BRIDLINGTON, Old Mill Caravan Park,

YORKSHIRE (NORTH)
HARROGATE, Shaws Trailer Park,
HELMSLEY, Foxholme Touring C & C Park,
PICKERING, Overbrook Caravan Park,
RICHMOND, Tavern House Caravan Park,
YORK (Near), Willow House Caravan Park,

YORKSHIRE (WEST)
LEEDS, Moor Lodge Caravan Park,

WALES
CARMARTHENSHIRE
CARMARTHEN, Pant Farm C & C Park,
CONWY
PENMAENMAWR, Tyddyn Du Touring Park,

DENBIGHSHIRE
RUTHIN, Dyffryn Ial Caravan Site,

PEMBROKESHIRE
FISHGUARD, Rosebush C & C Park,
HERMON, The Lamb Inn Touring Caravan Park,
TENBY, Red House Farm,

POWYS
CRICKHOWELL, Riverside C & C Park
LLANDRINDOD WELLS, Dalmore Caravan Park,
WELSHPOOL, Rhyd-Y-Groes Touring C & C P,

SCOTLAND
FIFE
LEVEN, Monturpie Caravan Park,

HIGHLANDS
INVERGARRY, Faichemard Farm C & C Park,

INDEX TO PARKS WITH FISHING ON SITE
Look for the County in which you wish to stay, then choose a Town, the Park name is shown alongside. Then simply refer to the main section of the guide to read more on the park you have selected.

ENGLAND
BUCKINGHAMSHIRE
OLNEY, Emberton Country Park,

CAMBRIDGESHIRE
EARITH, Westview Marina,
HUNTINGDON, Huntingdon Boathaven & Caravan Park,
HUNTINGDON, Quiet Waters Caravan Park,
HUNTINGDON, Stroud Hill Park,
HUNTINGDON, Wyton Lakes Holiday Park,
ST. NEOTS, C & C Club Site,
WISBECH, Virginia Lake Caravan Park,

CHESHIRE
CHESTER, Manor Wood Country Caravan Park,
CHESTER, Netherwood Touring Site,
MACCLESFIELD, Strawberry Wood C P,

CORNWALL
BUDE, Wooda Farm Holiday Park,
CRANTOCK, Treago Farm C & C Site,
HAYLE, Beachside Holiday Park,
ISLES OF SCILLY, Troytown Farm Campsite,
LISKEARD, Great Trethew Manor,
NEWQUAY, Trencreek Holiday Park,
NEWQUAY, Trevornick Holiday Park,
PADSTOW, Mother Ivey's Bay Holiday Park,
PERRANPORTH, Perran Springs Holiday Park,
POLZEATH, Tristram Camping & Caravan Park,
PORTSCATHO, Treloan Coastal Holidays,
ST. AUSTELL, Pensagillas Park,
TRURO, Cosawes Park,
WADEBRIDGE, Trewince Farm Holiday Park,

CUMBRIA
CARLISLE, Dalston Hall Caravan Park,
CONISTON, Coniston Hall Camping Site,
CONISTON, Pier Cottage Caravan Park,
DENT, Ewegales Farm,

CUMBRIA (cont'd)
EGREMONT, Tarnside Caravan Park,
KENDAL, Waters Edge Caravan Park,
KESWICK, Burns Farm Caravan Site,
PENRITH, Park Foot C & C Park,
PENRITH, Waterside House Campsite,
ULLSWATER, Waterfoot Caravan Park,
ULVERSTON, Bardsea Leisure,
WINDERMERE, Hill of Oaks Caravan Estate,

DERBYSHIRE
ASHBOURNE, Rivendale Caravan & L P,
BAMFORD, Swallowholme C & C Park,
BUXTON, Shallow Grange,
DERBY, Beechwood Park,
DERBY, Shardlow Marina Caravan Park,
RIPLEY, Golden Valley C & C Park,

DEVON
COMBE MARTIN, Newberry Valley Park,
EXETER, Springfield Holiday Park,
HARTLAND, Hartland C & C Park,
ILFRACOMBE, Watermouth Cove Holiday Park,
MORTEHOE, Twitchen House Holiday Village,
MORTEHOE, Warcombe Farm Camping Park,
NEWTON ABBOT, Twelveoaks Farm C P,
PUTSBOROUGH, Putsborough Sands C P,
SOUTH MOLTON, Riverside C & C Park,
TAVISTOCK, Harford Bridge Holiday Park,
UMBERLEIGH, Umberleigh C & C Club Site,
WOOLACOMBE, Golden Coast Holiday Village,
WOOLACOMBE, Woolacombe Bay Hol Village,

DORSET
BRIDPORT, Britt Valley
BRIDPORT, Britt Valley Campground,
BRIDPORT, Freshwater Beach Holiday Park,
CHARMOUTH, Manor Farm Holiday Centre,
CHIDEOCK, Golden Cap Holiday Park,
DORCHESTER, Lyons Gate Caravan Park,
SHAFTESBURY, Blackmore Vale C & C Park,
ST. LEONARDS, Back-of-Beyond Touring Park,
THREE LEGGED CROSS,
        Woolsbridge Manor Farm Caravan Park,
WAREHAM, East Creech C & C Site,

DURHAM
DURHAM, Finchale Abbey Caravan Park,
MIDDLETON-IN-TEESDALE, Mickleton Mill C P,

ESSEX
HALSTEAD, Gosfield Lake Resort,
MERSEA ISLAND, Waldegraves H & L Park,
SOUTHEND-ON-SEA, Riverside Village H P,
WEELEY, Homestead Lake Park,

GLOUCESTERSHIRE
CIRENCESTER, Second Chance Caravan Park,
GLOUCESTER, The Red Lion Inn C & C Park,
TEWKESBURY, Croft Farm L & WPark,
GLOUCESTERSHIRE
TEWKESBURY, Mill Avon Holiday Park,
TEWKESBURY, Winchcombe C & C Club Site,

HAMPSHIRE
BRANSGORE, Harrow Wood Farm C P,
FORDINGBRIDGE, Hill Cottage Farm C & C P,
RINGWOOD, Oakdene Forest Park,

HEREFORDSHIRE
BROMYARD, Boyce Caravan Park,
HEREFORD, Hereford C & C Club Site,
HEREFORD, Lucksall C & C Park,
LEOMINSTER, Pearl Lake Leisure Park,
PETERCHURCH, Poston Mill Park,
ROSS-ON-WYE, Broadmeadow Caravan Park,

HERTFORDSHIRE
HODDESDON, Lee Valley Caravan Park

ISLE OF WIGHT
SANDOWN, Adgestone C & C Club Site,
SANDOWN, Village Way C & C Park,
SHANKLIN, Ninham Country Holidays,

KENT
MARDEN, Tanner Farm Touring C & C Park,

LANCASHIRE
BENTHAM, Riverside Caravan Park,
GARSTANG, Claylands Caravan Park,
GARSTANG, Fell View Park
GARSTANG, Six Arches Caravan Park,
LANCASTER, Wyreside Lakes Fishery,

LEICESTERSHIRE
MARKET BOSWORTH, Bosworth Water Trust,

LINCOLNSHIRE
ALFORD, Woodthorpe Hall Leisure Park,
BOSTON, Orchard Park,
BOSTON, The Moorings,
BOSTON, Walnut Lake Lodges & Camping,
HORNCASTLE, Ashby Park,
HUTTOFT, Jolly Common Adult Only C P,
INGOLDMELLS, Hardy's Touring Site,
LINCOLN, Hartsholme Country Park,
LINCOLN, Oakhill Leisure,
LINCOLN, Shortferry Caravan Park,
MARKET DEEPING, The Deepings C P,
SKEGNESS, Pine Trees Leisure Park,
SKEGNESS, Skegness Water Leisure Park,

193

YORK (COUNTY OF)
YORK, Moorside Caravan Park,
YORK, Naburn Lock Caravan Park,

YORKSHIRE (EAST)
BRIDLINGTON, Thornwick & Sea Farm H C,
HULL, Sand-le-Mere Holiday Village
SKIPSEA, Skirlington Leisure Park,
STAMFORD BRIDGE, Weir Caravan Park,

YORKSHIRE (NORTH)
BENTHAM, Riverside Caravan Park,
BOROUGHBRIDGE, Boroughbridge C & C Site,
FILEY, Orchard Farm Holiday Village,
HARROGATE, High Moor Farm Caravan Park,
KNARESBOROUGH, Kingfisher C & C Park,
LEYBURN, Akebar Park,
MALTON, Ashfield Caravan Park,
PATELEY BRIDGE, Riverside Caravan Park,
RICHMOND, Brompton Caravan Park,
RICHMOND, Swale View Caravan Park,
RIPON, River Laver Holiday Park,
RIPON, Sleningford Watermill,
RIPON, Woodhouse Farm Caravan Park,
SELBY, Oakmere Caravan Park,
SKIPTON, Eshton Road Caravan Site,
YORK (Near), Cawood Park,
YORK (Near), Goosewood Holiday Park,
YORK (Near), Home Farm C & C Park,
YORK (Near), Willow House Caravan Park,

YORKSHIRE (SOUTH)
ROTHERHAM, Thrybergh Country Park,

WALES
ANGLESEY
BENLLECH, Golden Sunset Holidays,
LLANFWROG, Penrhyn Bay Caravan Park,
RHOSNEIGR, Ty Hen,

CAERPHILLY
ABERCARN, Cwmcarn Forest Campsite,
BARGOED, Parc Cwm Darran,

CARMARTHENSHIRE
LLANDDEUSANT, Blaenau Farm,
NEWCASTLE EMLYN, Afon Teifi C & C Park,

CEREDIGION
ABERYSTWYTH, Morfa Bychan Holiday Park,
LLANRHYSTUD, Morfa Caravan Park,
CEREDIGION
LLANRHYSTUD, Pengarreg Caravan Park,
NEW QUAY, Pencnwc Holiday Park,

CONWY
BETWS-Y-COED, Cwmlanerch Caravan Park,
BETWS-Y-COED, Y Giler Arms,
TY-NANT, Glan Ceirw Caravan Park,

DENBIGHSHIRE
CORWEN, Hendwr Caravan Park,
CORWEN, Llawr-Betws Caravan Park,
LLANGOLLEN, Ddol Hir Caravan Park,
RUTHIN, Dyffryn Ial Caravan Site,

GWYNEDD
ABERSOCH, Nant-Y-Big,
BALA, Glanllyn-Lakeside C & C Park,
BALA, Ty-Isaf Camping Site,
BALA, Tyn Cornel Camping & Caravan Park,
BANGOR, Dinas Farm Camping & Touring Site,
CAERNARFON, Bryn Gloch C & C Park,
CAERNARFON, Riverside Camping,
CLYNNOG FAWR, Aberafon Camping & Caravan Site,
CRICCIETH, Eisteddfa C & C Site,
DINAS MAWDDWY, Tynypwll C & C Site,
DOLGELLAU, Dolgamedd Camping & Caravan Site,
PWLLHELI, Hirdre Fawr C & C,
TYWYN, Cwmrhwyddfor Campsite,

MONMOUTHSHIRE
MONMOUTH, Bridge Caravan Park & Camping Site,
MONMOUTH, Glen Trothy Caravan Park,

PEMBROKESHIRE
FISHGUARD, Rosebush C & C Park,
HAVERFORDWEST, Nolton Cross Caravan Park,
MILFORD HAVEN, Sandy Haven Caravan Park,
NEWPORT, Llwyngwair Manor Holiday Park,
NEWPORT, Tycanol Farm Camp Site,
TENBY, Milton Bridge Caravan Park,

POWYS
BALA, Henstent Park,
BRECON, Lakeside Caravan Park,
BUILTH WELLS, Fforest Fields Camping & Caravan Park,
LLANDRINDOD WELLS, Disserth C & C Park,
LLANGAMMARCH WELLS, Riverside Park,
LLANSANTFFRAID, Vyrnwy Caravan Park,
MACHYNLLETH, Morben Isaf H H & T Park,
MIDDLETOWN, Bank Farm Caravan Park,
PENYBONTFAWR, Parc Farm,
PRESTEIGNE, Rockbridge Park,
WELSHPOOL, Carmel Caravan Park,
WELSHPOOL, Henllan Caravan Park,

Thank you for choosing Cade's to help you plan your touring holiday.
It will help us to continue to provide this information, if you would kindly mention
Cade's when replying to our advertisers.

Cade's provides a valuable source of website and email addresses too and it
would also help us if you would mention to advertisers that you discovered their
web address in Cade's.

Thank you.

Carbon monoxide can kill

Never use a fuel-burning appliance inside your tent or awning. Even a warm barbecue can be lethal.

Start 2013
in real style...

If you know of a touring Park that you would like to see included in Cade's, do please let us know by completing and returning this form.

Park Name ....

Address ....

....

.... Postcode ....

Telephone No. ....

Email Address. ....

Website ....

Please add your own details overleaf and return to:- Cade's Guides Limited,
Fairbourne Drive, Atterbury, Milton Keynes, MK10 9RG
or **Scan and Email to:-** enquiries@cades.co.uk

If you know of a touring Park that you would like to see included in Cade's, do please let us know by completing and returning this form.

Park Name ....

Address ....

....

.... Postcode ....

Telephone No. ....

Email Address. ....

Website ....

Please add your own details overleaf and return to:- Cade's Guides Limited,
Fairbourne Drive, Atterbury, Milton Keynes, MK10 9RG
or **Scan and Email to:-** enquiries@cades.co.uk

We would like Cade's to include the Touring Park named overleaf because:-

....

....

....

....

Name ....

Address ....

....

.... Postcode ....

Email Address. ....

We would like Cade's to include the Touring Park named overleaf because:-

....

....

....

....

Name ....

Address ....

....

.... Postcode ....

Email Address. ....

NOTES

If you have a favourite park that is currently not included in Cade's, do let us know. Email us enquiries@cades.co.uk.

NOTES

If you have a favourite park that is currently not included in Cade's, do let us know. Email us enquiries@cades.co.uk.

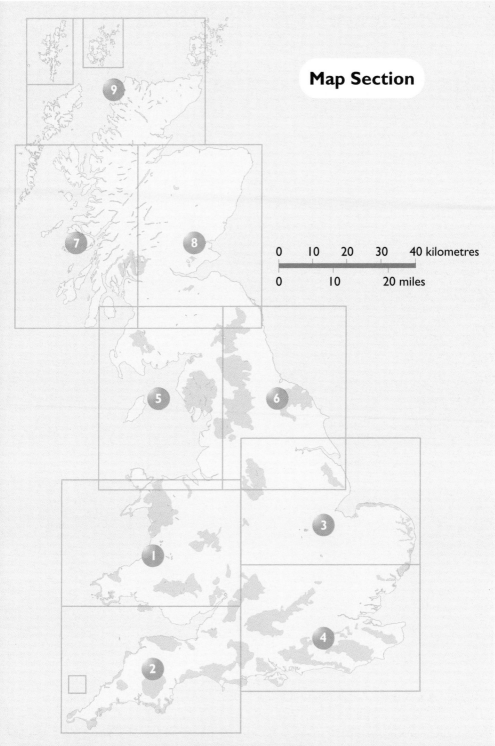

Map Section

0   10   20   30   40 kilometres

0   10   20 miles

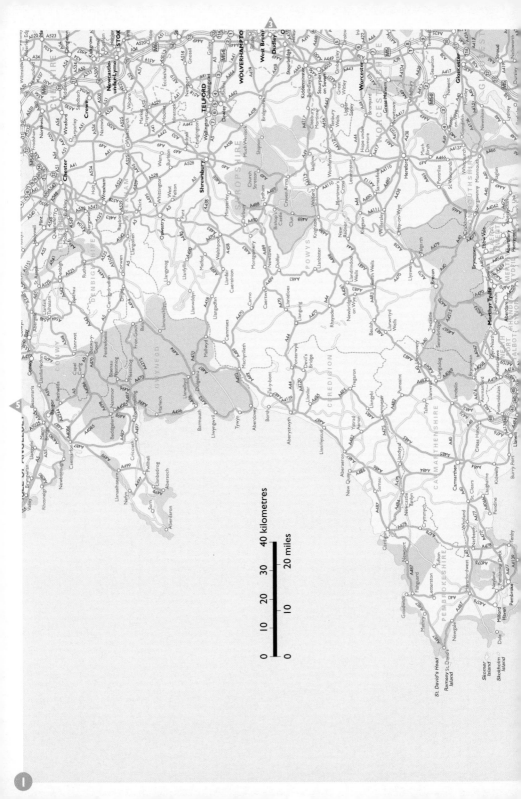

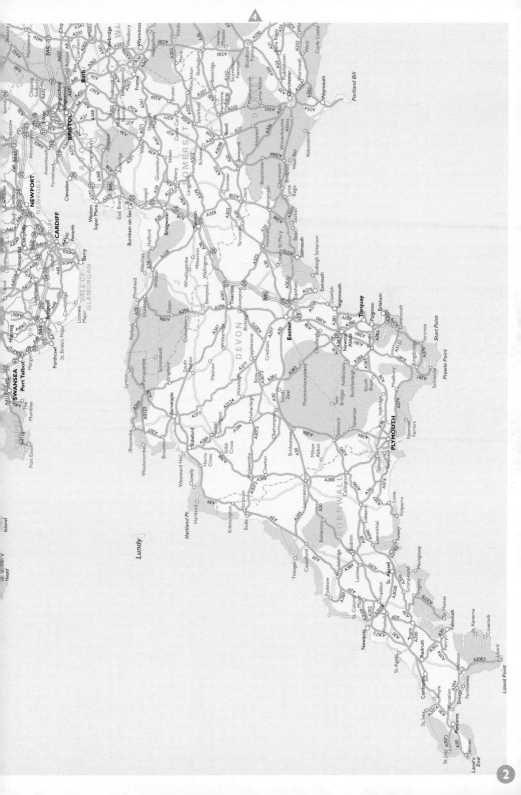

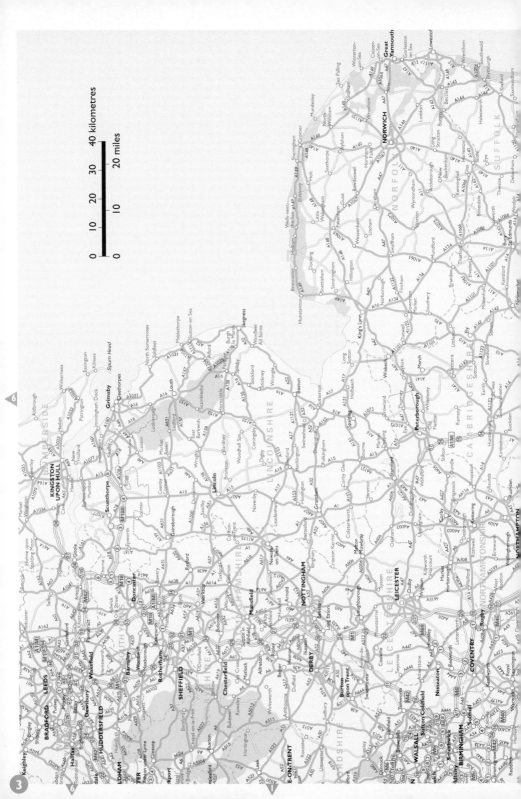

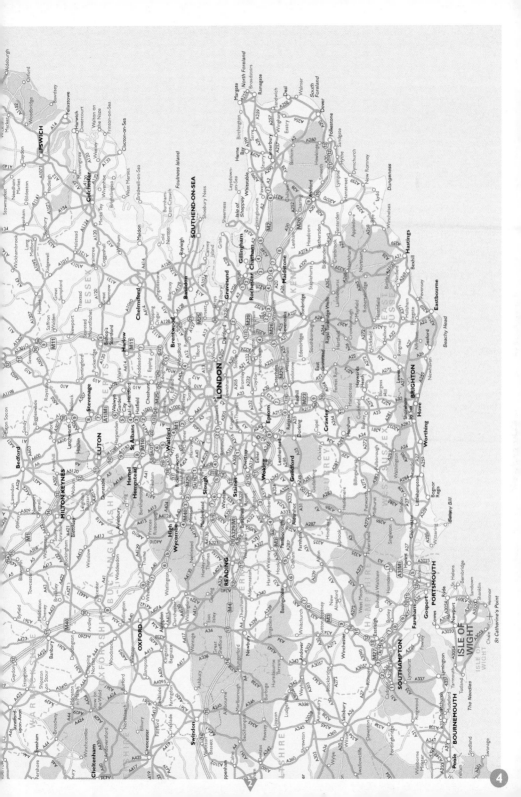

8

Kelso
Belford
Bamburgh
Wooler
Town Yetholm
Embleton
Alnwick
Lesbury
Newton-on-the-Moor
Amble
Rothbury
Rochester
Otterburn
Longhorsley
Newbiggin-by-the-Sea
NORTHUMBERLAND
Cambo
Morpeth
Ashington
Bellingham
Ridsdale
Blyth
Bedlington
Wark
Belsay
Whitley Bay
Simonburn
Chollerton
Ponteland
Gosforth
Wallsend
North Shields
Haydon Bridge
NEWCASTLE
SOUTH SHIELDS
Haltwhistle
Hexham
Corbridge
Hebburn
Jarrow
TYNE AND WEAR
Broomhaugh
GATESHEAD
Boldon
Allendale
Washington
SUNDERLAND
Knarsdale
Edmundbyers
Consett
Stanley
Houghton-le-Spring
Castleside
Chester-le-Street
Seaham
Alston
Lanchester
Easington
Durham
Peterlee
Wearhead
Stanhope
Tow Law
St. John's Chapel
Crook
Spennymoor
CLEVELAND
DURHAM
Bishop Auckland
Hartlepool
Sedgefield
Middleton-in-Teesdale
Newton Aycliffe
Redcar
West Auckland
Billingham
Marske-by-the-Sea
Appleby-in-Westmorland
Saltburn-by-the-Sea
Stockton-on-Tees
Eston
Brotton
Barnard Castle
MIDDLESBROUGH
Brough
Loftus
Darlington
Thornaby on Tees
Bowes
Guisborough
Yarm
Whitby
Kirkby Stephen
Sleights
Robin Hood's Bay
Stokesley
Scotch Corner
Great Smeaton
Reeth
Richmond
Catterick
Muker
Northallerton
Sedbergh
Leyburn
Lockton
Scalby
Scarborough
Hawes
Aysgarth
Bedale
Leeming Bar
Kirkbymoorside
Middleham
Thirsk
Helmsley
Pickering
Seamer
Filey
Masham
Staxton
Buckden
Hovingham
Reighton
NORTH YORKSHIRE
Ingleton
Ripon
Easingwold
Malton
Norton
Rillington
Foxholes
Flamborough
Flamborough Head
Clapham
Pateley Bridge
Boroughbridge
Sledmere
Langtoft
Bridlington
Settle
Grassington
Ripley
Long Preston
Shipton
Fridaythorpe
Driffield
Lissett
Blubberhouses
Harrogate
Knaresborough
Stamford Bridge
Skipsea
Gisburn
Skipton
Bolton Bridge
YORK
Pocklington
Bainton
Earby
Wetherby
Hornsea
Ilkley
Otley
Harewood
Leven
Clitheroe
Keighley
Bingley
Tadcaster
Escrick
Holme upon Spalding Moor
Market Weighton
Colne
Shipley
Beverley
Whalley
Nelson
Aldbrough
BRADFORD
LEEDS
Burnley
Pudsey
Selby
KINGSTON UPON HULL
HUMBERSIDE
Hebden Bridge
Accrington
Morley
Howden
South Cave
Hedon
Withernsea
BLACKBURN
Halifax
Castleford
Hessle
Darwen
Bacup
Rawtenstall
Todmorden
Batley
Brighouse
Knottingley
Snaith
Goole
New Holland
Patrington
Ramsbottom
Dewsbury
Wakefield
Pontefract
Barton upon Humber
Easington
Kilnsea
Rochdale
HUDDERSFIELD
Immingham
Immingham Dock
Bury
Heywood
Hemsworth
Thorne
Scunthorpe
Grimsby
Spurn Head
BOLTON
OLDHAM
Holmfirth
Adwick le Street
Keelby
Cleethorpes
Barnsley
SOUTH YORKS.
Brigg
Penistone
Wombwell
Doncaster
Epworth
Swallow
Eccles
MANCHESTER
Ashton under Lyne
Langsett
Mexborough
Scotter
Caistor
North Somercotes
Saltfleet
Salford
Glossop
Rawmarsh
Ludborough
Sale
Rotherham
Maltby
Tickhill
Bawtry
Caenby Corner
Market Rasen
Stockport
Gainsborough
Ludford
Louth
Altrincham
Hazel Grove
Bamford
SHEFFIELD
Blyth
Wilmslow
Whaley Bridge
Chapel-en-le-Frith
Retford
Dunholme
Wragby
East Barkwith
Alderley Edge
Knutsford
Dronfield
Worksop
Saxilby
Scamblesby
Macclesfield
Buxton
DERBYSHIRE
Lincoln
Alford
Baslow
Tuxford
CHESHIRE
Chesterfield
Bolsover
Warsop
Ollerton
Horncastle
Partney
Bakewell
Branston
Bardney
Carlton

3

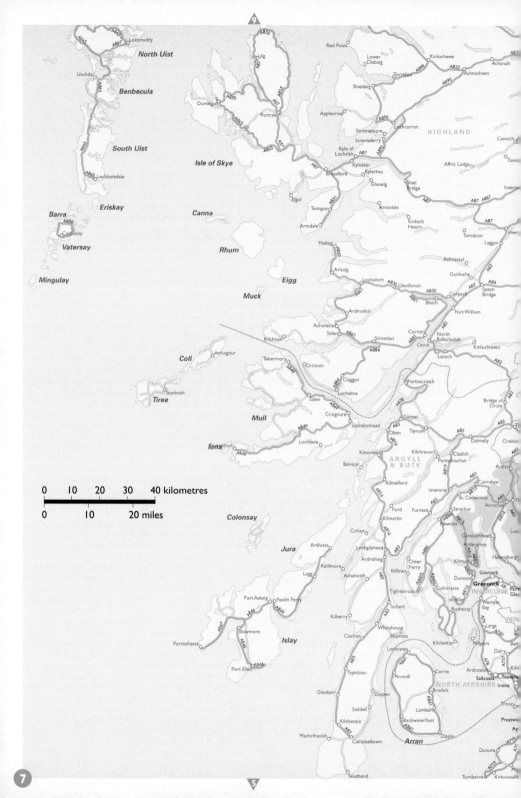

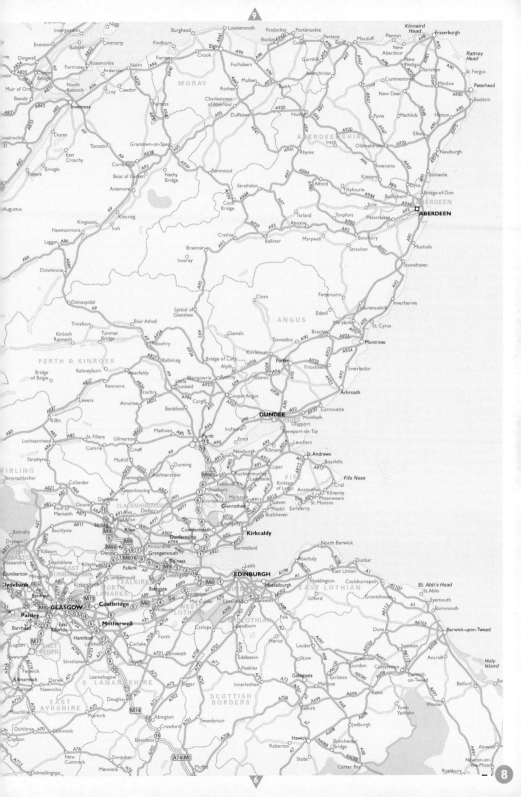

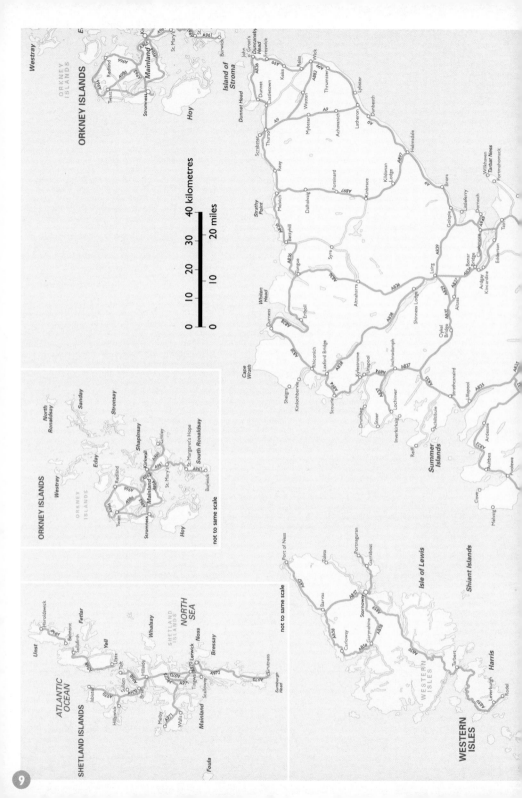

SHETLAND ISLANDS

ATLANTIC OCEAN

NORTH SEA

Unst
Haroldswick
Fetlar
Baltasound
Belmont
Gutcher
Yell
Whalsay
Ulsta
Noss
Aithsel
Voe
Bressay
Hillswick
Brae
Toft
Lerwick
Walls
Melby
Scalloway
Tingwall
Mainland
Sumburgh Head
Foula

A970
A968
A971

SHETLAND ISLANDS

not to same scale

ORKNEY ISLANDS

Westray

ORKNEY ISLANDS

Mainland
Stromness
Kirkwall
Tankerness
Redland
Hoy
Finstown
Twatt
St. Mary's
Burwick

A966
A986
A965
A961

ORKNEY ISLANDS

North Ronaldsay
Sanday
Stronsay
Eday
Shapinsay
Westray
Redland
Kirkwall
Finstown
Tankerness
Linksness
Stromness
St. Mary's
St. Margaret's Hope
South Ronaldsay
Burwick
Hoy
Twatt

A966
A986
A965
A961

not to same scale

Island of Stroma
Dunnet Head
Whiten Head
Cape Wrath
Strathy Point

John o'Groat's
Duncansby Head
Freswick
Wick
Keiss
Reiss
Thrumster
Lybster
Dunbeath
Helmsdale
Brora
Golspie
Littleferry
Dornoch
Tarbat Ness
Portmahomack
Tain
Edderton
Bonar Bridge
Ardgay
Kincardine
Alness
Invergordon

Duncansby Head

John o'Groat's
Dunnet
Castletown
Watten
Thurso
Scrabster
Reay
Bettyhill
Melvich
Strathy
Dalhalvig
Forsinard
Kinbrace
Kildonan Lodge
Mybster
Achavanich
Latheron
Ulbster

A836
A99
A9
A897
A882

Tongue
Durness
Eriboll
Altnaharra
Syre
Lairg
Shinness Lodge
Crask Inn
Oykel Bridge
Rosehall
Invershin
Lochinver
Inchnadamph
Strathcanaird
Ledmore
Elphin
Knockan
Ullapool
Kylestrome
Kylesku
Unapool
Scourie
Laxford Bridge
Rhiconich
Kinlochbervie
Sheigra

A838
A836
A839
A837
A835
A894
A837
A894

Drumbeg
Stoer
Inverkirkaig
Reiff
Achiltibuie
Summer Islands

A835

Poolewe
Aultbea
Melvaig
Cove
Aird
Gairloch

WESTERN ISLES

Isle of Lewis
Shiant Islands
Harris

Port of Ness
Galson
Barvas
Carloway
Garrynahine
Stornoway
Portnaguran
Garrabost
Achmore
Tarbert
Leverburgh
Rodel

A857
A858
A859
A866
A865

WESTERN ISLES

not to same scale

0   10   20   30   40 kilometres
0   10   20 miles

CADE'S · ONE POUND

CAMPING, TOURING & MOTOR CARAVAN SITE GUIDE 2013

PRESENT THIS VOUCHER TO THE SITE OPERATOR WHEN PAYING TO RECEIVE ONE POUND DISCOUNT PER VOUCHER, PER NIGHT. SEE CONDITIONS OVERLEAF. VALID UNTIL 31-12-13

CADE'S · ONE POUND

CAMPING, TOURING & MOTOR CARAVAN SITE GUIDE 2013

PRESENT THIS VOUCHER TO THE SITE OPERATOR WHEN PAYING TO RECEIVE ONE POUND DISCOUNT PER VOUCHER, PER NIGHT. SEE CONDITIONS OVERLEAF. VALID UNTIL 31-12-13

CADE'S · ONE POUND

CAMPING, TOURING & MOTOR CARAVAN SITE GUIDE 2013

PRESENT THIS VOUCHER TO THE SITE OPERATOR WHEN PAYING TO RECEIVE ONE POUND DISCOUNT PER VOUCHER, PER NIGHT. SEE CONDITIONS OVERLEAF. VALID UNTIL 31-12-13

CADE'S · ONE POUND

CAMPING, TOURING & MOTOR CARAVAN SITE GUIDE 2013

PRESENT THIS VOUCHER TO THE SITE OPERATOR WHEN PAYING TO RECEIVE ONE POUND DISCOUNT PER VOUCHER, PER NIGHT. SEE CONDITIONS OVERLEAF. VALID UNTIL 31-12-13

CADE'S · ONE POUND

CAMPING, TOURING & MOTOR CARAVAN SITE GUIDE 2013

PRESENT THIS VOUCHER TO THE SITE OPERATOR WHEN PAYING TO RECEIVE ONE POUND DISCOUNT PER VOUCHER, PER NIGHT. SEE CONDITIONS OVERLEAF. VALID UNTIL 31-12-13

CADE'S · ONE POUND

CAMPING, TOURING & MOTOR CARAVAN SITE GUIDE 2013

PRESENT THIS VOUCHER TO THE SITE OPERATOR WHEN PAYING TO RECEIVE ONE POUND DISCOUNT PER VOUCHER, PER NIGHT. SEE CONDITIONS OVERLEAF. VALID UNTIL 31-12-13

CADE'S · ONE POUND

CAMPING, TOURING & MOTOR CARAVAN SITE GUIDE 2013

PRESENT THIS VOUCHER TO THE SITE OPERATOR WHEN PAYING TO RECEIVE ONE POUND DISCOUNT PER VOUCHER, PER NIGHT. SEE CONDITIONS OVERLEAF. VALID UNTIL 31-12-13

CADE'S · ONE POUND

CAMPING, TOURING & MOTOR CARAVAN SITE GUIDE 2013

PRESENT THIS VOUCHER TO THE SITE OPERATOR WHEN PAYING TO RECEIVE ONE POUND DISCOUNT PER VOUCHER, PER NIGHT. SEE CONDITIONS OVERLEAF. VALID UNTIL 31-12-13

CADE'S · ONE POUND

CAMPING, TOURING & MOTOR CARAVAN SITE GUIDE 2013

PRESENT THIS VOUCHER TO THE SITE OPERATOR WHEN PAYING TO RECEIVE ONE POUND DISCOUNT PER VOUCHER, PER NIGHT. SEE CONDITIONS OVERLEAF. VALID UNTIL 31-12-13

CADE'S · ONE POUND

CAMPING, TOURING & MOTOR CARAVAN SITE GUIDE 2013

PRESENT THIS VOUCHER TO THE SITE OPERATOR WHEN PAYING TO RECEIVE ONE POUND DISCOUNT PER VOUCHER, PER NIGHT. SEE CONDITIONS OVERLEAF. VALID UNTIL 31-12-13

PITCH FEE DISCOUNT VOUCHERS

CONDITIONS OF USE

Vouchers will only be redeemed by those sites featuring a 🅴 symbol in the *facilities* line of their County entry. Presentation of this voucher to the Site Operator at the time of paying your balance will entitle you to a one pound discount per voucher, per night. (Only one voucher per night). Vouchers may be used in multiples i.e. five vouchers presented for a five night stay will entitle you to a discount of £5.00.

A **CADE'S CAMPING, TOURING & MOTOR CARAVAN SITE GUIDE 2013 EDITION** must be presented at the time of payment. Vouchers are valid for accommodation only. Vouchers may not be exchanged for cash. Not to be used with any other offer. Valid until 31-12-13.

CONDITIONS OF USE

Vouchers will only be redeemed by those sites featuring a 🅴 symbol in the *facilities* line of their County entry. Presentation of this voucher to the Site Operator at the time of paying your balance will entitle you to a one pound discount per voucher, per night. (Only one voucher per night). Vouchers may be used in multiples i.e. five vouchers presented for a five night stay will entitle you to a discount of £5.00.

A **CADE'S CAMPING, TOURING & MOTOR CARAVAN SITE GUIDE 2013 EDITION** must be presented at the time of payment. Vouchers are valid for accommodation only. Vouchers may not be exchanged for cash. Not to be used with any other offer. Valid until 31-12-13.

CONDITIONS OF USE

Vouchers will only be redeemed by those sites featuring a 🅴 symbol in the *facilities* line of their County entry. Presentation of this voucher to the Site Operator at the time of paying your balance will entitle you to a one pound discount per voucher, per night. (Only one voucher per night). Vouchers may be used in multiples i.e. five vouchers presented for a five night stay will entitle you to a discount of £5.00.

A **CADE'S CAMPING, TOURING & MOTOR CARAVAN SITE GUIDE 2013 EDITION** must be presented at the time of payment. Vouchers are valid for accommodation only. Vouchers may not be exchanged for cash. Not to be used with any other offer. Valid until 31-12-13.

CONDITIONS OF USE

Vouchers will only be redeemed by those sites featuring a 🅴 symbol in the *facilities* line of their County entry. Presentation of this voucher to the Site Operator at the time of paying your balance will entitle you to a one pound discount per voucher, per night. (Only one voucher per night). Vouchers may be used in multiples i.e. five vouchers presented for a five night stay will entitle you to a discount of £5.00.

A **CADE'S CAMPING, TOURING & MOTOR CARAVAN SITE GUIDE 2013 EDITION** must be presented at the time of payment. Vouchers are valid for accommodation only. Vouchers may not be exchanged for cash. Not to be used with any other offer. Valid until 31-12-13.

CONDITIONS OF USE

Vouchers will only be redeemed by those sites featuring a 🅴 symbol in the *facilities* line of their County entry. Presentation of this voucher to the Site Operator at the time of paying your balance will entitle you to a one pound discount per voucher, per night. (Only one voucher per night). Vouchers may be used in multiples i.e. five vouchers presented for a five night stay will entitle you to a discount of £5.00.

A **CADE'S CAMPING, TOURING & MOTOR CARAVAN SITE GUIDE 2013 EDITION** must be presented at the time of payment. Vouchers are valid for accommodation only. Vouchers may not be exchanged for cash. Not to be used with any other offer. Valid until 31-12-13.

CONDITIONS OF USE

Vouchers will only be redeemed by those sites featuring a 🅴 symbol in the *facilities* line of their County entry. Presentation of this voucher to the Site Operator at the time of paying your balance will entitle you to a one pound discount per voucher, per night. (Only one voucher per night). Vouchers may be used in multiples i.e. five vouchers presented for a five night stay will entitle you to a discount of £5.00.

A **CADE'S CAMPING, TOURING & MOTOR CARAVAN SITE GUIDE 2013 EDITION** must be presented at the time of payment. Vouchers are valid for accommodation only. Vouchers may not be exchanged for cash. Not to be used with any other offer. Valid until 31-12-13.

CONDITIONS OF USE

Vouchers will only be redeemed by those sites featuring a 🅴 symbol in the *facilities* line of their County entry. Presentation of this voucher to the Site Operator at the time of paying your balance will entitle you to a one pound discount per voucher, per night. (Only one voucher per night). Vouchers may be used in multiples i.e. five vouchers presented for a five night stay will entitle you to a discount of £5.00.

A **CADE'S CAMPING, TOURING & MOTOR CARAVAN SITE GUIDE 2013 EDITION** must be presented at the time of payment. Vouchers are valid for accommodation only. Vouchers may not be exchanged for cash. Not to be used with any other offer. Valid until 31-12-13.

CONDITIONS OF USE

Vouchers will only be redeemed by those sites featuring a 🅴 symbol in the *facilities* line of their County entry. Presentation of this voucher to the Site Operator at the time of paying your balance will entitle you to a one pound discount per voucher, per night. (Only one voucher per night). Vouchers may be used in multiples i.e. five vouchers presented for a five night stay will entitle you to a discount of £5.00.

A **CADE'S CAMPING, TOURING & MOTOR CARAVAN SITE GUIDE 2013 EDITION** must be presented at the time of payment. Vouchers are valid for accommodation only. Vouchers may not be exchanged for cash. Not to be used with any other offer. Valid until 31-12-13.

CONDITIONS OF USE

Vouchers will only be redeemed by those sites featuring a 🅴 symbol in the *facilities* line of their County entry. Presentation of this voucher to the Site Operator at the time of paying your balance will entitle you to a one pound discount per voucher, per night. (Only one voucher per night). Vouchers may be used in multiples i.e. five vouchers presented for a five night stay will entitle you to a discount of £5.00.

A **CADE'S CAMPING, TOURING & MOTOR CARAVAN SITE GUIDE 2013 EDITION** must be presented at the time of payment. Vouchers are valid for accommodation only. Vouchers may not be exchanged for cash. Not to be used with any other offer. Valid until 31-12-13.

CONDITIONS OF USE

Vouchers will only be redeemed by those sites featuring a 🅴 symbol in the *facilities* line of their County entry. Presentation of this voucher to the Site Operator at the time of paying your balance will entitle you to a one pound discount per voucher, per night. (Only one voucher per night). Vouchers may be used in multiples i.e. five vouchers presented for a five night stay will entitle you to a discount of £5.00.

A **CADE'S CAMPING, TOURING & MOTOR CARAVAN SITE GUIDE 2013 EDITION** must be presented at the time of payment. Vouchers are valid for accommodation only. Vouchers may not be exchanged for cash. Not to be used with any other offer. Valid until 31-12-13.

CADE'S   ONE POUND

CAMPING, TOURING & MOTOR CARAVAN SITE GUIDE 2013

PRESENT THIS VOUCHER TO THE SITE OPERATOR WHEN
PAYING TO RECEIVE ONE POUND DISCOUNT PER
VOUCHER, PER NIGHT. SEE CONDITIONS OVERLEAF.
VALID UNTIL 31-12-13

CADE'S   ONE POUND

CAMPING, TOURING & MOTOR CARAVAN SITE GUIDE 2013

PRESENT THIS VOUCHER TO THE SITE OPERATOR WHEN
PAYING TO RECEIVE ONE POUND DISCOUNT PER
VOUCHER, PER NIGHT. SEE CONDITIONS OVERLEAF.
VALID UNTIL 31-12-13

CADE'S   ONE POUND

CAMPING, TOURING & MOTOR CARAVAN SITE GUIDE 2013

PRESENT THIS VOUCHER TO THE SITE OPERATOR WHEN
PAYING TO RECEIVE ONE POUND DISCOUNT PER
VOUCHER, PER NIGHT. SEE CONDITIONS OVERLEAF.
VALID UNTIL 31-12-13

CADE'S   ONE POUND

CAMPING, TOURING & MOTOR CARAVAN SITE GUIDE 2013

PRESENT THIS VOUCHER TO THE SITE OPERATOR WHEN
PAYING TO RECEIVE ONE POUND DISCOUNT PER
VOUCHER, PER NIGHT. SEE CONDITIONS OVERLEAF.
VALID UNTIL 31-12-13

CADE'S   ONE POUND

CAMPING, TOURING & MOTOR CARAVAN SITE GUIDE 2013

PRESENT THIS VOUCHER TO THE SITE OPERATOR WHEN
PAYING TO RECEIVE ONE POUND DISCOUNT PER
VOUCHER, PER NIGHT. SEE CONDITIONS OVERLEAF.
VALID UNTIL 31-12-13

CADE'S   ONE POUND

CAMPING, TOURING & MOTOR CARAVAN SITE GUIDE 2013

PRESENT THIS VOUCHER TO THE SITE OPERATOR WHEN
PAYING TO RECEIVE ONE POUND DISCOUNT PER
VOUCHER, PER NIGHT. SEE CONDITIONS OVERLEAF.
VALID UNTIL 31-12-13

CADE'S   ONE POUND

CAMPING, TOURING & MOTOR CARAVAN SITE GUIDE 2013

PRESENT THIS VOUCHER TO THE SITE OPERATOR WHEN
PAYING TO RECEIVE ONE POUND DISCOUNT PER
VOUCHER, PER NIGHT. SEE CONDITIONS OVERLEAF.
VALID UNTIL 31-12-13

CADE'S   ONE POUND

CAMPING, TOURING & MOTOR CARAVAN SITE GUIDE 2013

PRESENT THIS VOUCHER TO THE SITE OPERATOR WHEN
PAYING TO RECEIVE ONE POUND DISCOUNT PER
VOUCHER, PER NIGHT. SEE CONDITIONS OVERLEAF.
VALID UNTIL 31-12-13

CADE'S   ONE POUND

CAMPING, TOURING & MOTOR CARAVAN SITE GUIDE 2013

PRESENT THIS VOUCHER TO THE SITE OPERATOR WHEN
PAYING TO RECEIVE ONE POUND DISCOUNT PER
VOUCHER, PER NIGHT. SEE CONDITIONS OVERLEAF.
VALID UNTIL 31-12-13

CADE'S   ONE POUND

CAMPING, TOURING & MOTOR CARAVAN SITE GUIDE 2013

PRESENT THIS VOUCHER TO THE SITE OPERATOR WHEN
PAYING TO RECEIVE ONE POUND DISCOUNT PER
VOUCHER, PER NIGHT. SEE CONDITIONS OVERLEAF.
VALID UNTIL 31-12-13

PITCH FEE DISCOUNT VOUCHERS

CONDITIONS OF USE

Vouchers will only be redeemed by those sites featuring a 🖼 symbol in the *facilities* line of their County entry. Presentation of this voucher to the Site Operator at the time of paying your balance will entitle you to a one pound discount per voucher, per night. (Only one voucher per night). Vouchers may be used in multiples i.e. five vouchers presented for a five night stay will entitle you to a discount of £5.00.

A **CADE'S CAMPING, TOURING & MOTOR CARAVAN SITE GUIDE 2013 EDITION** must be presented at the time of payment. Vouchers are valid for accommodation only. Vouchers may not be exchanged for cash. Not to be used with any other offer. Valid until 31-12-13.

CONDITIONS OF USE

Vouchers will only be redeemed by those sites featuring a 🖼 symbol in the *facilities* line of their County entry. Presentation of this voucher to the Site Operator at the time of paying your balance will entitle you to a one pound discount per voucher, per night. (Only one voucher per night). Vouchers may be used in multiples i.e. five vouchers presented for a five night stay will entitle you to a discount of £5.00.

A **CADE'S CAMPING, TOURING & MOTOR CARAVAN SITE GUIDE 2013 EDITION** must be presented at the time of payment. Vouchers are valid for accommodation only. Vouchers may not be exchanged for cash. Not to be used with any other offer. Valid until 31-12-13.

CONDITIONS OF USE

Vouchers will only be redeemed by those sites featuring a 🖼 symbol in the *facilities* line of their County entry. Presentation of this voucher to the Site Operator at the time of paying your balance will entitle you to a one pound discount per voucher, per night. (Only one voucher per night). Vouchers may be used in multiples i.e. five vouchers presented for a five night stay will entitle you to a discount of £5.00.

A **CADE'S CAMPING, TOURING & MOTOR CARAVAN SITE GUIDE 2013 EDITION** must be presented at the time of payment. Vouchers are valid for accommodation only. Vouchers may not be exchanged for cash. Not to be used with any other offer. Valid until 31-12-13.

CONDITIONS OF USE

Vouchers will only be redeemed by those sites featuring a 🖼 symbol in the *facilities* line of their County entry. Presentation of this voucher to the Site Operator at the time of paying your balance will entitle you to a one pound discount per voucher, per night. (Only one voucher per night). Vouchers may be used in multiples i.e. five vouchers presented for a five night stay will entitle you to a discount of £5.00.

A **CADE'S CAMPING, TOURING & MOTOR CARAVAN SITE GUIDE 2013 EDITION** must be presented at the time of payment. Vouchers are valid for accommodation only. Vouchers may not be exchanged for cash. Not to be used with any other offer. Valid until 31-12-13.

CONDITIONS OF USE

Vouchers will only be redeemed by those sites featuring a 🖼 symbol in the *facilities* line of their County entry. Presentation of this voucher to the Site Operator at the time of paying your balance will entitle you to a one pound discount per voucher, per night. (Only one voucher per night). Vouchers may be used in multiples i.e. five vouchers presented for a five night stay will entitle you to a discount of £5.00.

A **CADE'S CAMPING, TOURING & MOTOR CARAVAN SITE GUIDE 2013 EDITION** must be presented at the time of payment. Vouchers are valid for accommodation only. Vouchers may not be exchanged for cash. Not to be used with any other offer. Valid until 31-12-13.

CONDITIONS OF USE

Vouchers will only be redeemed by those sites featuring a 🖼 symbol in the *facilities* line of their County entry. Presentation of this voucher to the Site Operator at the time of paying your balance will entitle you to a one pound discount per voucher, per night. (Only one voucher per night). Vouchers may be used in multiples i.e. five vouchers presented for a five night stay will entitle you to a discount of £5.00.

A **CADE'S CAMPING, TOURING & MOTOR CARAVAN SITE GUIDE 2013 EDITION** must be presented at the time of payment. Vouchers are valid for accommodation only. Vouchers may not be exchanged for cash. Not to be used with any other offer. Valid until 31-12-13.

CONDITIONS OF USE

Vouchers will only be redeemed by those sites featuring a 🖼 symbol in the *facilities* line of their County entry. Presentation of this voucher to the Site Operator at the time of paying your balance will entitle you to a one pound discount per voucher, per night. (Only one voucher per night). Vouchers may be used in multiples i.e. five vouchers presented for a five night stay will entitle you to a discount of £5.00.

A **CADE'S CAMPING, TOURING & MOTOR CARAVAN SITE GUIDE 2013 EDITION** must be presented at the time of payment. Vouchers are valid for accommodation only. Vouchers may not be exchanged for cash. Not to be used with any other offer. Valid until 31-12-13.

CONDITIONS OF USE

Vouchers will only be redeemed by those sites featuring a 🖼 symbol in the *facilities* line of their County entry. Presentation of this voucher to the Site Operator at the time of paying your balance will entitle you to a one pound discount per voucher, per night. (Only one voucher per night). Vouchers may be used in multiples i.e. five vouchers presented for a five night stay will entitle you to a discount of £5.00.

A **CADE'S CAMPING, TOURING & MOTOR CARAVAN SITE GUIDE 2013 EDITION** must be presented at the time of payment. Vouchers are valid for accommodation only. Vouchers may not be exchanged for cash. Not to be used with any other offer. Valid until 31-12-13.

CONDITIONS OF USE

Vouchers will only be redeemed by those sites featuring a 🖼 symbol in the *facilities* line of their County entry. Presentation of this voucher to the Site Operator at the time of paying your balance will entitle you to a one pound discount per voucher, per night. (Only one voucher per night). Vouchers may be used in multiples i.e. five vouchers presented for a five night stay will entitle you to a discount of £5.00.

A **CADE'S CAMPING, TOURING & MOTOR CARAVAN SITE GUIDE 2013 EDITION** must be presented at the time of payment. Vouchers are valid for accommodation only. Vouchers may not be exchanged for cash. Not to be used with any other offer. Valid until 31-12-13.

CADE'S — ONE POUND	CADE'S — ONE POUND
CAMPING, TOURING & MOTOR CARAVAN SITE GUIDE 2013 PRESENT THIS VOUCHER TO THE SITE OPERATOR WHEN PAYING TO RECEIVE ONE POUND DISCOUNT PER VOUCHER, PER NIGHT. SEE CONDITIONS OVERLEAF. VALID UNTIL 31-12-13	**CAMPING, TOURING & MOTOR CARAVAN SITE GUIDE 2013** PRESENT THIS VOUCHER TO THE SITE OPERATOR WHEN PAYING TO RECEIVE ONE POUND DISCOUNT PER VOUCHER, PER NIGHT. SEE CONDITIONS OVERLEAF. VALID UNTIL 31-12-13
CADE'S — ONE POUND	CADE'S — ONE POUND
CAMPING, TOURING & MOTOR CARAVAN SITE GUIDE 2013 PRESENT THIS VOUCHER TO THE SITE OPERATOR WHEN PAYING TO RECEIVE ONE POUND DISCOUNT PER VOUCHER, PER NIGHT. SEE CONDITIONS OVERLEAF. VALID UNTIL 31-12-13	**CAMPING, TOURING & MOTOR CARAVAN SITE GUIDE 2013** PRESENT THIS VOUCHER TO THE SITE OPERATOR WHEN PAYING TO RECEIVE ONE POUND DISCOUNT PER VOUCHER, PER NIGHT. SEE CONDITIONS OVERLEAF. VALID UNTIL 31-12-13
CADE'S — ONE POUND	CADE'S — ONE POUND
CAMPING, TOURING & MOTOR CARAVAN SITE GUIDE 2013 PRESENT THIS VOUCHER TO THE SITE OPERATOR WHEN PAYING TO RECEIVE ONE POUND DISCOUNT PER VOUCHER, PER NIGHT. SEE CONDITIONS OVERLEAF. VALID UNTIL 31-12-13	**CAMPING, TOURING & MOTOR CARAVAN SITE GUIDE 2013** PRESENT THIS VOUCHER TO THE SITE OPERATOR WHEN PAYING TO RECEIVE ONE POUND DISCOUNT PER VOUCHER, PER NIGHT. SEE CONDITIONS OVERLEAF. VALID UNTIL 31-12-13
CADE'S — ONE POUND	CADE'S — ONE POUND
CAMPING, TOURING & MOTOR CARAVAN SITE GUIDE 2013 PRESENT THIS VOUCHER TO THE SITE OPERATOR WHEN PAYING TO RECEIVE ONE POUND DISCOUNT PER VOUCHER, PER NIGHT. SEE CONDITIONS OVERLEAF. VALID UNTIL 31-12-13	**CAMPING, TOURING & MOTOR CARAVAN SITE GUIDE 2013** PRESENT THIS VOUCHER TO THE SITE OPERATOR WHEN PAYING TO RECEIVE ONE POUND DISCOUNT PER VOUCHER, PER NIGHT. SEE CONDITIONS OVERLEAF. VALID UNTIL 31-12-13
CADE'S — ONE POUND	CADE'S — ONE POUND
CAMPING, TOURING & MOTOR CARAVAN SITE GUIDE 2013 PRESENT THIS VOUCHER TO THE SITE OPERATOR WHEN PAYING TO RECEIVE ONE POUND DISCOUNT PER VOUCHER, PER NIGHT. SEE CONDITIONS OVERLEAF. VALID UNTIL 31-12-13	**CAMPING, TOURING & MOTOR CARAVAN SITE GUIDE 2013** PRESENT THIS VOUCHER TO THE SITE OPERATOR WHEN PAYING TO RECEIVE ONE POUND DISCOUNT PER VOUCHER, PER NIGHT. SEE CONDITIONS OVERLEAF. VALID UNTIL 31-12-13

CONDITIONS OF USE

Vouchers will only be redeemed by those sites featuring a ▣ symbol in the *facilities* line of their County entry. Presentation of this voucher to the Site Operator at the time of paying your balance will entitle you to a one pound discount per voucher, per night. (Only one voucher per night). Vouchers may be used in multiples i.e. five vouchers presented for a five night stay will entitle you to a discount of £5.00.

A **CADE'S CAMPING, TOURING & MOTOR CARAVAN SITE GUIDE 2013 EDITION** must be presented at the time of payment. Vouchers are valid for accommodation only. Vouchers may not be exchanged for cash. Not to be used with any other offer. Valid until 31-12-13.

CONDITIONS OF USE

Vouchers will only be redeemed by those sites featuring a ▣ symbol in the *facilities* line of their County entry. Presentation of this voucher to the Site Operator at the time of paying your balance will entitle you to a one pound discount per voucher, per night. (Only one voucher per night). Vouchers may be used in multiples i.e. five vouchers presented for a five night stay will entitle you to a discount of £5.00.

A **CADE'S CAMPING, TOURING & MOTOR CARAVAN SITE GUIDE 2013 EDITION** must be presented at the time of payment. Vouchers are valid for accommodation only. Vouchers may not be exchanged for cash. Not to be used with any other offer. Valid until 31-12-13.

CONDITIONS OF USE

Vouchers will only be redeemed by those sites featuring a ▣ symbol in the *facilities* line of their County entry. Presentation of this voucher to the Site Operator at the time of paying your balance will entitle you to a one pound discount per voucher, per night. (Only one voucher per night). Vouchers may be used in multiples i.e. five vouchers presented for a five night stay will entitle you to a discount of £5.00.

A **CADE'S CAMPING, TOURING & MOTOR CARAVAN SITE GUIDE 2013 EDITION** must be presented at the time of payment. Vouchers are valid for accommodation only. Vouchers may not be exchanged for cash. Not to be used with any other offer. Valid until 31-12-13.

CONDITIONS OF USE

Vouchers will only be redeemed by those sites featuring a ▣ symbol in the *facilities* line of their County entry. Presentation of this voucher to the Site Operator at the time of paying your balance will entitle you to a one pound discount per voucher, per night. (Only one voucher per night). Vouchers may be used in multiples i.e. five vouchers presented for a five night stay will entitle you to a discount of £5.00.

A **CADE'S CAMPING, TOURING & MOTOR CARAVAN SITE GUIDE 2013 EDITION** must be presented at the time of payment. Vouchers are valid for accommodation only. Vouchers may not be exchanged for cash. Not to be used with any other offer. Valid until 31-12-13.

CONDITIONS OF USE

Vouchers will only be redeemed by those sites featuring a ▣ symbol in the *facilities* line of their County entry. Presentation of this voucher to the Site Operator at the time of paying your balance will entitle you to a one pound discount per voucher, per night. (Only one voucher per night). Vouchers may be used in multiples i.e. five vouchers presented for a five night stay will entitle you to a discount of £5.00.

A **CADE'S CAMPING, TOURING & MOTOR CARAVAN SITE GUIDE 2013 EDITION** must be presented at the time of payment. Vouchers are valid for accommodation only. Vouchers may not be exchanged for cash. Not to be used with any other offer. Valid until 31-12-13.

CONDITIONS OF USE

Vouchers will only be redeemed by those sites featuring a ▣ symbol in the *facilities* line of their County entry. Presentation of this voucher to the Site Operator at the time of paying your balance will entitle you to a one pound discount per voucher, per night. (Only one voucher per night). Vouchers may be used in multiples i.e. five vouchers presented for a five night stay will entitle you to a discount of £5.00.

A **CADE'S CAMPING, TOURING & MOTOR CARAVAN SITE GUIDE 2013 EDITION** must be presented at the time of payment. Vouchers are valid for accommodation only. Vouchers may not be exchanged for cash. Not to be used with any other offer. Valid until 31-12-13.

CONDITIONS OF USE

Vouchers will only be redeemed by those sites featuring a ▣ symbol in the *facilities* line of their County entry. Presentation of this voucher to the Site Operator at the time of paying your balance will entitle you to a one pound discount per voucher, per night. (Only one voucher per night). Vouchers may be used in multiples i.e. five vouchers presented for a five night stay will entitle you to a discount of £5.00.

A **CADE'S CAMPING, TOURING & MOTOR CARAVAN SITE GUIDE 2013 EDITION** must be presented at the time of payment. Vouchers are valid for accommodation only. Vouchers may not be exchanged for cash. Not to be used with any other offer. Valid until 31-12-13.

CONDITIONS OF USE

Vouchers will only be redeemed by those sites featuring a ▣ symbol in the *facilities* line of their County entry. Presentation of this voucher to the Site Operator at the time of paying your balance will entitle you to a one pound discount per voucher, per night. (Only one voucher per night). Vouchers may be used in multiples i.e. five vouchers presented for a five night stay will entitle you to a discount of £5.00.

A **CADE'S CAMPING, TOURING & MOTOR CARAVAN SITE GUIDE 2013 EDITION** must be presented at the time of payment. Vouchers are valid for accommodation only. Vouchers may not be exchanged for cash. Not to be used with any other offer. Valid until 31-12-13.

CONDITIONS OF USE

Vouchers will only be redeemed by those sites featuring a ▣ symbol in the *facilities* line of their County entry. Presentation of this voucher to the Site Operator at the time of paying your balance will entitle you to a one pound discount per voucher, per night. (Only one voucher per night). Vouchers may be used in multiples i.e. five vouchers presented for a five night stay will entitle you to a discount of £5.00.

A **CADE'S CAMPING, TOURING & MOTOR CARAVAN SITE GUIDE 2013 EDITION** must be presented at the time of payment. Vouchers are valid for accommodation only. Vouchers may not be exchanged for cash. Not to be used with any other offer. Valid until 31-12-13.

CONDITIONS OF USE

Vouchers will only be redeemed by those sites featuring a ▣ symbol in the *facilities* line of their County entry. Presentation of this voucher to the Site Operator at the time of paying your balance will entitle you to a one pound discount per voucher, per night. (Only one voucher per night). Vouchers may be used in multiples i.e. five vouchers presented for a five night stay will entitle you to a discount of £5.00.

A **CADE'S CAMPING, TOURING & MOTOR CARAVAN SITE GUIDE 2013 EDITION** must be presented at the time of payment. Vouchers are valid for accommodation only. Vouchers may not be exchanged for cash. Not to be used with any other offer. Valid until 31-12-13.

CADE'S ONE POUND	CADE'S ONE POUND
CAMPING, TOURING & MOTOR CARAVAN SITE GUIDE 2013 PRESENT THIS VOUCHER TO THE SITE OPERATOR WHEN PAYING TO RECEIVE ONE POUND DISCOUNT PER VOUCHER, PER NIGHT. SEE CONDITIONS OVERLEAF. VALID UNTIL 31-12-13	**CAMPING, TOURING & MOTOR CARAVAN SITE GUIDE 2013** PRESENT THIS VOUCHER TO THE SITE OPERATOR WHEN PAYING TO RECEIVE ONE POUND DISCOUNT PER VOUCHER, PER NIGHT. SEE CONDITIONS OVERLEAF. VALID UNTIL 31-12-13
CADE'S ONE POUND	CADE'S ONE POUND
CAMPING, TOURING & MOTOR CARAVAN SITE GUIDE 2013 PRESENT THIS VOUCHER TO THE SITE OPERATOR WHEN PAYING TO RECEIVE ONE POUND DISCOUNT PER VOUCHER, PER NIGHT. SEE CONDITIONS OVERLEAF. VALID UNTIL 31-12-13	**CAMPING, TOURING & MOTOR CARAVAN SITE GUIDE 2013** PRESENT THIS VOUCHER TO THE SITE OPERATOR WHEN PAYING TO RECEIVE ONE POUND DISCOUNT PER VOUCHER, PER NIGHT. SEE CONDITIONS OVERLEAF. VALID UNTIL 31-12-13
CADE'S ONE POUND	CADE'S ONE POUND
CAMPING, TOURING & MOTOR CARAVAN SITE GUIDE 2013 PRESENT THIS VOUCHER TO THE SITE OPERATOR WHEN PAYING TO RECEIVE ONE POUND DISCOUNT PER VOUCHER, PER NIGHT. SEE CONDITIONS OVERLEAF. VALID UNTIL 31-12-13	**CAMPING, TOURING & MOTOR CARAVAN SITE GUIDE 2013** PRESENT THIS VOUCHER TO THE SITE OPERATOR WHEN PAYING TO RECEIVE ONE POUND DISCOUNT PER VOUCHER, PER NIGHT. SEE CONDITIONS OVERLEAF. VALID UNTIL 31-12-13
CADE'S ONE POUND	CADE'S ONE POUND
CAMPING, TOURING & MOTOR CARAVAN SITE GUIDE 2013 PRESENT THIS VOUCHER TO THE SITE OPERATOR WHEN PAYING TO RECEIVE ONE POUND DISCOUNT PER VOUCHER, PER NIGHT. SEE CONDITIONS OVERLEAF. VALID UNTIL 31-12-13	**CAMPING, TOURING & MOTOR CARAVAN SITE GUIDE 2013** PRESENT THIS VOUCHER TO THE SITE OPERATOR WHEN PAYING TO RECEIVE ONE POUND DISCOUNT PER VOUCHER, PER NIGHT. SEE CONDITIONS OVERLEAF. VALID UNTIL 31-12-13
CADE'S ONE POUND	CADE'S ONE POUND
CAMPING, TOURING & MOTOR CARAVAN SITE GUIDE 2013 PRESENT THIS VOUCHER TO THE SITE OPERATOR WHEN PAYING TO RECEIVE ONE POUND DISCOUNT PER VOUCHER, PER NIGHT. SEE CONDITIONS OVERLEAF. VALID UNTIL 31-12-13	**CAMPING, TOURING & MOTOR CARAVAN SITE GUIDE 2013** PRESENT THIS VOUCHER TO THE SITE OPERATOR WHEN PAYING TO RECEIVE ONE POUND DISCOUNT PER VOUCHER, PER NIGHT. SEE CONDITIONS OVERLEAF. VALID UNTIL 31-12-13

CONDITIONS OF USE

Vouchers will only be redeemed by those sites featuring a symbol in the *facilities* line of their County entry. Presentation of this voucher to the Site Operator at the time of paying your balance will entitle you to a one pound discount per voucher, per night. (Only one voucher per night). Vouchers may be used in multiples i.e. five vouchers presented for a five night stay will entitle you to a discount of £5.00.

A **CADE'S CAMPING, TOURING & MOTOR CARAVAN SITE GUIDE 2013 EDITION** must be presented at the time of payment. Vouchers are valid for accommodation only. Vouchers may not be exchanged for cash. Not to be used with any other offer. Valid until 31-12-13.

CONDITIONS OF USE

Vouchers will only be redeemed by those sites featuring a symbol in the *facilities* line of their County entry. Presentation of this voucher to the Site Operator at the time of paying your balance will entitle you to a one pound discount per voucher, per night. (Only one voucher per night). Vouchers may be used in multiples i.e. five vouchers presented for a five night stay will entitle you to a discount of £5.00.

A **CADE'S CAMPING, TOURING & MOTOR CARAVAN SITE GUIDE 2013 EDITION** must be presented at the time of payment. Vouchers are valid for accommodation only. Vouchers may not be exchanged for cash. Not to be used with any other offer. Valid until 31-12-13.

CONDITIONS OF USE

Vouchers will only be redeemed by those sites featuring a symbol in the *facilities* line of their County entry. Presentation of this voucher to the Site Operator at the time of paying your balance will entitle you to a one pound discount per voucher, per night. (Only one voucher per night). Vouchers may be used in multiples i.e. five vouchers presented for a five night stay will entitle you to a discount of £5.00.

A **CADE'S CAMPING, TOURING & MOTOR CARAVAN SITE GUIDE 2013 EDITION** must be presented at the time of payment. Vouchers are valid for accommodation only. Vouchers may not be exchanged for cash. Not to be used with any other offer. Valid until 31-12-13.

CONDITIONS OF USE

Vouchers will only be redeemed by those sites featuring a symbol in the *facilities* line of their County entry. Presentation of this voucher to the Site Operator at the time of paying your balance will entitle you to a one pound discount per voucher, per night. (Only one voucher per night). Vouchers may be used in multiples i.e. five vouchers presented for a five night stay will entitle you to a discount of £5.00.

A **CADE'S CAMPING, TOURING & MOTOR CARAVAN SITE GUIDE 2013 EDITION** must be presented at the time of payment. Vouchers are valid for accommodation only. Vouchers may not be exchanged for cash. Not to be used with any other offer. Valid until 31-12-13.

CONDITIONS OF USE

Vouchers will only be redeemed by those sites featuring a symbol in the *facilities* line of their County entry. Presentation of this voucher to the Site Operator at the time of paying your balance will entitle you to a one pound discount per voucher, per night. (Only one voucher per night). Vouchers may be used in multiples i.e. five vouchers presented for a five night stay will entitle you to a discount of £5.00.

A **CADE'S CAMPING, TOURING & MOTOR CARAVAN SITE GUIDE 2013 EDITION** must be presented at the time of payment. Vouchers are valid for accommodation only. Vouchers may not be exchanged for cash. Not to be used with any other offer. Valid until 31-12-13.

CONDITIONS OF USE

Vouchers will only be redeemed by those sites featuring a symbol in the *facilities* line of their County entry. Presentation of this voucher to the Site Operator at the time of paying your balance will entitle you to a one pound discount per voucher, per night. (Only one voucher per night). Vouchers may be used in multiples i.e. five vouchers presented for a five night stay will entitle you to a discount of £5.00.

A **CADE'S CAMPING, TOURING & MOTOR CARAVAN SITE GUIDE 2013 EDITION** must be presented at the time of payment. Vouchers are valid for accommodation only. Vouchers may not be exchanged for cash. Not to be used with any other offer. Valid until 31-12-13.

CONDITIONS OF USE

Vouchers will only be redeemed by those sites featuring a symbol in the *facilities* line of their County entry. Presentation of this voucher to the Site Operator at the time of paying your balance will entitle you to a one pound discount per voucher, per night. (Only one voucher per night). Vouchers may be used in multiples i.e. five vouchers presented for a five night stay will entitle you to a discount of £5.00.

A **CADE'S CAMPING, TOURING & MOTOR CARAVAN SITE GUIDE 2013 EDITION** must be presented at the time of payment. Vouchers are valid for accommodation only. Vouchers may not be exchanged for cash. Not to be used with any other offer. Valid until 31-12-13.

CONDITIONS OF USE

Vouchers will only be redeemed by those sites featuring a symbol in the *facilities* line of their County entry. Presentation of this voucher to the Site Operator at the time of paying your balance will entitle you to a one pound discount per voucher, per night. (Only one voucher per night). Vouchers may be used in multiples i.e. five vouchers presented for a five night stay will entitle you to a discount of £5.00.

A **CADE'S CAMPING, TOURING & MOTOR CARAVAN SITE GUIDE 2013 EDITION** must be presented at the time of payment. Vouchers are valid for accommodation only. Vouchers may not be exchanged for cash. Not to be used with any other offer. Valid until 31-12-13.